SPATIAL
ANALYSIS

D. L. ANDERSON, *Northwestern University*

R. BACHI, *Hebrew University, Jerusalem*

A. M. BAKER, *University of Toronto*

B. J. L. BERRY, *University of Chicago*

L. W. BRINKMAN, *University of Iowa*

R. A. BRYSON, *University of Wisconsin*

I. BURTON, *University of Toronto*

G. A. P. CARROTHERS, *University of Pennsylvania*

R. J. CHORLEY, *Cambridge University*

M. CHOYNOWSKI, *Polish Academy of Sciences*

A. COURT, *San Fernando Valley State College*

L. CURRY, *University of Toronto*

M. F. DACEY, *Northwestern University*

W. L. GARRISON, *Northwestern University*

R. C. GEARY, *The Economic Research Institute, Dublin*

L. A. GOODMAN, *University of Chicago*

T. HÄGERSTRAND, *Royal University of Lund*

P. HAGGETT, *University of Bristol*

J. W. HARBAUGH, *Stanford University*

R. C. KAO, *The Rand Corporation*

M. G. KENDALL, *C.E.I.R., London*

L. J. KING, *Ohio State University*

D. S. KNOS, *University of Kansas*

J. B. LINDBERG, *University of Iowa*

I. S. LOWRY, *The Rand Corporation*

J. R. MACKAY, *University of British Columbia*

D. F. MARBLE, *Northwestern University*

I. MATUI, *Ochanomizu University, Tokyo*

J. D. NYSTUEN, *University of Michigan*

F. W. PRESTON, *University of Kansas*

A. H. ROBINSON, *University of Wisconsin*

M. E. SABBAGH, *University of Wisconsin*

J. Q. STEWART, *Formerly Princeton University*

E. N. THOMAS, *Northwestern University*

W. R. TOBLER, *University of Michigan*

W. WARNTZ, *Harvard University*

S. T. WONG, *Simon Fraser University, British Columbia*

J. K. WRIGHT, *Formerly American Geographical Society*

SPATIAL
ANALYSIS

A READER IN STATISTICAL GEOGRAPHY

BRIAN J. L. BERRY

University of Chicago

DUANE F. MARBLE

Northwestern University

PRENTICE-HALL, INC., ENGLEWOOD CLIFFS, NEW JERSEY

Library of Congress Catalog Card No.: 68-10856

PRINTED IN THE UNITED STATES OF AMERICA

Current printing (last digit):

10 9 8 7 6 5 4 3 2 1

PRENTICE-HALL INTERNATIONAL, INC., London
PRENTICE-HALL OF AUSTRALIA, PTY. LTD., Sydney
PRENTICE-HALL OF CANADA, LTD., Toronto
PRENTICE-HALL OF INDIA PRIVATE LTD., New Delhi
PRENTICE-HALL OF JAPAN, INC., Tokyo

PREFACE

This is a book about quantification in geography, and particularly about the geographical uses of statistical methods for spatial analysis. Most of the important literature is recent and much is fugitive. This reader was assembled to gather a representative sample of ongoing work in a single place, readily accessible to both professional geographer and to student.

As with all such compilations in a rapidly developing field, individual pieces are likely to become "dated" fairly quickly insofar as their substance is concerned. However, we feel that whatever the particular problems addressed by individual papers, the methods of analysis they illustrate will have greater longevity, and it is to illustrate the methods that the collection has been prepared.

Thus, the major sections of the book collect important pieces dealing with methodology, spatial data and spatial statistics, analysis of spatial distributions, study of spatial association, regionalization, and problems in the analysis of spatial series.

The student who reads this book in a course on methods will also need to use a good standard statistical text. What this volume contains are the examples of geographic uses of conventional inference statistics that such texts lack, and readings in the special problems of statistical analysis within geography, not an orderly set of proofs and description of procedures.

Many friends have provided us with insights and suggestions since an original group found itself at The University of Washington in 1955. We hope that we have expressed our thanks to these colleagues adequately elsewhere. Two special notes of appreciation are in order, however: to Bill Garrison, for his was the spark that set us all in motion; and to Jan and Jackie, who made the process so delightful. To each of them our debt is immeasurable.

BRIAN J. L. BERRY   DUANE F. MARBLE

CONTENTS

III

SPATIAL DATA AND SPATIAL STATISTICS

IV

ANALYSIS OF SPATIAL DISTRIBUTIONS

V

STUDY OF SPATIAL ASSOCIATION

VI

REGIONALIZATION

VII

PROBLEMS IN THE ANALYSIS OF SPATIAL SERIES

SPATIAL
ANALYSIS

I

INTRODUCTION

There has been a long history of quantification in geography, for quantification, viewed generally, implies many things: counting, development of classificatory systems, systematic study of variation, development of mathematical models, and emergence of axiomatic theories of measurement. Each of these elements is present in geography today, and most of them have characterized geographic study for a considerable time.

Similarly, geography and statistics have many origins in common. For example, when established in 1852, the American Geographical *and Statistical* Society (italics ours) included in its charter such purposes as to:

... read valuable papers on Geographical and Statistical subjects ...
... obtain ... the latest, completest, and most authentic information ... about countries ...
... increase the extent and accuracy of Geographical and Statistical knowledge ....

Even when the charter was amended in 1871 and the name of the society changed to the American Geographical Society, the following statement of objectives was retained:

The objects of the said Society shall be the advancement of the geographical science; the collection, classification and scientific arrangement of statistics and their results ... collection and diffusion of geographical, statistical and scientific knowledge.

This statement was, of course, perfectly consistent with the prevailing Jeffersonian notion that statistics were matters of state, and reflects the early relationship between record keeping and the performance of state functions.

It was actually August Meitzen, the acknowledged father of settlement geography, who recognized this statist tradition to be one of the two roots of modern statistics.[1] In 1866, Meitzen advanced the idea that the statistics of his time had developed from two different roots.[2] One originated in the middle of the seventeenth century in the work of the English political arithmeticians, such as Graunt and Petty, who coined the term. Political arithmetic had as its essence the idea that social problems could be subjected to quantitative analysis, and that causal relationships existed between quantitative variables.

The second root was German university statistics, the origins of which Meitzen attributed to Achenwall in the early eighteenth century, but which Lazarsfeld has traced back to Conring, a contemporary of Petty. University statistics had as its focus an intensive interest in the characteristics of a *state*, and from it comes the term "statistics." The essential effort of the university statistician was to derive systematically the best set of categories by which a state could be characterized.

At the end of the eighteenth century the English root of political arithmetic and the German root of university statistics became engaged, Meitzen records, in a controversy as to which was more scientific and useful. The former won, at least to the extent that it thereafter monopolized the term "statistician." What was left of university statistics reverted to political science and geography.

Some of the polemics of the debate seem strangely reminiscent of recent years in geography:

The vulgar statisticians have depraved the great art to "brainless busy work."
These stupid fellows disseminate the insane idea that one can understand the power of state if one just knows its size, its population, its national income, and the number of dumb beasts grazing around.
The machinations of those criminal political-statisticians in trying to tell everything by figures . . . is despicable and ridiculous beyond words.[3]

After the separation, geography's statistical work was entirely in the tradition of university statistics. The collection of data about countries and regions, and the attempt to derive the best sets of categories by which they could be characterized, was the object of geography's mainstream philosophy of areal differentiation.

Yet within geography there remained a deviation from the mainstream, one of *spatial analysis*, and within this deviant stream there remained an awareness of the interdependence of geography and geometry—of the science of spatial analysis and the mathematics of space.

Indeed, if the Greeks had not appropriated the term two thousand years ago, we might have called this book *geometrics*, just as other social sciences today have their econometrics, psychometrics, sociometrics, cliometrics, and even jurimetrics.

The spatial analysts kept alive only the awareness of a science of space, however. In the other tradition, that of German political arithmetic (later economics), a series of major works in location theory was completed, supplementing Thünen's work (1826) on agricultural location with the masterful twentieth-century works of Weber on industrial location (1909), and Christaller (1933) and Lösch (1939) on cities and the tertiary sector. It is from these theories that the first agreement as to significant research questions in spatial analysis emerged, as the work of the descendents of the university statisticians and political arithmeticians converged once again on the eve of the Second World War.

Prior to that war, few papers of a modern statistical nature had been published by geographers. Both before and immediately after the war, it was workers in other fields, not geographers, who provided many of the initial examples of applications of modern statistical methods to geographic problems, identified the major statistical problems of regional analysis, prepared the first experimental text on statistical geography, and thereby did much to set the pace and tone of statistical geography today. For example, M. G. Kendall (a statistician) showed in 1939 how principal components analysis could be used to develop a multivariate index that would portray the geographical distribution of crop productivity in England, and M. J. Hagood (a sociologist and statistician) used multiple-factor analysis in 1943 to define multivariable uniform regions. Kendall and G. U. Yule first recognized the problem of *modifiable units*, whereby if data refer to areas rather than to points, results of any analysis will in part be dependent upon the nature of the areal units of observation utilized. W. S. Robinson (a sociologist) provided the relevant relationship between individual and ecological (areal, set-type) correlations in 1950. A second problem, that of *contiguity* or *spatial autocorrelation* was examined by P. A. P. Moran (a statistician) in the nominal case in 1940 and R. C. Geary (an economist and statistician) more generally in 1954. Geary also applied his measures of contiguity to evaluation of lack of independence of residuals from regression in studies of spatial association. These studies are reviewed in O. D. Duncan, R. P. Cuzzort, and B. D. Duncan (sociologists), *Statistical Geography* (New York: Free Press of Glencoe, Inc., 1961) the first general book in the field. Further examination of autocorrelation in spatial series is to be found in B. Matern (a mathematician), *Spatial Variation* (Stockholm: Forest Research Institute, 1960), a major contribution to the literature of sampling. Spatial analysis remains basic to quantitative plant ecology and to much of epidemiology, and from these fields have come many of the ideas used in the study of pattern in point distributions and of spatial diffusion processes.

Besides these pioneering contributions from elsewhere, two other prewar antecedents can be identified that did involve quantitative work by geographers: centrography and social physics. To the former is due the idea of developing a special family of descriptive statistics for spatial distributions, and to the latter the recognition of certain classes of regularities in such distributions.

CENTROGRAPHY

During the early twentieth century there was a lively debate among statisticians concerning such measures as the center of the population of the United States. Part of the debate stemmed from publication by the Bureau of the Census of a piece entitled "Center of Population and Median Lines" in the first volume of the 14th Census of the United States (1920). Many articles were published, notably in the *Journal of the American Statistical Association* and *Metron*, concerning the relative advantages of alternative centers, such as the center of gravity, the spatial median, and the center of minimum aggregate travel. The Geography Branch of the United States Bureau of the Census still reports on the center of gravity of the population after each census.

The debate on centers gradually subsided in the United States, but in the Soviet Union centrography flourished during the 1920's and 1930's. In 1925, a centrographic laboratory was founded at Leningrad under the auspices of the Russian Geographical Society. Its director,

E. E. Sviatlovsky, pursued studies of the "actual" and "proper" centers and distributions of all manner of phenomena. However, the set of "proper" centers of economic activities proposed by him for the Gosplan of 1929 conflicted with the goals of the second Five Year Plan, and as a result the Mendeleev Laboratory was disbanded in Stalin's purges in the 1930's.

Recently the Israeli statistician, Roberto Bachi, has attempted to revive centrography with the development of a variety of measures of dispersion and association of spatial distributions. One of his papers appears below. Similarly, a group of urban planners at Cornell University, drawing on statistical mechanics for stimulus, has been attempting to apply centrography to the urban scene. Current interest within geography in the classic approach to centrography is slight, however, except as embraced by the social physicists.

SOCIAL PHYSICS

The attempt to describe human phenomena in terms of physical laws has a long history in every social science, with the Newtonian and Darwinian analyses most common. In geographical studies this attempt is represented by the use of gravity models to describe spatial interaction and the generalization of gravity concepts in potential models, designed as general summaries of the interdependencies existing simultaneously among all places in large areas. Such models have been argued by their proponents to correlate highly with the spatial distributions of a wide variety of social and economic phenomena in economically advanced countries.

Gravity models were first used in a relatively formal geographic way by E. J. Ravenstein in his seminal study "The Laws of Migration" (1885, 1889), although Henry Carey, among others, had made much earlier suggestions about gravitational concepts in social science. Thereafter, these models found wide application, for example in marketing geography (Reilly's laws of retail gravitation in 1929) or in postwar urban transportation studies describing interzonal travel. The basic idea is that interactions or movements between places are proportional to the product of the masses of those places and inversely proportional to some exponent of the distance separating them.

The gravity analogs were generalized by the astronomer J. Q. Stewart, who developed the idea of a potential surface that simultaneously describes the interactions of each place and every other. On this surface, the potential at any point i is given by:

$$P_i = \sum_{j=1}^{j=n} (M_j/d_{ij}^x)$$

The surface is obtained by interpolation from computations made at a sample of points in an area.

There is still considerable interest in social physics within geography, and new applications are continually being developed. The contributions of Mackay and Stewart and Warntz, below, show some of these.

The Postwar Period

Centrography, social physics, and other external stimuli, facilitated by developments in computer technology that enabled massive amounts of data to be handled conveniently for the first time, coming simultaneously with a resurgence of interest in problems of location theory by geography, combined, following 1950, to stimulate workers in geography's spatial tradition to work quantitatively. Reintegration of spatial analysis with statistical methods was at once facilitated and compelled, and this has been the dominant theme of postwar American geography. The older forms of cartographic analysis provided firm bases for this development, and many of the early studies were simply quantitative extensions of analyses cartographically conceived and executed. But the essence of the change was that the means were provided for matching observed facts with spatial theory, at a time when a new respect for theory was being incorporated into the field.

Although the change took place in the spatial tradition, it has not been confined to it. Statistical geography in some way has moved toward the mainstream of chorography and areal differentiation with increased use of multivariate analysis. A traditional chorographic problem is that of regionalization; an attempt is made to derive regions that are relatively uniform in terms of a complex of associated characteristics which they are observed to possess and which are also relatively different from other regions that possess other forms of the complex or other complexes. This kind of problem, involving mass data analysis, was traditionally attacked by overlaying maps. The advent of the modern computer, however, together with the use of factor analysis to reduce many variables to a few factors representing "complexes" of associated characteristics, and numerical taxonomy to derive the optimal classification of observations into regions, has provided a new and objective solution.

With the move back to the mainstream, the first flush of revolutionary change is over. A new paradigm has been implanted in geography, in which the implicit definition of legitimate problems and research methods is significantly different from that of a generation ago.[4] Peter Haggett,[5] in a seminal review of the substance of the work, uses the following outline to systematize locational models developed in human geography within the framework of the new paradigm:

I. Movement
  (a) movement and morphology
  (b) interaction (movement and distance)
  (c) "field" and "territory" (movement and area)
  (d) diffusions (movement and time)
II. Networks
  (a) location of routes
  (b) density pattern of route networks
  (c) models of network change
III. Nodes
  (a) morphology of settlement patterns
  (b) population clusters: the size continuum
  (c) size and spacing of clusters
IV. Hierarchies
  (a) functional hierarchies of settlements
  (b) specialized centers within the hierarchy
  (c) distortion due to agglomeration
  (d) distortion due to resource localization
V. Surfaces
  (a) surfaces and gradients
  (b) minimum-movement models
  (c) distortion of regular gradients

The argument used to tie these elements into a comprehensive conceptual scheme is derived from systems theory and states that regional organization needs a constant flow of people, goods, money, and information in order to maintain itself (*energy supplies*). An excess of inward movements must be met by changes associated with growth, as must a diminution in supply by decline and decay of parts (*form adjustments*). Areas of influence expand or contract to meet increased or decreased flows (*homeostatic adjustment*). Adjustments in the system frequently seem to be in the directions required to maintain system efficiency (*optimality*), while many regularities appear to exist and persist over space and time (*maintenance*). Cross-national comparisons also indicate that wide differences in causes may lead to the same results (*equifinality*).

THE BASE OF METHODS

What this review of substance omits, however, is an appreciation of the new technology that has been an essential part of the development. Under each of Haggett's headings, the studies reviewed have concerned themselves with one or another of three objectives:

1. determination of significant fact
2. matching facts with theory
3. articulation of theory.

These, in Kuhn's terms, are the activities of a "normal science,"[6] one in which an essential agreement exists on research questions and methods.

The methods enable the worker to pursue three kinds of studies:

1. of the nature of spatial distributions
2. of spatial associations—the covariance of distributions
3. of regionalization and areal differentiation.

Each kind of study involves use of one or both of two kinds of data:

1. structural (categorical)—the properties of places, or the categories that characterize them
2. functional (interactional)—the energy moving between places, or their spatial interactions.

Furthermore, work can apply to:

1. the current cross section of time
2. past cross sections, and comparisons of these cross sections

3. changes through time—developmental or longitudinal studies.

Any distinction between "qualitative" and "quantitative" work is probably inappropriate, for studies utilize one or more of several scales of measurement:

1. nominal (classificatory)
2. ordinal (ranking)
3. interval (measures without ratio properties)
4. ratio (full measurement, true zero).

Additionally, the studies involve any of the phenomena normally mapped by geographers —point, line, or area.

From these categories emerge the various sections of this book. Part II introduces the students to same basic methodological questions and provides some foundation for working with unfamiliar but important terms. Part III raises questions of the nature of geographic data, sampling, data storage, and data reduction. In Part IV the analysis of spatial distributions is introduced, and the topics covered include point, area, and surface pattern analysis, study of networks, interactions, and movements through time. Part V deals with spatial associations among such distributions, and if the previous section primarily addresses questions of what are significant spatial facts, this section essentially focuses upon matching facts with theory. Part VI considers the regionalization problem and related aspects of the formal study areal differentiation. Part VII raises the two most fundamental technical problems in spatial analysis: modifiability of the areal units of observation and contiguity, or the autocorrelation of spatial series.

THE CONCEPTUAL BASES

What are the important ideas that the student must grasp if he is to function as an intelligent geographer, able, at the minimum, to read and comprehend quantitative contributions to spatial analysis?

Burton, in the first article reprinted in this book, emphasizes that one should not be led astray by any emotional notions of a quantitative-qualitative dichotomy in geographic work, but should recognize that a variety of modes of inquiry may in fact be complementary. Measurement, he notes, embraces many levels, from simple classification (nominal), to ranking (ordinal), and thence to interval and ratio scales. And most important, quantitative analysis cannot function in the absence of a sound theoretical base.

Berry then classifies the various kinds of analysis in which the geographer engages:

1. systematic, or spatial—the study of spatial distributions and associations
2. regional—the description of particular places and codification of their areal differentiation
3. historical—either of the above in past cross sections of time, or any of the elements in the above compared through time.

Within these types of analysis Nystuen argues that there is a distinctly geographic point of view which can be captured by such underlying concepts as direction or orientation, distance, and connection or relative position. Further, common geographical problems can be thought of as a group of tensions: a dimensional tension between point, line, and area activities, or a tension between present activities and past facilities and institutions. And scale of the study is important, as is the relative scale of the elements within it.

What are the ways in which geographers can match concept and reality through use of models? Chorley differentiates between theory and model, and then develops a "model for models" showing how different stages and types of inquiry fit together. This is complemented by Lowry's essay on how to build analytic models.

The essence of these papers is that geographers should no longer feel as uneasy in the halls of modern science as they have in the past. If the philosophic mainstream of geography in the past century has been dominated by chorographic interest in areal differentiation, in the arrangements and associations of things that distinguish one area from another, the papers in Part II emphasize the postwar predilection for building accurate generalizations with predictive power by precise quantitative description of spatial distributions, spatial structure and organization, and spatial relation-

ships. Mainstream research is unashamedly empirical; the new interests are frankly theoretical. The major tool of the mainstream is the map; on the frontier, maps and graphs, statistics, mathematics, and formal logic all play their role as technical aids to analysis.

SPATIAL DATA AND SPATIAL STATISTICS

The tools are applied to data, but what are "geographic" or "spatial" data. In Part III Kao points out that two kinds should be distinguished:

1. locational data, values observed at some point
2. areal data, values for some geographic unit.

As Kao argues, the former are properties of some "point function" and the latter are those of a "set function." Yet data exist at different levels of measurement: nominal, ordinal, interval, and ratio. Moreover, cartographers have always emphasized that they must portray not only point and area data, but information referring to *lines* as well. The lines may simply indicate connections between places, but they may also rank the quality of those connections or scale the intensity, just as point and area symbols do. There is thus an extraordinary diversity in the kinds of spatial distributions studied by geographers. A brief set of examples includes the following: *a land use map:* scalar, nominal, of areas, an areal distribution; *a map of the United States showing the location of major cities by dots:* scalar, nominal, at points, a point distribution; *an airline route map:* vector, nominal, joining points; *a map of soil quality in Illinois:* scalar, ordinal, of areas; *a map showing average annual temperature in India:* scalar, interval, and if it shows averages by states or districts, discontinuous and areal (a choropleth map if different shadings are applied to the units), but if it shows the temperature varying over India as a surface, it is the continuous generalization of point observations (generally isopleth, since the surface will be depicted by contours) if generalized from the weather station data, but perhaps of areal data if interpolations were made with respect to the district averages treated as points central to each of the districts; *a state highway map with routes classified by quality:* vector, ordinal, joining points; *a map of city-to-city air passenger movements:* vector, ratio, joining points.

Two dominant themes emerge in spatial analysis of such maps: evaluation of the *pattern* of scalar distributions and of similarities in pattern over a number of such distributions, and evaluation of the *connectivity* evidenced by vector distributions and of similarities in the connectivity of several such distributions. Apparently, the fundamental properties of pattern include absolute location (position), relative location (geometry), and scale, with a family of interesting derived properties, including density and density gradients, spacing, directional orientation, and the like. Similarly, accessibility is central to the study of connectivity, and from it are derived such properties as centrality itself, relative dominance, degree of interdependence, etc. It is these two themes that merge in *spatial systems analysis*, where pattern and connectivity are examined in their association and mutual interdependency.

One of the main points of Kao's argument is that the development and spread of large modern computers provides an ability to maintain and exploit the geographic ordering of information in ways never before attempted. If locational coordinates are stored along with bits of data, maps may be drawn by computer. Summaries may be provided by whatever set of areal units the investigator deems necessary. There is complete flexibility to change scale and match results at different scales of analysis.

Other benefits also accrue. Emerging from Tobler's review of the projection problem in mapping is the clear understanding that if geographic data are stored with proper geographic identification (i.e., location codes), then it is possible to map, to change scale, to reaggregate, and to move easily not only from one conventional map projection to another, but also to graphic portrayals whatever the concept of space. Miles may be stretched or compressed according to differences in transport costs. The natural variability of the earth's surface may be "washed away" to compare what is left of reality with the idealized view of some theoretical model.

Ultimately there comes the problem of collecting data. Berry and Baker review methods of point sampling in the plane. Once collected, data must be summarized. Bachi presents the spatial statistics of centrography. Court uses the statistical theory of extremes to summarize temperature phenomena. Chorley seeks ways to describe the shape of drainage basins using probability papers. Mackay applies the gravity model to measure the effects of linguistic and political boundaries on communication, and Stewart and Warntz further develop the ideas of social physics.

These pieces variously touch upon descriptive statistics for point and area data, for functional units, such as drainage basins, and for surfaces. The descriptions may be of particular elements, for example the center, or they may try to summarize the whole, as with measures of shape. They do cover the major measures used today in geography, however.

ANALYSIS OF SPATIAL DISTRIBUTION

A great diversity of spatial distributions lies within the domain of the geographer. In analysis of such distributions, the critical feature to be captured is that of *pattern*, although its identification is but a first step in the search for the processes that have generated that pattern.

The simplest cases of pattern analysis involve points in area. Matui's classic study of 1932 uses probabilities of occurrence based upon the Poisson distribution to summarize such point patterns. King, on the other hand, shows how nearest-neighbor analysis can be used to the same end. Dacey elaborates on both methods. He shows, for example, that distances between neighbors in a random pattern may be generated by a gamma distribution, and in his second study examines how "mixed" probability distributions may be developed for special circumstances and postulates. The probability base of distributional analysis is reiterated by Choynowski in his study of the occurrence of rare diseases in the districts (areas) of Poland.

There are, however, other ways to look at pattern. Consider the case of a surface. Normally the geographer will look at it using an isoline map. Nonetheless Chorley and Haggett provide an excellent review of the benefits to be achieved by surface fitting using polynomials, and Harbaugh and Preston do the same for Fourier series where the phenomena are cyclic.

Garrison, using the mathematics of graph theory, then shows how indices of centrality can be derived from line and network patterns, and Sabbagh and Bryson use harmonic analysis to study the spatial distribution of phenomena that vary cyclically in time at different locations in different ways.

ANALYSIS OF SPATIAL ASSOCIATION

Given spatial distributions, how may they be compared? Knos provides an excellent, systematic passage from correlation and simple regression studies of single hypotheses to the use of multiple regression analysis to study multiple hypotheses simultaneously. But there are many difficulties in comparing distributions. Robinson, Lindberg, and Brinkman address the problem of studying data for which the units of observation vary widely, and Robinson shows how to generalize a set of small-area correlations.

Thomas then develops residual analysis, the procedure whereby the residue is separated from the known and examined in the search for more general concepts. Haggett provides a good example of the joint uses of regression and residual analyses, analysis of variance, and surface-fitting techniques to show a family of distributional and associational techniques in action. Wong's paper is included for several reasons. It provides another example of regression analysis at work. It also shows how factor analysis may be used to help resolve the collinearity problem that exists when the explanatory variables are not independent. In doing so it also provides an introduction to Part VI.

At this point in the book, Hägerstrand's paper using Monte Carlo methods to simulate the diffusion of innovations in space may seem a bit out of place at first. A little reflection may suggest otherwise, however, for we have examined associations among pairs or sets of distributions of areal data. Similar studies of flow materials exist in the literature. Yet the association of points in one place with those in another because of the operation of identifiable processes over space through time has not been addressed. This is the topic of Hägerstrand's seminal paper. The conclusion is at the same time satisfying and disconcerting. A spatial distribution may be replicated by simulating the processes by which it has spread. Yet it follows that the points in one area are then not independent of points in other areas, but linked over time by that process. In comparing the distribution with others by standard statistical means, then, the assumption of independence of the observations is violated.

REGIONALIZATION

Traditionally, geography's chorographic mainstream has accumulated and used masses of data to define regions and assess regional differences. The computer provides means of handling massive data files. Multivariate analysis provides ways of analyzing such data. Ultimately, quantitative spatial analysis had to take advantage of the computer, draw on multivariate methods, and return to re-evaluate the classic geographic problems of regionalization.

Kendall pointed the way in 1939 with his study of the geographic distribution of crop productivity in Britain. He showed how principal components methods could be used to summarize the common theme in many original variables, to index the theme, and to show its geographic distribution and regionalization by mapping it.

The mathematics of graph theory is taken by Nystuen and Dacey and used to derive nodal regions from a mass of communications data, so that mathematical solutions are provided to both the uniform and nodal region cases.

Berry then shows how factor analysis may be used to resolve multivariate spatial patterns to their fundamental bases and how dimensional methods provide measures of regional similarity. A related idea of dyadic analysis permits functional data to be placed in the same format as the formal data. Numerical taxonomy provides an optimal regionalization of either kind, but canonical analysis enables a joint formal and functional regionalization in a field theory context.

PROBLEMS IN THE ANALYSIS OF SPATIAL SERIES

Finally, problems of spatial analysis and aggregating areal data need to be pointed out. Goodman evaluates "ecological" correlations and regressions computed from areal data when the research worker is interested in the behavior of individuals. Geary then raises the question of contiguity, or geographic autocorrelation, and Dacey extends tests of contiguity in areal cases of nominal data. These contributions are suggestive of solutions, but more incisive tests have yet to be developed.

FOOTNOTES

[1] A. Meitzen, *Siedelung und Agrarwesen der Westgermanen und Ostgermanen, der Kelten, Römern, Finnen und Slawen* (Berlin, 1895).

[2] A. Meitzen, *History, Theory and Technique of Statistics* (Philadelphia: American Academy of Political and Social Science, 1891). Quoted in P. F. Lazarsfeld, "Notes on the History of Quantification in Sociology—Trends, Sources and Problems," *Isis*, **52** (1961). Meitzen attributes to Ritter the divergence in Germany between geography and statistics.

[3] Lazarsfeld, *op. cit.*, 293. Compare this with the debate summarized in I. Burton, "The Quantitative Revolution and Theoretical Geography," below, pp. 13–23.

[4] T. S. Kuhn, *The Structure of Scientific Revolutions* (Chicago: University of Chicago Press, 1962); Ad Hoc Committee on Geography, National Academy of Science-National Research Council, *The Science of Geography* (Washington: The Academy, 1965).

[5] P. Haggett, *Locational Analysis in Human Geography* (London: [Edward] Arnold [Publishers], Ltd., 1965).

[6] Kuhn, *op. cit.*

II

METHODOLOGY

1

THE QUANTITATIVE REVOLUTION
AND THEORETICAL GEOGRAPHY[1]

IAN BURTON

In the past decade geography has undergone a radical transformation of spirit and purpose, best described as the "quantitative revolution." The consequences of the revolution have yet to be worked out and are likely to involve the "mathematization" of much of our discipline, with an attendant emphasis on the construction and testing of theoretical models. Although the future changes will far outrun the initial expectations of the revolutionaries, the revolution itself is now over. It has come largely as the result of the impact of work by nongeographers upon geography, a process shared by many other disciplines where an established order has been overthrown by a rapid conversion to a mathematical approach.

Geographers may look with the wisdom of hindsight on a recent statement by Douglas C. North who points out that in the field of economic history "a revolution is taking place. . . . It is being initiated by a new generation of economic historians who are both skeptical of traditional interpretations of U.S. economic history, and convinced that a new economic history must be firmly grounded in sound statistical data."[2] North's paper has a familiar ring in geographical ears, but is not primarily concerned with where the revolution is likely to lead. If the example of other social sciences is any criterion, it will lead to a more mathematical, not solely statistical, economic history.

The movement which led to the revolution in geography was begun by physicists and mathematicians, and has expanded to transform first the physical and then the biological sciences. It is now strongly represented in most of the social sciences, including economics, psychology, and sociology. The movement is not yet strongly represented in anthropology or political science, and has scarcely been felt in history, although early rumblings may perhaps be heard from a new journal devoted to history and theory.[3]

This paper presents a discussion of the general characteristics of the quantitative movement, describes in somewhat greater detail

Reprinted from *The Canadian Geographer*, **7** (1963), 151–162, by permission of the author and editor.

the coming of the quantitative revolution to geography, and attempts an assessment of the value of quantitative techniques in the development of theory. Some scholars have chosen to regard the revolution in terms of a qualitative-quantitative dichotomy. It does not help to cast the debate in this form. For "what is philosophically distinctive about contemporary science is its disinterest in dubious dichotomies or disabling dilemmas,"[4] which fascinate and ensnare the mind because they give the illusion of coming close to the essential nature of things. O. H. K. Spate, in his paper on "Quantity and Quality in Geography," goes so far as to cry "down with dichotomies,"[5] but fails to heed his own advice and apply it to the title of his paper. Furthermore, to specify the presence or absence of an attribute or quality is merely to begin the process of measurement at its lowest level on a nominal scale. Viewed in this manner, observations of qualitative differences are but the prelude to measurements of a higher order on ordinal, interval, or ratio scales.

The quantity-quality dichotomy has also been allowed to embrace and perhaps conceal a number of related but distinct questions. These include measurement by instruments vs. direct sense data; rational analysis vs. intuitive perception; cold and barren scientific constructs vs. the rich variety of daily sense experience; continuously varying phenomena vs. discrete cases, nomothetic vs. ideographic, and the like.

The desire to avoid this confusion reinforces my inclination to side-step the quality-quantity issue, and to view the movement toward quantification as a part of the general spread and growth of scientific analysis into a world formerly dominated by a concern with the exceptional and unique.

Quantification as Indeterminism

Geography has long been a "following" rather than a "leading" discipline. The main currents of thought have had their origins in other fields. The mechanistic approach of much nineteenth-century science was represented to some extent among the environmental determinists from Ratzel (if he *was* a determinist) to Semple, Huntington, and Griffith Taylor. They were preoccupied by the notion of cause and effect, and were constantly seeking "laws." A similar

mechanistic flavor is present in much of the recent work by the "quantifiers." It is as if geography is re-emerging after the lapse into ideography which followed the retreat from environmental determinism. The quantitative revolution is taking us back much closer to environmental determinism. It is surely not coincidental that the quantitative revolution is contemporaneous with the appearance of neo-determinism in geography.[6]

It seems clear that a strong reaction to environmental determinism has served to delay the coming of the quantitative movement to geography, and has postponed the establishment of a scientific basis for our discipline that the quantifiers hope to provide (and which the determinists were seeking, although for the most part did not find).

It is not so surprising, therefore, that the quantitative revolution was resisted most strongly by American geographers, for it was in the United States that the reaction to environmental determinism was strongest. Characteristically, the source of strongest opposition is now the source of greatest support, and the United States has achieved a very favorable balance of trade in the commodity of quantitative techniques.

Although quantification in geography has been mechanistic, new techniques being used and others being developed are in line with the contemporary trend in science in that they are probabilistic. The probabilistic approach as exemplified in Curry's work on climatic change,[7] and Hägerstrand's simulation of diffusion[8] offers a most promising vista for future research. As Bronowski notes, statistics "is the method to which modern science is moving.... This is the revolutionary thought in modern science. It replaces the concept of inevitable effect by that of probable trend."[9] It is more accurate, therefore, to refer to some of the later examples of quantification in geography as indeterministic. With Jerzy Neyman, "one may hazard the assertion that every serious contemporary study is a study of the chance mechanism behind some phenomena. The statistical and probabilistic tool in such studies is the theory of stochastic processes, now involving many unsolved problems."[10]

Of great significance in the development of laws in the social sciences is the scale of analysis. As Emrys Jones explains:

The lack of stringency lies in the finite numbers dealt with in the social sciences as opposed to the infinite numbers dealt with in the physical sciences. At this latter extreme, statistical regularity is such that it suggests extreme stringency or absolute validity; while at the other end statistical variations and exceptions are much higher, and deviations themselves warrant study.[11]

THE END OF A REVOLUTION

Although its antecedents can be traced far back, the quantitative revolution in geography began in the late 1940's or early 1950's; it reached its culmination in the period from 1957 to 1960, and is now over. Ackerman remarks that:

Although the simpler forms of statistical aids have characterized geographic distribution analysis in the past, the discipline is commencing to turn to more complex statistical methods—an entirely logical development. The use of explanatory models and regression, correlation, variance, and covariance analysis may be expected to be increasingly more frequent in the field. In the need for and value of these methods geography does not differ from other social sciences.[12]

Similarly, Hartshorne says that:

to raise ... thinking to the level of scientific knowing, it is necessary to establish generic concepts that can be applied with the maximum degree of objectivity and accuracy and to determine correlations of phenomena with the maximum degree of certainty. Both purposes can best be accomplished if the phenomena can be fully and correctly described by quantitative measurements and these can be subjected to statistical comparisons through the logic of mathematics.[13]

Spate, although somewhat skeptical about quantitative methods, concedes that "increasingly young geographers will feel that they are not properly equipped without some statistical nous,"[14] and adds parenthetically that he is relieved not to be a young geographer.

An intellectual revolution is over when accepted ideas have been overthrown or have been modified to include new ideas. *An intellectual revolution is over* when the revolutionary ideas themselves become a part of the conventional wisdom. When Ackerman, Hartshorne, and Spate are in substantial agreement about something, then we are talking about the conventional wisdom.

Hence my belief that the quantitative revolution is over and has been for some time. Further evidence may be found in the rate at which schools of geography in North America are adding courses in quantitative methods to their requirements for graduate degrees.

Many would concur with Mackay's comment that "the marginal return on arguing for the need of quantitative methods is now virtually nil."[15] This does not deny that many ramifications of the revolution remain to be worked out. Nor does it mean that the ramifications will be painless. It is not easy to agree with Spate's argument that the need for statistical nous applies only to young geographers. Is the field to progress only as rapidly as the turnover in generations? The impact of cybernation is already creating unemployment at the white-collar level. Its impact on the managerial and professional strata is likely to mean more work, not less. It is no flight of fancy to foresee the day when geographers, if they are to remain abreast of developments, must relearn their craft anew every decade. Nor is it difficult to see that the present generation of quantifiers may rapidly be replaced by younger men more thoroughly versed in mathematics.

Although the quantitative revolution is over, it is instructive to examine its course, because to do so tells us something about the sociology of our profession, and because it provides a background for the question, "quantification for what?" considered below.

THE COURSE OF THE QUANTITATIVE REVOLUTION IN GEOGRAPHY

Although the origins of the revolution lie in the fields of mathematics and physics, the direct invasion came from closer to home. A list of the more important antecedents, having a direct or indirect impact on geography, would include von Neuman (a mathematician) and Morgenstern (an economist) for their *Theory of Games and Economic Behavior*,[16] first published in 1944; Norbert Wiener, whose 1948 volume on cybernetics[17] emphasized the necessity of crossing academic boundaries; and Zipf, who published *Human Behavior and the Principle of Least Effort*[18] in 1949.

Geographers began to look for quantitative techniques that could be applied to their problems, and some nongeographers began to bring new methods to bear on old geographic questions. One example is physicist J. Q. Stewart's paper, "Empirical Mathematical Rules Concerning the Distribution and Equilibrium of Population," published in the *Geographical Review*[19] as early as 1947.

Stewart has been a leader in the development of social physics, and the declaration of interdependence signed by a group of physical and social scientists at the Princeton conference in 1949 is a landmark in the growth of the application of mathematics to the social sciences.[20] That economists were engaging in methodological debate at this time, in a way that geographers were to do five years later, is evidenced by the Vining and Koopmans controversy in the *Review of Economics and Statistics for 1949*.[21]

The impact of quantification began to be felt in geography almost immediately. It was initiated by a number of statements calling for quantification. Such calls had been issued earlier. For example, in 1936 John Kerr Rose, in his paper on corn yields and climate, argued that "the methods of correlation analysis would seem especially promising tools for geographical investigation."[22] This call went largely unheeded. Similar statements in 1950, however, were followed up. An outstanding early plea was made by Strahler in his attack on the Davisian explanatory-descriptive system of geomorphology,[23] and his endoresement of G. K. Gilbert's dynamic-quantitative system.[24]

QUANTITATIVE GEOMORPHOLOGY AND CLIMATOLOGY

If Gilbert's 1914 paper was as sound as Strahler seems to think, why was it not adopted as a signpost to future work in geomorphology, instead of being largely forgotten and ignored for thirty years? The answer may be, as Strahler himself seems to imply, that geomorphology was a part of geography. Hydrologists and geologists did not direct their major interest toward such matters, or when they did they followed Davis. The followers included Douglas Johnson, C. A. Cotton, N. M. Fenneman, and A. K. Lobeck. Strahler held that they made "splendid contributions to descriptive and regional geomorphology," and "have provided a sound base for studies in human geography,"[25] but they did not greatly advance the scientific study of geomorphological process. This is not to say that there was no quantitative work in geomorphology prior to Strahler.[26]

One immediate response to Strahler's attack on Davis came from Quam, who wondered whether mathematical formulae and statistical analysis might not give a false impression of objectivity and accuracy.[27] A more violent response, however, came from S. W. Wooldridge, who notes that:

There has been a recent attempt in certain quarters to devise a "new" quasi-mathematical geomorphology. At its worst this is hardly more than a ponderous sort of cant. The processes and results of rock sculpture are not usefully amenable to treatment by mathematics at higher certificate level. If any "best" is to result from the movement, we have yet to see it; it will be time enough to incorporate it in the subject when it has discovered or expressed something which cannot be expressed in plain English. For ourselves, we continue to regard W. M. Davis as the founder of our craft and regret the murmurings of dispraise heard occasionally from his native land.[28]

Lester King is inclined to support Strahler.

Statistical analysis is essentially the method of the bulk sample, and is admirable for the study of complex phenomena and processes into which enter a large number of variables. As yet few geomorphic topics provide data suited directly to statistical treatment, and methods may have to be adapted to the new field of inquiry, so that too facile results should not be expected. The net result must be, however, a greater precision in geomorphic thinking.[29]

Several geomorphologists, including Chorley,[30] Dury,[31] Mackay,[32] Wolman,[33] and others, in addition to Strahler, are using quantitative methods, and the practice seems likely to spread.

There has been little argument about the application of quantitative techniques to climatology. This branch of our subject embraces the most apparently manageable and quantifiable continuum that geographers have been concerned to study. Thornthwaite and Mather,[34] Hare,[35] Bryson,[36] and others have been applying quantitative techniques to climatic problems for some time, and with great effect. The quality of their work has virtually silenced the potential critics.

QUANTIFICATION IN HUMAN AND ECONOMIC GEOGRAPHY

By far the greatest struggle for the acceptance of quantitative methods has been in human and economic geography. This is not surprising in view of the possibilist tradition.[37] It is here that the revolution runs up against notions of free will and the unpredictability of human behavior. Here the comparison with physical science is helpful. Physicists working on a microcosmic level encounter the same kinds of problems with quanta and energy that social scientists do with people. The recognition of such parallels is cause for rejoicing, not for despair. To be accepted and accorded an honored place in our society, social science needs to acquire demonstrable value as a predictive science without a corresponding need to control, restrict, or regiment the individual. A social science which recognizes random behavior at the microcosmic level and predictable order at the macrocosmic level is a logical outgrowth of the quantitative revolution.

The catalogue of claim and counter-claim, charge and countercharge that appeared in the literature in the 1950's is a long one. It includes Garrison's[38] comment on Nelson's[39] service classification of American cities; the Reynolds-[40] Garrison[41] exchange of 1956 on the (then) little use of statistical methods in geography; the Spate-Berry editorial exchange in *Economic Geography* in which the former reminds us that "statistics are at best but half of life. The other half is understanding and imaginative interpretation,"[42] and the latter defends the quantifiers for their clear distinction between facts, theories, and methods, and in turn accuses his critics of creating a quantitative bogey-man and tilting at windmills;[43] Dacey's[44] criticism of Burghardt's[45] conclusions on the spacing of river towns, and Porter's defense with the fable of "Earnest and the Orephagians";[46] the Zobler[47]-Mackay[48] exchange on the use of chi-square in regional geography; Arthur Robinson's classification of geographers into "Perks and Pokes;"[49] the debate between Luckermann[50] and Berry[51] on a "geographic" economic geography, and so on.

By 1956, the quantifiers were arguing with each other through the medium of the professional journals as well as with their opponents. In so doing, they occupied an increasing amount of attention and space. In 1956 also the Regional Science Association was established and gave further impetus to quantification in geography.

The erstwhile revolutionaries are now part of the geographic "establishment," and their work is an accepted and highly valued part of the field.

THE OPPOSITION TO QUANTIFICATION

The opposition to the quantitative revolution can be grouped into five broad classes. There were those who thought that the whole idea was a bad one and that quantification would mislead geography in a wrong and fruitless direction. If such critics are still among us, they have not made themselves heard for some time. There were those like Stamp who argued that geographers had spent too long perfecting their tools (maps, cartograms, and other diagrammatic representations) and should get on with some real building. Stamp was "a little alarmed by the view that the geographer must add to his training a considerable knowledge of statistics and statistical method, of theoretical economics and of modern sociology. Sufficient perhaps to appreciate what his colleagues are doing so that team work may be based on mutual appreciation seems to me the right attitude."[52] This seems to be another dubious dichotomy. The notion that geographers either improve their tools or engage in research with available tools seems false. Surely advances in technology are most likely to occur at the moment when we are grappling with our toughest problems. Furthermore, to argue that geographers should not use statistical methods comes close to defining geography in terms of one research tool—namely, the map. One weakness of this position has been well demonstrated by McCarty and Salisbury, who have shown that visual comparison of isopleth maps is not an adequate means of determining correlations between spatially distributed phenomena.[53]

A third kind of opposition holds that statistical techniques are suitable for some kinds of geography, but not all geography, because there are certain things that cannot be measured. This may be true for some variables. However, even with qualitative characteristics, nominal observations can be made and there is an expanding body of literature on the analysis of qualitative data.[54] A variant of this argument is that the variables with which geography is concerned are too numerous and complex for statistical analysis. Quantifiers claim that it is precisely because of the number and complexity of the variables that statistical techniques are being employed.

Another class of objections is that although quantitative techniques are suitable and their application to geographic problems is desirable, they are nevertheless being incorrectly applied; ends are confused with means; quantitative analysis has failed on occasion to distinguish the significant from the trivial; the alleged discoveries of the quantifiers are not very novel; and so on. That these criticisms have a grain of truth cannot be denied, but to the valid, correct use of quantitative methods (and this is surely what we are concerned with) they are merely irrelevant. Incorrect applications have been and no doubt will continue to be made, and in some cases for the wrong reason, such as fashion, fad, or snobbery. More often, however, they are genuine and honest attempts to gain new knowledge and new understandings.

A final kind of criticism to note is in the *ad hominem* that quantification is all right but quantifiers are not. They are perky, suffer from overenthusiasm, vaulting ambition, or just plain arrogance. To this charge also perhaps a plea of guilty with extenuating circumstances (and a request for leniency) is the most appropriate response. When you are involved in a revolution, it is difficult not to be a little cocky.

THE CONSEQUENCES OF THE REVOLUTION

The revolution is over, in that once-revolutionary ideas are now conventional. Clearly this is only the beginning. There is a purpose other than the establishment of a new order. If the revolution had been inspired by belief in quantification for its own sake, or by fad and fashion, then it would have rapidly run its course and quickly died. But the revolution had a different purpose. It was inspired by a genuine need to make geography more scientific, and by a concern to develop a body of theory. Dissatisfaction with ideographic geography lies at the root of the quantitative revolution. The development of theoretical, model-building geography is likely to be the major consequence of the quantitative revolution.

Description, or as some have said, "mere description,"[55] may be an art or at least call for the exercise of certain talents best described as artistic. Nevertheless, description is an essential part of the scientific method. In examining the real world, our first task is to describe what we see, and to classify our observations into meaningful groups for the sake of convenience in handling. The moment that a geographer begins to describe an area, however, he becomes selective (for it is not possible to describe everything) and in the very act of selection demonstrates a conscious or unconscious theory or hypothesis concerning what is significant.

In his examination of significance in geography, Hartshorne rejects the notion that significance should be judged in terms of appearance, that is, as in objects in a landscape, and establishes as an alternative the criterion that observations should express "the variable character from place to place of the earth as the world of man."[56] In many geographic pursuits, man is the measure of significance, and spatial variations the focus. But how else can significance to man be measured except in terms of some theory of interrelationships?

In this connection there is reason to question Strahler's assertion, quoted above, that the Davisian geomorphologists "provided a sound basis for studies in human geography." The genetic and morphological landform classifications they produced may have provided a sound basis for most studies in human geography prior to 1950, but they are not truly anthropocentric. No attempts to assess significance to man were made until the work was substantially completed. This can be contrasted with Sheaffer's recent stream classification,[57] based on flood-to-peak interval, a variable known to be of significance for human adjustment.

The observation and description of regularities, such as those in the spatial arrangement of cultural features, human activities, or physical variables, are first steps in the development of theory. Theory provides the sieve through which myriads of facts are sorted, and without it the facts remain a meaningless jumble. Theory provides the measure against which exceptional and unusual events can be recognized. In a world without theory there are no exceptions; everything is unique. This is why theory is so important. As Braithwaite puts it, "the function of a science is to establish general laws covering the behavior of empirical events as objects with which the science in question is concerned . . . to enable us to correct together our knowledge of the separately known events, and to make reliable predictions of events yet unknown."[58]

The need to develop theory precedes the quantitative revolution, but quantification adds point to the need, and offers a technique whereby theory may be developed and improved. It is not certain that the early quantifiers were consciously motivated to develop theory, but it is now clear to geographers that quantification is inextricably intertwined with theory. The core of scientific method is the organization of facts into theories, and the testing and refinement of theory by its application to the prediction of unknown facts. Prediction is not only a valuable by-product of theory building, it is also a test by which the validity of theory can be demonstrated. Scientific inquiry may or may not be motivated by the desire to make more accurate predictions. Whatever the motivation, the ability to predict correctly is a sound test of the depth of our understanding.

Given the need to comply with the rigorous dictates of the scientific method, the need to develop theory, and to test theory with prediction, then mathematics is the best tool available to us for the purpose. Other tools—language, maps, symbolic logic—are also useful and in some instances quite adequate. But none so well fulfills our requirements as mathematics.

The quantification of theory, the use of mathematics to express relationships, can be supported on two main grounds. First, it is more rigorous. Second, and more important, it is a considerable aid in the avoidance of self-deception.

These points may be illustrated by reference to a paper by Robinson, Lindberg, and Brinkman on rural farm population densities in the Great Plains.[59] The authors point out that the statistical-cartographic techniques which they use may be properly employed after the establishment of "tentative descriptive hypotheses regarding the mutuality that may exist among the distributions of an area, inferred through the study of individual maps and other sorts of data. Coefficients of correlation and related indices provide general quantitative statements of the degree to which each hypothesis is valid."[60]

My submission is that the testing of hypotheses does not make much sense unless these hypotheses are related to a developing body of theory. High correlation does not necessarily confirm a hypothesis, and it is well known that nonsense correlations are possible. The authors propose rural farm population density as a dependent variable and proceed to examine spatial variations using average annual precipitation, distance from urban centers, and percentage of crop land in the total land area as explanatory variables. Having calculated correlation coefficients, the authors conclude that the general hypothesis concerning the association of spatial variations of these variables is confirmed.[61] This use of quantitative techniques demonstrates rigor to the extent that precise measurements of association are made. It also demonstrates the need and possibility of avoiding self-deception.

Nowhere in the paper is it possible to find an explicit statement of theory. Nowhere are we told why rural farm population density is highly correlated with average annual precipitation. Perhaps the explanation lies in the fact that as precipitation decreases, larger farm units are required to support a farm family, owing to lower yields of the same crops, or the cultivation of less remunerative crops. This is a theory, and a test of it would be to examine rural farm population density and farm size. It is conceivable that these two variables are not closely correlated. If this is the case, the theory will need revision. It is surely not much of an explanation, however, to correlate rural farm population density with precipitation. If there is a causal relationship here, it is an indirect one and several links have been omitted.

A more logical treatment would relate farm population to farm size, farm size to yields and land use, yields and land use to precipitation; but it is by no means certain that the causal chain of relationships could be carried so far. The correlations which John K. Rose[62] obtained between corn yields and July precipitation are not as high as Robinson, Lindberg, and Brinkman obtained for average annual precipitation and rural farm population. Admittedly, the two studies were concerned with different measurements, in different areas, at a different point in time. Nevertheless, it is significant that the Robinson group was able to show higher correlation between remotely connected variables than Rose could show between much more closely connected variables.

Robinson's study is deficient because it is not related to an explicit statement of theory. Quantitative analysis of variables cannot be justified for its own sake. The mere restatement of accepted ideas in numerical form instead of in "plain English" is not what the quantitative revolution is about. Examination of spatial variables of rural farm population of the Great Plains in terms of an explicit theory would have led Robinson, *et al.*, to select other, or at least additional, variables than those considered. Some might argue that the hypothesis relating rural farm population and average annual precipitation is a theory. If so, it sounds dangerously like the old deterministic hypotheses and has the same quality of inferring a causal relationship without any explanation or testing of a connecting process leading from cause to effect.

CONCLUSION

Quantitative techniques are a most appropriate method for the development of theory in geography. The quantitative era will last as long as its methods can be shown to be aiding in the development of theory, and there can be no end to the need for more and better theory. If follows that any branch of geography claiming to be scientific has need for the development of theory, and any branch of geography that has need for theory has need for quantitative techniques.

Not all statements of theory need to be expressed quantitatively in their initial form. Firey, for example, has developed a general theory of resource use[63] without resort to hypothesis testing in a formal sense. Such statements of theory are extremely valuable, and many more of them are needed in geography. Once formulated they should not long remain untested, but the testing need not be undertaken by the same person, or even by persons in the same discipline.

The development and testing of theory is the only way to obtain new and verifiable knowledge and new and verifiable understandings. As Curry points out:

Methods of representing various phenomena of nature and speculation about their interrelationships are closely tied together. It is too often forgotten that geographical studies are not descriptions of the real world, but rather perceptions passed through the double filter of the author's mind and his available tools of argument and representation. We cannot know reality, we can have only an abstract picture of aspects of it. All our descriptions of relations or processes are theories or, when formalized, better called models.[64]

Curry relates model building to another element in recent geographical work—the problem of perception, which may soon come to merit a place alongside the quantitative revolution in terms of significant new viewpoints.[65]

Our literature is replete with ideographic studies. There is a strong urge to get something into the literature because it has not been described before. If these ideographic studies and new descriptions are to have lasting value, their theoretical implications must be shown. In an increasing number of cases, the relationship to theory can best be shown in quantitative terms. In some instances a simple description of an exceptional case may serve to highlight defects in theory. The theory can then be revised or modified to take account of another kind of variation not previously noted, or the theory may have to be abandoned. Theories are not usually abandoned, however, because a few uncomfortable facts do not happen to fit. Theories are abandoned when newer and better theories are produced to take their place. Although observation and description of exceptional cases may be achieved without quantification,[66] the eventual incorporation of modifications into a theory will normally require the rigor of statistical techniques to demonstrate their validity.

There is not a very large literature in theoretical geography. Our discipline has remained predominantly ideographic.[67] A small proportion of the large volume of central place literature can be described as theoretical.[68] It is appropriate to speak of central place theory as one relatively well-developed branch of theoretical economic geography. A recent volume by Scheidegger has emphasized the theoretical aspects of geomorphology.[69] Wolman comments that "the emphasis on principles that Scheidegger stresses directs attention to interrelationships and hopefully lessens the tendency to observe, measure, and record everything because it's there."[70] This remark can be applied with equal value to the development of theory in other branches of geography.

Geographers are now making a conscious effort to develop more theory. A recent volume on theoretical geography[71] attempts to develop theory basic to some areas of the subject. In particular, the author presents a measurement of shape and discusses a general theory of movement and central place theory. This volume will help to focus the attention of geographers on the need for theory. Perhaps a rash of attempts to develop geographic theory will begin. Such a development seems unlikely, however. For while the use of quantitative methods is a technique that can be learned by most, few seem to have that gift of insight which leads to new theory. North comments that a difficult problem is "the development of the theoretical hypotheses necessary for shaping the direction of quantitative research."[72]

Attempts to develop theory in geography need not mean a wholesale shift in emphasis. Many an ideographic study could be of greater value if it contained but two paragraphs showing the theoretical implications of the work. This is often easier or at least possible for the author, while it is more difficult or even impossible for others who try to use the work at a subsequent time to develop or test theory. Of course, if case studies are designed with a theory in mind, it is likely that they will differ considerably from studies unrelated to a conscious statement of theory.

Theoretical geography does not mean the development of an entirely new body of theory exclusive to geography. Scheidegger has not attempted to develop new laws of physics, but has merely refined and adapted these laws to the study of geomorphological phenomena and processes. Central place theory is in keeping with some schools of economic theory. One role of an economic geographer is to refine and adapt available economic theory. In doing so he will improve the theory he borrows. If the Anglo-Saxon bias in economics has been to ignore the spatial aspects of economic activity, the geographer is one of those to whom we should look for the remedy. It need not be thought that the growth of regional science completely fills the gap. Those geographers who study drainage networks, highway networks, power distribution systems, flood problems, airline routes, social organization, and the venation of leaves all have in common a concern for a "flow" between "points" over a network of links arranged in a particular pattern. Graph theory is a branch of mathematics concerned with networks and may be adapted to fit all manner of collection, distribution, and communications systems. It is conceivable that a body of useful theory could be built up around the application of graph theory to geographical problems.[73] This is an example of what is meant by theoretical geography. It is a direction that an increasing number of geographers are likely to follow. Let us hope that the effort will meet success.

FOOTNOTES

[1] A shorter version of this paper was presented at the thirteenth annual meeting of the Canadian Association of Geographers, Quebec City, June 1963. The author thanks the following persons for aid and comments: Brian J. L. Berry, J. W. Birch, W. C. Calef, Michael Church, John Fraser Hart, Robert W. Kates, Leslie King, Jacob Spelt.

[2] D. C. North, "Quantitative Research in American Economic History," *American Economic Review*, **53** (1961), 128 130.

[3] See, for example, I. Berlin, "History and Theory: The Concept of Scientific History," *History and Theory*, **1** (1960), 1–3.

[4] From the editor's introduction, D. Lerner, ed., *Quality and Quantity* (New York: Free Press of Glencoe, Inc., 1961), p. 22.

[5] O. H. K. Spate, "Quantity and Quality in Geography," *Annals of the Association of American Geographers*, **50** (1960), 377–394.

[6] See, for example, Spate, "Toynbee and Huntington: A Study in Determinism," *Geographical Journal*, **118** (1952); also Spate, *The Compass of Geography* (Canberra: Australian National University, 1953), pp.

14–15. "There are signs of at least a neodeterminism, more subtle than the old, less inclined to think of environment as exercising an almost dictatorial power over human societies, but convinced that it is far more influential than the current view admits; and with this trend I would identify myself." Quoted in E. Jones, "Cause and Effect in Human Geography," *Annals of the Association of American Geographers*, **46** (1956), 369–377 (see 370). See also A. F. Martin, "The Necessity for Determinism," *Transactions and Papers, Institute of British Geographers*, **17** (1951), 1–11.

[7] L. Curry, "Climatic Change as a Random Series," below, pp. 184–194.

[8] T. Hägerstrand, "On Monte Carlo Simulation of Diffusion," and *The Propagation of Innovation Waves*, Lund Studies in Geography Series B, **4** (1952).

[9] J. Bronowski, *The Common Sense of Science* (New York: Random House, Inc., 1959).

[10] J. Neyman, "Indeterminism in Science and New Demands on Statisticians," *Journal of the American Statistical Association*, **55** (1960), 625–639.

[11] Jones, *op. cit.*, 373.

[12] E. A. Ackerman, *Geography as a Fundamental*

Research Discipline, University of Chicago, Department of Geography, Research Paper No. 53 (1958), p. 11.

[13] R. Hartshorne, *Perspective on the Nature of Geography* (Chicago: Rand McNally & Co., 1959), p. 161.

[14] Spate, "Quantity and Quality," *op cit.,* 386. Spate makes a similar statement in "Lord Kelvin Rides Again," *Economic Geography,* **36** (1960), preceding 95.

[15] Personal communication (March 30, 1963).

[16] J. von Neuman and O. Morgenstern, *Theory of Games and Economic Behavior* (Princeton: Princeton University Press, 1944).

[17] N. Wiener, *Cybernetics* (New York: John Wiley & Sons, Inc., 1948).

[18] G. K. Zipf, *Human Behavior and the Principle of Least Effort* (Reading, Mass.: Addison-Wesley Publishing Company, Inc., 1949).

[19] J. Q. Stewart, "Empirical Mathematical Rules Concerning the Distribution and Equilibrium of Population," *Geographical Review,* **37** (1947), 461–485.

[20] J. Q. Stewart, "The Development of Social Physics," *American Journal of Physics,* **18** (1950), 239–253.

[21] R. Vining, "Methodological Issues in Quantitative Economics," *Review of Economics and Statistics,* **31** (1949), 77–86. See also T. C. Koopman's reply and Vining's rejoinder, 86–94.

[22] J. K. Rose, "Corn Yield and Climate in the Corn Belt," *Geographical Review,* **26** (1936), 88–102. For a much earlier paper on a similar topic, see R. H. Hooker, "Correlation of the Weather and Crops," *Journal of the Royal Statistical Society,* **70** (1907), 1–51.

[23] A. N. Strahler, "Davis' Concepts of Slope Development Viewed in the Light of Recent Quantitative Investigations," *Annals of the Association of American Geographers,* **40** (1950), 209–213.

[24] G. K. Gilbert, *The Transportation of Debris by Running Water,* U.S. Geological Survey, Professional Paper No. 86 (Washington: U.S. G.P.O., 1914).

[25] Strahler, *op cit.,* 210.

[26] Strahler notes that important work was initiated in the Soil Conservation Service in the middle and late 1930's. In addition, in 1945 there is R. E. Horton's classical paper on quantitative morphology, "Erosional Development of Streams and Their Drainage Basins: Hydrophysical Approach to Quantitative Morphology," *Bulletin of the Geological Society of America,* **56** (1945), 275–370.

[27] See L. O. Quam, "Remarks on Strahler's Paper," *Annals of the Association of American Geographers,* **40** (1950), 213.

[28] S. W. Wooldridge and R. S. Morgan, *An Outline of Geomorphology* (London: Longmans, Green & Company, Ltd., 1959), 2nd ed., p.v.

[29] L. King, *Morphology of the Earth* (Edinburgh: Oliver & Boyd, Ltd., 1962), p. 231.

[30] See, for example, R. J. Chorley, "Climate and Morphometry," *Journal of Geography,* **65** (1957), 628–638.

[31] See, for example, G. H. Dury, "Contribution to a General Theory of Meandering Valleys," *American Journal of Science,* **252** (1954), 193–224; also "Tests of a General Theory of Misfit Streams," *Transactions and Papers, Institute of British Geographers,* **25** (1958), 105

118; and "Misfit Streams: Problems in Interpretation, Discharge and Distribution," *Geographical Review,* **50** (1960), 219–242.

[32] J. R. Mackay, "Pingos of the Pleistocene Mackenzie Delta Area," *Geographical Bulletin,* No. 18 (1962), 21–63; and *The Mackenzie Delta Area,* N.W.T. Department of Mines & Technical Surveys, Geographical Branch (Ottawa, 1963).

[33] See, for example, M. G. Wolman, *The Natural Channel of Brandywine Creek, Pa.,* U.S. Geological Survey, Professional Paper No. 271 (Washington: U.S. G.P.O., 1955).

[34] Much of the work of C. W. Thornthwaite and J. R. Mather has appeared in the Thornthwaite Associates Laboratory of Climatology, *Publications in Climatology* (Centerton, N.J.).

[35] See, for example F. K. Hare, "Dynamic and Synoptic Climatology," *Annals of the Association of American Geographers,* **45** (1955), 152–162; also "The Westerlies," *Geographical Review,* **50** (1960), 345–367.

[36] See, for example, L. H. Horn and R. A. Bryson, "Harmonic Analysis of the Annual March Precipitation over the United States," *Annals of the Association of American Geographers,* **50** (1960), 157–171. Also M. E. Sabbagh and R. A. Bryson, "Aspects of the Precipitation Climatology of Canada Investigated by the Method of Harmonic Analysis," below, pp. 250–265.

[37] A useful summary is provided by G. Tatham, "Environmentalism and Possibilism," in G. Taylor, ed., *Geography in the Twentieth Century* (New York: Philosophical Library, 1951), pp. 128–162.

[38] W. L. Garrison, "Some Confusing Aspects of Common Measurements," *Professional Geographer,* **8** (1956), 4–5.

[39] H. J. Nelson, "A Service Classification of American Cities," *Economic Geography,* **31** (1955), 189–210.

[40] R. B. Reynolds, "Statistical Methods of Geographical Research," *Geographical Review,* **46** (1956), 129–132.

[41] W. L. Garrison, "Applicability of Statistical Inference to Geographical Research," *Geographical Review,* **46** (1956), 427–429.

[42] Spate, "Lord Kelvin Rides Again," *op cit.*

[43] B.J.L. Berry, "The Quantitative Bogey-Man," *Economic Geography,* **36** (1960), preceding 283.

[44] M. F. Dacey, "The Spacing of River Towns," *Annals of the Association of American Geographers,* **50** (1960), 59–61.

[45] A. F. Burghardt, "The Location of River Towns in the Central Lowland of the United States," *Annals of the Association of American Geographers,* **49** (1959), 305–323.

[46] P. W. Porter, "Earnest and the Orephagians: A Fable for the Instruction of Young Geographers," *Annals of the Association of American Geographers,* **50** (1960), 297–299.

[47] L. Zobler, "Decision Making in Regional Construction," *Annals of the Association of American Geographers,* **48** (1958), 140–148.

[48] J. R. Mackay, "Chi-Square as a Tool for Regional Studies," *Annals of the Association of American Geographers,* **48** (1958), 164. See also Zobler, "The Distinction Between Relative and Absolute Frequencies in Using Chi-Square for Regional Analysis," *ibid.,* 456–457;

and Mackay and Berry, "Comments on the Use of Chi-Square," *ibid.*, **49** (1959), 89.

⁴⁹ Arthur H. Robinson, "On Perks and Pokes," *Economic Geography*, **10** (1958), 2–10.

⁵⁰ F. Luckermann, "Toward a More Geographic Economic Geography," *Professional Geographer*, **37** (1958), 2–10.

⁵¹ B. J. L. Berry, "Further Comments Concerning 'Geographic' and 'Economic' Economic Geography," *Professional Geographer*. **11** (1959), 11–12.

⁵² D. L. Stamp, "Geographical Agenda: A Review of Some Tasks Awaiting Geographical Attention," *Transactions and Papers, Institute of British Geographers*, **23** (1957), 1–17 (see 2).

⁵³ H. H. McCarty and N. E. Salisbury, *Visual Comparison of Isopleth Maps as a Means of Determining Correlations Between Spatially Distributed Phenomena*, University of Iowa, Department of Geography, Publication No. 3 (1961).

⁵⁴ A. E. Maxwell, *Analyzing Qualitative Data* (London: Methuen & Co., Ltd., 1961).

⁵⁵ F. K. Shaefer, "Exceptionalism in Geography: A Methodological Examination," *Annals of the Association of American Geographers*, **43** (1953), 226–249.

⁵⁶ Hartshorne, *op. cit.*, pp. 36–47.

⁵⁷ J. R. Sheaffer, "Flood-to-Peak Interval," in G. F. White, ed., *Papers on Flood Problems*, University of Chicago, Department of Geography, Research Paper No. 70 (1961), pp. 95–113. Also I. Burton, [whose] *Types of Agricultural Occupance of Flood Plains in the United States* (University of Chicago, Department of Geography, Research Paper No. 75 [1962]) represents a similar attempt to classify flood plains on the basis of characteristics significant for agricultural occupance.

⁵⁸ R. B. Braithwaite, *Scientific Explanation* (New York: Cambridge University Press, 1955).

⁵⁹ A. H. Robinson, J. B. Lindberg, and L. W. Brinkman, "A Correlation and Regression Analysis Applied to Rural Farm Population Densities in the Great Plains," below, pp. 211–221.

⁶⁰ *Ibid.*, 211.

⁶¹ *Ibid.*, 215.

⁶² Rose, *op. cit.*, 95–97, Figs. 7–8.

⁶³ W. Firey, *Man, Mind and Land: A Theory of Resource Use* (New York: Free Press of Glencoe, Inc., 1960).

⁶⁴ Curry, *op cit.*, 21.

⁶⁵ One recent publication in this newly developing field of geography is R. W. Kates, *Hazard and Choice Perception in Flood Management*, University of Chicago, Department of Geography, Research Paper No. 78 (1962).

⁶⁶ See, for example, my description of a dispersed city as an exception to the classical central place theory in "A Restatement of the Dispersed City Hypothesis," *Annals of the Association of American Geographers*, **53** (1963), 285–289.

⁶⁷ W. R. Siddall, "Two Kinds of Geography," *Economic Geography*, **51** (1961), preceding 189.

⁶⁸ B. J. L. Berry and A. Pred, *Central Place Studies: A Bibliography of Theory and Applications*, Bibliography Series No. 1 (Philadelphia: Regional Science Research Institute, 1961).

⁶⁹ A. E. Scheidegger, *Theoretical Geomorphology* (Berlin: Springer Verlag, 1961).

⁷⁰ Wolman, review of *ibid.*, in *Geographical Review*, **53** (1963), 331–333.

⁷¹ W. Bunge, *Theoretical Geography*, Lund Studies in Geography, Series C, No. 1 (1962).

⁷² North, *op. cit.*, 129.

⁷³ Some recent work has been done in this direction. See W. L. Garrison, "Connectivity of the Interstate Highway System," below, pp. 239–249; J. D. Nystuen and M. F. Dacey, "A Graph Theory Interpretation of Nodal Regions," below, pp. 407–418; K. Kansky, *Structure of Transportation Networks: Relationships Between Network Geometry and Regional Characteristics*, University of Chicago, Department of Geography, Research Paper No. 84 (1963); I. Burton, "Accessibility in Northern Ontario: An Application of Graph Theory to a Regional Highway Network," unpublished report to Ontario Department of Highways (Toronto, 1962).

2

APPROACHES TO REGIONAL ANALYSIS:
A SYNTHESIS

BRIAN J. L. BERRY

All discord, harmony not understood.
—ALEXANDER POPE, *Essay on Man*, 1:289

In my dictionary I find a synthesis defined as "a complex whole made up of a number of parts united."[1] The suggestions of complexity and unity are bothersome, however, because the synthesis of approaches to regional analysis presented in this paper is simplistic at best, and we have all found that the parts hardly seem united at times. There is perhaps only one advantage to be gained from the simplification—that poorly developed or new approaches to studying the geography of an area[2] may be identified more readily.

The paper begins with certain assertions concerning geography's role among the sciences. A synthesis of apparently dichotomous approaches to geographic understanding is then proposed,[3] and the concluding remarks are directed to the question of new approaches. The route toward such new approaches begins with analysis of the inadequacies of the pro-posed synthesis, and continues with discussion of possible solutions to the inadequacies via generalizations produced in general systems theory.[4]

GEOGRAPHY AMONG THE SCIENCES

James Conant describes science as an interconnected series of concepts and conceptual schemes that have developed as a result of experimentation and observation and are fruitful of further experimentation and observation as man explores his universe. He characterizes the methods of exploration—scientific method—as comprising speculative general ideas, deductive reasoning, and experimentation. Like all

Reprinted from *Annals of the Association of American Geographers*, **54** (1964), 2–11, by permission of the author and editor.

brief statements on any subject, these are ambiguous and incomplete outside of the expanded context given them by the author. They do provide a useful setting for the first thesis of this paper, however, that *geographers are like any other scientists, identified not so much by the phenomena they study, as by the integrating concepts and processes that they stress.*[5] James Blaut expresses the point nicely, saying that the objects dealt with by science are not natural entities, ultimate objects, but are rather sets of interlocking propositions about systems.[6]

Systems may be viewed in a variety of ways, and hence the variety of propositions that may be developed concerning them. The particular set of propositions stressed by any science depends upon its point of view, the perspective in looking at systems that it instills into its members as they progress from novices to accepted membership in that select professional core that serves as guardian and proponent of the viewpoint. As Kenneth Boulding has said, subjects "carve out for themselves certain elements of the experience of man and develop theories and patterns of research activity which yield satisfaction in understanding, and which are appropriate to their special segments."[7] Within this context, our second and third theses are thus that *the geographic point of view is spatial* and that *the integrating concepts and processes of the geographer relate to spatial arrangements and distributions, to spatial integration, to spatial interactions and organization, and to spatial processes.*[8]

But the experience of man encompasses many systems, and the geographer does not apply his spatial perspective to all. The second and third theses define the way of viewing, but not that which is viewed. Which system is examined by geographers? Hartshorne properly describes it as comprising "the earth as the home of man." A geographer is so trained and inclined that he assumes a spatial perspective in his analysis. But this perspective is not his sole perquisite, for other scientists take such a viewpoint. His contribution is that it is he who provides the spatial perspective so important to any understanding of the system comprising the earth as the home of man. This definition logically excludes from geography studies of other systems from a spatial viewpoint. We are well aware, for example, that when certain physical systems covering the

earth are studied apart from their relevance to man, even from a spatial point of view, the job is done by people in other disciplines—geologists, meteorologists, and oceanographers, among others. Similarly, bubble chamber work proceeds from a spatial viewpoint at the microlevel, and is undertaken by physicists.

What is this system comprising the earth as the home of man? It can be described as the complex, worldwide, man-earth ecosystem.[9] An ecosystem logically comprises populations of living organisms and a complex of environmental factors, in which the organisms interact among themselves in many ways, and in which there are reciprocal effects between the environments and the populations.[10] Biologists, botanists, and ecologists study such ecosystems from a spatial point of view, of course, but the geographer is the person who concentrates upon the spatial analysis of that worldwide ecosystem of which man is a part. The earth as the home of man is a gigantic ecosystem in which man, with culture, has become the ecological dominant. His earthly environments are thus not simply—and less and less—the physical and biological, but also the cultural of his own creating. The fourth thesis thus becomes: *Geography's integrating concepts and processes concern the worldwide ecosystem of which man is the dominant part.*

There is a further problem which emerges at this point. Definition of the system which geography studies from a spatial point of view is perfectly adequate to differentiate geography's role from that of the physical and biological sciences. Many social sciences study the man-made environments, however: political, economic, social, cultural, psychological, and the like, studied by political scientists, economists, sociologists, anthropologists, and psychologists. We resort to our second thesis. None of these sciences examines the man-made environments from a spatial point of view, whether it be to examine spatial distributions or associations of elements, the organization of phenomena over space, or the integration of diverse phenomena in place. Other distributional and organizational themes are stronger and more central to the other social sciences. Thus, whereas it is the system which is studied which differentiates geography from the physical and biological sciences, in studies of man and his works it is the spatial perspective that differentiates. Within the worldwide ecosystem of which man is the dominant part, man creates for himself many environments. These environments are not studied in their totality by geographers, only in their spatial facets.

DICHOTOMIES WITHIN GEOGRAPHY

Debate about approaches to geographic understanding has traditionally run to dichotomies: natural as opposed to human; topical or systematic vs. regional; historical or developmental as contrasted with functional and organizational; qualitative vs. quantitative; perks vs. pokes. Richard Hartshorne has gone to great lengths to show that many of these dichotomies are either meaningless or useless,[11] but the fact that dichotomies have emerged at all suggests that *the spatial viewpoint has several facets.* In his seminal paper "Geography as Spatial Interaction," Edward Ullman has gone so far as to argue that the essential intellectual contributions of human geography can be summarized in terms of a dichotomy, the dual concepts of *site* and *situation.*[12] Site is vertical, referring to local, man-land relations, to form and morphology. Situation is horizontal and functional, referring to regional interdependencies and the connections between places, or to what Ullman calls spatial interaction.

Existence of several facets poses problems, even if we agree that, as dichotomies, they are of little utility. Boulding argues that the most significant "crisis in science today arises because of the increasing difficulty of profitable talk among scientists as a whole." Very descriptively, he says that

"Specialization has outrun Trade, communication . . . becomes increasingly difficult, and the Republic of Learning is breaking up into isolated subcultures with only tenuous lines of communication between them. . . . One wonders sometimes if science will not grind to a stop in an assemblage of walled-in hermits, each mumbling to himself in a private language that only he can understand. . . .

Is this to be our fate within geography, with analytically minded economic urbanists off building their fragile models, anthropologically oriented cultural ecologists sequestered in some primitive backwoods contemplating their navels, and the like? As Boulding continues, "the spread of specialized deafness means that someone who

ought to know something that someone else knows isn't able to find it out for lack of generalized ears." His solution is "general systems theory to develop those generalized ears . . . to enable one specialist to catch relevant communications from others."[13]

A system is an entity consisting of specialized interdependent parts. Most systems can be subdivided into subsystems by searching for modules with high degrees of internal connectivity and lower degrees of intermodule interaction. If larger modules can be partitioned into smaller modules, it is possible to talk of a hierarchy of systems and subsystems.[14]

What we will try to do here is to construct a simple system that depicts the variety of approaches to regional analysis. The traditional dichotomies will be included either as parts of the frame of reference which specifies how the system is separated from the rest of science (the balance of science can be termed the "environment" of the system) or as modules of the system. It is this system that constitutes the synthesis of approaches to regional analysis. The fact that a system has been created emphasizes the unity of the spatial viewpoint. The many facets are not dichotomous or polychotomous, but interdependent; each feeds into and draws upon the others. Moreover, by treating the system so created as one would any other system within the framework of general systems theory, poorly developed or new approaches to the geography of large areas may be identified and elaborated. In this way the gift of the "generalized ears" can be used to catch communications from scientists who have forged ahead of us in the development of their particular sets of propositions about the systems they see and study.

A GEOGRAPHIC MATRIX[15]

Reflect for a moment on the nature of a single observation recorded from the spatial point of view. Such an observation refers to a single characteristic at a single place or location, and may be termed a "geographic fact." This geographic fact usually will be one of a set of observations, either of the same characteristic at a series of places, or of a series of characteristics at the same place. The two series need to be examined more closely. If the characteristic recorded at the series of places varies from place to place, it is common to refer to its spatial variations. These variations may be mapped, for just as the statistician's series are arranged in frequency distributions, geographers like to arrange theirs in spatial distributions. Study of the resulting spatial patterns displayed in the map is one of the essentials of geography. As for the series of characteristics recorded at the same place, they are the stuff of locational inventories and the geography of particular places. With such inventories it is the geographer's common practice to study the integration of phenomena in place.

Now assume [that] a whole series of characteristics has been recorded for a whole series of places. Perhaps we can imagine that complete "geographic data files" are available (whether such a dream may really be a nightmare is another topic). An efficient way to arrange the resulting body of data is in a rectangular array, or matrix. What does this "geographic matrix" look like? Each characteristic accounts for a row, and each place for a column, as in Fig. 1. The intersection of any row and column defines a cell, and each cell is filled by a geographic fact, the characteristic identified in the row, and the place in the column.

At this juncture one might object and say that there is surely an infinity of characteristics and therefore an infinity of possible rows, and at the limit also an infinity of infinitesimal locations on the earth's surface providing an

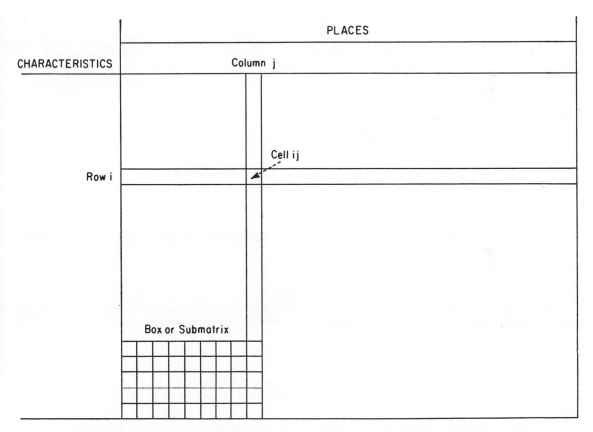

FIGURE 1. *The Geographic Matrix.* A row of this matrix presents the place-to-place variation of some characteristic, or a spatial pattern of the variable which can thus be mapped. Each column contains the locational inventory of the many characteristics of some place. Every cell therefore contains a "geographic fact": the value assumed by some characteristic at some place. Comparison of complete columns is the study of areal differentiation in its holistic sense, and leads to regional geography. Comparison of rows implies the study of spatial covariations and associations, and leads to topical or systematic geography.

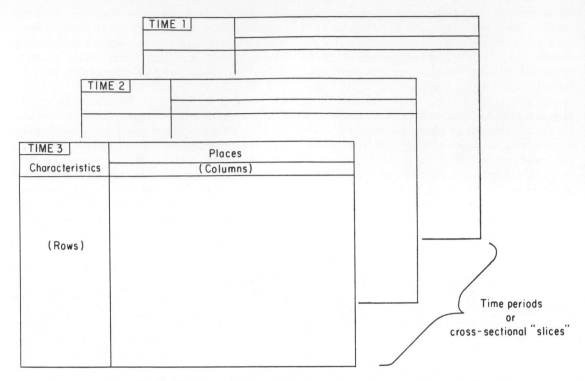

FIGURE 2. *A Third Dimension.* The third dimension, time, may be introduced by arraying a whole series of geographic matrices such as were presented in Fig. 1 in their correct temporal sequence. Each time period thus forms a "slice" of the three-dimensional cake, and every slice has all the features described in Fig. 1. It will be obvious that such an arrangement makes possible examination of rows through time, of columns through time, and of boxes through time.

infinite number of possible columns. This is true; all converges to infinity in the long run. However, to quote Keynes's well-worn maxim, in the long run we shall all be dead. In practice, for any particular problem in any particular context there is some specification of rows (characteristics) and columns (places) that is meaningful and useful. The present discussion is phrased so as to be applicable whenever there is such a problem, whatever the problem and consequent specification of the rows and columns may be, just so long as the viewpoint is spatial.

Given a geographic matrix as described above, how many approaches to regional analysis are possible? One can examine:

(*a*) the arrangement of cells within a row or part of a row; or
(*b*) the arrangement of cells within a column or part of a column.

The former leads to study of spatial distributions and maps, the latter to the study of localized associations of variables in place and to locational inventories. Surely we would agree that the two approaches are the bases of all geography.

Next steps might be:

(*c*) comparison of pairs or of whole series of rows; and
(*d*) comparison of pairs of columns or of whole series of columns.

The former involves studies of spatial covariations, or spatial association. If the columns are complete, running across all characteristics outlined in Fig. 1, the latter implies the study of areal differentiation in its holistic sense.[16]

A fifth possibility is:

(*e*) the study of a "box" or submatrix (see

It is evident that this kind of study could involve some or all of steps (*a*)-(*d*) above, but with something additional—the ability to use findings, say, from studies of spatial association to enrich an understanding of areal differentiation in the partitive sense of the box, or of areal differentiation to explain cases which deviate from some generally expected pattern of spatial association between variables. Each approach could indeed feed into and enrich the other.

A THIRD DIMENSION

The definition of a geographic fact presented to this point is deficient in one respect, since a single characteristic observed at a single location must necessarily also be observed *at a particular point in time*. At any other time it would be different; variation is temporal as well as spatial. Time, too, may be subdivided infinitely, but it is useful to think of the geographic matrix with a third dimension arranged as in Fig. 2 in a series of cross sections or "slices" taken through time in the same manner as rows were drawn through the infinity of characteristics and columns through the infinity of places. Each slice thus summarizes or captures the variations of characteristics from place to place at a certain period of time. Our historical geographers follow this pragmatic procedure. Andrew Clark, for example, noted that "the cross sections which geography cuts through the dimension of time . . . must have a certain thickness or duration, to provide a representative picture of existing situations."[17]

It will be obvious that for any time period, each of the five possible approaches to geographic analysis previously outlined may be taken. "Geographies of the past" can be studied in this way. Yet there are additional possibilities introduced by the temporal dimension:

(*f*) comparison of a row or part of a row through time, the study of changing spatial distributions;

(*g*) comparison of a column or part of a column through time, the study of the changing character of some particular area through a series of stages, otherwise termed the study of sequent occupance;

(*h*) study of changing spatial associations;

(*i*) study of changing areal differentiation;

and

(*j*) comparison of a submatrix through time, a process that could involve all of the preceding approaches individually, but more properly undertaken requires their interplay.

THE TEN APPROACHES

It is thus possible to conceive of ten modes of geographical analysis which may be applied to further an understanding of geographic data files such as are depicted in Fig. 2. These ten modes fall into three series. The first ([*a*], [*c*], [*f*], and [*h*]) includes studies of the nature of single spatial distributions, of the covariance of different distributions at the same period of time or of the distribution of the same phenomenon at different periods of time, and of the covariance of different distributions through time. A similar series of three levels characterizes the second series ([*b*], [*d*], [*g*], and [*i*]), which spans locational inventories, studies of areal differentiation and of sequent occupance, and investigations of changing areal differentiation. The third series ([*e*] and [*j*]) involves, at its simplest, the cross-sectional interplay of studies of spatial distributions and associations, locational inventories and areal differentiation, and at its more elaborate level the interplay of all nine of the earlier analytic modes.

TRADITIONAL GROUPINGS OF ROWS AND COLUMNS

Figure 3 shows the ways in which geographers have traditionally grouped rows and columns of the matrix, and also the conventional ways of grouping the cross-sectional slices, for which we are indebted to historians.[18]

The most common categorization of variables is into one of geography's classic dichotomies, human and physical. Within the human it is conventional to differentiate between variables dealing with collections of people and their numerical and biological characteristics, and those dealing with culture, here used in the holistic sense of the set of man-made variables intervening between man and the earth's surface. These intervening variables may be classified into urban, settlement, transportation, political, economic, and the like. Each of these can be, and has at times been, further sub-

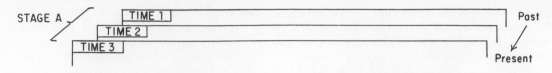

FIGURE 3. *Traditional Grouping of Dimensions.* Geographers have traditionally grouped variables into an ascending hierarchy of rows, the topical subfields. The broadest distinction is between human and physical geography. Within the former it is possible to isolate that part concerned with culture in its holistic sense, and within culture, the social, economic, and political. Economic is further subdivided into resources, industrial, etc. Industrial itself has been further subdivided, and so forth. Hartshorne also speaks of the study of areal differentiation as leading toward the identification of a hierarchy of world regions, formed by successive grouping of places and smaller regions into larger more general regions. This is to be seen in the arrangement of the columns. Finally, arrangement of the successive slices into "stages" is the work of the historian. Given this reference framework, it is possible to locate such things as "changing industrial structure of the English Midlands and the Ruhr during the industrial revolution" with ease, and to ascertain their immediate relevance to other undertakings in geography.

divided to create further systematic "fields." Economic, for example, is often subdivided into: resources, agricultural, manufacturing, and commercial. These in turn involve further subdivisions, until very limited groups of associated characteristics may be said to define "topical fields." Such is always the pressure of increasing specialization, and, at the extreme, overspecialization.

Clearly, row-wise groupings of variables of

interest correspond with the topical or systematic branches of geography. The essence of this kind of geography is thus the first of the three series of modes of geographical analysis. By the same token, groups of columns form regions (most conventionally, such groupings have been based upon countries and continents, or upon physiographic or climatic criteria). Analysis of such groups of columns is regional geography, with its basis the second series of modes of geographical analysis, emphasizing locational inventories and areal differentiation. *If the object of systematic geography is to find those fundamental patterns and associations characterizing a limited range of functionally interrelated variables over a wide range of places, the object of regional geography is to find the essential characteristics of a particular region—its "regional character" based upon the localized associations of variables in place—by examining a wide range of variables over a limited number of places.*

Yet neither a topical specialty nor study of a particular region can be sufficient unto itself. More profound understanding of spatial associations can only come from "comparative systematics" cutting across several topical fields, from an understanding of local variabilities, and from appreciation of the development of patterns through time. Indeed, geography's first, unlamented, theories about man's distribution on the surface of the earth, those of environmental determinism and their wishy-washy derivatives, possibilism and probabilism, postulated particular patterns whereby arrangements of characteristics from place to place in the "human rows" of Fig. 3 were determined by arrangements of physical characteristics in the physical rows with, in many respects, the former as a reflected image of the latter. The whole idea of study of man-land relationships is the idea of comparative systematics.

Similarly, "regional character" can only be evaluated in its integrative sense by proper comparative study of regions, the study of areal differentiation. But here we must pause. What is the basis of regional character? Is it the repetitive appearance of a common theme or themes throughout the entire set of variables recorded for the places within the region, which theme or themes differs from those of other regions? If it is, and there is every reason to believe so, then the understanding of regional

character presumes an analysis of spatial associations, simplified because it is undertaken for a relatively small number of places, but complicated because it must be defined for many variables. Only by such study can underlying and repetitive themes be identified. Much the same point can be made for topical studies as well. They are regional because they involve the study of a certain number of variables within the confines of a certain set of places. Whether we call a study topical or regional, then, is basically a function of the relative *length* and *breadth* of the portion of the geographic matrix which is studied. Likewise, whether we classify a study as historical geography or not depends upon the *depth* of the portion of the matrix studied relative to its length or breadth, or else the distance of the slice studied from the present.

To extend the argument further, selection of the columns to be studied is not entirely independent of the rows under investigation in American geography today. If a person is studying things in the economic, urban, and transportation rows, it is likely that his studies will also be confined to those columns encompassing "modern" urban-industrial societies. Similarly, if the rows under study involve culture in its partitive sense of cultures, settlement forms, language, religion, ecology, and man-land relations, then it is quite probable that the columns embracing the study will be restricted to preliterate and/or "nonwestern" or "preindustrial" societies. Although there are different modes of analysis, on no account, therefore, can it be said that the several series are undertaken independently of one another, nor should they be.

PERSPECTIVES ON THE ECONOMIC GEOGRAPHY OF THE UNITED STATES

Let us now use this matrix, and later a critique of its inadequacies, to see how well or how thoroughly we have studied the economic geography of the United States.[19] We should first define a submatrix in which the rows embrace those variables of interest to economic geography and the columns encompass all places in the United States. By projecting the box backward, we get historical depth.

Studies of this box *per se* have been done

very well. The spatial distribution and associations of many variables have been mapped and analyzed. The character of the economic enterprises of most places is well known, as is the historical development of most of the major industries. Attempts of varying degrees of quality have been made to define the relatively homogeneous economic regions of the country both in the partitive sense of agricultural regions, manufacturing regions and the like, and in the holistic sense of real, multivariate, uniform economic regions. Spatial aspects of the economic growth of the country have been the subject of many investigations.

Yet serious limitations to a general understanding of the economic geography of the country should also be noted. We have already argued that an understanding of the spatial association of any single set of variables requires an evaluation of their actual covariance and theoretical relationship to many other sets of variables, since we are dealing with a system of which interdependence is the essence. Explicit and implicit hypotheses relating to such broader associations are restricted to something which varies between hard-nosed and softheaded environmentalism. Similarly, more profound understanding of areal differentiation hinges upon comparative regional investigations. This literature is also limited. A third problem is that the model we have developed embraces most of the approaches conceived and undertaken by geographers, but not all; the model itself is limited. There are important geographic questions which the matrix we have developed does not show.

The discussion was initially phrased in terms of general systems theory. This theory tells us what some of these unanswered questions are. Any system, including the "world-wide eco-system of which man is the dominant part" can be viewed at a variety of levels, the first three of which are those of *static structure*, *connectivity of parts (functional organization)*, and *dynamic processes*. Figure 3 shows the ways in which the system of interest to geography may be viewed at the first of these levels, that of static structure—of frameworks and patterns in space and time. It says nothing at all about the second level of interconnections across areas, connectivity of places, flows and interactions, let alone of the third, that of dynamic, interrelated processes. Studies of the economic geography of the United States at the second level are fewer in number and more limited in scope compared with those at the static level, in spite of the early efforts of Platt and the later investigations of Harris and Ullman. The growing central place literature is undoubtedly the best example of the level at which the spatial organization of the United States economy is understood. This literature refers to a single sector, the distributive, and is generally confined to the local level of very small urban places. There is no understanding of the spatial organization of the United States economy that compares with our understanding of the static patterns, no functional regionalization to match the uniform.

There is no longer any real reason why this gap should exist, in spite of the complexity of the system which has to be clarified. What needs to be grasped is roughly as follows:

1. We live in a specialized society in which there is a progressively greater division of labor and scale of enterprise, accompanied by increasing degrees of regional specialization.

2. But in spite of the increasing diversity of people as producers, as consumers they are becoming more and more alike from one part of the country to another, consuming much the same "basket of goods" wherever they may live, as well as increasingly large baskets because of rising real incomes.

3. The physical problem in the economic system is therefore one of articulation—ensuring that the specialized products of each segment of the country are shipped to final consumers; seeing that consumers in every part of the country receive the basket of goods and services they demand and are able to purchase; bringing demands and supplies into equality over a period of time.

4. Articulation requires flows of messages, of goods and services, and of funds. The flows appear to be highly structured and channeled, with major metropolitan centers serving as critical articulation points, as follows: products move from their specialized production areas to transshipment or shipping points in the locally dominant metropolitan centers; a complete matrix of intermetropolitan product transfers takes place on a national basis, with each metropolitan center shipping out the specialized products of its hinterland, and collecting the entire range of specialized products from

other metropolitan centers spread throughout the country to satisfy the demands of the consumers residing in the area it dominates; distribution then takes place from the metropolis to its hinterland through the medium of wholesale and retail contacts organized in the familiar central place hierarchy. In the reverse direction move both requests for goods and services and funds to pay for goods and services received, so that the flows are not unidirectional.

The foregoing seems simple enough *but it is mostly unsupported by substantive studies of the spatial organization of the economy of the United States.* Here is a pressing need for careful analysis and synthesis. The amount we do not know at only the second level of viewing the system of interest to geographers is immense, without raising such third-level questions as the ways in which the complex spatial organization of the country is changing through time, and why. The challenge is great, and if these considerations constitute poorly developed or new approaches to the economic geography of the United States, it is toward their solution that we should be moving.

FOOTNOTES

[1] *The Oxford Universal Dictionary on Historical Principles*, 3rd ed. (1955).

[2] As applied later in the paper, and as befits the purpose of the President's program, the particular area of concern is the United States, but the remarks should apply generally.

[3] The ideas are directly attributable to J. S. Berliner, who developed them in his review of anthropology: "The Feet of the Natives Are Large: An Essay on Anthropology by an Economist," *Current Anthropology*, **3** (1962), 47–77.

[4] The idea of general systems theory was originally formulated by L. von Bertalanffy, "General System Theory: A New Approach to Unity of Science," *Human Biology*, **23** (1951), 303–361. The journal *General Systems* is a basic source for all interested in general systems theory.

[5] This contrasts with Hartshorne's view that geography is a chorological science similar to the chronological sciences but contrasting with the sciences classified by categories of phenomena. See *The Nature of Geography* (Washington: Association of American Geographers, 1949), Chaps. 4, 5, and 9, and *Perspective on the Nature of Geography* (Chicago: Rand McNally & Co., 1959), Chaps. 2, 3, and 11. We are not alone in questioning Hartshorne's views, for a similar debate has been raging for some time in history. Anyone interested in this debate should refer to the journal *History and Theory*.

[6] J. M. Blaut, "Object and Relationship," *The Professional Geographer*, **14** (1962), 1–7.

[7] K. E. Boulding, "General Systems Theory—The Skeleton of Science," *Management Science*, **2** (1956), 197.

[8] A caveat is appropriate at this point. Edward Shils' remarks concerning sociology, which appear in the *Epilogue* to his monumental collection *Theories of Society* (with Talcott Parsons, Kasper D. Naegele, and Jesse R. Pitts, 2 vols. [New York: Free Press of Glencoe, Inc., 1961]), might well have been written about the scientific status of contemporary geography:

> Insofar as a science is a coherent body of empirically supported propositions which retain their stability within a particular theoretical framework, sociology is not a science today. The empirically verified propositions at a level of low particularity are many; as they rise toward generality they become fewer, not because the structure of any science requires it, but because of the deficient coherence of the analytical scheme that explicitly or implicitly guides these inquiries, and because the techniques of research have still not been sufficiently well adapted to the observation of more abstractly formulated variability. Nor, for that matter, has theory become sufficiently articulated and explicit. The gap between general theory and actual observation is still considerable.

This statement subsumes R. B. Braithwaite's views concerning the structure of a science, namely, that a science properly includes several elements: (*a*) the facts observed and the simple, inductive generalizations based upon these facts; (*b*) abstract logical constructs; and (*c*) scientific theories, which are initially stated as hypothesis, and only assume the status of valid and accepted theory when the simple inductive generalizations and the final deductions of the abstract logical constructs coincide. "Coincidence" is achieved when a satisfactory level of explanation of the inductive generalizations from the deductive constructs is achieved. Nagel provides an excellent discussion of the four modes on scientific explanation, strictly logical, genetic, functional, and probabilistic. See R. B. Braithwaite, *Scientific Explanation* (London: Cambridge University Press, 1953), and E. Nagel, *The Structure of Science* (New York: Harcourt, Brace & World, Inc., 1962). Adherence to these views we consider basic to this paper.

[9] E. A. Ackerman, "Where Is a Research Frontier?" *Annals of the Association of American Geographers*, **53** (1963), 429–440.

[10] R. P. McIntosh, "Ecosystems, Evolution and Relational Patterns of Living Organisms," *American Scientist*, **51** (1963), 246–267.

[11] *Ibid.*

[12] E. L. Ullman, "Geography as Spatial Interaction," *Proceedings of the Western Committee on Regional*

Economic Analysis, D. Revzan and E. A. Englebert, eds. (Berkeley: University of California Press, 1954), pp. 1–13.

[13] *Boulding, op. cit.*, 198–199.

[14] I am indebted to discussions with Alex Orden for clarification of many concepts concerning systems and general systems theories.

[15] This "geographic matrix" differs from the matrix developed for anthropology by Berliner only in that the columns are *places* for geography and *cultures* for anthropology. This difference perhaps indicates the kind of variability of major interest to the anthropologist vis-à-vis the geographer, and thus the different perspective in looking at the same systems taken by the two subjects.

[16] R. Hartshorne, "On the Concept of Areal Differentiation," *The Professional Geographer*, **14** (1962), 10–12.

[17] A. H. Clark, "Praemia Geographiae: The Incidental Rewards of a Professional Career," *Annals of the Association of American Geographers*, **52** (1962), 230, quoting Hartshorne.

[18] In this grouping I relied upon P. E. James and C. F. Jones, eds., *American Geography: Inventory and Prospect* (Syracuse: Syracuse University Press, 1954).

[19] The evidence supporting these remarks will be found in B. J. L. Berry and T. D. Hankins, *A Bibliographic Guide to the Economic Regions of the United States*, a study prepared for the Commission on Methods of Economic Regionalization of the International Geographical Union, and published as Research Paper No. 87, Department of Geography Research Series, University of Chicago (1963).

3

IDENTIFICATION
OF SOME FUNDAMENTAL
SPATIAL CONCEPTS

JOHN D. NYSTUEN

The objective of this paper is to consider how many independent concepts constitute a basis for the spatial point of view, that is, the geographical point of view. Geographers have a common subject matter which reveals itself in certain words used again and again. The problems found interesting and being investigated in all branches of the discipline are defined using this common set of words—the controversy over the definition of geography notwithstanding. These words describe spatial arrangements and associations of activities and processes in geographical space. We adopt a spatial point of view whether the problem considered is one of physiography, cultural diffusion, economic expansion, or any of the diverse problems found attractive to geographers. Some of the words I refer to are: *distance, pattern, relative position, site,* and *accessibility.* Many others come to mind. What subset of these common words are necessary and sufficient to employ the geographical point of view? Given such a subset, what meanings do the basic words have? Answers to these questions will set into bold relief the essential geographical nature of a problem or situation.

THE SEARCH FOR A BASIS OF THE GEOGRAPHICAL POINT OF VIEW

The definitions of the words we employ to invoke a spatial point of view are tautological. We break the circle of definitions at some point and settle on a group of words which are accepted as undefined. We must, however, describe the properties of the concepts to which the undefined words refer. This is best done operationally by describing how the concept is observed. For example, distance is a funda-

Reprinted from *Papers of the Michigan Academy of Science, Arts, and Letters*, **48** (1963), 373–384, by permission of the author and editor.

mental concept in most geographical studies. But distance may have several properties. In one study it may be scaled off in miles, feet, or some other unit measure. In another circumstance the distances between elements under study may only be ranked as nearest, next nearest, and so on, without reference to a scalar measure. This is a different type of distance, and these differences have important bearing on understanding the differences between geographical problems. Different types of distances are only one example. The properties of all the basic concepts may vary in subtle but important ways. Operational definitions of the words and subsequent consistent use of the words representing the concepts in the particular context under study are necessary.

Each word in the basis is required for a complete description but does not duplicate the meaning of other words in the basis, that is, each word is necessary and independent. All other concepts will be compounds of this basic set. Obviously there can be more than one basis because synonyms of basic words may replace them, giving a new set of words which convey the same concepts. I will present one basis here, and I stand ready to enlarge it at your suggestions so long as the additions do not say the same thing using different words. What I am searching for is the complete minimum set of concepts necessary to the spatial point of view of geographers.

ADVANTAGES OF ABSTRACT GEOGRAPHICAL SYSTEMS

Certain incentives prompt me in this search. The main purpose is to clarify my objectives in studying geography so that I may study geography in the abstract. I want to remove my investigations from real world subject matter but, at the same time, carry into abstract formulations just those concepts essential to the geographical point of view. To study a problem completely in the abstract has many advantages. The main ones are simplicity and clarity. The elements in an abstract system possess only the properties explicitly assigned to them. In the real world, behavior of a variable is often due to causes not included in the explanation because they were not thought of or because chains of causes and effects are so

involved they cannot be traced through. In considering a problem in the abstract, one can restrict the properties of the object under study to a bare minimum and allow only simple associations to exist. By doing this the problem may become simple enough to understand. The abstract systems which are of use to geographers are precisely those in which the elements in the systems retain some geographically significant properties.

Thünen understood this value of abstract systems when he implored the reader:

... not to be deterred by the initial assumptions which deviate from reality and not to consider them as arbitrary and without purpose. On the contrary, these assumptions are necessary in order to clearly understand the effect which a given variable has. In actual life we have only a vague idea of the effect and operation of any single variable because it appears always in conflict with other variables operating at the same time. This procedure has thrown light on so many problems in my life and seems to me to be so generally applicable that I consider it the most important feature of my work.[1]

The work he spoke of was his study of an isolated state, in which he addressed himself to the question of how agriculture land use patterns would develop on farmland associated with a single market place in a plain that was flat, homogeneously fertile, and equal in every respect from place to place.

Geographers frequently recoil at such a landscape. A common reaction to the homogeneous plain assumption is to assert that there is no geography without variation from place to place. Indeed, geography has usually been defined as the "study of areal differentiation." See, for example, Hartshorne's chapter on areal differentiation in his *Perspective on the Nature of Geography*.[2] On page 14 of that work he cites four authorities employing this definition with slight variations and additions.

Hartshore complains that none of the short statements defining geography reveals the background thinking out of which the definitions of geography have evolved.[3] As a counterpoise to the study of differences over the earth's surface he cites "special interest" in cases in which separate areas appear to be alike. Thus the study of areal differentiation becomes the study of like places when you understand the full breadth of the meaning of the term.

He also argues with Ullman's suggestion that "areal differentiation" be considered a sub-concept of geography as "spatial interaction." This seems to Hartshorne, " . . . to result from a misconception of the former term, if not also the latter."[4] He implies that Ullman does not understand the fullness of the original term. This type of argument over semantics will be endless as long as the definitions of words such as "areal differentiation" remain flexible enough to include all aspects and nuances of geographical content simply by expanding the background thinking out of which the definition has evolved.

Clearly, if we are attempting to define an abstract system with the simplest geographical properties, we must use a set of simple words with clearly defined meanings rather than to invoke broad, compound, and complicated expressions in an attempt at being all inclusive in our definitions. Even Hartshorne admits to the difficulties of the all-embracing expressions. He concludes his chapter on areal differentiation:

If the phrase "areal differentiation" can be accepted as a label referring to that full description, rather than whatever the two words may appear to mean from dictionary definitions, it may be convenient—though perhaps risky—to continue to use the term as a shorthand label, but *only among professional colleagues who have learned what it is intended to represent.*[5]

Under these circumstances, to say geography is the study of areal differentiation is to say geography is the study of geography.

There is a contrast here in the use of words which reflects one fundamental methodological difference between those who strive for a geography which is a complete explanation of place and those who strive to isolate only certain geographical aspects of a place for analysis. The systematic fields of geography consider only parts of regions. The urban and transportation geography which interested Ullman led to a theoretical geography, and beyond to an abstract geography. An abstract geography must use definitions which isolate certain geographical properties and consciously exclude other geographical properties.

Few geographers have advocated a completely abstract geography implied by an extreme of the latter approach. Yet even an extremely abstract approach has some merit. Ackerman extends a timid suggestion:

. . . a theoretical framework is probably as important at this time as definition of the earth's physical matrix for observation was at an earlier stage in the science. Geography thus far has been notably weak in its attention to this possible building block. While the science has a voluminous literature on methodology and procedure, geographers have done comparatively little toward considering their subject in the abstract . . .[6]

An abstract geography will be an aid in generalization. We may expect essential similarities to emerge from extremely unlike circumstances. More penetrating and critical empirical studies may be planned based on suggestions from theoretical or abstract studies. New questions for empirical investigation will arise. I do not anticipate that an abstract geography would drift from central themes of empirical investigations. Each complements and is an inspiration to the other. Empirical work is well developed in geography. Let it remain strong. Effort should also be made to build an abstract geography equally rich.

An Example of an Abstract Space —The Isotropic Plain

Hägerstrand uses the words "isotropic plain" for the elementary, abstract, geographical space that has no difference from place to place or in one direction to another; that is, not only are places the same, but movement effort is the same in all directions from every place. The isotropic plain is not, incidentally, one of my basic words. I will use the device, however, to show how spatial properties of elements emerge with great clarity in abstract systems.

Imagine a concrete example of an isotropic plain. The interior of a mosque will do. This analogy was suggested to me by Torsten Hägerstrand, and we subsequently developed it quite far in a casual conversation. A mosque is normally devoid of furniture, illuminated by a diffused light, and has a flat, highly polished tile floor—a good representation perhaps of an isotropic surface. Let me introduce a group of people to the mosque and let them be engaged in an activity—a teacher teaching the word of Allah and his attending pupils. The teacher settles himself on the polished floor, choosing no place in particular, nor does he face in any particular direction. The pupils, however, do not choose random positions. We can imagine they arrange themselves in a very determinate fashion. They settle close in front of the teacher —but not too close. The first row forms a half-circle. Before the first row extends very far around the teacher a second row begins to develop. It is more desirable to be in the second row directly in front of the teacher than in the first row far off to one side. The second row is probably staggered so that pupils in this position can see past the heads of the ones in the first row. The arc of the students and the number of rows grow in an interdependent fashion. This relationship will depend upon the teacher's voice, how loud it is, how well he enunciates, whether there is an advantage in seeing his mouth as he speaks, etc.

Another set of variables is also important. Each pupil occupies, with his flowing robes, a certain area—call it a unit area. Also, some distance separates each pupil from another to prevent crowding. Like the number of rows, this separation depends upon the number in the class. Crowding will occur if the class is very large. There is probably a greater tendency for crowding near the front than at the rear of the class. At some distance, the teacher's voice no longer carries the message distinctly. A certain amount of shuffling around occurs, some pupils look around or sit facing other directions. They might even start talking among themselves. Given my own experience as a teacher, I can conceive of some pupils [who] might even seek out a location in the last row and beyond the cover of the teacher's eye.

The size of the mosque relative to the size of the class might eventually become a factor too, but that complicates the picture with the difficult problem of the effects of boundaries. Usually the isotropic surface is unbounded. Are there any geographical elements in the scene described? I am sure you recognize some, even though I described a model of a region with no distinguishable features. All of the geography present is created by intragroup association.

DIRECTIONAL ORIENTATION

There is a directional quality to the teacher's voice. In fact, the teacher and pupils sit face-to-face if possible. The human form has a natural orientation—a front and back—which defines a line of sight. A location or point and a line of sight or ray are necessary and sufficient to define orientation—one basic geographical property I recognize. If elements in the space have no intrinsic orientation, it is necessary and sufficient that two points exist and that direction be indicated from one to the other, perhaps by an arrow on the line connecting them.

DISTANCE

The effectiveness of the teacher's voice falls with distance. Distance, or separation, is a fundamental geographical property also. Intensity of communication falling off continuously with distance is a property shared by many, but not all, phenomena. An example of the opposite effect of distance is a transportation cost which normally rises with distance. Other phenomena are invariant with distance—at least within some range. Legal jurisdiction is as binding at the borders of a state as in its center.

The distance between two points is usually defined as a geodesic, that is, the shortest path between two points in whatever space and unit measure being considered. There are many spaces and measures possible. These spaces are defined by assigning properties to the distance measure. I will not define a distance suitable for all geographical problems. There is none. The problem must be evaluated and then the properties of the distance measure specified. Distance might be measured by simple ranking, or it may be asymmetric, e.g., the distance from a to b is not the same as the distance from b to a. An example of the latter is travel on a one-way street system.

Distance in a metric space has several useful properties which will affect most activities in the space. One such property is the triangular inequality in which

$$d(a) \leq d(ac) + d(cb)$$

where a, b, and c are points and $d(ab)$ is the distance between a and b. To what extent properties of this type may be extended into different spaces is significant for geographical study because many familiar geographical problems seem to be associated with something other than the familiar Euclidean space. Using the example above, distances which separate points for a traveler on a one-way street system are non-Euclidean because of their lack of symmetry.

CONNECTIVENESS

We may remove measures of distance and direction from a geographical study and speak of connection only. Some other words for this property of space are adjacency, contiguity, or simply relative position. This is best thought of as a topological property of space. The properties of connectiveness may remain invariant under transformations which change direction and distance relations. A map of the United States may be stretched and twisted, but so long as each state remains connected with its neighbors, relative position does not change. Connectiveness is independent of direction and distance—all three properties are needed to establish a complete geographical point of view.

FUNCTIONAL ASSOCIATIONS AND SPECIFICATION OF THE SPACE UNDER STUDY

Important problems may be investigated when one or more of the above properties are not defined. In urban studies direction is often eliminated by drawing an average profile through the city center showing rent, traffic density, etc. The familiar diagram of decreasing intensity of activity with distance from the center of a city implies no differences in direction from the center. Circular isolines appear in the plane projection of the rotation of this function about its central axis and directional differences are eliminated.

Both distance and direction are eliminated in studies concerned with networks of connections only. A simple example are route maps on railroad schedules which show only the sequence of stops.

Connections need not be adjacent boundaries or physical links. They may be defined as functional associations. Functional associations of spatially separate elements are best revealed by the exchanges which take place between the elements. The exchanges may often be measured by the flows of people, goods, or communication. The term Ullman uses for these functional relations is "interaction."[7] He calls for a greater concentration of research on these connections between areas, and he is correct in his emphasis. In the absence of site characteristics, such as I described in the example of the mosque, with its perfectly flat, polished surface, the pattern or arrangement of the people depends entirely upon their functional associations. The exchange in this case is a flow of words. By specifying the properties of this functional relation and identifying each person's role, the geographical pattern of this group of people engaged in this activity may be anticipated. If the same group of people engage in another activity, for example, social dancing, or a tug-of-war, new arrangements would arise. To study relations abstractly requires explicit recognition of the properties of the relationship. One property mentioned above is symmetry. Many relations are not symmetrical. For example, the largest flow of telephone calls from a small city may be to a large central city, but the largest flow of telephone calls of the large central city need not be to the smaller city. Mathematicians have studied such relations in great detail. It is very possible we can borrow many of their theorems to our advantage if we can specify the properties of the functional relation between spatially separate elements.

ELEMENTS AND PROCESSES IN GEOGRAPHICAL SPACE

In order to talk about the properties on an isotropic plane I introduced a subject matter—the teacher and his pupils—and specified a functional association between them—the reciprocal acts of teaching and learning. These steps are necessary in order to apply a geographical point of view. Activities or processes associating the elements in a study over space must be assumed.

There is one special case where elements in space are not related to one another in any fashion whatsoever or, what amounts to the same thing, the elements are associated in so many ways that no finite set of associations can describe the resulting pattern. The special case results in a random distribution in space. There are certain advantages in addressing ourselves to this special case, but we will not consider them here.

We are interested in those activities and processes which explain how the elements under study are arranged and associated in space. I use the words "activities" and "processes" as synonyms just to emphasize [that] I mean spatial association between groups of people as well as spatial association of all nonhuman elements or the interaction between both these classes of elements.

SITE AND SITUATIONAL CHARACTERISTICS

To return to my analogy once more, if I took the class out of the mosque and settled them down in a garden or out in a woods, site characteristics would modify the arrangement of the class. A wind blowing, or the direction of the sun, might shift the orientation of the pupils. The arrangement of rocks or benches would affect the arrangement also. All of the geographical elements present inside the mosque are still present, but their effects are modified by the characteristics of the site chosen.

The difference between these two sets of influences on geographical patterns is implied in the terms "site" and "situation" or in the terms "place" and "location." It is sometimes difficult to separate "site" from "situational properties." This is probably true because the classification is artificial and depends to some extent upon the scale of observation. Nevertheless I consider the distinction useful in clarifying the geographical features of a problem.

BASIC GEOGRAPHICAL PROBLEMS

Themes recur when defining the geographical elements of a study. Recognizing them helps to identify basic similarities between apparently unlike phenomena.

HISTORICAL TENSION

Certain site characteristics are extremely important. If my study group from the mosque are using benches of stone set down by a prior group for some other purpose, very likely they will accommodate themselves to the existing arrangement rather than take the effort of reorganizing the heavy benches. The benches represent the accumulated benefit and legacy of the past. In many studies this legacy from the past may be the single most important fact. Existing facilities and institutions will always be not quite suitable for the present because society is always creating new activities which, for greatest efficiency, require new arrangements.

This tension of present activities with past arrangements is a fundamental geographical problem which arises again and again.

DIMENSIONAL TENSION

There are other tensions which create problems of great interest. Geographical elements may be characterized as points, lines, or areas. In fact, even more dimensions are added if we accept as significant such concepts as social distance. For example, there are geographical effects from the social distances separating races in our big cities.

Dimensional tension is created between point- and area-occupying activities. [On] a national scale, agricultural activities are area-occupying, whereas factories may be thought of as points. A dimensional tension is created by the fact we require association with, and the products of, both farm and factory. This is what central place theory is all about. Given the need to distribute a set of point-occupying functions over an area, what is the optimum arrangement of the points?

TIME-SPACE TENSION

Similarly there is a time-space tension which creates interesting geographical problems. When time is short, space is conserved. When an activity has a deadline associated with it, congestion in space is likely. This is essentially the problem of highway congestion in the journey-to-work hours. The concentration of the women's dress industry in New York City and the concentration of wholesale fresh fruit and vegetable markets in large urban areas are also examples of the time-space tensions.

SCALE OF OBSERVATION AND UNIT AREAS

There is undoubtedly great advantage in considering geographical elements as points, because this will very likely simplify the abstract relations. Whether it will be useful to do so or not will depend on the scale of observation and the relative scale of the elements under study to the entire study area. On a world-wide scale there is little error in considering cities as points. At a county level this same abstraction would cause great error. In my example of the class in the mosque, the area occupied by each person was important in establishing the arrangement of the class and could not be ignored. This unit area or internal dimension is of fundamental importance. Many terms used by geographers are compounds of this term with counts of other elements. Density, intensity crop yield, rent, or land value are calculated on this basis.

SUMMARY

The terms which seem to me to contain the concepts of a geographical point of view are *direction* or *orientation, distance,* and *connection* or *relative position*. Operational definitions of these words are the axioms of the spatial point of view. Other words, such as pattern, accessibility, neighborhood, circulation, [etc.], are compounds of the basic terms. For abstract models, the existence of these elements and their properties must be specified. The properties such as a metric unit, unit area, symmetry, transitivity, and others depend upon the particular set of elements and their processes or activities under study. These subject matters must be in mind when deciding which properties the space will possess.

Spatial relationships will be clarified if a class of site or place phenomena is distinct from a class of situational or locational phenomena. Certain themes recur when applying a spatial point of view. They may be included in an abstract study or not, but a conscious choice of inclusion or omission will be very valuable in evaluating the results.

Common geographical problems may be thought of as a group of tensions: a dimensional tension between point, line, and area activities; a time-space tension in current activities; or a tension between present activities and past facilities and institutions. The scale of the study cannot be ignored, nor can the relative scale of elements in the study, because upon these scale differences will depend the appropriateness of the abstractions used.

There may be fundamental concepts which I have omitted. I have not thought through the question of boundaries. Two questions arise in boundary considerations. First, how may the boundaries be defined, and second, what influence do the boundaries have on other activities and phenomena?

I feel boundaries should be included in this statement of the basis of the geographical point of view. If you see other omissions, I would appreciate your comments.

FOOTNOTES

[1] J. H. von Thünen, *Der isolierte Staat in Beziehung auf Landwirtschaft und Nationalökonomie,* in K. W. Kapp and L. L. Kapp, eds., *Readings in Economics* (New York: Barnes & Noble, Inc., 1949), p. 299.

[2] R. Hartshorne, *Perspective on the Nature of Geography* (Chicago: Rand McNally & Co., 1959), pp. 12 ff.

[3] *Ibid.,* pp. 14–15.

[4] *Ibid.,* p. 19. The article referred to is E. L. Ullman, "Human Geography and Area Research," *Annals, of the Association of American Geographers,* **43** (1953), 54–66.

[5] *Ibid.,* p. 21. (Emphasis mine.)

[6] E. A. Ackerman, *Geography as a Fundamental Research Discipline,* University of Chicago, Department of Geography, Research Paper No. 53 (1956), pp. 28–29.

[7] E. Ullman, *op. cit.*

4

GEOGRAPHY AND ANALOG THEORY

RICHARD J. CHORLEY

One of the most striking characteristics of geographical analysis which this subject has in common with the other natural and social sciences is the high degree of ambiguity presented by its subject matter and the attendantly large "elbow room" which the researcher has for the manner in which this material may be organized and interpreted. This characteristic is a necessary result of the relatively small amount of available information which has been extracted in a very partial manner from a large and multivariate reality, and leads not only to radically conflicting "explanations" of geographical phenomena, but to differing opinions regarding the significant aspects of geographical reality which are worth exploring. Even within a circumscribed body of information there is no universally appropriate manner of treatment, and such treatment is often conditioned either by the general systematic framework which one (often subconsciously) adopts as an appropriate setting for the information[1] or by the type of question which one is prepared to ask about the "real

world." The change in character between the geographical methodologies of the nineteenth and twentieth centuries (and, for that matter, between the methodologies of botany or social anthropology), for example, lies very largely in the abandonment of attempts at causal explanation in favor of functional studies.

Where such ambiguity exists, scholars commonly handle the associated information either by means of *classifications* or *models*. Much has been written on the subject of geographical classifications, which usually result from the accumulation of a backlog of information which is then dissected and categorized in some convenient manner. Model building, which sometimes may even precede the collection of a great deal of data, involves the association of supposedly significant aspects of reality into a system which seems to possess some special properties of intellectual stimulation. This is not to imply that classifications and

Reprinted from *Annals of the Association of American Geographers*, **54** (1964), 127–137, by permission of the author and editor.

models do not share some common ground, and, indeed, the "genetic classifications" of national economic stages[2] and of shorelines[3] form something of a link between them. However, in their extreme forms, classifications and models are sharply differentiated, and it is with the employment of model building, or *analog theory*, in geography that this paper is concerned.

The Use of Models

The use of analogy has long been recognized as a powerful tool both in the reasoning process and in throwing a new light on reality. The concept of analogy was first applied by the Greeks to expose a similarity in geometrical proportion between two objects, but was later extended to include a much wider range of similarities, including qualitative ones.[4] Reasoning by analogy involves the assumption of a resemblance of relations or attributes between some phenomenon or aspect of the real world in which one is interested and an analog, or model. The basic assumption involved is that "two analogs are more likely to have further properties in common than if no resemblance existed at all, and that additional knowledge concerning one consequently provides some basis for a prediction of the existence of similar properties in the other."[5] A model, or analog, must belong therefore to a more familiar realm than the system to which it is applied.[6] In other words, the problem is translated into more familiar or convenient terms, such that a useful model involves a more simplified, accessible, observable, controllable, rapidly developing, or easily formulated phenomenon from which conclusions can be deduced, which, in turn, can be reapplied to the original system or real world.

"In general, any two things, whether events, situations, creatures, or objects, can be said to be analogs if they resemble each other to some extent in their properties, behavior, or mode of functioning, so that, in practice, the term analog is used rather loosely to cover a wide range of degrees of resemblance."[7] This wide range of resemblance may lead the model builder to employ as varied analogs as a past situation or happening in the real world, a mathematical simplification, or a construction built of string and wire.

Obviously the use of analogs in any process of reasoning involves very apparent difficulties and dangers, some of which will be treated in later sections. However, their use can be extremely productive providing there is no reason to believe that the points of similarity between the analog or model and the real world situation are irrelevant to the matter under investigation, or that there is "no a priori knowledge that the two analogs differ in such a way as to prohibit any similarity in the particular property which is the subject of the prediction."[8] In spite of the dangers of analogy, physical scientists have used it freely in the past because the conclusions can usually be checked by experiment or further observation;[9] but, largely deprived of these checks, social scientists have been more cautious in their use. One of the more obvious exceptions to this has been the development of "social physics,"[10] in which physical principles have been used as models for the behavior of man in society, such that, for example, the size and spacing of towns have been examined from the standpoint of Newton's gravitational law, the equalization of social classes and races have been viewed in the context of a thermodynamic model as a tendency toward maximum "social entropy," and, in somewhat the same manner, the political state and human society have been treated by the social Darwinists in the light of the organic model provided by the theory of evolution. Although many of these attempts have failed, for reasons which will be treated later, some have proved important vehicles for analysis and research. As Bunge has pointed out, it is one of the features of geographical methodology that the idea of uniqueness of geographical phenomena (the "idiographic" notion) has retarded the overt application of analog theory to the subject, although the latter is very commonly employed as a means of explanation and analysis in less obvious ways.[11]

Finally, in the field of definition, it is important to differentiate between models and theories. Analogy is often a fruitful source of suggestion for hypotheses for further inductive investigation, but alone it cannot "prove" anything. A model becomes a theory about the real world only when a segment of the real world has been successfully mapped into it, both by avoiding the discarding of too much information in the stage of abstraction (see next section) and by carrying out a rigorous *interpretation* of the model results into real world

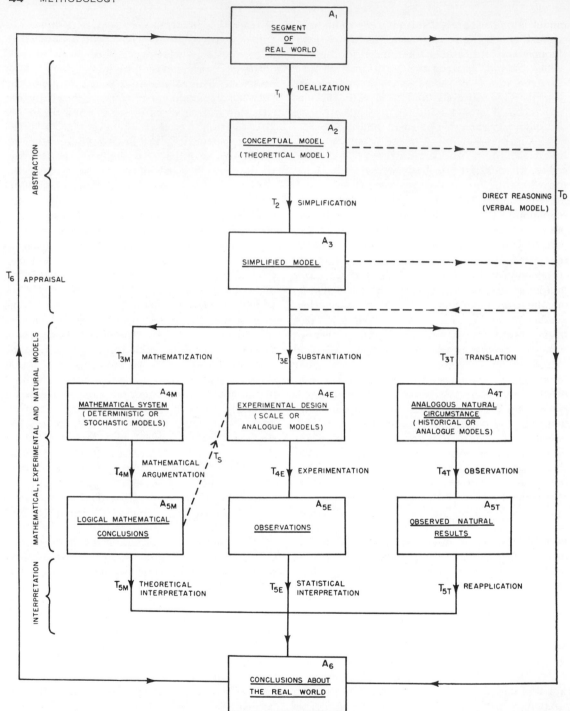

FIGURE 1. A model for models

terms. "As a theory, [a model] . . . can be accepted or rejected on the basis of how well it works. As a model, it can only be right or wrong on logical grounds. A model must satisfy only internal criteria; a theory must satisfy external criteria as well."[12] In short, reasoning by analogy is a step toward the building of theories, such that "a promising model is one with implications rich enough to suggest novel hypotheses and speculations in the primary field of investigation."[13]

A MODEL FOR MODELS

Following the efforts of Coombs, Raiffa, and Thrall[14] and of Aronow[15] to formalize broad sectors of the analogy reasoning processes, an attempt has been made in Fig. 1 to provide a more detailed analysis of the ways in which models may be employed both in scholarship as a whole and in geography in particular. It is important to stress at the outset that this diagram differs from a board designed for a child's dice game in that success is seldom measured in terms of the model builder's ability to negotiate all the hurdles on the course (although the most important model builders have done so), the only proviso being that the course must be completed in some manner. The diagram is simply composed of a series of *steps* (A_{1-6}), each of which contains some aspect of the real world, model, observation, or conclusion; these are connected, sometimes in a very loose and varied manner, by *transformations* (T_{1-6}) whereby the reasoning process is advanced or checked upon. Each of these transformations introduces (in the language of the information theorist) the possibility of "noise," insofar as the processes of simplification and translation involve, on the one hand, the discarding of information, some of which may eventually be proved to have been useful information (popularly, though rather inaccurately, termed "throwing out the baby with the bath water"), and, on the other, the possibility of the introduction of new information which is irrelevant (commonly termed "clouding the issue" or "introducing a red herring"). The most useful employment of analogs is that which succeeds in causing the least noise.

ABSTRACTION

This sequence of steps represents the most difficult type of model building because, in developing a simplified but appropriate model for a given object system or segment of the real world (A_1), huge amounts of available information are being discarded (T_1 and T_2), and therefore much noise is being potentially introduced. The transformation of *idealization* (T_1) is especially difficult, and its successful negotiation is very much a function of the intuition, luck, knowledge, experience, and genius of the model builder. It involves extracting from the mass of information about the real world those aspects which are held to be especially significant, in that they seem to fit together into some sort of pattern,[16] and it is readily apparent that the appropriateness and significance of those parts of reality so abstracted depend very much on the creative ability and vision of the model builder.[17] One of the major sources of noise in this transformation is introduced by the phenomenon of *feedback*. This occurs because our belief as to what "facts" about the real world are important, appropriate, significant, or even existent is to a certain extent conditioned by the framework of thought which we have consciously or unconsciously adopted.[18] Idealization largely involves reaching some conclusion about the relationships in the real world which really matter[19] so that the irrelevant "dead wood" can be pruned away to expose the significant relationships then susceptible to further examination. An example of the operation of feedback is provided by geophysics, in which the selection and interpretation of the "facts" of seismograph recordings largely depend on the previous notions of the operator regarding the internal structure of the earth.

By such means a *conceptual model* (A_2) is derived which, having some basis of observed facts and regularities, contains a mental image of the significant "web of reality" that may have come quite unambiguously from the simplification of previous empirical knowledge or may seem to have sprung largely from intuition or imagination.[20] Many attempts at model building depart from formality at this point and pass by *direct reasoning* (T_D) to a *hypothesis* or some *conclusions about the real world* (A_6) which, if successfully *appraised* (T_6) against the real world, may form the basis of a *theory*. Usually, however, the conceptual model is still too complex to handle and it is subjected to further *simplification* (T_2) by the discarding of still more extraneous information to lay bare to the bone what are considered to be the simplest and most significant aspects of the basic matter at issue. This transformation is somewhat less noisy than T_1 because both ends of it are more completely understood[21] and in practice it may represent a whole series of simplifications, the aim of which is to retain the simplest and most significant aspects of the problem, while removing any irrelevant material which might obscure the fundamental relationships and prevent a satisfactory solution. The final product of abstraction is often a *simplified model* (A_3) which, if at all successful, has been reduced, by the laying aside of minor variables and the discarding of irrelevant information, to a condition where the fundamental symmetries and relationships lie exposed for precise definition and further treatment.

Usually, however, the simplified model is to a greater or lesser extent unsatisfactory, and this is because the whole process of abstraction forces the model builder to strike a balance between his desire to distill the problem down to its essence and to eliminate the possible sources of noise which excessive simplification may introduce. There are consequently few examples of largely successful simplified models. Newton's model of gravitation is the most outstanding. In geography, most attempts at model building by abstraction have met with minimal success, but it is notable that those which are currently judged as most successful are the conceptual models in which excessive simplification has been avoided. These contrast with the overly simplified geographical models of a deterministic character so popular in the nineteenth century. Thus the simplified "place, work, people" concept of Le Play[22] seems to us to be a less real and appropriate model than the "regional synthesis" of Vidal de la Blache,[23] in which too much information has been retained but very little noise introduced. So too the simplified economic models of von Thünen[24] and Weber,[25] with their assumption of fixed markets and sources of raw materials, seem less attractive than the freer and more complex models of Christaller[26] and Lösch.[27] It is natural that the excessive pruning of simplified models should recommend them to certain scholars, and it is very interesting that Wooldridge has written of the "superbly 'clean' and intellectually attractive quality" of W. M. Davis' cyclical concept of landform development.[28] To these scholars the less simplified model of landform development adopted by G. K. Gilbert has little to commend it by comparison.[29] In short, one often has to choose between the clean but noisy model of Davis and the less clean but relatively quiet model of Gilbert.

Simplified models abound in geography and related fields, exhibiting various degrees of failure to measure up to reality within an oversimplified framework. Ritter's notions regarding the development of peoples under differing geographical conditions,[30] Mackinder's "Heartland" theory,[31] Malthus' population growth model,[32] Frederick Jackson Turner's "frontier hypothesis" of national development,[33] and Suess's eustatic theory[34] are examples of such simplified models in which too much truth has been sacrificed for too much simplicity. It must not be assumed, however, that in all instances (except under the hand of genius) increasing simplification produces detrimental results. Some simplification may be significant or successful in that it transforms a segment of the real world into a new dimension which is neither "better nor worse" but merely different and interesting. One has only to compare a realistic landscape painting from the Dutch School, with an impressionist landscape painting from the French Impressionist School and an abstract modern "landscape" painting to be impressed both by this transformation and by the unity of knowledge which is fostered by attention to analog theory. A Cezanne painting is cleaner but more noisy than one by Van Ruysdael!

MATHEMATICAL, EXPERIMENTAL, AND NATURAL MODELS

The derivation of some form of simplified model enables structures and relationships to appear which are capable of further exploitation, commonly in such a manner that prediction can be attempted. This exploitation can be pursued by means of mathematical, experimental, or natural models.

MATHEMATICAL MODELS Mathematical models include those which have been most spectacularly employed by the model builders of genius, and involve the adoption of "a number of idealizations of the various details of the phenomena studied and in ascribing to the various entities involved some strictly defined properties."[35] The essential features of the phenomena are then "analogous to the relationship between certain abstract symbols, which we can write down. The observed phenomena resemble closely something extremely simple, with very few attributes. The resemblance is so close that the equations are a kind of working model, from which we can predict features of the real thing which we have never observed."[36] The first task in the construction of a mathematical model is the language transformation (T_{3M}) from the words of the simplified model to mathematical symbols (*mathematization*) so as to produce a *mathematical system* (A_{4M}). These systems can be of two broad kinds: deterministic or stochastic.[37]

Deterministic models are based on the classic mathematical notion of direct cause and effect, and consist of a set of mathematical assertions from which consequences can be derived by logical mathematical argument.[38] Commonly the reasoning exploits the assumed simple or multiple relationships between a number of interlocked factors which have been identified in the simplified model.[39] The best example of the application of this type of reasoning to geomorphology is provided by Jeffreys, who developed a mathematical model for the denudation of the land surface by runoff, and by this means deduced theoretically the form of the resulting peneplain.[40] The most popular geomorphic application of deterministic mathematical models has been in the deduction of the forms accompanying slope recession, summarized by Scheidegger,[41] and a similar method has been employed by Miller and Zeigler[42] to predict the expected patterns of coastal sediment size and sorting. Most mathematical models of the atmospheric circulation are of the deterministic sort, as are those involved in numerical forecasting.[43]

Deterministic mathematical models having relevance to human geography commonly possess a strongly experimental flavor, demonstrating the lack of reality in any rigid separation of mathematical, experimental, and natural models, which inevitably grade into one another. Thus Beckmann has attempted to minimize the costs of interlocal commodity flows by the theoretical use of the hydrodynamics "equation of continuity";[44] Lighthill and Whitham used the principle of kinematic waves, suggested by theories of flow around supersonic projectiles and of flood movement in rivers, to investigate the flow and concentration of traffic on crowded arterial roads;[45] and Richards similarly investigated traffic flow on the basis of the mathematics of fluid flow.[46]

Stochastic models, based upon probability instead of mathematical certainty, are obviously of more promise in investigations relating to human geography rather than to the physical branches of the discipline. However, Leopold and Langbein have used the thermodynamic engine model to illustrate the steady-state concept applied to the longitudinal profile of a river, as well as the mathematical random-walk model to rationalize the stream network geometry of a drainage basin.[47] In the human field, Isard has constructed a spatial economic model of a statistical character,[48] Hägerstrand's "innovation wave" model is similarly based,[49] as is the mathematical theory of population clusters by Neyman and Scott, which was inspired by the kinetic gas theory.[50] More recently, Garrison has suggested the employment of an electronic computer to develop a stochastic mathematical model for city growth.[51]

Both the deterministic and stochastic mathematical models must be susceptible to logical *mathematical argumentation* (T_{4M}), a transformation which is virtually noise free and involves the solution of the equations forming the basis of the mathematical system to provide *logical mathematical conclusions* (A_{5M}). Although these conclusions are susceptible to *theoretical interpretation* (T_{5M}) into *conclusions about the real world* (A_6), it is important to recognize that, of themselves, mathematical models do not provide explanations of the real world, but merely allow conclusions to be drawn from the original mathematical assumptions.[52] Some authors even take the extreme position that "the mathematician, as such, has no responsibility whatever for the degree to which idealizations may represent a real situation. His work consists in discovering, developing, and/or applying methods of abstract logic dealing with form, structure, quantity, etc., and his responsibility is discharged completely and with honor if he avoids *internal* error."[53] A more balanced view of the need to anchor mathematical models to reality in the earth sciences has been given by Jeffreys, who wrote:

Such treatment is . . . highly desirable; for a mathematical investigation enables us to specify accurately the causes we are taking into account, and the correspondence or divergence between the effects it predicts and the actual phenomena indicated the extent to which we have succeeded in tracing the more important causes. The differences revealed may then lead to the discovery of further causes, and thus observed facts may gradually become understood in greater completeness and detail.[54]

EXPERIMENTAL MODELS   A second manner in which a simplified model can be further treated, in order to examine certain phases of its operation or to attempt predictions about it, is by *substantiation* (T_{3E}). In this process the concepts of the simplified model are reproduced as tangible structures (i.e., the usual concept of a "model") by a transformation which is inherently very noisy. Two types of experimental models may be conveniently differentiated, the scale model and the analog model.

Scale models are closely imitative of a segment of the real world, which they resemble in some very obvious respects (i.e., being composed mostly of the same type of materials), and the resemblance may sometimes be so close that the scale model [is] considered as merely a suitably controlled portion of the real world.[55] Thus scale models have been employed with much success in physical geography, Friedkin describing the use of scale models to investigate the phenomenon of meandering,[56] and Rouse the use of model techniques in meteorological research.[57] The most obvious advantages of the use of scale models are the high degree of control which can be achieved over the simplified experimental conditions and the manner in which time can be compressed. However, the fundamental problem attending their construction is that changes of scale affect the relationships between certain properties of the model and of the real world in different ways. Problems of scaling and of dimensional similarity have been well treated by Langhaar[58] and Duncan,[59] while Strahler[60] and Stahl[61] have treated the application of dimensional analysis to the natural sciences. This inherent lack of one's ability to produce faithful scale models is most strikingly exemplified by the discrepancy between geometric and kinematic model ratios. Such discrepancies can be circumvented in any of three interrelated ways. First, a distortion of one important attribute can (usually by rule of thumb) be reduced or eliminated by the distortion of another attribute—for example,

a distortion of the vertical scale of river models enables the effects due to turbulence to be more or less faithfully reproduced. The second, and most important, way in which analogous model ratios can be produced is by dimensionless combinations of attributes. Thus a combination of density, velocity, depth, and viscosity (combined in the Reynolds number) enables viscous effects to be accurately reproduced; and a combination of velocity, length, and the acceleration of gravity (e.g., the Froude number) is important where gravity effects need to be accurately scaled in the model. Third, one or more of the media can be changed in the model to assist the true scaling of other effects, and early German experiments with wave tanks even involved the substitution of lower density brandy for the more conventional water! Such considerations naturally lead into the second type of experimental models, the analog model.

Analog models involve a radical change in the medium of which the model is constructed. They have a much more limited aim than scale models in that they are intended to reproduce only some aspects of the structure or web of relationships recognized in the simplified model of the real world segment.[62] Such a transformation is obviously rather difficult and a great potential source of noise. Although such analog models can, at best, merely furnish the basis for plausible hypotheses, rather than proofs, their use can be extremely valuable. An electronic computer may be considered as an experimental analog model of the human brain. Other such models of special interest to the physical geographer include the construction of a hydraulic analog model to simulate freezing and thawing of soil layers;[63] Lewis and Miller's use of a kaolin mixture to simulate some features of the deformation and crevassing of a valley glacier;[64] Reiner's rheological models for the simulation of different types of deformation;[65] and Starr's "dishpan" analog, in which the circulation of water in a heated and rotating pan was made to exhibit many of the gross features of the atmospheric circulation in a hemisphere.[66] It is, however, in the fields abutting on human geography that analog experimental models have been most strikingly applied. Hotelling early used a non-constructed heat flow analog to present a theory of human migration.[67] But it is the spatial economists who have been especially interested in the use of these models. Enke employed electric circuits to attack a problem of spatial price equilibrium, in which voltage was identified with price and current with real goods;[68] Brink and de Cani similarly employed an electrical analog machine in determining the location of service points to serve a number of customers of known demand, so as to minimize transport costs;[69] and Stringer and Haley constructed a pulley and weight "transport optimizing machine."[70] Needless to say, most such machines have been displaced in favor of the electronic analog computer.

Whether a scale or analog experimental model is used, their construction is followed by *experimentation* (T_{4E}), leading to a set of experimental *observations* (A_{5E}) which remain to be interpreted in terms of the real world in a manner similar to the theoretical interpretation of the conclusions from a mathematical model. Very occasionally these results from a mathematical model are transformed (T_8) into experimental terms (a very noisy process) as a further step in testing their agreement with the real world.[71]

NATURAL MODELS The third manner in which simplified models can be exploited and used as a basis for further analysis and prediction is by their *translation* (T_{3T}) into some *analogous natural circumstance* (A_{4T}) believed to be simpler, better known, or more readily observable. Such translations are inherently of two kinds—historical and analog.

The employment of historical natural models involves a translation of the simplified model into a different time and/or place, on the assumption that what has happened before will happen again, or that what happens here will happen there.[72] Such a translation is an obvious source of noise because the multicomponent character of most models means that, even where a reasonable analog can be found, "it is to be expected that the importance of each of these factors will be different in the two cases, and frequently the dominant influence in each case is exerted by a different factor."[73] However, some historians have naturally been attracted to the historical analog concept (e.g., Toynbee). For example, assumptions have been made that the present demography of India has some features in common with that of preindustrial revolution Europe, or that similarities exist between the characteristics of feudalism in seventeenth/eighteenth-century Russia and Medieval Europe. The most obvious geographical analog which is applied to a different time (apart from some of the broad historical geographical analogs used in the last century, e.g., by Ritter and Ratzel) is presented by the analog forecasting methods at present being developed in meteorology.[74] Reasoning from "experience" of analogous situations elsewhere is a common basis for current geographical planning, but an obvious general example of such a spatial analogy translation is the fashion model who is considered by the prospective purchaser of a dress to share some analogous features with her.

Analog natural models imply the translation of the simplified model into a different natural medium—a process of the most noisy kind. Problems of social geography are being attacked on the basis of physical analogs. Bunge[75] has compared the shift of highways with the shift of rivers, and has applied the mathematics of crystallography to central place theory in considering the growth and shrinkage of market areas as similar to the patterns associated with two-dimensional crystals; and Garrison has developed an "ice-cap analogy" of city growth.[76] The social physicists obviously utilize such models; and in the field of physical geography, Chorley has attempted some mechanical explanation for the variation in drumlin shape on the basis of some of the factors controlling the shape of birds' eggs.[77] The introduction of noise into such a transformation stems from the very real danger of comparing the original phenomenon with another which is equally, or even more, complicated and equally unknown.[78] Comparisons with living organisms are thus especially dangerous, as has been shown by failure of organic theories of the state popular among geopoliticians. Even the use of the "loaded" terms of "youth," "maturity," and "old age" by Davis has introduced into modern geomorphology a great deal of quite extraneous evolutionary noise.[79]

In any event, an appropriate analogous natural circumstance, if subjected to appropriate *observation* (T_{4T}), may yield *observed natural results* (A_{5T}) which, through *reapplication* (T_{5T}), may lead to some testable conclusions about the real world situation in which one is interested.

INTERPRETATION AND APPRAISAL

Little further remains to be said regarding the problems of interpreting the conclusions derived from mathematical, experimental, or natural models (T_5) to reach conclusions which are appropriate to the real world situation (A_6), except to stress the potential noise of this transformation. It is interesting that many lines of reasoning in geography reach these conclusions by a process of more or less *direct reasoning* (T_D)—sometimes with a minimum of model building, by what has been graphically termed the "eyeball" method. The value of this method is obviously very much determined by the degree of shortsightedness of the operator and the tint of his spectacles.

Successful *appraisal* (T_6) involves the checking of conclusions derived from model building with the real world, so that a hypothesis can be developed. If sufficient checks of this kind lead to similar conclusions, a *theory* may be developed. This appraisal is an indispensable step, no matter what the simplicity or sophistication of the previous model building, and on this the success or failure of the whole reasoning process hinges.

CONCLUSION

The use of analogous models, in the wide sense here employed, is an important, and it might be argued instinctive, adjunct to the reasoning process in the natural and social sciences. In these disciplines, where so much ambiguity exists in the manner in which phenomena may be interpreted, it seems characteristic that much of the most satisfying scholarship includes the utilization of some sort of model, the successful construction of which involves the highest levels of intellectual attainment. It is important, therefore, that the geographic applications of analog theory should be placed on as rigorous a footing as possible, so that we may recognize in the work of ourselves and others the possibilities and dangers attendant upon reasoning by analogy. These dangers have been stressed throughout the present analysis, and involve questions of the following character: Is the analog model truly analogous in the sense in which it has been applied? Has an excessive discarding of information introduced so much noise that the simplified model is effectively divorced from reality? Is reality of too multivariate a character to be susceptible to reasoning by analogy? Are leaps into different domains justifiable? Above all, does the use of models introduce too great a detour into the reasoning process, and the repeated "decanting and filtering" destroy the reality which must necessarily be preserved in scientific analysis? It would appear that, where analogy is used in a controlled and careful manner, the answer to all these questions must be a satisfactory one. Just as no analog model is completely successful, and even the most significant ones (e.g., that of Newton) are eventually superseded, so, few models are without some value. Model theories are like torches of varying size and intensity, shining in different directions, and each illuminating some novel aspect or relationship of reality. With all their defects and distortions, they are often the most convenient vehicles for analyzing, interpreting, and expressing our concepts of the real world. Any better understanding of analog theory cannot but help us to reach toward a deeper appreciation of the methodological basis, essential character, and limitations which geographical scholarship shares with other natural and social sciences.

FOOTNOTES

[1] R. J. Chorley, "Geomorphology and General Systems Theory," U. S. Geological Survey, Professional Paper No. 500-B (Washington: U.S.G.P.O., 1962).

[2] W. W. Rostow, *The Stages of Economic Growth* (London: Cambridge University Press, 1960).

[3] D. W. Johnson, *Shore Processes and Shoreline Development* (New York: John Wiley & Sons, Inc., 1919).

[4] V. Daniel, "The Uses and Abuses of Analogy," *Operational Research Quarterly*, **6** (1955), 32–46.

[5] A. W. Ross, "Approximate Methods in Operational

Research," in M. Davies, R. T. Eddison, and T. Page, eds., *Proceedings of the 1st International Conference on Operational Research* (Oxford: English Universities Press, 1958), p. 58.

[6] M. Black, *Models and Metaphors* (Ithaca: Cornell University Press, 1962), Chap. 13.

[7] Ross, *op. cit.*, p. 58.

[8] *Ibid.*, p. 59.

[9] Daniel, *op. cit.*

[10] See, for example, G. K. Zipf, *Human Behavior and the Principle of Least Effort* (Reading, Mass.: Addison-Wesley Publishing Company, Inc., 1949).

[11] W. Bunge, *Theoretical Geography*, Lund Studies in Geography, Series C, No. 1 (1962), pp. 7–13.

[12] C. H. Coombs, H. Raiffa, and R. M. Thrall, "Some Views on Mathematical Models and Measurement Theory," in R. M. Thrall, *et al.*, eds., *Decision Processes* (New York: John Wiley & Sons, Inc., 1954), pp. 25–26.

[13] Black, *op. cit.*

[14] Coombs, Raiffa, and Thrall, *op. cit.*

[15] S. Aronow, "A Theory of Analogs," *Proceedings of the 1st International Biophysics Conference*, H. Quastler and H. J. Morowitz, eds. (New Haven: Yale University Press, 1959), pp. 27–34.

[16] *Ibid.*

[17] Coombs, Raiffa, and Thrall, *op. cit.*

[18] Chorley, *op. cit.*

[19] Daniel, *op. cit.*

[20] H. G. Andrewartha, "The Use of Conceptual Models in Population Ecology," *Cold Spring Harbor Symposia on Quantitative Biology*, **22** (1957), 226.

[21] Aronow, *op. cit.*

[22] F. Le Play, *Les Ouvriers européens*, 1st ed. (Paris, 1855).

[23] P. Vidal de la Blache, *La France de l'est* (Paris, 1917).

[24] J. H. von Thünen, *Der isolierte Staat in Beziehung auf Landwirtschaft und Nationalökonomie* (Hamburg, 1826).

[25] A. Weber, *Über den Standort der Industrien*, Part. 1 (Tübingen, 1909).

[26] W. Christaller, *Die zentralen Orte in Süddeutschland* (Jena: G. Fischer Verlag, 1935).

[27] A. Lösch, *The Economics of Location*, 2nd ed., W. G. Woglom, trans. (New Haven: Yale University Press, 1954).

[28] S. W. Wooldridge, "The Study of Geomorphology: A Review of 'Geographical Essays' by W. M. Davis," *Geographical Journal*, **121** (1955), 90.

[29] J. T. Hack, "Interpretation of Erosional Topography in Humid Temperate Regions," *American Journal of Science*, Bradley Volume, **258-A** (1960), 80–97. Chorley, *op. cit.*

[30] K. Ritter, *Die Erdkunde im Verhältnis zur Natur und zur Geschichte des Menschen* (Berlin, 1817–1818), 2 vols.

[31] H. J. Mackinder, *Democratic Ideals and Reality: A Study in the Politics of Reconstruction* (London: Constable & Co., Ltd., 1919).

[32] T. R. Malthus, *An Essay on the Principle of Population as it Affects the Future Improvement of Society* (London, 1798), 1st ed.

[33] F. J. Turner, "The Significance of the Frontier in American History," *Proceedings of the State Historical Society of Wisconsin*, **41** (1894), 79–112.

[34] E. Suess, *The Face of the Earth*, H. B. C. and W. J. Sollas, trans. (London: Oxford University Press, 1906), Vol. II.

[35] J. Neyman and E. L. Scott, "On a Mathematical Theory of Populations Conceived as a Conglomeration of Clusters," *Cold Spring Harbor Symposia on Quantitative Biology*, **22** (1957), 109.

[36] Daniel, *op. cit.*, 34.

[37] Andrewartha, *op. cit.*

[38] Coombs, Raiffa, and Thrall, *op. cit.*

[39] J. Haynel, "Mathematical Models in Demography," *Cold Spring Harbor Symposia on Quantitative Biology*, **22** (1957), 97–102.

[40] H. Jeffreys, "Problems of Denudation," *Philosophical Magazine* 6th Series, **36** (1918), 179–190.

[41] A. E. Scheidegger, "Mathematical Models of Slope Development" *Bulletin of the Geological Society of America*, (1961), 37–49.

[42] R. L. Miller and J. M. Zeigler, "A Model Relating Dynamics and Sediment Pattern in Equilibrium in the Region of Shoaling Waves, Breaker Zone and Foreshore," *Journal of Geology*, **66** (1958), 417–441.

[43] O. G. Sutton, *Understanding Weather* (Harmondsworth, England: Penguin Books Ltd., 1960), pp. 134–156.

[44] M. Beckmann, "A Continuous Model of Transportation," *Econometrica*, **20** (1952), 643–660.

[45] M. J. Lighthill and G. B. Whitham, "On Kinetic Waves: II, A Theory of Traffic Flow on Long Crowded Roads," *Proceedings of the Royal Society of London*, Series A, **229**, No. 1178 (1955), 317–345.

[46] P. I. Richards, "Shock Waves on the Highway," *Journal of the Operations Research Society of America*, **4** (1956), 42–51.

[47] L. B. Leopold and W. B. Langbein, "The Concept of Entropy in Landscape Evolution," U.S. Geological Survey, Professional Paper No. 500-A (Washington: U.S.G.P.O., 1962).

[48] W. Isard, *Location and Space-Economy* (New York: John Wiley & Sons, Inc., 1956).

[49] T. Hägerstrand, *The Propagation of Innovation Waves*, Lund Studies in Geography, Series B, No. 4 (1952).

[50] Neyman and Scott, *op. cit.*, 109–120.

[51] W. L. Garrison, "Notes on the Simulation of Urban Growth and Development," University of Washington, Department of Geography, Discussion Paper No. 34 (1960).

[52] Black, *op. cit.*

[53] G. D. Camp, "Models as Approximations," in J. Banbury and J. Maitland, eds. *Proceedings of the 2nd International Conference on Operational Research* (Aix-en-Provence, 1960), (1961), 22.

[54] Jeffreys, *op. cit.*, 179.

[55] Aronow, *op. cit.;* Black, *op cit.*

[56] J. F. Friedkin, "A Laboratory Study of the Meandering of Alluvial Rivers," U.S. Waterways Experiment Station, Vicksburg, Miss. (1945).

[57] H. Rouse, "Model Techniques in Meteorological Research," in H.R. Byers, *et al.*, eds., *Compendium of Meteorology*, (Boston: American Meteorological Society, 1951), pp. 1249–1254.

[58] H. L. Langhaar, *Dimensional Analysis and Theory of Models* (New York: John Wiley & Sons, Inc., 1951).

[59] W. J. Duncan, *Physical Similarity and Dimensional Analysis* (London: [Edward] Arnold [Publishers], Ltd., 1953).

[60] A. N. Strahler, "Dimensional Analysis Applied to Fluvially Eroded Landforms," *Bulletin of the Geological Society of America*, **69** (1958), 279–300.

[61] W. R. Stahl, "Similarity and Dimensional Methods in Biology," *Science*, **137** (1962), 205–212.

[62] Black, *op. cit.*

[63] Massachusetts Institute of Technology, "Design and Operation of an Hydraulic Analog Computer for Studies of Freezing and Thawing of Soils," Massachusetts Institute of Technology, Soil Engineering Division, Department of Civil Engineering, Technical Report No. 62, Corps of Engineers, U.S. Army (May, 1956).

[64] W. V. Lewis and M. M. Miller, "Kaolin Model Glaciers," *Journal of Glaciology*, **2** (1955), 535–538.

[65] M. Reiner, "The Flow of Matter," *Scientific American*, **201**, No. 6 (1959), 122–138.

[66] V. P. Starr, "The General Circulation of the Atmosphere," *Scientific American*, **195**, No. 6 (1956), 40–45.

[67] H. Hotelling, "A Mathematical Theory of Migration," unpublished master's thesis, University of Washington (1921).

[68] S. Enke, "Equilibrium Among Spatially Separated Markets: Solution by Electric Analogue," *Econometrica*, **19** (1951), 40–47.

[69] E. L. Brink and J. S. de Cani, "An Analogue Solution of the Generalized Transportation Problem, with Specific Application to Marketing Location," in M. Davies, R. T. Eddison, and T. Page, eds., *Proceedings of the 1st International Conference on Operational Research* (Oxford: English Universities Press, 1957), (1958), pp. 123–137.

[70] S. Stringer and K. B. Haley, "The Application of Linear Programming to a Large-Scale Transportation Problem," *ibid.*, pp. 109–122.

[71] Aronow, *op. cit.*

[72] L. von Bertalanffy, "General System Theory—A Critical Review," *General Systems*, **7** (1962), 15.

[73] Ross, *op. cit.*, p. 59.

[74] Sutton, *op. cit.*, pp. 170–172.

[75] Bunge, *op. cit.*, pp. 27–31.

[76] W. L. Garrison, lecture given in the "Regional Science Seminar," held at the University of California, Berkeley (Aug. 1962).

[77] R. J. Chorley, "The Shape of Drumlins," *Journal of Glaciology*, **3** (1959), 339–344.

[78] Daniel, *op. cit.*

[79] W. M. Davis, "The Geographical Cycle," *Geographical Journal*, **14** (1899), 481–504.

5

A SHORT COURSE IN MODEL DESIGN

IRA S. LOWRY

The growing enthusiasm for the use of computer models as aids to urban planning and administration derives less from the proven adequacy of such models than from the increasing sophistication of professional planners and a consequent awareness of the inadequacy of traditional techniques. As Lowdon Wingo has put it, planners are now prisoners of the discovery that in the city everything affects everything else:

In the good old days we tackled the slum in a straightforward way by tearing it down. Now we know the slum to be a complex social mechanism of supportive institutions, of housing submarkets, of human resources intertwined with the processes of the metropolitan community as a whole. . . . To distinguish favorable policy outcomes from unfavorable ones is no longer a simple matter. Decisions by governments, firms, and individuals in metropolitan areas turn on the state of such interdependent spatial systems as use of recreation facilities, transportation and communication nets, and the markets for land, housing, and even labor, rather than on the highly localized consequences directly elicited by policy actions. The rapid evolution of a genus of mathematical techniques, or models, to conditionally predict certain locational aspects of the behavior of urban populations has been both cause and consequence of these developments.[1]

. . . During the coming decade, it is safe to predict, many of our readers will be called upon to evaluate proposals for such models, or to participate in their construction. In this essay, I hope to provide some orientation to the model builder's way of thinking, interpret the jargon of his trade, and suggest a few standards for the evaluation of his product.[2]

Granted the complexity of the urban environment and the potentially extensive ramifications of planning decisions, we may ask, first of all, how computer models improve the planner's ability to generate sound policy and effective programs. The answer is certainly not that computers are wiser than their masters, but rather that they perform the most monotonous and repetitive tasks at high speed and

Reprinted from *Journal of the American Institute of Planners* **31** (1965), 158–165, by permission of the author and editor.

with absolute mechanical accuracy. The model builder can make use of this capacity only insofar as he is able to perceive repetitive temporal patterns in the processes of urban life, fixed spatial relationships in the kaleidoscope of urban form.

If he can identify such stable relationships, he may then find it possible to use them as building-blocks, or elements of a computer model. These elements, replicated many times, can be combined and manipulated by the computer (according to rules specified by the model builder) to generate larger, quasi-unique patterns of urban form and process which resemble those of the real world. The model literally consists of "named" variables embedded in mathematical formulae (structural relations), numerical constants (parameters), and a computational method programmed for the computer (algorithm). The pattern generated is typically a set of values for variables of interest to the planner or decision maker, each value tagged by geographic location and/or calendar date of occurrence.

THE USES OF MODELS

The model thus constructed may fall into any of three classes, depending on the interest of the client and the ambition of the model builder. In ascending order of difficulty, these are: descriptive models, predictive models, and planning models.

DESCRIPTIONS

The builder of a descriptive model has the limited objective of persuading the computer to replicate[3] the relevant features of an existing urban environment or of an already observed process of urban change. Roughly speaking, the measures of his accomplishment are: (1) the ratio of input data required by the model to output data generated by the model; (2) the accuracy and cost of the latter as compared to direct observation of the variables in question; and (3) the applicability of his model to other times and places than that for which it was originally constructed.

Good descriptive models are of scientific value because they reveal much about the structure of the urban environment, reducing the apparent complexity of the observed world to the coherent and rigorous language of mathematical relationships. They provide concrete evidence of the *ways* in which "everything in the city affects everything else," and few planners would fail to benefit from exposure to the inner workings of such models. They may also offer a shortcut to fieldwork, by generating reliable values for hard-to-measure variables from input data consisting of easy-to-measure variables.[4] But they do not directly satisfy the planner's demand for information about the future, or help him to choose among alternative programs. For these purposes, he must look to the more ambitious predictive and planning models.

PREDICTIONS

For prediction of the future, an understanding of the relationship between form and process becomes crucial. In a descriptive model it may suffice to note that X and Y are covariant (e.g., that the variable Y consistently has the value of $5X$, or equivalently, that $X = .2Y$); but when the aim is to predict the value of Y at some future time, the model must specify a causal sequence (e.g., that a one-unit change in the value of X will *cause* the value of Y to change by five units). If one is able to postulate the direction of causation, knowledge of the future value of the "cause" enables one to predict the future value of the "effect."[5]

Thus the first task of the builder of a predictive model is to establish a logical framework within which the variables of interest to his client stand at the end rather than at the beginning of a causal sequence. (Variables in this terminal position are often described as "endogenous.") His second task is to make sure that those variables which stand at the beginning (prime causes, often called "exogenous") can be plausibly evaluated as far into the future as may be necessary. These requirements may enlarge his frame of reference far beyond that which would serve for a merely descriptive model.[6]

The second requirement is partly relaxed in the case of *conditional* predictions, which are in any case of greater interest to planners than the unconditional variety. The planner is ordinarily interested in the state of the world following some contemplated act on his part, or following some possible but uncertain event outside his control. The model may then be allowed to respond in the form, "if X occurs, then Y will follow," without explicitly asserting the likelihood of X's occurrence. But explicit predictions must still be made for other exogenous events, since these may reinforce or counteract the effects of the hypothetical change in X.

A special case of conditional prediction is called "impact analysis." Here the interest is focused on the consequence that should be expected to follow a specified exogenous impact (change in X), if the environment were otherwise undisturbed.

PLANNING

Finally, there are planning models, a class whose technology is not far developed. A planning model necessarily incorporates the method of conditional prediction, but it goes further in that outcomes are evaluated in terms of the planner's goals. The essential steps are as follows: (1) specification of alternative programs or actions that might be chosen by the planner; (2) prediction of the consequences of choosing each alternative; (3) scoring these consequences according to a metric of goal achievement; and (4) choosing the alternative which yields the highest score.

The best-known species of planning model executes these steps by means of a "linear program," a computational routine allowing the efficient exploration of a very wide spectrum of alternatives—albeit under rather special restrictions as to permissible cause-effect relationships, and assuming complete information about alternatives and their consequences at the time of choice. Perhaps more relevant to urban planners is the problem of making a sequence of choices, the effects of each choice conditioning the alternatives available for subsequent choices. Since at each decision point there are as many "branches" as alternatives available, the spectrum of possible final outcomes can easily become astronomical. If steps (3) and (4) above are programmed for the computer, it is feasible to trace a fairly large number of alternative decision sequences through to their final outcomes; and mathematicians have reported some success with "dynamic programs" for identifying optimal sequences more efficiently than by trial-and-error.[7]

THEORIES AND MODELS

I have indicated that the model builder's work begins with the identification of persistent relationships among relevant variables, of causal sequences, of a logical framework for the model. In so doing, he must develop or borrow from theories of urban form and process. Although "theory" and "model" are often used interchangeably to denote a logico-mathematical construct of interrelated variables, a distinction can be drawn. In formulating his constructs, the theorist's overriding aims are logical coherence and generality; he is ordinarily content to specify only the conceptual significance of his variables and the general form of their functional interrelationships. The virtuosity of the theorist lies in rigorous logical derivation of interesting and empirically relevant propositions from the most parsimonious set of postulates.

The model builder, on the other hand, is concerned with the application of theories to a concrete case, with the aim of generating empirically relevant output from empirically based input. He is constrained, as the theorist is not, by considerations of cost, of data availability and accuracy, of timeliness, and of the client's convenience. Above all, he is required to be explicit, where the theorist is vague. The exigencies of his trade are such that, even given his high appreciation of "theory," his model is likely to reflect its theoretical origins only in oblique and approximate ways. Mechanisms that "work," however mysteriously, get substituted for those whose virtue lies in theoretical elegance.

The theoretical perspective of the model builder is most clearly visible in the set of structural relations he chooses as the framework of his model. A neatly articulated model will consist of a series of propositions of the general form, $Y = f(U, V, X, Z \ldots)$.[8] These propositions embrace the variables in which he is interested and specify the ways in which these variables act on one another. For most models relating to policy issues, it is useful to classify the propositions in terms of their content as technological, institutional, behavioral, or accounting.[9] While there may well be alternative sets of such propositions that convey the same meaning, the model builder is at least bound by rules of consistency (no contradictory propositions) and coherence (as many independent propositions as there are variables). Within these rules, his choice of structures is guided mostly by his sense of strategic advantage.

The pure theorist is often satisfied with the general forms indicated above, or with these forms plus a few constraints or restrictions. The model builder must be much more explicit, detailing the exact functional forms of his structural relations (e.g., $Y = \log U + a(V/X) - Z^b$); he must also fit his variables (Y, U, V, X, Z) and parameters (a, b) from empirical sources.

THE STRATEGY OF MODEL DESIGN

The "dirty work" of transforming a theory into a model is further discussed below ("Fitting a Model"). At this point I want to review some strategic alternatives of design open to the model builder, choices which demand all his skill and ingenuity since they bear so heavily on the serviceability of his model to its pre-determined purposes. Typically, these decisions must be made in an atmosphere of considerable uncertainty with respect to problems of implementation and eventual uses, and there are no clear canons of better and worse. Though the model builder can profit from the experience of others who have dealt with similar problems, he is to a large extent thrown back on his intuitive perceptions and his sense of style.

THE LEVEL OF AGGREGATION

Perhaps his most important choice concerns the level of aggregation at which he finds it profitable to search for regularities of form and process. While there is an accepted distinction between macroanalysis and microanalysis, the differences between these modes of perception can be elusive. Neither is the exclusive property of a particular academic discipline, but in urban studies, macroanalysis is closely associated with urban geography, demography, social physics,

and human ecology, while microanalysis is typically the métier of economics and social psychology.

The geographers, demographers, ecologists, and social physicists prefer to deal with statistics of mass behavior and the properties of collectivities. The elements of a model based on this tradition are likely to be stock-flow parameters, gravity or potential functions, matrices of transition probabilities.[10] Faced with the same *explanandum*, the economist is much more likely to think in terms of a market model, in which resources are allocated or events determined through competitive interaction of optimizing individuals whose behavior is predicated on a theory of rational choice. The social psychologist also works from a theory of individual choice, and has his own version of the market model—though it is less articulate because it embraces a much wider variety of transactions.[11]

The principal criticism of the macroanalytic approach is that its "theory" consists in large part of descriptive generalizations which lack explicit causal structure. Thus a macromodel of residential mobility may consist essentially of a set of mobility rates for population subgroups classified by age, sex, or family status, rates based on historical evidence of the statistical frequency of movement by the members of such groups. For purposes of prediction, one may assume that these rates will apply to future as well as past populations; but since the reasons people move are not explicit in such a model, the assumption of continuity in behavior cannot be easily modified to fit probable or postulated future changes in the environment of this behavior.

A second objection to macroanalytic approaches is that they do not lend themselves easily to financial accounting schemes. These are of particular relevance to planning models whose purpose is to distinguish among better and worse alternatives of policy or program. Strictly speaking, such distinctions can only be made if goal achievement is reducible to a single metric, and the most comprehensive metric available in our society, whether we like it or not, is money.[12] Thus in choosing among alternative transportation plans, the objective may be to maximize net social return to transportation investments—for example, to maximize the difference between benefits to be derived from the investment and costs allocable to it. Even though a gravity-model representation of the journey-to-work/residential location relationship may "work" in the sense of generating accurate predictions of population distribution and travel patterns, it will not yield financial data so easily as a market model of travel behavior and residential site selection, since the latter operates throughout in terms of price-defined alternatives faced by households.

The microanalytic approach also has its problems. Chief among these is that a model based on the theory of rational choice can be implemented only if the chooser's system of relative values—technically, his "preference system"—can be specified in considerable detail. The search for an empirical technique to achieve this detailed specification has frustrated generations of economists, and approximations to date are both crude in detail and based on highly questionable operating assumptions. Lacking the ability to observe these preference systems directly, the modeler is restricted to a very meager menu of empirically relevant propositions concerning the complementarity and substitutability of economic goods, propositions deducible from general theoretical principles.

The second problem of the microanalytic approach is the implementation of a comprehensive market model—one embracing the entire range of transactions which substantially affect the patterns of urban development and land use. Given complete information about the demand schedules of buyers and the supply schedules of sellers, the classical theory of a perfectly competitive market for a homogeneous commodity is simple enough, having a determinate solution for both the volume of transactions and the emergent price of the commodity. But the model builder is faced, empirically, with a congeries of interrelated markets, subtly-differentiated commodities, imperfections in communication, and inequities of bargaining position, all of which rule out the easy mathematical resolutions of the classical case. The fact is that we are presently able to implement only quite crude and tenuous approximations of market models.[13]

THE TREATMENT OF TIME

Except for the simple descriptive case, a model usually purports to represent the outcome of a process with temporal dimensions. Beginning with the state of the (relevant) world at time t, it carries us forward to the state of that world at $t + n$; thus a land-use model may start with a 1960 land-use inventory in order to predict the 1970 inventory. The way in which this time dimension is conceived is a matter of considerable strategic significance; the choice lies among varying degrees of temporal continuity, ranging from comparative statics at one extreme, through various types of recursive progression, to analytical dynamics at the other extreme.

At first glance, the choice seems to hinge merely on the question, how often need results be read out? But the issues go deeper, involving the model builder's perception of the self-equilibrating features of the world represented by his model, the empirical evaluation of response lags among his variables, and his interest in impact analysis as distinguished from other types of conditional or unconditional prediction.

The method of comparative statics implies a conviction that the system is strongly self-equilibrating, that the endogenous variables respond quickly and fully to exogenous changes. The model's parameters, fit from cross-section data, represent "equilibrium" relationships between exogenous and endogenous variables; a prediction requires specification of the values of the exogenous variables as of the target date. The process by which the system moves from its initial to its terminal state is unspecified.[14]

Alternatively, comparative statics may be used for impact analysis, where no target date is specified. Assuming only one or a few exogenous changes, the model is solved to indicate the characteristics of the equilibrium state toward which the system would tend in the absence of further exogenous impacts.

Self-equilibration is not a necessary assumption for analytical dynamics, an approach which focuses attention on the processes of change rather than on the emergent state of the system at a specified future date. Technically, this type of model must be formulated as a set of differential equations, at least some of which include variables whose rates of change are specified with respect to time.

Implementation of such a model requires only specification of its structural parameters and the "initial conditions" of its variables.

Thereafter, all processes are endogenous except time, and the time path of any variable can be continuously traced. The state of the system can be evaluated at any point in time. If the system *is* self-equilibrating, the values of its variables should converge on those indicated by analogous comparative statics; but without self-equilibrating properties, the system may fluctuate cyclically, explode, or degenerate.

Because comparative statics requires such strong equilibrium assumptions (seldom warranted for models of urban phenomena), and because analytical dynamics requires virtually complete closure (all variables except time are endogenous), most model builders compromise on recursive progressions. This method protrays the system's changes over time in lock-step fashion by means of lagged variables, for example:

(1) $Y_{t+1} = a + b\,X_t$
(2) $X_t = c + d\,Y_{t-1}$

Starting with initial values for either X or Y, one carries the system forward by alternately solving Eqs. 1 and 2. Of course in this example, a bit of algebraic manipulation suffices to evaluate Y_{t+n} directly from a given Y_t; but the case is seldom so simple—and the model builder is likely to want to inject periodic exogenous changes into this recursive sequence.

THE CONCEPT OF CHANGE

Any model dealing with changes over time in an urban system must distinguish (at least implicitly) between variables conceived as "stocks" and variables conceived as "flows." A stock is an inventory of items sufficiently alike to be treated as having only the dimension of size or number—for example, dwelling units, female labor-force participants, acres of space used for retail trade. This inventory may change as items are added or deleted; such changes, expressed per unit of time, are called flows. A model builder may choose to focus either on the factors which determine the magnitude of each stock, or on the factors which determine the magnitude of each flow.[15]

Since a stock is by definition the integral over time of the corresponding flow, it must also have the same determinants as the flow. But if the model builder limits his attention to flows which occur over any short span of time,

he can afford to take a number of shortcuts. Exogenous variables whose effects on stocks are visible only in the long run can be ignored or treated as fixed parameters. Whereas nonlinear expressions may be necessary to represent the long-run growth of a stock, marginal increments in the short run can often be represented by linear expressions. By accepting the initial magnitude of a stock as historically "given," one avoids the necessity of replicating the past and can devote himself to modeling the events of the present and near future.

Consider a model of retail location whose eventual application will be a five-year projection of the distribution of retail establishments within an urban area. The existing pattern (initial stock) of retail establishments in a large city reflects locational decisions made over the course of a century or more, during which time the transportation system, merchandising techniques, and patterns of consumption all have changed slowly but cumulatively. Most of the present stock of retail establishments will still be in operation at their present sites five years hence.

If the model builder is willing to organize his design around the *present* characteristics of the transportation network, of merchandising methods, of consumption patterns, his task may be greatly simplified. And the resulting model may be quite adequate for the prediction of short-run *changes* in retail location (say, as a consequence of population growth), even though it would not be able to recapitulate the city's history of retail development.

Clearly the model builder must weight the advantages of such simplifications against the fact that his model will have a shorter useful life. Since its structure postulates stability in a changing environment, the model will soon lose its empirical relevance.[16] By way of compromise, many model builders make use of "drift parameters": structural "constants" which are programmed for periodic revision to reflect changing environmental conditions, conditions which cannot conveniently be made explicit in the model.

SOLUTION METHODS

An integral part of the strategy of model design is a plan for operating the model—an algorithm or method of solution. This plan describes the concrete steps to be taken from the time that input data is fed to the computer until final results are read out. Four general methods are prominent; the choice among them is largely governed by the degree of logico-mathematical coherence of the model itself.

The neatest and most elegant method is the analytic solution. Ordinarily this method is applicable only to models which exhibit very tight logical structures and whose internal functional relationships are uncomplicated by nonlinearities and discontinuities. In substance, the set of equations constituting the model is resolved by analysis into a direct relationship between the relevant output variables and the set of input variables; intervening variables drop out of the "reduced form" equations. The paradigm system used above to illustrate recursion (Eqs. 1 and 2) can be solved analytically; for example:[17]

$$(3) \qquad Y_{t+4} = (a + bc)\,(1 + bd) + (bd)^2 Y_t$$

For models lacking complete logical closure, or whose structures are overburdened with inconvenient mathematical relationships, an alternative to the analytic solution is the iterative method. This method comprises a search for a set of output values which satisfy all the equations of the model; it proceeds initially by assuming approximate values for some of the variables and solving analytically for the remainder. These first-round solutions are then used as the basis for computing second approximations to replace the initially estimated values, and so on. Except for various degenerate cases, the solution values eventually "converge"—that is, further iterations fail to result in significant changes in the solution. Mechanically, the process is quite similar to recursive progression of a self-equilibrating system, but the iterative process need not imply either a sequence over time or a causal sequence. A drawback of this method is that it fails to signal the existence of alternative solution sets; a possibility that may have considerable importance for the interpretation of results.[18]

Ambitious models of urban processes may not meet the requirements for either the analytic or iterative methods of solution because of their scope: In the attempt to embrace a wide range of obviously relevant phenomena, one easily loses mathematical rigor and logical closure. For models of this class—loosely articulated

"system analyses"—machine simulation may be the best resort. The model specifies an inventory of possible "events" and indicates the immediate consequences of each event for one or more variables representing a "stock" or population. A change in the magnitude of a stock has specified (endogenous) consequences in the form of inducing new events; but characteristically, the major source of new events is exogenous. Indeed, the more sophisticated simulations (Monte Carlo or stochastic models) generate exogenous events by random choice from a given frequency distribution of possibilities. The computer's principal task is to keep a running account of all stocks and to alter them in response to events. This method is less appropriate for explicit projections than for tests of the sensitivity of the model (and by implication, of the real-world system represented by the model) to various possible constellations of exogenous events.

Finally, there is the method of "man-machine simulation," in which computer processing of input data is periodically interrupted, and the intermediate state of the system is read out for examination by a human participant. He may adjust intermediate results to correspond with his judgment as to their inherent plausibility, or he may use these intermediate results as a basis for a "policy" decision which is then fed back to the computer model as an exogenous change in values for specified variables or parameters. The human participant is ordinarily included for educational reasons—to give him practice in responding to planning problems—but on occasion, he is there simply because the model builder does not fully trust his model to behave "sensibly" under unusual circumstances.[19] (See below, "Parameters.")

FITTING A MODEL

Once the model builder has selected a theoretical perspective, designed a logical framework large enough to encompass his objectives, and postulated the existence of enough empirical regularities to permit the resolution of his problem, his next task is to "fit" or "calibrate" the model. This task involves two types of transformation: the variables mentioned in the model must be given precise empirical definition, and numerical values must be provided for the model's parameters.

VARIABLES

The first transformation always involves compromise. A variable conceived in general terms (household income) must be related to an available statistic (median income of families and unrelated individuals as reported by the U. S. Census of 1960 on the basis of a 25 per cent sample), and the restrictions and qualifications surrounding the data must be carefully explored to be sure they do not seriously undermine the proposed role of the variable in the model (aggregation of medians is difficult; response errors may create serious biases in the data; sampling variability of figures reported for small areas may be uncomfortably large).

A variable included in the model because of its theoretical significance may not be directly observable in the real world, so that some more accessible proxy must be chosen. Thus many land-use models deal in "location rents" (defined as that portion of the annual payment to an owner of a parcel of land which is attributable to the geographical position of the parcel as distinct from its soil or slope characteristics, existing structural improvements, or services provided by the landlord), but empirical sources tell us only about "contract rents" (the total contractual payment of tenant to landlord). Can contract rents be statistically standardized to serve as a reliable proxy for location rents?

I know of no formal canon of method for fitting variables, although I can think of some scattered principles to be observed.[20] More frequently than not, the problems encountered at this step force the model builder to backtrack and revise parts of his logical structure to lessen its sensitivity to bad data or to make better use of what data is actually available. Since few published statistics are exactly what they seem to be from the table headings and column stubs, it is very easy for one inexperienced in the generation of a particular class of data to misinterpret either its meaning or its reliability.

PARAMETERS

The fitting of parameters—numerical constants of relationship—is necessary for two reasons: (1) theoretical principles and deductive reasoning therefrom are seldom sufficient to indicate more than the appropriate sign (positive or negative) and probable order of magnitude for such constants; and (2) since these constants are measures of relationship between numerical variables, the precise empirical definition of the variable affects the value of the parameter. For instance, the appropriate value of a labor-force participation rate depends among other things on whether the pool from which participants are drawn is defined to include persons 15 to 60 or persons 14 to 65.

Parameter fitting is a highly developed branch of statistical method.[21] The most common tool is regression analysis, the simplest case being the estimation of parameters for a linear function of two variables, $Y = a + bX$. From a set of coordinate observations of the values of X and Y, one can estimate values for a and b in such a way as to minimize the expected error of estimate of Y from known values of X.

If the model can be formulated as a set of simultaneous linear equations, an elaboration of this method can be used to locate "best fit" values for all parameters in the system.[22] Models fitted in this way are often described as "econometric," although the method is equally applicable to noneconomic variables. A significant drawback of econometric fitting is that the criterion of selection for the values assigned to each parameter is the best *overall* fit of the model to a given array of data. The values generated for individual parameters are often surprising, yet it is difficult to look "inside" the fitting process for clues of explanation.

Alternatives to a comprehensive econometric fit can be described generally as "heuristic" methods. The model is partitioned into smaller systems of equations—some perhaps containing a single parameter—so that the parameters of each subsystem can be fit independently. This is in fact the typical approach, since few large models of urban form and process can be formulated as a single system of linear equations and still meet the objectives of the client.

Methods for obtaining estimates of the various parameters in these subsystems may vary considerably. A model ordinarily contains parameters whose function is nominal, and a model builder anxious to get on with his job may simply assign an arbitrary but plausible value to such a parameter. Where the context rules out direct methods for deriving simultaneous "best fits" even for the parameters of a limited subsystem, trial-and-error methods can be used to find a set of parametric values which seem to work. Or parametric values may be taken directly from empirical analogs, without regard for "best fit" in the context of the model.[23]

Finally, I should mention that model builders sometimes despair of finding a mathematically exact expression of relationship among certain of their model variables, so resort instead to "human" parameters. At the appropriate point in the operation of the model, intermediate or preliminary results are scanned by persons of respected judgment, who are asked to alter these outputs to conform to an intuitive standard of plausibility based on their experience in the field. The altered data are then fed back to the computer for further processing.

TESTING A MODEL

Fitting a model is analogous to the manufacture and assembly of a new piece of electrical machinery. A work team, guided by engineering drawings, fabricates each component and installs it in proper relation to other components, connecting input-output terminals. Along the way, considerable redesign, tinkering, and mutual adjustment of parts is inevitable; but eventually the prototype is completed. However carefully the individual components have been tested, and their interconnections inspected, a question remains about the final product: Will it really work?

Industrial experience indicates that the best way to answer this question is to turn the machine on and apply it to the task at hand. This precept applies also to computer models of urban form and process, with the important reservation that it is extremely difficult to select a "fair" but revelatory task, or to establish clear and objective standards of performance.

The appropriate test for a model depends, of course, on its predetermined function. It is unfair to ask a descriptive model to make a prediction, or a predictive model to find the optimal solution to a planning problem. But it is unfortunately the case that even an appropriate test may be infeasible.

The easiest model to test is the descriptive variety. Thus, for a model of urban form, the appropriate test would be its ability to replicate the details of an existing urban pattern on the basis of limited information concerning the area in question. Since most such models are built with a particular urban area in mind, and fitted with reference to this area's characteristics one ordinarily has detailed observations (for example, concurrent and otherwise compatible inventories of land use, structures, human populations, business enterprises, transportation facilities, and so forth) against which the model's output may be checked. The limitations of the test should also be apparent: The model's structure and parameters may be so closely locked into the patterns evident in this particular area and time that its descriptive abilities may have no generality; applied to another city the model may fail miserably.

The appropriate test for a predictive model is to run a prediction and verify the details of its outcome. The more distant the horizon of forecast, the more stringent the test; it would be easy to predict the distribution of workplaces in Boston tomorrow if one were given today's inventory. But few clients have the patience to finance several years of model building, then wait several more years to verify the model's first predictions. And even if one were willing to wait, there is the further problem that the model will almost certainly be designed for *conditional* predictions, and it would be remarkable indeed to discover in retrospect that all postulated conditions had been fulfilled.

The more accessible alternative is *ex post facto* prediction: Take the state of the world in 1950 as a starting point and apply the model by forecasting for 1960, then compare the forecast values to the observed values for 1960.[24] This procedure is likely to suffer from the same limitation of semicircularity that plagues the testing of descriptive models. More likely than not, the predictive model was *fitted* to the recorded processes of change, 1950–60. And if not, the reason is likely to be that comparable data are not available for the two dates. A predictive model is oriented to the problems of the future, and the model builder is anxious to feed his model the most recent additions to the menu of urban data—indeed, he may well initiate field work on a new series to provide it with a balanced diet. Why limit his freedom by insisting that his model be able to subsist on the more limited menu available a decade ago?

The test of a planning model has two distinct phases. The first is a check on its ability to trace through the consequences of a given planning decision or set of decisions; this phase is a form of conditional prediction, and subject to all the hazards described above. The second phase is a check on the ability of the model to select an optimal result from a spectrum of alternative outcomes. It may fail to do so because (1) short-cut methods may eliminate as suboptimal some outcomes which have more promise than they immediately show; (2) the evaluation of outcomes may be very sensitive to engineering estimates of cost or imputation of benefits, and these are intrinsically nebulous; or (3) the criteria of selection may be poorly stated, so that an outcome which would in fact be acceptable to the client is classified as unacceptable by the model.

"Sensitivity testing" is sometimes urged as a more accessible substitute for the performance tests discussed above; although it is easy to perform and applicable to a wide variety of models, sensitivity testing elicits indications of the "strength" of a model's design rather than of its descriptive or predictive or evaluative accuracy. The procedure is as follows: By varying the value of a single parameter (or even of an input variable) in successive runs of the model, one can measure the difference in outcome associated with a given parametric change. If the model's response to wide differences in parametric values is insignificant, this may be an indication that the parameter—and the associated network of functional relations—is superfluous. On the other hand, extreme sensitivity of outcomes to parametric changes indicates either that the parameter in question had better be fit with great care, or that some further elaboration of this component of the model is in order—on the grounds that the analogous real-world system must in fact have built-in compensations to forestall wild fluctuations in outcome.

EVALUATION

The picture I have painted above is rather grim, but I think it is accurate. The truth is that the client ordinarily accepts from the model builder a tool of unknown efficacy. The tests that the client can reasonably insist upon are at best partial and indecisive. Perhaps worst of all, those who must make the major decisions about sponsoring a model-building project are unlikely to have the time or training to evaluate a proposal, and later, having footed a large bill, have a vested interest in the model hardly second to the professional stake of its builder. In the absence of incontrovertible evidence to the contrary, the builder and sponsor will agree that the model "works."

In the face of such ambiguities, it is not hard to imagine a reasonable man's refusal to participate in such a probable boondoggle. But for the reasons indicated at the beginning of this article, I do not anticipate any shortage of sponsorship for model-building projects: It is better to try something—anything—than to merely wring one's hands over the futility of it all. Sponsors and model builders too can take comfort in the thought that they are building for the distant if not the near future.

Above all, the process of model building is educational. The participants invariably find their perceptions sharpened, their horizons expanded, their professional skills augmented. The mere necessity of framing questions carefully does much to dispel the fog of sloppy thinking that surrounds our efforts at civic betterment. My parting advice to the planning profession is: If you do sponsor a model, be sure your staff is deeply involved in its design and calibration. The most valuable function of the model will be lost if it is treated by the planners as a magic box which yields answers at the touch of a button.

FOOTNOTES

[1] Wingo in W. Z. Hirsch, ed., *Elements of Regional Accounts* (Baltimore: Johns Hopkins Press, 1964), p. 144. Model building has also been greatly encouraged by the electronic revolution in data processing and computation; mathematical models have an insatiable appetite for numbers.

[2] An immensely important topic in the field of model design which is not covered by this article is the joint effort of model builder and client to define the "problem" to which a model offers a possible "solution." On this point, I know of no better reference than a RAND book on systems analysis, E. S. Quade, ed., *Analysis for Military Decisions*. R-387-PR (Santa Monica: The RAND Corporation, 1964), particularly the essays of R. D. Specht ("The Why and How of Model-Building"), R. McKean ("Criteria"), and E. S. Quade ("Pitfalls in Systems Analysis").

[3] Some model builders would freely substitute "simulate" for my "replicate." All models are intended in some sense to simulate reality, but this usage is the source of some confusion in the literature since "simulation" has acquired another, more technical meaning descriptive of a class of algorithms. In this essay, I use the term only in the latter sense. See, below, "Solution Methods."

[4] For example, traffic analysts use zonal interchange models to generate estimates of zone-to-zone traffic flows from inventories of the land uses in each zone. One prominent member of the profession is so convinced of the descriptive reliability of these models that he sees no further need for direct surveys of traffic movements (O & D studies).

[5] Philosophers of science view the concepts of "cause" and "effect" with jaundiced eyes. For lesser mortals these concepts are most helpful, and not at all dangerous so long as they are applied within the framework of a system of interdependence. H. A. Simon, *Models of Man* (New York: John Wiley & Sons, Inc., 1957), Chaps. 1–3.

[6] No variable is intrinsically endogenous or exogenous. These terms, like the statistician's "dependent" and "independent," merely define the position of a variable within a particular model. A further useful distinction can be made between exogenous variables subject to policy control and those which are not, and between endogenous variables of direct interest to the planner and those which are included only because they are necessary to complete the logical structure of the model. S. Sonenblum, and L. H. Stern. "The Use of Economic Projections in Planning," *Journal of the American Institute of Planners*, **30** (1964), 110–123.

[7] The fundamentals and applications of linear programming are summarized in very readable form by W. J. Baumol, "Activity Analysis in One Lesson," *American Economic Review*, **48** (1958), 837–873. I cannot find any simple exposition of dynamic programming, but see R. Bellman, *Dynamic Programming* (Princeton: Princeton University Press, 1957) for a brief account of the class of problems to which the technique is applicable.

[8] "The value of Y is a function of (depends on) the values of U, V, X, and Z, and so forth." For a gentle introduction to the notation and methods of mathematical modeling, Beach is an excellent source. E. F. Beach, *Economic Models: An Exposition* (New York: John Wiley & Sons, Inc., 1957).

[9] Some examples, in prose rather than symbols:

Technological: The maximum vehicular capacity of a roadway is a function of the number of lanes, the average distance between signals, and the weather.

Institutional: Disposable family income is a function of gross family earnings and the tax rate.

Behavioral: The level of housing density chosen by a family depends on disposable family income, the average age of family members, and the location of the work place of the principal wage earner.

Accounting: Total land in use is the sum of land in residential use, in retail use, in manufacturing use, and so forth.

[10] The essays in Part II of G. K. Zipf, *Human Behavior and the Principle of Least Effort* (Reading, Mass.: Addison-Wesley Publishing Company, Inc., 1949) should give the reader a "feel" for the macroanalytic perspective in urban models. See also G. A. P. Carrothers, "An Historical Review of the Gravity and Potential Concepts of Human Interaction," *Journal of the American Institute of Planners*, **22** (1956), 94–102 and B. J. L. Berry, "Cities as Systems Within Systems of Cities." Paper presented at the Annual Meeting of the Regional Science Association, Chicago (Nov. 1963).

[11] Dyckman provides an excellent review of the theory of rational choice in a planning context. J. W. Dyckman, "Planning and Decision Theory," *Journal of the American Institute of Planners*, **27** (1961), 335–345. Any introductory text in economics will describe the microanalytic underpinnings of demand and supply schedules and will also review a family of market models. The most ambitious microanalytic model ever undertaken in the social sciences is described in G. H. Orcutt, M. Greenberger, J. Korbel, and A. M. Rivlin, *Microanalysis of Socioeconomic Systems: A Simulation Study* (New York: Harper & Row, Publishers, 1961). For models that embrace more than "economic" man, see Simon, *op. cit.* or P. F. Lazarsfeld, ed., *Mathematical Thinking in the Social Sciences* (New York: Free Press of Glencoe, Inc., 1954).

[12] N. Lichfield, "Cost-Benefit Analysis in City Planning," *Journal of the American Institute of Planners*, **26** (1960), 273–279.

[13] It is my personal conviction—not shared by all members of the fraternity of model builders—that the macroanalytic approach to modeling urban form and processes shows the greater promise of providing reliable answers to concrete problems of prediction and planning. For a contrary view, see the forceful statement by B. Harris, "Some Problems in the Theory of Intra-Urban Location." Paper prepared for a seminar sponsored by the Commitee on Urban Economics of Resources for the Future, Washington, D. C. (Apr. 1961).

[14] Descriptive models of urban form are nearly always static or "equilibrium" models, and are sometimes used for quasi-predictions (comparsative tatics). For convenient examples, see B. Harris, "A Model of Locational Equilibrium for Retail Trade." Paper prepared for the Seminar on Models of Land Use Development, Institute of Urban Studies, University of Pennsylvania, Philadelphia (Oct. 1964) or I. S. Lowry, *A Model of Metropolis*. RM-4035-RC (Santa Monica: The RAND Corporation, 1964).

[15] Contrast the emphasis on stocks in the San Francisco CRP model designed by Arthur D. Little, Inc., "A Simulation Model of the Residential Space Market in San Francisco." Paper prepared for the Seminar on Models of Land Use Development, Institute

of Urban Studies, University of Pennsylvania, Philadelphia (Oct. 1964), with the emphasis on flows in R. S. Bolan, W. B. Hansen, N. A. Irwin, and K. H. Dieter, "Planning Applications of a Simulation Model." Paper prepared for the New England Section, Regional Science Association, Fall Meeting, Boston College (Oct. 1963) or with the several "growth allocation" models described in this issue of the *Journal*.

[16] R. V. Black, "Scientific Versus Empirical Projections," *Journal of the American Institute of Planners*, **26** (1960), 144–145.

[17] The reader is warned that Eq. 3 is not a general solution for any Y_{t+n}, but merely the simplest expression for Y_{t+4}.

[18] An example of the iterative technique is given in some detail in Lowry, *op. cit.*, pp. 12–19.

[19] A good bibliography in simulation methods is M. Shubik, "Bibliography on Simulation, Gaming, Artificial Intelligence and Allied Topics," *Journal of the American Statistical Association*, **55** (1960), 736–751. M. A. Geisler, W. W. Haythorn, and W. A. Steger, *Simulation and the Logistics Systems Laboratory*. RM-3281-PR (Santa Monica: The RAND Corporation, 1962) offer a quick and readable review of the field, with emphasis on man-machine simulation, or "gaming." N. D. Grundstein, "Computer Simulation of a Community for Gaming." Paper prepared for the Annual Meeting of the American Association for the Advancement of Science, Denver (Dec. 1961), describes a "community game" for the training of planners and municipal administrators.

[20] Special data problems encountered in modeling urban form and process are discussed by B. Harris, "An Accounts Framework for Metropolitan Models," in Hirrch, *op. cit.*, 107–127. Also See W. A. Steger, "Data and Information Management in a Large Scale Modelling Effort: The Pittsburgh Urban Renewal Simulation Model." Paper prepared for the Seminar on Models of Land Use Development, Institute of Urban Studies, University of Pennsylvania, Philadelphia (Oct. 1964), 1–6.

[21] Beach, *op. cit.* Part II, provides an especially good introduction to statistical and econometric methods.

[22] The convenience of this method is so great that it is often applied to systems containing known nonlinearities, on the grounds that a linear approximation is better than nothing. Simultaneous estimation of the parameters of nonlinear systems is possible, but more difficult; the outstanding example among land-use models is Karl Dieter's Program Polimetric for fitting an exponential model with a great many parameters. (The model, but not the fitting method, is described in R. S. Bolan, *op. cit.*

[23] J. H. Niedercorn, *An Econometric Model of Metropolitan Employment and Population Growth*. RM-3758-RC (Santa Monica: The RAND Corporation, 1963). His model is partitioned into three subsystems, each of which was fit independently. The discussion on pp. 14–15 illustrates the variety of estimating methods ordinarily required to fit a model. See also Harris, *op. cit.* for a discussion of the "gradient search" method of estimating parameters.

[24] D. M. Hill, "A Growth Allocation Model for the Boston Region—Its Development, Calibration and Validation." Paper prepared for the Seminar on Models of Land Use Development, Institute of Urban Studies, University of Pennsylvania, Philadelphia (Oct. 1964), reports with unusual thoroughness on a test of this type for the EMPIRIC Model developed for Boston by Traffic Research Corporation.

SPATIAL DATA
AND SPATIAL STATISTICS

1

THE USE OF COMPUTERS
IN THE PROCESSING AND ANALYSIS
OF GEOGRAPHIC INFORMATION

RICHARD C. KAO

The purpose of this paper is to assess—at least on a modest scale—the impact of high-speed computers on the collection and use of data in geographic research. Geographic data are customarily classified into two distinct types: locational and areal. By locational data are not necessarily meant only the geodetic coordinates of a small point on earth with respect to some arbitrarily chosen reference system (for example, latitude and longitude), but almost any other form of information which can be associated with that point (for example, its altitude above mean sea level or the normal atmospheric pressure thirty feet above it along the plumb line). Areal data, on the other hand, are those which characterize a region on the globe (the population of Kenya or the amount of oil deposits off the California coast, for example). Locational data are the values of a "point function," areal data those of a "set function." In either case the domain of definition of the function is the outer shell of the earth—Hettner's *Erdhulle* or Hartshorne's *earth shell*. That this definition includes also points in space is a natural consequence of the kind of reality studied by geographers.[1]

IMPACT OF COMPUTERS ON FUTURE GEOGRAPHIC RESEARCH

It is probably trite to say that any geographic research must have to do with either locational or areal data of some sort. It is equally trite to say that automation in the form of high-speed computers is here to stay. Everyone knows that one of the things these giant brains are supposed to do is to process data on a grand scale and at awe-inspiring speed. A fundamental question then arises: What impact, if any, may they exert on data collection and utilization in future geographic research? This is a large question, to which no neat and simple answer can be given at present. However, two examples may serve to illustrate the manner in which such impact is already . . . felt.

Reprinted from *Geographical Review*, **53** (1963), 530–547, by permission of the editor.

THE GEOGRAPHIC ORDERING OF INFORMATION

The first example may be called the "geographic ordering of information."[2] All geographers are aware that information in their research must be spatially ordered. However, in the past, owing to certain technologic constraints, such information was often ordered in a nongeographic or quasi-geographic format. Some of these constraints are fast disappearing since the introduction of the computer, but the methodology developed within their context lingers on. A typical case is census data. Traditionally, each census tract is given an arbitrary code designation, and a list of characteristics of the tract is appended. Information so provided can be meaningfully analyzed without any reference whatever to the exact location of the tract. But such analysis is almot by definition nongeographic or, at best, quasi-geographic. The code designation does specify in which state and which county a tract is located, but it is completely random as to location within the county. A geographic analysis that needs the location of a census tract can therefore be made only by the help of supplementary information. This information is typically in the form of a map showing the exact location of the census tracts. The published tables of information by census tracts can then be spatially ordered and geographically analyzed.

Another familiar method of presenting geographic data is a lexicographic listing of geographic areas with associated information; for example, an alphabetic listing of the states or of counties within a given state. To analyze such information geographically, it is necessary first to extract the information from the listing and transfer it to a map. With the ready availability of computers, it is not difficult to picture the possibility of direct analysis without the transference from tables to maps now required.

Perhaps the most extreme form of the traditionally accepted ordering of geographic data is the metes and bounds system still used in some states for legal description of real property. The description uses bench marks, which may be anything from an oak tree[3] to an abandoned well. This system is as confused and inconvenient as the British coinage system, something to be cherished only by future historians or present-day Englishmen. The township and range system used in the Survey of the Public Lands of the United States, though a considerable improvement over the meters and bounds system for cadastral surveys, still leaves much to be desired. Basically, the township and range system is a combination of an areal (or set, as against point) coordinate system and a lexicographic listing. By an areal coordinate system is meant a coordinate system not for individual points, but for unit areas (point sets) on the globe. In the Public Lands Survey, the unit areas are the six-mile-square townships. These quadrilateral unit areas are approximately equal in size and are ordered in east-west (range) and north-south (township) directions as points in the plane. Thus, with reference to the San Bernardino Base and Meridian, the unit area with coordinate Township 4 North, Range 9 West, is in the "second quadrant" of the areal coordinate system, and that with coordinate Township 2 South, Range 1 East, is in the "fourth quadrant." Superimposed on this "coarse" areal coordinate system is a lexicographic (in this case, numerical) listing of the thirty-six sections for each unit area arranged in a serpentine fashion beginning with the northeast corner of the unit area.

Two observations are in order. First, to the extent that the township and range system is a partition of areas, its units are similar to census or county units. Second, the entire Public Lands Survey system is a collection of different areal coordinate systems with not only limited, but uneven coverage. For example, there is no unit area with coordinate Township 36 South, Range 140 East, Mount Diablo Base and Meridian. For such a unit would be close to Albuquerque, New Mexico, where the reference point is the New Mexico Principal (106° 53′12″ W., 34°15′35″ N.) rather than Mount Diablo (121°54′47″ W., 37°52′54″ N.).[4] That the coverage of different areal coordinate systems is uneven is well known. What may not be generally known is the degree to which unevenness exists. Take, for example, the Humboldt Base and Meridian system and the San Bernardino Base and Meridian system in California. The area covered by the San Bernardino is at least ten times larger than that covered by the Humboldt. These observations serve to point out the highly sectionalized nature of the township and range system, which is clearly a heritage from the preautomation era—not only chronologically, but also conceptually.[5]

The three types of geographic ordering of information mentioned above—census tracts, lexicographic listing, and bench-mark system—are sufficient to prove my first point of contention: that is, as computers are used more widely to process data, geographers will find it more convenient and necessary to order information in an analytic rather than a descriptive form. There are many problems badly in need of research now or soon, before such a transition is possible. For instance, just imagine what geographers would have to do in order to give a workable analytic definition of the seemingly trivial concept of "contiguity."

An excellent illustration of the need to order geographic information in analytic rather than descriptive form is a study by Torsten Hägerstrand.[6] The Swedish census reports information on individual households by street address—a mixture of a lexicographic listing and a bench-mark system. Hägerstrand translated all street addresses into coordinates of the Swedish military grid—an analytic form—and data on each household and the coordinates of that household were punched on Hollerith cards. A listing of this information turns out to be both convenient and sufficient for a wide variety of geographic analyses; for example, analysis of population or income distribution by provinces, or the construction of such useful statistics as the average distance of a household to the nearest neighbor, or the correlation between the distribution of schoolchildren and that of teachers under forty years of age. The objective of Hägerstrand's study is "to investigate if a possibility exists to give to the space aspect of statistical material the same neutrally objective status as the time aspect always had."[7]

NEW LIGHT ON OLD PROBLEMS

The second example is somewhat different. Besides inducing geographers to abandon some old customs, computers may permit new light to be focused on old problems. A concrete illustration may be taken from the field of cartography. Among all available map projections, geographers are inclined to use equivalent (or equal-area) maps the most; mathematicians, conformal maps the most. Presumably the reason for the difference is a matter both of interest and of emphasis. Geographers are primarily concerned with studying geographic environment, which usually makes reference to

area as the variable;[8] only rarely are angles of much significance except for problems connected with navigation. Mathematicians, on the other hand, usually study maps as a special case of the general theory of transformations. When only a system of two functions of two variables, representing two distinct sets of coordinate systems, is concerned, there is available a rather elegant mathematical theory called "conformal mapping." However, this theory may or may not have relevance in a particular piece of geographic research.

In a study involving real-time simulation of a great mass of geographic data some years ago,[9] I found geometric (or perspective) maps to be far superior to conformal maps, for the simple reason that the property of conformality, being at best a local isometry, is of relatively little importance to the problem, whereas properties in the large, such as a great-circle path or the property of a point lying inside or outside a region, are far more relevant. As a consequence, metric methods are subordinated to projective or topological methods for both the description and the analysis of the problem.[10] In order that visual aesthetics will not be entirely eliminated, subroutines are prepared that permit instantaneous display of simulated air pictures on a cathode-ray tube in the form of a conformal map. But the real work is carried out in terms of projective coordinates in the computer program, because these are found to be particularly suitable for rapid arithmetic manipulation. Here is an instance in which a class of maps generally considered to be uninteresting and antiquated could, because of the computer, compete on equal footing with a class which has hitherto been accepted almost ex cathedra as being the ultimate in cartography. Until computers can perform the function of information storage and retrieval as efficiently as, or even more efficiently than, that of calculation, geometric maps will continue to receive increasing attention both in theory and in practice.

Perspective maps are also becoming more important in another context, that of space exploration, particularly satellite reconnaissance. If we stay sufficiently close to the earth's surface, relatively little distortion is introduced by assuming the surface to be flat. However, as we go to higher altitudes, the curvature of the earth can hardly be ignored. By the very nature of the geometry, the satellite is taking a perspective map if we assume light to travel in a straight line, probably the best approximation if we confine ourselves to the gravitational field around the earth.[11] It is sometimes instructive to stop and think back a little. Perspective maps were first studied because of their intimate connection with certain physical problems; if staying close to the real problem is the criterion, then we can hardly throw away these maps and use others simply because the others may be more appealing from a mathematical standpoint. Great mathematicians—for example, Hilbert and Poincaré—always insisted on staying close to the real problem, even when a most difficult mathematical theory was being developed. They would be the last to abandon the real problem and concentrate on some arbitrary abstraction of it to suit their own convenience. Felix Klein said some fifty years ago: "I should like to emphasize, however, that precisely in geographic practice use is often made of *representations in which angles are not preserved*, so that conformal transformations should not be regarded, as is often done, as the only important ones."[12] If geographic research calls for other maps, there is no scientific rationale to require everybody to use conformal maps exclusively.[13] When we place our emphasis in cartography not so much on the end product of a highly technical process called map making as on the relation between a pair of maps (data processing of geographic information),[14] we may find some old, long-forgotten maps to be handy at times. Hence computers may not only force geographers to abandon old habits; they may also garb geographers in old habits that are no longer considered fashionable, though with good reason.

COMPUTERS AND TYPES OF GEOGRAPHIC PROBLEMS

In case the impression has been given that computers can only *solve* problems, not *create* them, let us turn to a brief discussion of the different types of geographic problems that are likely to arise with the increasingly widespread use of high-speed computers. Obviously computers cannot create problems that do not already exist. However, as computers become increasingly available for their use, geographers either are forced into harder thought in some areas of research or are beginning to gain new

hope for the solution of hitherto "insoluble" problems. It is in this context that the subsequent discussion should be interpreted.

DATA-REDUCTION PROBLEMS

The first class of problems has to do with the preparation of inputs—the so-called data-reduction problems. These problems are not confined to high-speed computers. But as we use them more and more, we are some-how brought to greater awareness of the presence and nature of these problems. The basic question is the translation of geographic information from the iconic to the analytic level.[15] Take, for example, photogrammetry for surveying and mapping. The inputs collected for analysis are in iconic, or pictorial, form. Before the computer can process and analyze them, the images must somehow be translated into analytic form acceptable to it. This is a rather difficult problem without satisfactory solution as yet and in computer programming comes under such various terms as "artificial intelligence" and "pattern recognition." It is not possible here to go into a deeper discussion of this problem,[16] but it is well to point out the intimate connection between its solution and the prospects for observation satellites in military intelligence and weather forecasting.[17]

DATA-PROCESSING PROBLEMS

The second class of problems has to do with the manipulation of geographic inputs (already in analytic form) by the computer program—the so-called data-processing problems. Here a sharp distinction must be made between two subclasses that for convenience may be labeled as "book-keeping" and "computation." Book-keeping problems are those in which the computer is used more or less as an efficient accounting machine in the analysis of the problems. Data are grouped or regrouped by different criteria, and simple statistics, such as means or dispersions, can be computed. The end result is in general some sort of cartogram with certain derived statistics on an areal basis, but this result need not hold any predictive value. By and large, geographers' problems fall into this subclass when the computer is used.[18]

It is important to note that the limiting factor in the performance of the computer here is that of an information-storage-and-retrieval device.

The computer is like a huge library in which a lot of individual bits of information are stored. Depending on the nature of the problem, a specific type of storage device may be used. A rough classification is given in Table 1. The adjectives used in the table are all relative. Core memory and drum storage are generally considered to be only temporary devices, since the same unit has to be used, in general, for subsequent tasks on the same computer. Disc, tape, and card storage may be considered more or less permanent, since their relatively low cost makes it possible to use separate units for different tasks. For the same reason, the storage capacity of the computer may be adjusted to any level merely by using more units.

Accessibility to the stored information also differs among these devices. This may be illustrated by borrowing some terms from the theory of Markov chains.[19] Let the individual information locations be denoted by $E_i (i = 1, \ldots, n)$, where the subscript i denotes the order in which these locations follow one another. For core memory, i denotes simply the cell number in the memory unit; for cards, i denotes the position of a particular card in a given deck. Let a_i denote the initial probability that information may be associated with (that is, stored into or retrieved from) E_i, where $\sum_{i=1}^{n} a_i = 1$ and p_{ij} is the conditional probability that information may be associated with E_j on the next trial, given that it has already been associated with E_i on some trial. Then a sequenced-access device (tape or card) may be characterized by

$$a_i = \begin{cases} 1 \text{ if } i = 1 \\ 0 \text{ if } i \neq 1 \end{cases} \quad p_{ij} = \begin{cases} 1 \text{ if } j = i + 1 \\ 0 \text{ if } j \neq i + 1 \end{cases}$$

whereas they may be arbitrary for random-access devices. In particular, for core memory $p_{ij} = p_{ik}$ for every pair $j, k (j \neq k)$, whereas for drum or disc, p_{ij}'s are, for fixed i, inversely related to $|i - j|$.

Just as information-storage-and-retrieval devices may differ from one computer to another, or even on the same computer, book-keeping problems involving geographic information may differ from one area to another. Specifically, two criteria may be used to distinguish among these problems. The first is the degree to which individual bits of information are correlated on a geographic basis, and the second is the frequency with which the same bit of information recurs over time. Table 2 gives this twofold classification with some typical illustrations. For instance, life-insurance companies may generally expect losses to be geographically independent, barring epidemics or natural hazards, just as fire departments may expect alarms to be geographically independent, barring arson or hoax. In either case, the recurrence time is long, indeed infinite for a loss payoff on a life-insurance policy. On the other hand, billing taxes according to an assessment roll also has a long recurrence time; that is, such billing typically takes place only twice a year. However, owing to the

TABLE 1

Storage devices and their associated characteristics

Type	Duration	Capacity	Access	Access time	Cost
Core memory	Temporary	Limited	Random	Short, constant	High
Drum	Temporary	Limited	Random	Short, variable	High to medium
Disc	Permanent	Unlimited	Random	Medium, variable	Medium
Tape	Permanent	Unlimited	Sequenced	Medium to long, variable	Medium to low
Card	Permanent	Unlimited	Sequenced	Long, variable	Low

TABLE 2

Relation between bits of Information	Recurrence time	
	Long	Short
Independent	Life-insurance statistics	Distribution of telephone calls
Correlated	Assessment roll	Weekly payroll of city employees

ad valorem nature of the assessment, taxes must be paid on every parcel of real property except those reserved for public or charitable uses. In other words, the degree to which taxes on different parcels of ground as different bits of geographic information are correlated is nearly perfect. It is normally the exemptions that are to be separately treated.[20] A good example for a problem involving short recurrence time but relatively independent information bits is the distribution of telephone calls. The same phone may ring twenty-five times a day, but phones situated close together geographically need not have anything to do with each other. Finally, the weekly payroll of, say, public offices is a book-keeping task which must be performed rather frequently (short recurrence time) and which requires that all employees be paid (high correlation between information bits).

A comparison of Tables 1 and 2 instantly suggests the relative efficiency of various storage devices for data processing in book-keeping problems involving geographic information. For example, tape or card storage would be suitable and adequate for assessment or payroll book-keeping problems, whereas core memory would probably be needed to facilitate the "automatic" channeling of communication links in telephone service. In general, data-processing problems of the book-keeping type call for a great many storage-and retrieval operations on the computer, and programming techniques exist that may "optimize" storage efficiency for a given storage device. Such optimization programming techniques are related to the optimal assignment, or "traveling salesman," problem in mathematical programming.

The other subclass of data-processing problems, computation, is most closely related to simulation research, where the limiting factor lies in the computer's ability to carry out real-time computation. Most geographers may be only partly aware of the potential of computers in this line of research or may consider such problems to lie outside their realm of investigation. However, there is a growing tendency away from this traditional attitude. Hägerstrand's studies of "The Propagation of Innovation Waves" and "On Monte Carlo-Simulation of Diffusion"[21] are outstanding examples of a new trend in geographic research; so are traffic studies conducted at several transportation or regional science centers in this country.[22] My

own experience with computers as applied to geographic data has also been confined largely to this area, except that the real-time requirement is rather stringent. Briefly described, a computer program must be so designed as to produce a "motion picture" of, for example, air defense exercises (battles and all) on a cathode-ray tube of a radar scope when outside the laboratory nothing is happening. Keeping up with real time is crucial, and the nature of the problem is such that different bits of information need not be highly correlated (uncertainty in enemy penetration, saturation tactics, and the like) and the recurrence time is relatively short. Since most present-day high-speed computers possess one common characteristic —". . . storage and retrieval of data is relatively expensive, whereas calculating and recalculating derived data is fairly cheap"[23]—one must be prepared either to manipulate repeatedly the same bits of geographic information to produce derived quantities in real time or to resort to table look-up in core memory if storage capacity and tolerance requirements permit. This is the reason that perspective maps are particularly suitable for real-time simulation of geographic inputs.

An example may be given to illustrate the basic difference between the two subclasses of data-processing problems. As was indicated earlier, the first, or book-keeping, class comprises problems for which no urgency exists for using the processed or derived information for prediction. The term "book-keeping" as used here serves to emphasize the fact that processing of data already collected is not required for the collection of "future" data. It is done primarily as an aid for the analysis and interpretation of a stable state of affairs, namely the given geographic environment for which we seek to collect relevant data. The second, or computation, subclass, on the other hand, comprises problems for which processing of data is needed, often in real time, principally as a means of predicting the future course of events. This implies, in particular, an unstable or dynamic geographic environment for which we desire to obtain vital and timely information. Take, for example, title companies and the recording system used in most counties in the United States. A parcel of land will ordinarily not be sold more than twice a year; nevertheless, there must be on hand a complete inventory of all the parcels. Hence the problem here is primarily efficient information storage and retrieval. In contrast, meteorologists or navigators are likely to need their information in terms of minutes, hours, or days. For them it is sometimes crucial to be able to keep up with things in real time as they unfold. A civil-defense authority would certainly want to have progress information on the path of a moving fireball or tornado. Here the emphasis is on efficient transformation and transmission of stored information for something that is essentially predictive. In a broad way, the distinction between the two kinds of examples is related to recurrence time (Table 2).

SPECIAL-PURPOSE COMPUTERS

The third class of geographic problems arises from special-purpose hardware that is beginning to appear increasingly on the market. There is a slow but healthy trend to design smaller, special-purpose computers to handle special problems. Present-day computers are designed primarily for efficient *arithmetic* operations. It is conceivable that new computers will handle other types of problems more efficiently; for example, direct processing of photographic, sonar, or seismic inputs,[24] or instrumentation and control-engineering problems.[25] All this may sound overwhelming, but the idea is by no means farfetched. Those who are familiar with Soviet computer technology can bear witness to the fact that the Russians seem to have placed quite different emphasis on the design of their computers. Some of their machines are supposed to accept linguistic inputs that are not only audio, but also cultural.[26] It is no more improbable that a computer may be built to handle information-retrieval problems more efficiently,[27] the lack of which seems to be the Achilles' heel in present-day computer technology.

A word may be added here on the difference between special-purpose computers and the mere application of a general-purpose computer for special problems. A special-purpose computer is designed to handle *inputs* that arise from, or are peculiar to, a particular problem. A general-purpose computer may be used to produce *outputs* in some special form, which we consider only an application. The literature abounds with such applications, ranging from machine translation to musical composition.[28] In each case a computer program is prepared, based on an idealized model of the problem, and the computer is used as a logico-arithmetic blackbox to produce an output of the desired form. Problems of this nature are usually "simpler" than those related to the design of special-purpose computers. Much confusion has arisen in the computing field because this fundamental distinction is not made. Take, for example, all the discussion centering around "intelligent" machines. If a computer possesses no "intelligence," no amount of program writing and rewriting will give it the desired intelligence. An "intelligent" computer must be a special-purpose machine designed to reproduce partly or wholly the nervous system of the human brain. Clearly, a prerequisite would be a thorough, if not complete, understanding of how the human brain processes sensory impulses to form thoughts. Without this requirement the best one can hope for is simulated or definitional intelligence.

COMPUTERS AND MAPS

A rough picture has been given of the various kinds of problems that could arise, and that need to be carefully thought through, when computers are used to process or analyze geographic information. A modern computer can perform many functions, though generally not with equal efficiency. Also it is conceivable that special computers may be constructed for specific purposes. It is therefore rather difficult to say which objectives should be given priority.

The desirability of the adoption of a universal mapping system by users of geographic information has been much discussed.[29] But before we decide which particular system to adopt, it is well to ask ourselves what a universal mapping system can accomplish. Such a mapping system is by its very nature only a labeling system. It cannot get to the heart of every conceivable type of problem in which geographic data are being used. What it does provide is a useful and certainly important means of easy communication between users of maps, but easy communication should not always be the overriding criterion when a diversity of problems arise. An analogy may illustrate the point. It cannot be assumed that the adoption of Esperanto, presumably a universal linguistic system, would cause all the peoples in the world to iron out their differences, because it wouldn't. The problems will always exist, whether Esperanto exists or not. One thing we may do well to remember is this: by making any system of representation more *general*, we are at the same time also reducing its usefulness for a *particular* application.

It is perhaps instructive to make a general observation here on various maps that have been either proposed or used to process geographic information. If popularity is to be the criterion, most of these tend to fall into two types—maps without projections[30] and maps without applications. Maps without projections are generally inventions by users who merely need some sort of geographic representation to plot some data. They either do not care about, or are not fully aware of, the implications of the representation invented or chosen. The information so obtained or represented has no "transfer" values, in the sense that no one else can use it with any degree of assurance as to either the limitations or the probable error. Such maps may be called "unreferenced systems,"[31] whose exact relations to the terrestrial reference of geodetic coordinates are not known.

Maps without applications have been invented largely as mathematical curiosities. The best illustration is the class of conformal maps. Apparently the only basis for the construction of some of these is the fundamental theorem in the theory of a complex variable: every complex analytic function of a complex variable gives rise to a conformal map, and conversely. Since it is also true that composing two analytic functions leads to another analytic function, one may immediately begin a rampage of printing out as many conformal maps as one pleases without any regard whatever as to the utility of most of them. A relevant comment is that in mathematics it is usually the general theory that is of interest and not any particular realization of that theory.

These two extremes may be partly mitigated by the adoption of a universal mapping system. But the choice of such a system can best be made after, not before, a careful determination of all requirements that are likely to arise in problems involving geographic information.

COMPUTERS AND TYPES OF USERS OF GEOGRAPHIC DATA

Let us turn now to the nature of the problems facing users of geographic data. By users of geographic data I mean people in various disciplines who are likely to have need for computers in their work, presumably with reference to geographic information. Typical users would be workers in the earth sciences. We may take the list of component societies of the Division of Earth Sciences, National Academy of Sciences –National Research Council, and ask in each case: "Why and how would an individual in this particular discipline use a computer in his work?" The result is a continuum that more or less represents a gradation of potential uses of the computer in the various disciplines, ranging from the book-keeping type to the computation type. Each discipline may be depicted as a distribution over this continuum with a mean value situated somewhere within the range indicated. There may, of course, be greater dispersion within disciplines than between them, but our representation is probably accurate when the entire discipline is considered. Geography does not appear on the continuum, since this subject seems too encompassing or dispersed to fit into any one place. Indeed, one needs only to recall the various kinds of geography studied to appreciate the dilemma. To put the matter differently, it may be necessary to draw a multimodal distribution to represent geography on this continuum. However, it is likely that the highest of the modes would fall within the one-quarter interval at the left end of the continuum. There is, of course, no neces-

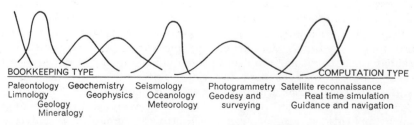

BOOKKEEPING TYPE   COMPUTATION TYPE

Paleontology	Geochemistry	Seismology	Photogrammetry	Satellite reconnaissance
Limnology	Geophysics	Oceanology	Geodesy and	Real time simulation
Geology		Meteorology	surveying	Guidance and navigation
Mineralogy				

sary implication in the continuum of a one-to-one correspondence between disciplines and the peak values of distributions on it. Geography is one example; many others might be given. One that might be mentioned—just to illustrate the range of the problems we must be prepared to face before we can choose this or that particular universal mapping system as best for purpose—is civil defense. The reason for using this example is twofold: the problem is becoming one of the central issues in the discussion of national security policy, and very little is known or done about it.

Problems in civil defense are generally of three types, belonging to the preattack, during-attack, or postattack phase.[32] In the preattack period, the primary interest is in stockpile or inventory statistics of transportation, production, and the like. We want to know what types of survival articles to store and how much of them, where to store them, and according to what priorities they are to be stored. Food, fuel, and medical supplies undoubtedly head the list, then perhaps come spare parts for machinery, implements for restoring power and communication, fertilizers, and so on.[33] The basic problem is to produce a cartogram of inventory statistics that will provide a basis for rational planning.

When attack has been initiated and is continuing, we are faced with new and radically different problems that require solution in real time to provide a useful basis for immediate action. Warning and bomb-alarm systems certainly will be of no value if information updating has not been possible or is too slow. Problems of action, such as civilian evacuation and dispersal and determination of fallout coverage and direction, will be likely to have time as the limiting factor. Hence the problem of updating information in real time has been added on top of the stockpiling problem of the preattack stage.

The postattack period has two types of problems: those related to immediate survival and those related to long-term recovery. For immediate survival, new estimates of supplies and personnel are needed, which must be correlated with the estimates made in the preattack phase for proper adjustment and execution of the preattack plan, since stockpiles and personnel included in the original plan were themselves possible targets and may have been destroyed during the attack. Real-time determination of these types of information is an absolute requirement. On the other hand, types of information for long-term recovery are directed toward possible economic reorganization and political reorientation, and may evolve slowly with time. It is not crucial that such information be forthcoming in a day or so. Reliable and carefully determined information would be preferable to rough and perhaps highly unreliable information, which could, however, be generated very quickly.

It would seem, then, that there are basically two distinct types of problems in civil-defense planning, each requiring its own kind of attention. It would be a mistake not to carry out a thorough study but to pick some arbitrary universal mapping system to store all the needed stockpiling and personnel statistics. Perhaps it might even be desirable to have these statistics stored in different forms to meet the different requirements described above.

A less sanguinary but somewhat related problem is poll prediction. Basically this problem is of the book-keeping type, though large and complicated. However, computers can now carry out this book-keeping job so efficiently that results in early election returns could be made available to "influence" later returns.[34] Consideration of the possibility and its political implications was voiced in Congress in regard to the future role of the various mass media and communication systems.[35] What it means is that a job previously assumed to be time-consuming and hence politically "neutral" can now be performed with such efficiency as to provide a basis for shaping an instrument of policy. This example clearly shows the dynamic character of a problem that results from increased efficiency in processing and communicating information that is basically of a geopolitical character. It comes down to this, then. Although a universal mapping system is highly desirable as a common frame of reference for all geographic data, its users should be as willing to abandon it as they are to adopt it. Only by doing so can we keep up with the progress of time.

FOOTNOTES

[1] See H. Carol, "Geography of the Future," *Professional Geographer*, **13** (1961), 14–18, esp. 14–15. From now on I shall avoid using the cumbersome phrase "geographic or spatial data" and shall employ the word "geographic" in its more comprehensive sense.

[2] This example and the discussion of it are based largely on W. R. Tobler, "Geographic Ordering of Information," University of Washington, Department of Geography, Discussion Paper No. 38 (1960).

[3] "Surveyors Find Witness Trees 131 Years Old," *Surveying and Mapping* **21** (1961), 84.

[4] Coordinates from *Manual of Instructions for the Survey of the Public Lands of the United States, 1947* Bureau of Land Management, U. S. Department of the Interior (Washington: U.S.G.P.O., 1947).

[5] W. D. Pattison, The Original Plan for an American Rectangular Land Survey," *Surveying and Mapping*, **21** (1961), 339–345. See also D. B. Clement, "Progress in Cadastral Surveys," *ibid.*, 79–84; L. F. Jones, "Cadastral Surveys—The Rectangular System Surveys and Protractions," *ibid.*, **20** (1960), 459–468.

[6] "Statistiska primäruppgifter, flygkartering och "Data Processing"-maskiner: Ett kombinerings-projekt," *Svensk Geogr. Årsbok*, **31** (1955), 233–255 (with summary in English, 254–255). (Also as separate, *Meddelanden från Lunds Univ. Geogr. Instn. No. 344* [1955].)

[7] *Ibid.*, 254.

[8] The basic units in the township and range system are approximately equal in (areal) size. Hence this system is approximately equal-areal but is not a map projection according to the usually accepted definition.

[9] R. C. Kao, "Geometric Projections in System Studies," in W. L. Garrison, ed., *Quantitative Geography* (Evanston: Northwestern University, Department of Geography, 1967).

[10] For an illuminating discussion on the topological, as distinct from the metric, properties of coordinates, see H. Reichenbach, *The Philosophy of Space and Time*, M. Reichenbach and J. Freund, trans. (New York: Dover Publications, Inc., 1958), p. 244.

[11] It is interesting to speculate here on the extent to which a computer may be substituted for (or complement) an optical device for the correction of the earth's curvature in photogrammetry. In theory, a computer program may be so prepared as to transform photographic inputs from one perspective map into another (or into an analytic map). Such transformation is now facilitated by direct optical devices (camera lens or prism), the design of which requires an increasingly higher marginal cost for further improvement in performance as the limit of technology is approached. One possible trade-off would be a special-purpose computer designed to carry out the necessary transformation on the inputs—preferably in real time —such as the new "space computer" mentioned by P. J. Klass, "New Data System Proposed for Space," *Aviation Week and Space Technology*, **76** (1962), 77–79.

[12] F. Klein, *Elementary Mathematics from an Advanced Standpoint*, E. R. Hedrick and C. A. Noble, trans. (New York: The Macmillan Company, 1932–1940), Part 2, p. 103.

[13] Cf. below, "Computers and Maps."

[14] See R. C. Kao, "Geometric Projections of the Sphere and the Spheroid," *Canadian Geographer*, **5** (1961), 12–21.

[15] Cf. W. R. Heath and J. C. Sherman, "Cartographic Expression in Geography," *Professional Geographer*, **10** (1958), 22–24.

[16] A recent doctoral dissertation in geography was written on precisely this type of problem in system analysis: M. F. Dacey, *Identification of Patterns on Maps with Special Reference to Data Reduction for Systems Analysis*, unpublished Ph. D. thesis, University of Washington (1960). See also A. L. Samuel, "Artificial Intelligence: A Frontier of Automation," *Annals of the American Academy of Political and Social Science*, **340** (1962), 10–20; H. A. Simon, "Modelling Human Mental Processes," *Proceedings of the Western Joint Computer Conference, Los Angeles, California, 1961* (New York: Institute of Radio Engineers, 1961), 111–119, and the references cited therein; *ibid.*, 545–585.

[17] See Katz, *op cit., passim*. Also, S. M. Greenfield and W. W. Kellogg, "Weather Reconnaissance by Satellites," *Astronautics*, **4** (1959), 32–33, 77–78. The interested reader may wish to associate Katz's paper with L. C. Peltier, "The Potential of Military Geography," *Professional Geographer*, **13** (1961), 1–5, in order to determine both the requirements for, and the problems of, using observation satellites in military intelligence. A recent . . . RAND study by Katz suggests the application of observation satellites to the estimation of agricultural production in Iron Curtain countries.

[18] Cf., for example, J. R. Anderson, "Toward More Effective Methods of Obtaining Land-Use Data in Geographic Research," *Professional Geographer*, **13** (1961), 15–18, esp. 17.

[19] See W. Feller, *An Introduction to Probability Theory and Its Applications*, 2nd ed. (New York: John Wiley & Sons, Inc., 1957), Vol. I Chap. 15.

[20] See "Tax Center," *Los Angeles Times* (Aug. 9, 1962), Part III, 9. It may be unfortunate but true that, as Benjamin Franklin observed, ". . . in this world nothing can be said to be certain, except death and taxes."

[21] T. Hägerstrand, *The Propagation of Innovation Waves*, Lund Studies in Geography, Series B, No. 4 (1952); Hägerstrand, "On Monte Carlo-Simulation of Diffusion," see pp. 368–384. Hägerstrand is one of the first geographers to use computers in simulation research.

[22] For example, Brown University (G. F. Newell), University of California, Berkeley (H. Davis, D. L. Trautman), University of Michigan (H. H. Goode, J. Nystuen), Northwestern University (W. L. Garrison, L. N. Moses), University of Pennsylvania (W. Isard), University of Washington (R. Morrill). See A. Glickstein and S. L. Levy, "Application of Digital Simulation Techniques to Highway Design Problems," *Proceedings*

of the *Western Joint Computer Conference, op. cit.,* pp. 39–51, and the references cited therein.

[23] L. T. Reinwald, "A Computer for Geographers," draft of a paper presented at the annual meeting of the Association of American Geographers, East Lansing, Michigan (Aug. 29, 1961), 4.

[24] See, for example, L. W. Andrukonis, "Surveying Equipment Under Development for the Army," *Surveying and Mapping,* **20** (1960), 45–48; "Earthquakes Located by Electronic Computers," *ibid.,* 468; R. E. Herndon, Jr., "Aerospace Cartography," *ibid.,* **21** (1961), 31–43, esp. 41 (on shadow-progression technique for relief mapping); M. Cunietti, "Generalizzazione dei procedimenti di calcolo ed operativi nella triangolazione aerea analitica," *Boll. di Geodesia e Scienze Affini,* **19** (1960), 589–608; "Design of the Perceptron," *Datamation,* **4** (1958), 25–27. For an excellent survey of the basic principles of automatic computers, see W. F. Gunning, "A Survey of Automatic Computers— Analog and Digital" p-356 (Santa Monica: The RAND Corporation, 1952).

[25] Some of these special-purpose computers are a "reservations computer" by The Teleregister Corporation, New York City, built for American Airlines at La Guardia Airport; a "flight-plan computer" by the Engineering Research Division, Remington Rand Corporation, St. Paul, Minn., built for the Civil Aeronautics Authority; a "check-clearing computer" by the International Telemeter Corporation, West Los Angeles; "Magnifile" by W. S. MacDonald Company, Cambridge, Mass.; and "Speed-tally" by Engineering Research Associates for inventory control and automatic accounting; and the "space computer" mentioned by Klass, *op cit.*

[26] Cf. J. P. LaSalle, "Automation and Control in the Soviet Union," in R. Bellman, ed., *Mathematical Optimization Techniques* (Berkeley: University of California Press, 1963), Chap. 15; and, by The RAND Corporation, W. H. Ware, *Soviet Computer Technology —1959,* RM-2541 (Mar. 1, 1960); E. A. Feigenbaum, *Soviet Cybernetics and Computer Sciences, 1960,* RM-2799-PR (Oct. 1961); and P. Armer, *Attitudes Toward Intelligent Machines,* P-2114-1 (May 1, 1962), pp. 20–29. See also the announcement of a Research Training Institute on Heuristic Programming sponsored by The RAND Corporation, June 18 to July 27, 1962, in *Evening Outlook* (May 17, 1962), 28.

[27] Recent announcement of a highly efficient information retriever shows that field documents can be scanned at the rate of 6400 pages a minute ("Task of Paper Control Eased by File Search," *Los Angeles Times* [July 10, 1962], Part III, 5).

[28] See, for example, S. Cameron and H. Kantner, "A Hybrid Data Processor with Magnetic Tape Input and Direct Pictorial Output" (Chicago: Armour Research Foundation, 1958); J. D. Carroll, Jr., *et al.,* "The Cartographatron," *C[hicago] A[rea] T[ransportation] S[tudy] Research News,* **2** (1958), 3–20; A. Newell, "On New Areas of Application," *Datamation,* **7** (1961), 15–16; Simon, *op cit.*; H. Jacoby, Subdivision Calculation by Electronic Computation," *Surveying and Mapping,* **21** (1961), 205–209; *Instruments and Automation* (May 1958). See also such journals as *Automation, Computing Reviews, Datamation, Journal of the Association for Computing Machinery, IRE Transactions on Electronic Computers,* and *IBM Journal of Research and Development.*

[29] A universal mapping system is a system of coordinates for storage of spatial data that could be used with equal facility by earth scientists or civil, governmental, and military agencies on a national (or even international) basis. See J. A. O'Keefe, "The Universal Transverse Mercator Grid and Projection," *Professional Geographer,* **4** (1952), 19–24; and *The Universal Grid Systems,* U. S. Department of the Army Technical Manual 5-241; U. S. Department of the Air Force Technical Order 16–1–233, Washington: U.S.G.P.O., 1951). I have also benefited from private correspondence with Professor E. B. Espenshade, Jr., of Northwestern University; Dr. J. A. O'Keefe, Theoretical Division, NASA, Goddard Space Flight Center; and Professor W. R. Tobler of the University of Michigan.

[30] R. E. Dahlberg, "Maps Without Projections," *Journal of Geography,* **60** (1961), 213–218.

[31] W. R. Tobler, "Coordinates for Geographic Inventories," draft of unpublished paper, University of Michigan (1962), 9–10.

[32] See B. F. Massell and S. G. Winter, Jr., "Postattack Damage Assessement: A Conceptual Analysis," RM-2844-PR. (Santa Monica: The RAND Corporation, Nov. 1961).

[33] See, for example, two papers by D. V. T. Bear and P. G. Clark, "Industrial Survival in Nuclear War," *Quarterly Review of Economics and Business,* **1** (1961), 39–51, and "The Importance of Individual Industries for Defense Planning," *American Economics Review,* **51** (1961), 460–464; and H. Mitchell, "Ecological Problems and Postwar Recuperation: A Preliminary Survey from the Civil Defense Viewpoint," RM-2801 (Santa Monica: The RAND Corporation, Aug. 1961).

[34] See *Datamation,* **7** (1961), 35–40.

[35] Witness, for example, the following debate (Amendment of Communications Act Relating to Broadcasting of Returns of Presidential Elections, *Congressional Record,* **107**, No. 3 (Jan. 5, 1961), 166):

Mr. GOLDWATER: Mr. President, on election night just past, the radio and television stations of the eastern part of the United States were broadcasting results of the election in precincts, cities, and States before the polls had closed in California and other Western States. I think it takes unfair advantage of the time difference in the United States.

Therefore, I have had prepared a bill that would prohibit any radio station—which means also television station—from broadcasting, prior to 12 midnight Eastern Standard Time on the day of an election for President or Vice President, reports of the election in any one or more precincts in any state.

I send the bill to the desk and ask that it be appropriately referred.

The PRESIDING OFFICER: The bill will be received and appropriately referred.

The bill (S. 56) to amend the Communications Act of 1934 with respect to the broadcasting of returns of Presidential elections, introduced by Mr. Goldwater, was received, read twice by its title, and referred to the Committee on Interstate and Foreign Commerce.

2

GEOGRAPHIC AREA
AND MAP PROJECTIONS

WALDO R. TOBLER

A basic truism of geography is that the incidence of phenomena differs from place to place on the surface of the earth. Theoretical treatises that assume a uniformly fertile plain or an even distribution of population are to this extent deficient. As Edgar Kant has put it:

The theoretical conceptions, based on hypotheses of homogeneous distribution, must be adapted to geographical reality. This implies, in practice, the introduction of corrections with regard to the existence of *blank districts*, *deserts of a phenomenon*, *massives*, or *special points*. That is to say that in practice we have to take into special consideration the anisotropical qualities of the *area geographica*.[1]

The *ceteris paribus* assumptions that are repugnant to a geographer are those which conflict seriously with the fundamental fact that the distribution of phenomena on the surface of the earth is highly variable. Von Thünen,[2] for example, postulates a uniform distribution of agricultural productivity; his economic postulates are no less arbitrary, but they disturb the geographer somewhat less. Christaller's central-

place theory is in a similar category, for the necessary simplifying assumptions, among them a uniform distribution of purchasing power, are unsatisfactory from a geographic point of view.[3] In order to test the theory empirically, one must find rather large regions in which the assumptions obtain to a fairly close approximation. The theory can, of course, be made more realistic by relaxing the assumptions, but this generally entails an increase in complexity. An alternate approach, hopefully simpler but equivalent, is to remove the differences in geographic distribution by a modification of the geometry or of the geographic background. This has been attempted by other geographers with some success, but without clear statement of the problem.

Map projections always modify certain geometric relations and hence would seem well suited to the present task. However, instead of considering the earth to be an isotropic closed surface (as is traditional in the study of map

Reprinted from *Geographical Review*, **53** (1963), 59–78, by permission of the author and editor.

projections), account can be taken of an uneven distribution of a phenomenon on this surface—the *area geographica*. The topic is approached by an examination of a number of published maps called cartograms in current cartographic parlance. Attention is here directed toward those types of cartograms which appear amenable to the metrical concepts of the theory of map projections, with no attempt at definition of the rather vague term "cartogram."

Examples of Cartograms

Cartograms are of many types. [Figure 1], showing "A New Yorker's Idea of the United States of America," contains several interesting notions. The thesis of cognitive behaviorism suggests that people behave in accordance with the external environment, not as it actually is, but as they believe it to be.[4] In this vein, the cartogram presented can be considered to illustrate one type of psychological distortion of the geographic environment that may occur in the minds of many persons. It is clear that the distortion is related to distance. Furthermore, the areas of the states are not in correct proportion; Florida, for example, appears inordinately large. Hence distortion of area can be recognized, though a complete separation of the concepts of distance and area is not possible in this instance.

The second illustration is also a distorted view of the United States (Fig. 2), but the purpose of this cartogram is somewhat different. The areas of the states and cities are shown in proportion to their retail sales, rather than in proportion to the spherical surface areas enclosed by their boundaries. Harris's point is that the expendable income, not the number of square miles, is a more proper measure of the importance of an area—at least for the purposes of the location of economic activity. Harris also presents cartograms of the United States with map areas of the states in proportion to the number of tractors on farms and to the number of persons engaged in manufacturing.[5] Raisz[6] presents a cartogram with the areas of the states in proportion to their populations. Hoover[7] stresses a point of view similar to that of Harris and presents a different cartogram of the United States, with map areas of the cities and states in proportion to their populations. Weigert[8] recognizes that the importance of a country

may be more directly proportional to its population than to its surface area and presents a cartogram placing the countries of the world in this perspective. Woytinsky and Woytinsky[9] make extensive use of a similar cartogram, reproduced here as Fig. 3. Zimmermann[10] presents further examples—cartograms of world population and of output of steel by country.

Whether all these cartograms are to be considered maps, based on projections, is a matter of definition and, as such, is not really important. Raisz stresses the point that his rectangular statistical cartograms are not map projections. The network of latitude and longitude on the Woytinskys' population cartogram (Fig. 3) suggests a map projection but is actually spurious, as the Woytinskys themselves remark. However, since all maps contain distortion, the diagrams can be regarded as maps based on some unknown projection. Certainly the definition that considers a map projection to be an orderly arrangement of terrestrial positions on a plane sheet suffices. It also seems adequate to demonstrate that diagrams similar to these cartograms can be obtained as map projections. But what is the nature of these projections? No such map projections are given in the literature of the subject. The question is approached by a detailed examination of a simpler problem posed by Hägerstrand.

Hägerstrand has been concerned with the study of migration. In discussing the cartographic problem, he states:

> The mapping of migration for so long a period, giving the exchange of one single commune with the whole country in *countable* detail, cannot be made by ordinary methods. All parts of the country have through the flight of time been influenced by migration. However, different areas have been of very different importance. With the parishes bordering the migrational center, the exchange has numbered hundreds of individuals a decade. At long distances only a few migrants or small groups are recorded. A map partly allowing a single symbol to be visible at its margin, partly giving space to the many symbols near its center, calls for a large scale since *we wish to be able to count on the map.*[11]

It is desired to count symbols on the map. This is a clear statement of a common cartographic problem. The situation occurs frequently in the mapping of population, where high concentrations appear in restricted areas

FIGURE 1. This map is interesting viewed as a projection. The present emphasis is on distortion of area. (*Courtesy of Daniel K. Wallingford.*)

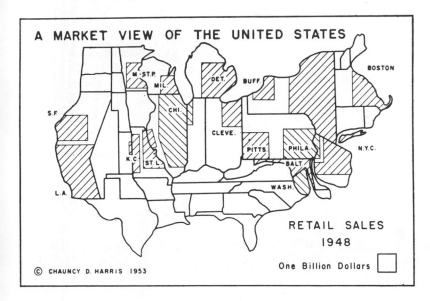

FIGURE 2. Sizes of states proportional to retail sales, 1948. Major cities are shaded. From Harris, "The Market as a Factor in the Localization of Industry" (see note 5). (*Courtesy of Chauncy D. Harris.*)

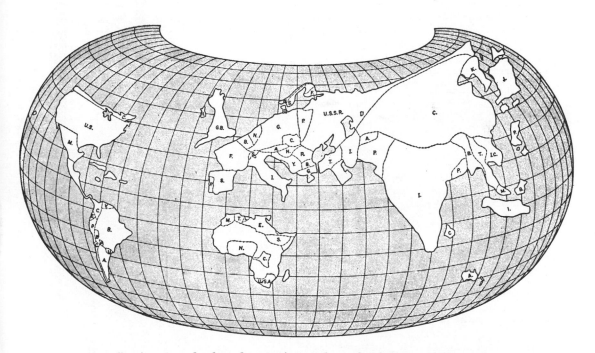

FIGURE 3. Continents and selected countries on the scale of their population. The background of latitude and longitude is spurious. From Woytinsky and Woytinsky, "World Population and Production" (see note 9). (*Courtesy of the Twentieth Century Fund.*)

and smaller numbers are spread more thinly throughout the remainder of the map. Certainly every cartographer has at some time wished for a distribution of a phenomenon which did not seem to require that all the symbols overlap. One solution has been the introduction of so-called three-dimensional symbols.[12] An alternate solution is here suggested, based on the theory of map projections. Also note the distinction between the common geographic use of an equal-area map to illustrate the distribution of some phenomenon and Hägerstrand's emphasis on the recovery of information recorded on the map.

In the problem as formulated by Häger-strand, the exchange of migrants is known not to be distributed arbitrarily, but is a function of distance from a center, the commune being studied. More commonly, differences from one area to another vary much more irregularly, as in, for example, the distribution of population throughout the world. Careful reading of Hägerstrand's statement suggests that the functional dependence is one of decreasing migratory exchange with increasing distance from the center. This can be recognized as a simple distance model often employed by geographers. In particular, the suspected function of distance can be postulated to be continuous and differentiable, strictly monotone decreasing, and independent of direction. If these postulates are accepted, the functional dependence can be shown on a graph as a continuous curve, in this instance a curve of negative slope. The curve can be considered a profile along an azimuth, and the expected incidence of migration could be shown on a map by isolines. This suggests that variants of the solution to Hägerstrand's problem can be applied to many isoline maps. Population density, for example, is often illustrated by isolines drawn on maps, and an approach to the population cartograms is suggested. Hägerstrand's own solution is as follows:

The problem is solved by the aid of a map projection in which the distance from the center shrinks proportionally to the logarithm of the real distance. (The method was suggested to the author by Prof. Edg. Kant. Maps of a similar kind are used for the treatise *Paris et l'agglomération parisienne*.) The rule obviously cannot be applied to the shortest distances. Thus the area within a circle of one km radius has been reduced to a dot. The distortion in relation to the conventional map is of course considerable.[13]

The basis for the choice of the logarithmic projection (Fig. 4) is not clearly indicated in this statement. An azimuthal projection that yields the desired result seems to have been plucked out of thin air. Working backward, however, the radial scale distortion is seen to be ρ^{-1} (where ρ is the spherical distance), and it can be inferred that the projection was obtained by taking the suspected function of distance as the radial scale distortion, as can be done for any of the distance models employed by geographers.[14] The space elimination at the origin is appropriate, for it excludes the commune being studied (which does not belong to the domain of migration). But is Hägerstrand's the most valid solution to the problem as formulated? The concept of primary concern is not distance but area. This is implicit in the statement that it is desired to be able to count symbols on the map. The suggestion is that the map show the areas near the center at large scale and those at the periphery at small scale. Such maps would be useful in most studies of

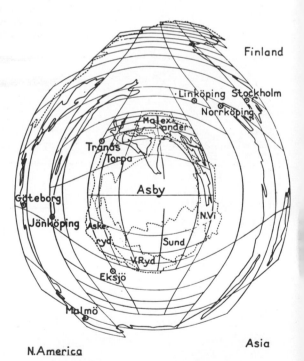

FIGURE 4. Hägerstrand's logarithmic map. The numbers and grid lines refer to the Swedish plane coordinate system. From Hägerstrand, "Migration and Area" (see note 11). (*Courtesy of Torsten Häger-strand.*)

nodal regions. Hägerstrand's solution achieves this objective, as can be verified by calculation of the areal distortion, at least for areas near the center of the map. But so do the orthographic projection, the square-root projection, and many others. The azimuthal equidistant centered on the antipodal point also yields the desired solution and has been used for this purpose by Michels.[15] Kagami[16] suggests an alternate solution when faced with an almost identical problem. Charts for aircraft pilots have also been prepared using maps that have a large scale near the center and a small scale at the periphery.[17]

CARTOGRAMS AS PROJECTIONS

To clarify the situation, one should note that it is the areal scale, and not the linear scale, which is important. Furthermore, it is natural to require that the areal distortion be *exactly* the same as the expected or observed distribution. Somewhat more precisely, Hägerstrand's problem can be generalized in the following manner. In the domain under consideration there are locations from which migration to the center originates. If we consider the beginning point of each migration to be an "event," each small region (element of area) will (or is likely to) contain a certain number of events. Hence with each proper partition of the domain is associated a number, and the area contained within the boundaries of the corresponding partition on the map is to be proportional to this number. The similarity to the cartograms previously presented is now clearer. In each instance a set of nonnegative numbers (people, dollars) has been associated with a set of bounded regions (cities, states, nations). The objective is to display the regions on a diagram in such a manner that the areas within the boundaries of the regions on the diagram are proportional to the number associated with the particular region. Harris recognizes the similarity of the concepts, for his cartogram "A Farm View of the United States"[18] is accompanied by a histogram of the number of tractors by states. On an equal-area projection, the number associated with each partition is the spherical (or ellipsoidal) surface area.

There seem to be two methods of attacking the details of these map projections. One assumes differentiability; the other is an analog of the first but employs what might be called

rule-of-thumb procedures. Each method has advantages and disadvantages. The differentiable cases display the similarity to equal-area map projections somewhat better, whereas the approximation methods are simpler to use with empirically obtained data. The differentiable cases also allow explicit solution for the pair of functions necessary to define a map projection. No attempt is made here to duplicate the specific cartograms illustrated; the purpose is only to indicate the class of projections to which they belong.

The data are somewhat difficult to manipulate when the partitions of area are large. It is therefore convenient to reduce the values associated with each portion of the domain to density form, and to think in terms of a continuous (integrable and differentiable) distribution that can be represented by isolines on a sphere. The details of this device are well known and can be omitted here.[19] The map area between given limits is then to be proportional to the total distribution between corresponding limits. The density distribution on the surface of a sphere is assumed to have been described by an equation. For equal-area projections, the density of spherical surface area is always constant (unity), so that correct values are also obtained in this special situation. As is true of area, finite densities sum to a finite value, so that the density-preserving property of the projections to be achieved obtains both locally and in the large. The use of density values also facilitates the further objective that common boundaries between regions should again coincide on the final map.

The derivation of the cartograms under consideration as map projections follows directly from the preceding discussion. A mathematical analysis of this class of map projections is given in the Appendix. A special case, of some practical interest, is given here to illustrate the general method.

The distribution of population in an urban area can be described as a density function $D(\delta, \gamma)$ on a plane, using polar coordinates δ, γ. Horwood[20] has suggested one such distribution in which the density decreases monotonically from the center but also varies from one direction to the next (Fig. 5). The specific theoretical function taken by Horwood is such that the density is highest along symmetrically spaced radial streets (n in number) and less in the interstitial areas, which is not unrealistic and

FIGURE 5. **FIGURE 5.** This illustration can be considered as either (a) isolines of population density or (b) polar coordinates after a transformation.

is easily described by trigonometric functions or Fourier Series. The population is then given by the integral

$$\iint_R \delta D(\delta,\gamma)d\delta d\gamma$$

To transform this to the map plane so that all map areas have identical densities, set

$$\iint_{R'} r\,dr\,d\theta = \iint_R \delta D(\delta,\gamma)d\delta d\gamma$$

or

$$\iint_{R'} r\,|J|\,d\delta d\gamma = \iint_R \delta D(\delta,\gamma)d\delta d\gamma$$

which is equivalent to

$$r|J| = \delta D(\delta,\gamma)$$

where

$$\pm J = \frac{\partial r}{\partial \delta}\frac{\partial \theta}{\partial \gamma} - \frac{\partial \theta}{\partial \delta}\frac{\partial r}{\partial \gamma}$$

For one solution, not necessarily the most appropriate but simple, stipulate that the transformation is to be azimuthal, that is, that $\theta = \gamma$. Then

$$\frac{\partial \theta}{\partial \delta} = 0,\ \frac{\partial \theta}{\partial \gamma} = 1,\ \text{and}\ J = \frac{\partial r}{\partial \delta}$$

The equation to be solved for r is consequently

$$r^2 = 2\pi \int \delta D(\delta,\gamma)d\delta + g(\gamma)$$

and the remaining details are matters of integration and root extraction. This example could be extended to a sphere or spheroid, but for an urban area there is little point in such extension. The image of the original polar coordinates on the final map might appear as shown in Fig. 5.

Although further details are in the Appendix, certain results from the mathematical analysis are worth noting here. It is easily shown that the transformations are a generalization of equal-area projections in the sense that *all* equal-area projections represent a special case. Moreover, this class of projections can be obtained by setting Tissot's measure of areal distortion equal to the given (expected, probable) density distribution. It is also apparent that there are an infinite number of solutions for any specific density. This suggests that additional conditions be applied. Of the many possible conditions, two are of particular interest. Since this class of projections is equivalent to projections with areal distortion, and since all conformal projections of a sphere distort area, it follows that a conformal projection with a specific areal distortion should yield a solution. The transformation also may be taken so that cost or time distances from the map center are correctly represented.

Occasionally the assumption of continuity of a distribution is not warranted. The data are often in the form of discrete locations, as on a population dot map; or are grouped into areal units, such as census tracts; or refer to areal units rather than to infinitesimal locations, such as land values that refer to specific parcels of land. In these cases an analytic solution usually is not feasible and rule-of-thumb approximations are useful. Even in the case of continuous distributions, descriptive equations are difficult to obtain and, at present, are not available for geographic data, though theoretically possible. Approximation methods, therefore, are useful. They can also be used to demonstrate some of the different types of particular solutions available and some of the additional conditions that may be applied. The approximation methods are no less valid than the methods used in the differentiable cases and can be formalized to the same extent, but they are more akin to topological transformations than to those traditionally associated with cartography.

The only known description of the method used in the preparation of the cartograms previously mentioned is that given by Raisz;[21] the method used by others is presumably similar. The populations of the states are taken as given, and rectangles proportional to population are drawn on a sheet of paper; adjacent rectangles are adjusted until neighbor relations and overall shape are approximately correct. This is illustrated in Fig. 6. Though the example is very simple, there are still an infinite number of solutions, but some seem more appropriate than others. Preservation of the internal topology is one condition that seems desirable; this is in fact a requirement that the map (not the distribution) be continuous (a homeomorphism —neighborhoods are preserved under the mapping). Preservation of the shape of the external boundary is another condition that might be applied. Alternately, one might wish the boundary to map into a specific shape. These last two conditions are difficult to specify even in the analytic case.

If one thinks in terms of a map of a part of the earth's surface, an obvious difficulty is that the immediately foregoing examples do not indicate where positions within the original areal units are to be placed within the corresponding partitions of the transformed image. Stated in another way, if locations in the original are described by latitude and longitude, where are the images of these lines in the transformed image? If the partitions represent states, the placement of cities is rather arbitrary, and so on. Here the differentiable cases display a distinct advantage. However, if a coordinate system is introduced in the original, and an assumption of uniform density within each partition (for example, states) is made, the difficulty can be circumvented by estimating lines of equal increments of density on the original. These lines then correspond to an equal-area grid system on a plane, and the converse. A similar method can be employed when the original data are given in the form of a dot map. If a partition has no entries, the map area should vanish, a collapsing of space or a many-to-one mapping. Figure 3 actually consists of several domains; otherwise, ocean areas would be eliminated (lines of latitude and/or longitude coincide), just as Greenland and Antarctica do not appear on the map. Although there is some population in the ocean areas, the amounts are so small as to be negligible. In the continuous case with zero density,

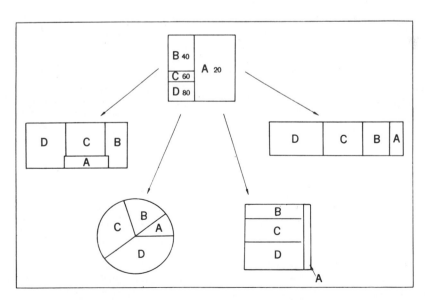

FIGURE 6. Sample transformations of a unit square with different amounts of a phenomenon in different portions illustrating several of the possible solutions.

the transformation becomes many-to-one (a collapsing of space) for this part of the domain.

The approximation methods need not be discussed in more detail; they are fairly simple and do not reveal information that is not readily apparent from an examination of the equations given in the Appendix. More interesting, and more difficult to evaluate, are the geographic uses of maps obtained by the foregoing types of projections or transformations. These applications should also suggest the additional conditions to be applied in selection of a specific transformation from the infinite variety of particular solutions available.

Geographic Applications

Obviously the map projections obtained can be used as were the cartograms previously presented, for they were derived by consideration of such cartograms. These many applications need not be repeated. Further, any distribution plotted on a map using such a transformation shows a ratio; income symbolized on a map equalizing population density shows per capita income, and so on. The projections may likewise be useful as base maps in simulation or other studies in which data are plotted by computer.

It is also clear that any grid system which partitions the area of the plane map into units of equal size will yield a partitioning of the basic data into regions containing an equal number of elements when mapped back to the original domain. For example, states might be partitioned into electoral districts in such a manner that all districts contained an equal number of voters. The specific equal-area grids on a plane are infinite in number, so that this procedure is not really of much assistance. Equal-area grids are also difficult to define along irregular boundaries, and partitionings (electoral districts, and so on) are usually required to satisfy numerous additional conditions (coincide with city and county boundaries, and so on). To attempt to use the transformations in this manner seems politically impractical, though theoretically suggestive.

More interesting applications can perhaps be found in the theories of von Thünen and Christaller. It is in this context that Harris and Hoover attempted to use their cartograms. Von Thünen assumes a uniform fertility of agricultural land, Christaller a uniform distribution of rural population or income, though both attempt to relax these unrealistic assumptions somewhat. If one postulates that agricultural fertility can be measured and varies from place to place—that is, that fertility can be described by a relation $F = f(\phi, \lambda)$—and if one then applies a transformation of the type described, areas of high fertility will appear enlarged. One can then plot[22] an even yield (for example, in bushels) per unit of map area and, using the inverse transformation, return to the original domain. The even distribution of yields will now be uneven, and in fact corresponds to the distribution of fertility. This becomes more interesting if one adds the condition that cost distances from (or to, but not both) a market place appear as map distances from the center of the map and that the intensity of use (yields) decreases with cost distance. That is, on the map transformed so that all areas appear of equal fertility, returns are to be plotted as decreasing from the center of the map, as in the von Thünen model. The inverse transformation will then display a distribution of intensity of use that takes into account fertility and cost distance from the market place. The measurement of agricultural fertility is by no means easy. Dunn[23] doubts that such measurement can be achieved, but the United States Department of Agriculture publishes detailed information with a ranked classification (measurement on an ordinal scale) of rural land based on its economic value. Cost distances are used in the preparation of the map projection as another application of the notion that the earth should perhaps not be treated as an isotropic sphere. It is necessary to take into account not only the shape of the earth, but also the realities of transportation on its surface. Automobiles, trains, airplanes, and other media of transport can be considered to have the effect of modifying distance relations—measured in temporal or monetary units—in a complicated manner. It can be shown (see Appendix) that a density-preserving projection with a continuous and monotonic but otherwise arbitrary centrally symmetric distance function can be obtained. This distance function can be the empirically obtained cost- or time-distance from the market place.[24]

Just as the von Thünen model can be applied to cities,[25] the foregoing discussion can be rephrased using "suitability for construction" instead of fertility. Many urban areas are already built up, and construction is no longer feasible; other areas are blighted and have but little appeal; some locations have high prestige value; site and topographic factors vary; and so on. Undoubtedly, measurement of these values is difficult. Requirements for different classes of land use differ, and some measure of intensity of use seems required. Land costs are biased, since they reflect accessibility and an estimate of potential returns. Nevertheless the transformation and its inverse can be used as before. Such a transformation takes into account only two factors and is therefore of only limited assistance in explaining the totality of urban land uses. The currently available models of urban structure are not outstandingly more successful.

Christaller in his work on geographic location[26] assumes a uniform distribution of the underlying rural population and then obtains sets of nested hexagonal service areas and a hierarchy of cities regularly spaced throughout the landscape. It has been shown how an uneven distribution may be made to appear uniformly distributed, and the pertinent question is whether Christaller's resulting pattern will now be observed. The answer is difficult for several reasons. Given an empirical distribution of income and market areas, the transformation is to make the income densities uniform and to send the market areas into hexagons. It is not clear how this latter condition is to be specified in choosing a particular transformation from the infinite set. Christaller obtains hexagons from consideration of circular service areas, and it is known that only the stereographic projection sends all circles into circles. The stereographic projection, however, will certainly not result from the density-preserving transformation in the general case. Conformal projections in general preserve circles as circles, but only locally, and would require satisfying both conditions of conformality and a specific areal distortion. For relatively small service areas conformal transformations may be suitable. The solution (if one exists) to this problem is obscure. It is possible, of course, to draw hexagons on a map of some region transformed in such a manner that densities are uniform and, by use of the inverse transformation, to examine the resulting pattern of curvilinear polygons in the original domain. There is a slight problem here of specifying an initial orientation for the hexagons and of fitting hexagons to the boundaries of the image region. The appearance of the transformed hexagons will, of course, differ for each transformation in the infinite set. Nevertheless an experiment of this nature has recently been completed by Getis, using expendable income data for the city of Tacoma.[27] Richardson's conformal transformations of hexagonal patterns are somewhat similar.[28] Some such procedure is also implied by Isard's schematic diagrams of a hypothetical landscape.[29] Conceptually Isard's notions are correct, but the boundaries of the service areas will almost certainly not be straight lines, as they have been drawn in his illustrations. Conversely, one might use Vidale's method of partitioning a landscape into service areas,[30] apply a transformation, and examine the images of the service areas to see whether they resemble hexagons. Such an empirical experiment does not appear difficult; one can choose simple density distributions and use the simpler and more obvious transformations. None of these methods is as satisfactory as a theoretical solution, of course, though they may shed further light on the nature of the problem. Christaller's hexagons also need not be retained. Another approach is to consider threshold populations, not hexagons. From this point of view the boundaries of service areas overlap and are somewhat indeterminate. Adding the concept of the range of a good enables one to define the region in terms of cost distances. In this instance the useful map projections are those which make cost distances from some location proportional to map distances from that location and which distribute densities evenly.

Christaller is also concerned with distances; his circular service areas are more akin to geodesic circles using a "subjectively valued time-cost distance" (sic), and his spacing of cities stipulates some distance between cities. Yet distances are not preserved by the transformations; preservation of all distances is certainly not possible if densities are to be uniformly distributed on a plane map. Clearly, then, application of the suggested transformations to theories similar to those of von Thünen and Christaller is difficult and only partly successful, though promising and capable of improvement. The deficiencies are to a certain extent due to the inadequacies of the theories themselves, for at present they are neither sufficiently general nor explicitly formulated.

Valuable map projections can be obtained that do not conform to the traditional geographic emphasis on the preservation of spherical surface area but rather distort area deliberately to "eliminate" the spatial variability of a terrestrial resource endowment. In many ways these maps are more realistic than the conventional maps used by geographers and would be of value even if the earth were a disk, as some ancients believed. The important point, of course, is not that the transformations distort area, but that they distribute densities uniformly. It is hoped that future textbook presentations on the subject of map projections will include discussion of this interesting and highly useful class of transformations.

APPENDIX

1. The element of area on a locally Euclidean (but otherwise arbitrary) two-dimensional surface is given by the well-known formula due to Gauss:[31] $dA = (EG - F^2)^{1/2} dudv$. The element of density on a surface is given by $dD = D(u, v)dA$, where $D(u, v)$ represents the given (expected, probable) value at the point u, v. The general problem hence reduces to one of finding u' and v' as functions of u and v to satisfy

$$(1.1) \quad \begin{aligned} &\iint_{R'} (E'G' - F'^2)^{1/2} \, du'dv' = \\ &\iint_{R} D(u,v)(EG - F^2)^{1/2}dudv \end{aligned}$$

or

$$(1.2) \quad (E'G' - F'^2)^{1/2}|J| = D(u,v)(EG - F^2)^{1/2}$$

For a sphere $EG - F^2$ is equal to $R^4 \cos^2 \phi$, using geographical coordinates ϕ and λ, or to $R^4 \sin^2 \rho$, using spherical coordinates ρ and λ. In the present instance the interest is only in plane maps; for a plane, $E'G' - F'^2$ is equal to 1, using rectangular coordinates x and y, or to r^2, using polar coordinates r and θ. The interesting cases will generally be oblique projections, but this requires only a relabeling.

When the Jacobian determinant (J) is written out in full, the following partial differential equations obtain:

$$(1.3) \quad \frac{\partial x}{\partial \lambda} \frac{\partial y}{\partial \phi} - \frac{\partial x}{\partial \phi} \frac{\partial y}{\partial \lambda} = \pm D(\phi,\lambda) R^2 \cos \phi$$

$$(1.4) \quad r\left[\frac{\partial r}{\partial \rho} \frac{\partial \theta}{\partial \lambda} - \frac{\partial r}{\partial \lambda} \frac{\partial \theta}{\partial \rho}\right] = \pm D(\rho,\lambda) R^2 \sin \rho$$

2. The difficulty of an explicit solution to 1.3 or 1.4 will depend on the specific form of the density function and the additional conditions applied. As is typical of differential equations, in general there will be an infinitude of particular solutions. Certain simple solutions, however, are immediately apparent. For example, if $\partial x/\partial \phi = 0$ and $\partial x/\partial \lambda$ is arbitrary, then

$$(2.1) \quad y = R^2 \int \frac{\pm D(\phi,\lambda) \cos \phi}{\partial x/\partial \lambda} d\phi + g(\lambda)$$

Or if $\partial y/\partial \lambda = 0$, and $y = f(\phi)$ is given, then

$$(2.2) \quad x = R^2 \int \frac{\pm D(\phi,\lambda) \cos \phi}{\partial y/\partial \phi} d\lambda + g(\phi)$$

In polar coordinates a similar procedure is available. Taking $\partial \theta/\partial \rho = 0$ and a given $\partial \theta/\partial \lambda$ yields

$$(2.3) \quad r^2 = 2R^2 \int \frac{\pm D(\rho,\lambda) \sin \rho}{\partial \theta/\partial \lambda} d\rho + g(\lambda)$$

An azimuthal projection is obtained if $\theta = \lambda$, conic projections if $\theta = n\lambda$. Taking $\partial r/\partial \lambda = 0$, and with $r = f(\rho)$ selected arbitrarily, yields

$$(2.4) \quad \theta = R^2 \int \frac{\pm D(\rho,\lambda) \sin \rho}{r(\partial r/\partial \rho)} d\lambda + g(\rho)$$

3. The condition that a map of the sphere be equal-area can be written as

$$(3.1) \quad \frac{|J|}{R^2 \cos \phi} = 1 \text{ (or constant)}$$

Hence it follows immediately that equal-area projections represent the special case $D = 1$ (or constant).

4. Areal distortion (S) is, by definition, the ratio of the element of area on the map to the element of area on the original. In other words,

$$(4.1) \quad S = \frac{dA'}{dA} = \frac{(E'G' - F'^2)^{1/2}}{(EG - F^2)^{1/2}}$$

From a simple substitution it is seen that the density is the same as the areal distortion (i.e., $D = S$). In Tissot's notation $S = ab$, the product of the linear distortion in two orthogonal directions. Knowing this relation, we can obtain the desired transformations by choosing the areal distortion to match exactly the expected or known density distribution.

5. If the density is given by $\cos^{-4}(\rho/2)$ and an azimuthal projection is desired, Eq. 2.3 yields the stereographic projection. Although such a density is unlikely, this demonstrates the existence of conformal projections within this class of projections. The suggestion is that a conformal version exists among the solutions for many, if not all, nonconstant densities. Though the areal distortion on conformal projections is easily calculated, the existence of conformal projections with a given areal distortion involves more subtle considerations, which are not presented here.[32]

6. According to Tissot, every nonconformal transformation retains as orthogonal curves one, and only one, pair of curves orthogonal on the original. An interesting question is whether the transformation can be determined so that the lines of latitude and longitude are the lines that remain orthogonal. For densities that depend on only one parameter the condition is readily obtained. For example, if $D = D(\phi)$ and $\partial x/\partial \lambda = 1$, Eq. 2.1 yields a cylindrical projection. Korkine's analysis of equal-area projections may be of use in obtaining the general case.[33]

7. Transport costs are often said to increase at a decreasing rate with distance, i.e., $\partial^2 r/\partial \rho^2 < 0$. If $r = f(\rho)$ and a density $D(\rho, \lambda)$ is given, Eq. 2.4 yields a solution that renders map distances proportional to transport costs and distributes densities evenly (see 8.4). An even more interesting result would be the simultaneous solution of 1.4 with an arbitrary $r = f(\rho, \lambda)$.

8. A few particular solutions may be of interest. From 2.3 an azimuthal projection for a linearly decreasing density $D = a\rho + b$, $a < 0 < b$, yields

$$(8.1) \qquad r = [2R^2(-a\rho \cos \rho - b \cos \rho + a \sin \rho)]^{1/2}$$

If the density distribution in Hägerstrand's problem is assumed to be ρ^{-1}, the appropriate azimuthal projection is

$$(8.2) \qquad r^2 = 2R^2 \int \frac{\sin \rho}{\rho} d\rho = 2R^2 \left(\rho - \frac{\rho^3}{3 \cdot 3!} + \frac{\rho^5}{5 \cdot 5!} - \frac{\rho^7}{7 \cdot 7!} + \frac{\rho^9}{9 \cdot 9!} \cdots \right)$$

Additional azimuthal projections for densities equaling $\exp(-\rho)$ or $(2\pi)^{-1/2} \exp(-\rho^2/2)$ would appear to be of geographic interest, and are relatively easily obtained.

From 2.4 one obtains an equidistant version with $r = R\rho$ and $D = \pi - \rho$:

$$(8.3) \qquad \theta = (-1 + \pi/\rho)\lambda \sin \rho$$

Also from 2.4 but with $r = R(\rho)^{1/2}$, $D = \pi - \rho$, one has

$$(8.4) \qquad \theta = 2\lambda(\pi - \rho) \sin \rho + g(\rho)$$

In all these instances it is necessary to examine the resulting transformation for one-to-oneness. Choice of the constants of integration may be of importance. In some instances the substitution of difference equations for the differential equations may be appropriate. The author has calculated further special cases, which will be made available to interested parties.

9. It is suggested that these projections be referred to by their mathematical name; that is, as transformations of surface integrals.

FOOTNOTES

[1] E. Kant, "Umland Studies and Sector Analysis," *Studies in Rural-Urban Interaction*, Lund Studies in Geography, Series B, No. 3 (1951), 5.

[2] J. H. von Thünen, *Der isolierte Staat in Beziehung auf Landwirtschaft und Nationalökonomie* (Hamburg, 1826).

[3] C. W. Baskin, *A Critique and Translation of Walter Christaller's "Die zentralen Orte in Süddeutschland,"* unpublished Ph.D. thesis, University of Virginia, Department of Economics (1957).

[4] H. Sprout and M. Sprout, "Environmental Factors in the Study of International Politics," *Journal of Conflict Resolution*, **1** (1957), 309–328.

[5] C. D. Harris, "The Market as a Factor in the Localization of Industry in the United States," *Annals of the Association of American Geographers*, **44** (1954),

315–348. See also C. D. Harris and G. B. McDowell, "Distorted Maps: A Teaching Device," *Journal of Geography*, **54** (1955), 286–289.

[6] E. Raisz, "The Rectangular Statistical Cartogram," *Geographical Review*, **24** (1934), 293 (Fig. 2).

[7] E. M. Hoover, *The Location of Economic Activity* (New York: McGraw-Hill Book Company, 1948), p. 88 (Fig. 5.6).

[8] H. W. Weigert, *et al.*, *Principles of Political Geography* (New York: Appleton-Century-Crofts, 1957), p. 296 (Fig. 9.2).

[9] W. S. Woytinsky and E. S. Woytinsky, *World Population and Production* (New York: Twentieth Century Fund, 1953), pp. lxix–lxxii, 42–43, *et passim*.

[10] E. W. Zimmermann, *World Resources and Industries*, rev. ed. (New York: Harper & Row, Publishers, 1951), p. 97. Another cartogram can be seen in D. Greenhood, *Down to Earth: Mapping for Everybody* rev. ed. (New York: Holiday House, Inc., 1951) p. 236. The Library of Congress map collection also contains a large number of maps of this type.

[11] T. Hägerstrand, "Migration and Area," in *Migration in Sweden*, Lund Studies in Geography, Series B, No. 13 (1957), p. 73.

[12] Cf. A. H. Robinson, *Elements of Cartography*, 2nd ed. (New York: John Wiley & Sons, Inc., 1960), pp. 169–170 (Figs. 9.16–9.17).

[13] Hägerstrand, *op. cit.* 74. The reference is to P.-H. Chombart de Lauwe, *et al.*, *Paris et l'agglomération parisienne*, 2 vols. (Paris, 1952).

[14] For further details on this procedure see W. R. Tobler, *Map Transformations of Geographic Space*, unpublished Ph. D. thesis, University of Washington (1961), pp. 114–117.

[15] F. W. Michels, "Drie nieuwe Kaartvormen," *Tijdschrift Kon. Nederl. Aardrijksk. Genootschap*, Series 2, **76** (1959), 203–209. See also D. M. Desoutter, "Projection by Introspection," *Aeronautics*, **40** (1959), 42–44.

[16] K. Kagami, "The Distribution Map by the Method of Aeroview," *Geographical Review of Japan*, **26** (1953), 463–468 (with English abstract).

[17] L. Y. Dameron, "Terminal Area Charts for Jet Aircraft," *Military Engineer*, **52** (1960), 227.

[18] Harris, *op. cit.*, 338.

[19] See C. E. P. Brooks and N. Carruthers, *Handbook of Statistical Methods in Meteorology*, M.O. 538 (London: Her Majesty's Stationery Office, 1953), pp. 161–165; or C. F. Schmid and E. H. MacCannell, "Basic Problems, Techniques and Theory of Isopleth Mapping," *Journal of the American Statistical Association*, **50** (1955), 220–239.

[20] E. M. Horwood, *A Three-Dimensional Calculus Model of Urban Settlement*, paper presented at the Regional Science Association Symposium, Stockholm (Aug. 1960).

[21] E. Raisz, "Rectangular Statistical Cartograms of the World," *Journal of Geography*, **35** (1936), 8–10; and "The Rectangular Statistical Cartogram," *op. cit.*

[22] The plotting can be conceptual, or it can be internal in a digital computer, and need not actually be performed.

[23] E. S. Dunn, Jr., *The Location of Agricultural Production* (Gainesville: University of Florida Press, 1954), pp. 67–69.

[24] A more extensive discussion of this topic can be found in Tobler, *op. cit.*, pp. 78–141.

[25] W. Alonso, *A Model of the Urban Land Market: Locations and Densities of Dwellings and Business*, unpublished Ph. D. thesis, University of Pennsylvania (1960).

[26] W. Christaller, *Die zentralen Orte*, *op. cit.*

[27] A. Getis, *A Theoretical and Empirical Inquiry into the Spatial Structure of Retail Activities*, unpublished Ph. D. thesis, University of Washington (1961), pp. 89–102.

[28] L. F. Richardson, "The Problem of Contiguity," appendix to *The Statistics of Deadly Quarrels* (Pittsburgh: The Boxwood Press, 1960), in *General Systems*, **6**, (1962), 139–187.

[29] W. Isard, *Location and Space-Economy* (Cambridge: Massachusetts Institute of Technology Press, 1956), pp. 272, 277, 279 (Figs. 52–54).

[30] M. Vidale, "A Graphical Solution of the Transportation Problem," *Operations Research*, **4** (1956), 193–203.

[31] See, for example, D. J. Struik, *Lectures on Classical Differntial Geometry* (Reading, Mass.: Addison-Wesley Publishing Company, Inc., 1950), or any other text on differential geometry. Einstein's more convenient notation is not employed in cartography.

[32] See, for example, Richardson, *op. cit.*, 158 (Eq. 4.54).

[33] A. Korkine, "Sur les Cartes géographiques," *Mathematische Annalen*, **35** (1890), 588–604. Also note the similarity to equations derived by the Russian Urmaev, as discussed in D. H. Maling," A Review of Some Russian Map Projections," *Empire Survey Review*, **15** (1959–1960), 210–213.

3

GEOGRAPHIC SAMPLING

BRIAN J. L. BERRY and ALAN M. BAKER

Geography is only one of the disciplines concerned with the spatial distribution of phenomena. In his study *Spatial Variation*, Matérn outlines as examples of the extensive range of interests in spatial problems the following:

1. the spatial distribution of microscopic particles suspended in a liquid or in the air
2. the distribution of galaxies in space
3. the pattern of various rock formations in a geologic map
4. the spatial distribution of plants or animals in the field, of trees in a forest
5. the variation of tensile strength of a piece of metal
6. the microscopic pattern of the surface of a manufactured product (photographic film, sheets of veneer, paper, metal, etc.)[1]

To identify one interesting part of this range, he used the term "topographic variation" to denote the subset of spatial distributions involving maps of fertility, vegetation, geologic and climatic occurrences, and land use. It is on this subset that this paper will focus. Matérn argued that in one respect the subset was no different from the other types of spatial variation; however, patterns are often so complex that only a statistical description can be attempted.

Yet the development of concepts and terms for the properties of spatial variation may be of value in several situations . . . . It may be helpful in investigating the underlying mechanism. It may provide a means of specifying certain properties . . . which are of technical or economic significance. Furthermore, from the statistician's point of view, it is important to have a good knowledge of the spatial variation in a region where a sample survey, or field experiment, is to be conducted.[2]

It is in the latter spirit that this paper on geographic sampling is provided.

The manner in which a phenomenon varies

The assistance of Thomas D. Hankins in his work for the Northeastern Illinois Planning Commission is acknowledged.

from place to place is itself varied, and the variations vary from time to time. In order to assess such variations, surveys must be conducted. A complete inventory is likely to be time-consuming and economically infeasible; therefore sampling procedures are preferable to permit rapid collection of data or updating of a data bank, to facilitate study of change, to minimize costs of the survey, and to permit greater scope and accuracy than would be achieved with a complete survey.

In particular, we focus on problems of making estimates of land coverage in land-use studies, or of evaluating changes in land use, or of reconstructing a land-use map from sample data. Sources of such data are likely to be varied. Coverage estimates and change studies may be made from existing land-use maps, aerial photographs, locationally coded statistics, or by field observation. Field observation at sample points may be utilized to construct a complete land-use map.[3] The question to be addressed is: what kind of geographic sampling procedure appears to be most generally useful, and how may it be applied?

BASIC TERMS

In a sample only a part of the whole is observed. Thus perfect agreement should not be expected between *sample estimates* and the true *population values* (such estimates might include: proportion of land in various uses; numbers of individuals with specified properties; a map reproducing the complete spatial distribution from the sample data). Estimates based on any given sampling procedure are distinguished by two properties: *accuracy* and *precision*.

Accuracy refers to correctness in estimating the population value. If there is consistent over- or underestimation of this value, the sample is said to be *biased*. Any sampling procedure should produce estimates that differ from the true value only by some random disturbance factor introduced by the fact that a sample is being taken in the first place.

Precision refers to the spread of estimates of the population value around the true value. An *efficient* sample has a relatively small spread of such errors of estimation.

The prime requirement of any sampling procedure is accuracy. Among alternative unbiased (i.e., accurate) procedures, relative efficiency

(i.e., relative sizes of estimation errors) provides the criterion for selecting one method as opposed to another. Only one circumstance arises in which these requirements may be reversed. This is in studies of changes through time in which the bias is constant and the biased procedure provides greater efficiency, since in the temporal comparisons the bias may be eliminated.

TYPES OF SAMPLES

There is a variety of geographic sampling procedures: random, systematic, stratified, or any combination of these. In addition, the units of observation may differ, being either points, lines (traverses), or areas (quadrats).

A *random sample* is one in which each point, traverse, or quadrat is chosen randomly.

A *systematic sample* has an initial point chosen randomly and all others determined by a fixed interval.

A *stratified sample* is one in which the study area is subdivided into strata. Sampling points within strata may be chosen randomly, systematically, or in an aligned fashion. *Alignment* fixes the intervals between points within strata.

Figures 1-5 illustrate how each of these samples may be constructed in the case of points.

The first depicts a random geographic point sample. In this sample each point is selected by entering a table of random numbers and selecting two such numbers, one within the range of coordinate values of the ordinate, the other within the range of coordinate values of the abscissa. The random ordinate and abscissa

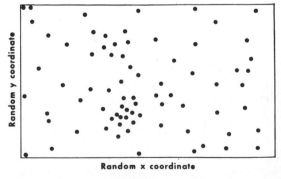

A RANDOM AREAL SAMPLE

Random y coordinate

Random x coordinate

FIGURE 1

values thus obtained locate the sample element. Note the uneven areal coverage which can emerge.

The second figure adds the element of stratification. In a stratified random areal sample, elements are located by selecting random pairs of coordinates within blocks of the larger area. The example has three points so located within each block, although *variable sampling proportions* could have been used such that the number of points is larger within more variable blocks, or within blocks which have more of the phenomena of interest. Note that areal coverage is better than that of a simple random areal sample.

Figure 3 is systematic. Such a checkerboard sample has a perfectly even spread of points, with regular spacing on both abscissa and ordinate after point A has been located at random. But such a selection procedure implies that all parts of the study area do not have an equal chance of being included in the sample. Furthermore, if there are periodicities in the data being collected, the regularly spaced points could hit the same point on a cycle time and again and give completely biased pictures of the spatial variations of the phenomena under study.

The fourth figure shows a "stratified systematic unaligned sample." It is constructed as follows: First, point A is selected at random. The x coordinate of A is then used with a new random y coordinate to locate B, a second random y coordinate to locate E, and so on across the top row of strata. By a similar process, the y coordinate of A is used in combination with random x coordinates to locate point C and all successive points in the first column of strata. The random x coordinate of C and y coordinate of B are then used to locate D, of E,

A STRATIFIED RANDOM AREAL SAMPLE

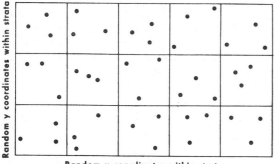

FIGURE 2

A STRATIFIED SYSTEMATIC UNALIGNED SAMPLE

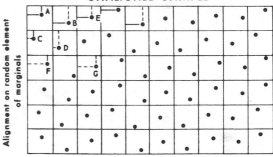

FIGURE 4

A SYSTEMATIC ALIGNED (CHECKERBOARD) SAMPLE

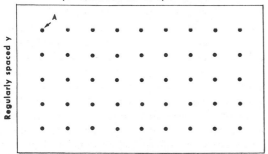

FIGURE 3

and F to locate G, and so on until all strata have sample elements. The resulting sample combines the advantages of randomization and stratification with the useful aspects of systematic samples, while avoiding possibilities of bias because of the presence of periodicities.

Figure 5 shows how one simple two-stage (hierarchical) sample may be constructed. Study areas (blocks) are selected with random pairs of coordinates, and then points are selected at random within the blocks so obtained.

Figure 6 provides similar illustrations for traverses. If areas (quadrats) are used as the observational units, they may be selected either randomly, with or without stratification, as in

ONE HEIRARCHICAL SAMPLE

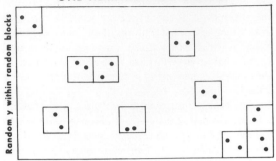

FIGURE 5

TRAVERSES: SYSTEMATIC AND RANDOM

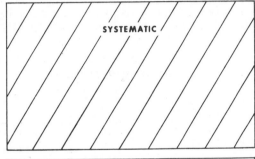

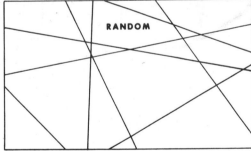

FIGURE 6

the manner of points in Figs. 1–2, or they may be laid out systematically, as with points in Fig. 3. Alternatively, as in the case of forest surveys, they may be spaced in some random or other way along systematic or random traverses.[4]

CHOICE OF SAMPLING PROCEDURE

Choice of sampling procedure for any phenomenon depends on how that phenomenon is distributed. If the spatial distribution being studied is *random*, each of the above procedures will give unbiased estimates with approximately equal variances. Thus the simplicity of systematic sampling is to be preferred. If *linear trends* are present in the data, stratified and systematic sampling will be more precise than random sampling; further, stratified sampling will be more precise than systematic because it permits within-strata errors to be cancelled out.

Serial correlation of the data presents more profound problems.[5] Relative precision of the sampling procedures depends upon the shape of the serial correlation function. If serial correlations are positive and decrease with increasing separation of the sampling points, stratified sampling is more precise than random. If periodicities are present in the function, other procedures will be preferred to systematic because of the risk of consistently hitting the same point on the periodic surface.[6]

When the exact nature of the distribution of the phenomena is unknown, a choice of an optimal sampling procedure cannot definitely be made. However, it appears that a *stratified systematic unaligned sample* includes the most desirable features of the others, and has the greatest efficiency under these circumstances. Thus for most land use work it is to be preferred, especially since the underlying serial correlations are unknown. Because it contains systematic, stratified, and random elements it appears to have the advantage of foreseeing most possible eventualities.[7]

A CASE STUDY IN STRATIFIED SYSTEMATIC UNALIGNED SAMPLING

How may a stratified systematic unaligned sample of points be taken in a given area? Whether data come from maps, air photos, or statistical sources, it is essential at the outset to adopt a carefully chosen system of geographic coding. This not only facilitates sampling, but also is of fundamental importance to spatial analysis, data storage, and machine mapping. Geographic coding implies attaching to each observation a pair of coordinates that assign it to a unique location.[8] Because of the usual problems of representing the curved surface of the earth on flat paper, it is desirable to use an orthogonal, two-dimensional grid. If necessary, a grid can be drawn arbitrarily on large-scale maps or vertical air photos. But generally, areal data will be most useful if the coordinates used for geographic coding are part of a widely adopted system, such as the State Plane Coordinate Systems,[9] the British Ordinance Survey grid, or the Universal Transverse Mercator Grid used for military purposes and by the U. S. Census. It is then possible to fit local study areas into large regions, to coordinate data from different sources, and to calculate distances and areas easily. On a world scale, other grid systems may be constructed to achieve the desired mapping.[10]

The criteria for a generally acceptable coordinate system have been set forth by Tobler as follows:

1. coordinates should permit accurate computation
2. coordinates should permit economical computation
3. coordinates should be compatible with systems used elsewhere
4. coordinates should be convenient for use at a local, national, or international level
5. coordinates should be determined by a rapid and accurate method
6. coordinates should be long-lasting—at least fifty years.

There are three coordinate systems that meet the above criteria:

1. latitude and longitude
2. state plane coordinates—for land surveyors (established in 1930 and used in twenty-seven states)
3. transverse Mercator grid.

These or any related by known mathematical equations can be used.

Once the points in the sample have been chosen by the identification of their coordinates, the next step is to locate them on the photos or maps used as data sources. If statistical data sources are being used, then of course this step is unnecessary. Points can be located on maps or air photos by direct plotting or by the use of a transparent overlay on which the points have been plotted. It is especially important to make sure that the points are not incorrectly located because of distortions resulting from projection of the curved earth surface onto a plane. With large-scale maps or vertical air photos, such distortions may be small enough to ignore, depending on the accuracy required.

In the case of air photos, locational distortions can result also from tip, tilt, and altitudinal variation and from differences in relief. In general, the use of rectified vertical photos is desirable in order to minimize such distortions.[11] It should be noted that special problems are likely to be encountered in using air photos of areas having great relief.

Theoretically, the data source is assumed to consist of an infinite population of points which can be classified into a set of mutually exclusive classes, such as different land uses. From this population a sample is selected and the proportions of points in the various classes are used to infer the true proportions present in the population. Practically, the points that are plotted on photos or maps will, of course, be small dots occupying some area rather than ideal points having no area. A dot represents the point being sampled, which may be thought of as occupying the center of the dot. Similarly, lines bounding different classes on the data source also have area in practice, but are taken to represent ideal lines having no area. A dot which appears to fall exactly on such a boundary line must be assigned to one class or another. Possible errors from this source intuitively seem less likely to be cumulative if each such decision is given the same directional bias by taking the dot to fall, say, to the north and east of the line.

The method described above has been used in a land-use study designed to meet the needs of the Northeastern Illinois Planning Commission and the Chicago Area Transportation Study.[12] The major purpose of the study was to update land-use data for the six counties which comprise the Chicago Standard Metropolitan Statistical Area. The primary data source was a set of air photo enlargements at a scale of one inch to 400 feet, made from vertical black-and-white photography flown by Chicago Aerial Surveys early in 1964. The system of land-use classification adopted was derived from the systems used in previous studies by the two agencies.[13] Limited availability of funds, personnel, and time led to the adoption of a sampling procedure for the study rather than the more usual procedure of delimiting and identifying the land use of every parcel of land in the study area.

The mechanics of the actual sampling procedure were as follows: An acetate overlay was placed over the photo, and on it were

TABLE 1

Percentages of land uses in test area indicated by eight samples
having a mean density of 46.6 points per square mile

Sample number	1	2	3	4	5	6	7	8	Mean	Variance	Std. dev.
LAND USE:											
Estate	0.5	0.0	0.5	1.0	0.6	0.0	0.0	0.5	0.4	0.1	0.3
Single-family residential	25.6	32.3	35.4	30.3	34.9	32.6	31.6	30.8	31.7	7.3	2.7
Multifamily residential	0.0	1.0	1.0	0.5	0.0	1.1	0.5	1.0	0.6	0.2	0.5
Commercial	2.7	1.0	2.6	1.1	1.1	1.1	2.7	1.5	1.7	0.6	0.8
Manufacturing	1.1	1.0	1.1	1.1	1.1	0.6	2.2	1.5	1.2	0.2	0.5
Mining	0.0	0.0	0.0	0.0	0.0	0.0	0.0	0.0	0.0	0.0	0.0
Transport, communications, utilities	0.5	0.0	0.5	0.0	0.0	0.6	0.5	0.0	0.3	0.4	0.2
Public buildings	0.6	0.5	1.0	1.1	1.1	0.6	0.5	0.5	0.7	0.1	0.3
Open space (recreational)	15.2	19.8	16.7	17.0	16.6	18.5	17.1	18.0	17.4	0.4	0.6
Agricultural and vacant	44.0	39.1	38.0	38.3	39.4	39.3	36.9	41.6	39.6	0.2	0.5
Access streets	6.0	4.2	2.1	4.8	4.0	3.4	4.8	3.6	4.1	1.3	1.1
Through streets and highways	3.8	1.1	1.1	4.8	1.2	2.2	3.2	1.0	2.3	1.9	1.4

TABLE 2

Measured percentages of land uses in test area

LOCATION:					
Township	40N	40N	40N	40N	Four-
Range	11E	11E	11E	11E	section
Section	15	16	21	22	totals
LAND USE:					
Estate	0.0	0.0	0.0	1.5	0.4
Single-family residential	46.2	30.4	14.7	30.2	30.5
Multifamily residential	0.0	0.0	2.3	0.0	0.6
Commercial	5.0	1.0	1.4	0.0	1.9
Manufacturing	0.6	6.2	1.1	0.0	2.0
Mining	0.0	0.0	0.0	0.0	0.0
Transport, communications, utilities	1.0	0.1	0.0	0.0	0.3
Public buildings	0.2	1.3	0.8	0.7	0.7
Open space (recreational)	0.4	35.7	37.1	0.7	18.2
Agricultural and vacant	39.7	20.4	35.6	61.0	39.3
Access streets	4.9	3.5	5.1	2.6	4.0
Through streets and highways	2.0	1.4	1.9	3.3	2.1

drawn locational reference lines, i.e., the boundaries of one-quarter square-mile units. Then the sample points were marked on this overlay after having been located by means of a random placement of another transparent overlay having on it dots distributed according to the sampling method. Thus there was preserved on the overlay a record of the locations of the sample points, together with the reference grid, for future verification and for possible use in studying land-use changes through time. The land use occurring under each dot was interpreted, coded, and recorded. The number of dots falling in each class was then tallied for each one-quarter square mile. Data for these one-quarter square-mile units can thus be aggregated into various samples whose boundaries coincide with those of groups of squares. It may be noted that the geographic coding in this study consisted of a pair of coordinates for each square rather than a pair for each point.

The sampling procedure was tested empirically on one photo selected as being representative of the study area in respect to variety in land uses, in size of parcels, and in patterns of land use. Eight samples of land use were taken for this area. All samples were of approximately the same size, averaging 46.6 points per square mile. Percentages of land in the various classes were calculated for each sample, and means, variances, and standard deviations were calculated from these eight sets of figures (Table 1). It must be noted that the assumption of randomness has been violated, the assumptions of a normal distribution and independence have not been demonstrated, and most of the sample means are positively skewed. Hence these variances and standard deviations must be regarded as indicators rather than as measures with precise mathematical properties.[14] Under these conditions there is no theoretical basis for interpreting confidence limits about the mean calculated in the usual manner.

An alternative procedure was adopted for evaluating the sampling results. Land use on the same photo was interpreted in detail for the entire four square miles shown, and areas in the various land-use classes were delimited by drawing lines on an acetate overlay. All areas thus delimited were then measured (by counting squares of side one-twentieth of an inch), tabulations of the various uses were made, and percentages of land in the various uses were

calculated (Table 2). These figures were taken to be true values for the population sampled.

If Tables 1 and 2 are compared, the closeness of sample estimates and measured percentages will be evident.

FURTHER EXAMPLES

Other examples have been reported by Berry.[15] Tests of relative efficiency of the more usual statistical kind were undertaken in two areas: Coon Creek and Montfort.[16] However, it should be noted that whether all the assumptions of these tests were satisfied is uncertain.

In the Coon Creek area (about ten square miles) a map of land use was available and is shown in Fig. 7. Planimetered estimates of the proportions of total area occupied by different types of land use were 40.8 per cent woodland, 32.5 per cent cropland, 22.5 per cent pasture, 2.0 per cent gallery, and 2.2 per cent other uses. Four stratified systematic unaligned samples were taken, randomly oriented with respect to each other, as recommended by Quenouille.[17] One of these is shown in Fig. 8. Each sample contains an average of one point per ten acres, so that the 660 points have an average spacing of one-eighth of a mile, or 660 feet.[18]

Estimates of percentage of woodland cover were 40.49, 40.96, 40.24, and 41.07 in the four samples. The mean is thus 40.69 per cent and the variance is 0.17. In a simple random areal sample, the expected variance for a sample of this size is 3.66, so that the relative efficiency of the systematic sample over the simple random is 21.5.

For comparison of relative errors, the area was stratified into one-quarter-mile square blocks, and four points were located at random in each block to create a stratified random areal sample. This was repeated four times. The per cent woodland coverage estimates from these four samples yielded a mean of 41.4 per cent and a variance of 0.96. The relative efficiency of the systematic over stratified random areal samples is thus 5.65, much the same as in the results of experiments reported by Cochran.[19] Similarly, for pasture the relative efficiency of systematic over stratified random samples was 2.3 and the systematic stratified unaligned sample is to be preferred.

In the Montfort area a complete, detailed land-use survey had been undertaken, and the

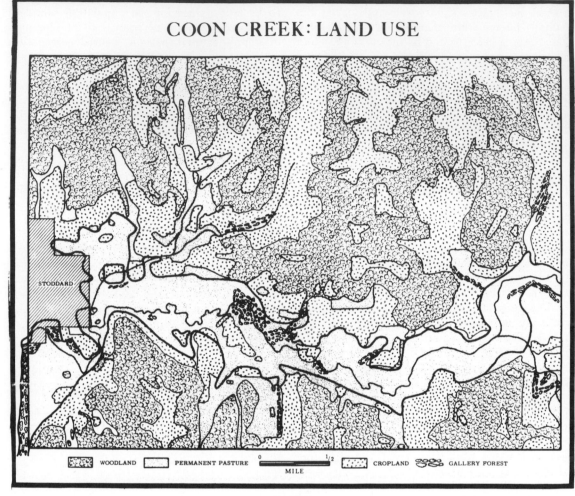

COON CREEK: LAND USE

WOODLAND PERMANENT PASTURE 0 1/2 CROPLAND GALLERY FOREST
MILE

STODDARD

FIGURE 7

results published in the volume *Geographic Surveys* in 1933. Of the total area of 29,396 acres, 55.4 per cent was in cultivated land. Relatively small samples were taken, with sample size equaling 184, or about one point to every 160 acres.

With a sample of this size, the expected variance of simple random samples is 13.4. Four systematic unaligned samples were taken, and they yielded an overall estimate of the mean of 54.7 per cent, with a variance of 10.2. The variance of four stratified random samples was 11.3, of four checkerboard systematic samples 12.8, of systematic traverses 13.5 (50.5 per cent, 48.7 per cent, 51.4 per cent, 57.2 per cent), and of random traverses 11.0. Although gains in efficiency are less impressive than in the Coon Creek case, the systematic unaligned

sample again provides the most efficient of the sampling methods, even when compared with traverses.

SUMMARY

For land-use data, where geographic autocorrelation is known to decline monotonically with increased distance, experiments show that greatest relative efficiency is obtained by systematic sampling. However, if the shape of the autocorrelation function is unknown and linear trends or periodicities may occur, addition of stratification and randomization to the systematic sample to produce a stratified systematic unaligned sample appears to yield both greatest relative efficiency and safety to estimation procedures.

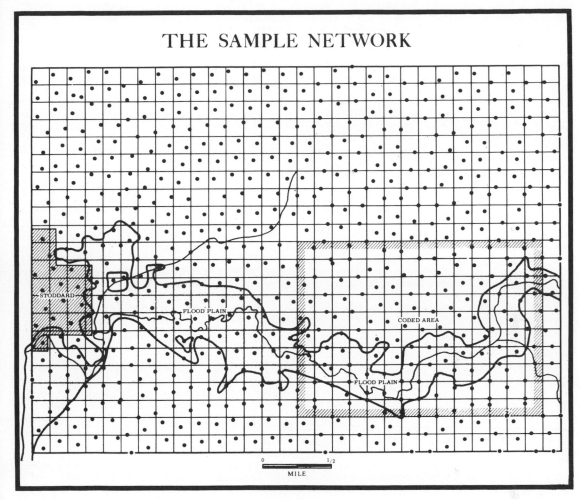

THE SAMPLE NETWORK

FIGURE 8

FOOTNOTES

[1] Bertil Matérn, *Spatial Variation*, Meddelanden fran Statens Skogsforsknings-institut, **5**, No. 3 (Stockholm, 1960).

[2] *Ibid.*

[3] For other items on geographic sampling, particularly of land use see: B. J. L. Berry, *Sampling, Coding, and Storing Flood Plain Data*. Agriculture Handbook No. 237 U. S. Department of Agirculture (Washington: U.S.G.P.O., 1962); J. W. Birch, "The Delimitation of Farming-Type Regions with Special Reference to the Isle of Man," *Transactions of the Institute of British Geographers*, No. 20 (1964), 141–158; J. W. Birch, "A Note on the Sample Farm Survey and Its Use as a Basis for Generalized Mapping, *Economic Geography*, **36** (1960), 254–259; J. M. Blaut, "Microgeographic Sampling: A Quantitative Approach to Regional Agricultural Geography," *Economic Geography*, **35** (1959), 79–88; H. Gauthier, "Sampling Techniques in Land-Use Analysis," unpublished paper, Northwestern University, Department of Geography (1960); E. E. Houseman, *et al.*, *Application of Probability Area Sampling to Farm Surveys*, Agriculture Handbook No. 67, U. S. Department of Agriculture (Washington: U.S.G.P.O., 1954); N. C. Matalas, "Geographical Sampling," *Geographical Review*, **53** (1963), 606–608; R. C. Mayfield, "Line Sampling and Land-Use Estimation in a Complex Rural Area: An Example from a North Indian Valley," unpublished paper, Southeastern State College (Durant, Okla.) Department of Geography; Northeastern Illinois Planning Commission, *Metropolitan Planning Guidelines: Land Use* (Chicago: The Commission, 1965); M. J. Proudfoot, "Sampling with Transverse Traverse Lines," *Journal of the American Statistical Association*, **37** (1942), 265–270; R. Steiner, *An Investigation of Selected Phases of Sampling to Determine Quantities of Land Use Types*, unpublished thesis, University of Washington (1954); R. Steiner, "Some Problems in Designing

Samples of Rural Land Use," *Yearbook of the Association of Pacific Coast Geographers*, **19** (1957), 25–28; W. E. Wood, "Use of Stratified Random Samples in a Land-Use Study," *Annals of the Association of American Geographers*, **45** (1955), 350–367. Useful texts on sampling include: W. G. Cochran, *Sampling Techniques* (New York: John Wiley & Sons, Inc., 1953); F. Yates, *Sampling Methods for Censuses and Surveys* (London: Charles Griffin & Company, Ltd., 1949); M. R. Sampford, *An Introduction to Sampling Theory* (Edinburgh: Oliver & Boyd, Ltd., 1962). Material from related fields of value includes: S. Cain and G. M. de Oliveria Castro, *Manual of Vegetation Analysis* (New York: Harper & Row, Publishers, 1959); P. G. Smith, *Quantitative Plant Ecology* (New York: Academic Press, Inc., 1957).

[4] Cain and Castro, *op. cit.*

[5] Serial correlation exists when the values observed at any given set of points correlate in some way with the values observed at contiguous points. The simplest case is when the correlations are highest for adjacent pairs of points and decline monotonically with increasing distance. See J. C. Obsorn, "Sampling Errors of Systematic and Random Surveys of Cover-Type Areas," *Journal of the American Statistical Association*, **37** (1942), 256–264; W. Youden and A. Mehlich, "Selection of Efficient Methods of Soil Sampling," *Proceedings of the Boyce Thompson Institute*, **9** (1937), 59–70; J. A. Neprash, "Some Problems in the Correlation of Spatially Distributed Variables," *Journal of the American Statistical Association*, **29**, supplement (1934), 167–168.

[6] Matérn writes that serial correlations of land-use data generally: (*a*) decrease monotonically with increased distance; (*b*) are often nearly isotropic but may show directional bias; and (*c*) can be smoothed by curves that have negative derivates near the origin and are downward convex in the vicinity of the origin. From his studies he concludes that "it seems hardly possible, however, to construct a random design which would be superior to the best systematic scheme of the rectangular type under the assumption of exponential correlation." (*Ibid.*, p. 100.)

[7] Berry, *op. cit.*, reports this form of sample to have the greatest efficiency in a series of experiments. See also M. H. Quenouille, "Some Problems of Plane Sampling," *Annals of Mathematical Statistics*, **20** (1949), 355–375.

[8] W. Tobler, "Automation and Cartography," *Geographical Review*, **44** (1959), 536–544.

[9] H. Mitchell and L. Simmons, *The State Plane Coordinate Systems* (Washington: U. S. Coast and Geodetic Survey, 1945).

[10] H. P. Bailey, "Two Grid Systems that Divide the Entire Surface of the Earth into Quadrilaterals of Equal Area," *Transactions of the American Geographical Union*, **37** (1956), 628–635.

[11] For discussions of rectification see American Society of Photogrammetry, *Manual of Photogrammetry* (Washington: The Society, 1952), pp. 449–501; and American Society of Photogrammetry, *Manual of Photographic Interpretation* (Washington: The Society, 1960), pp. 164–165.

[12] The two agencies have reported the method and results in S. Hadfield, "A Sampling Procedure for Updating the Suburban Land-Use Inventory," *CATS Research News*, **6** (June 26, 1964), 2–5; and Northeastern Illinois Planning Commission, *Metropolitan Planning Guidelines*, *op. cit.*

[13] Chicago Area Transportation Study, *Land Use Manual* (Chicago: The Study, 1956); and Northeastern Illinois Metroplitan Area Planning Commission, *Land Use Handbook* (Chicago: The Commission, 1961).

[14] F. F. Stephan, "Sampling Errors and Interpretations of Social Data Ordered in Time and Space," *Journal of the American Statistical Association*, **29**, supplement (1934), 165–166.

[15] *Op. cit.*

[16] For detailed study of the former see I. Burton, *Types of Agricultural Occupance of Flood Plains in the United States*. University of Chicago, Department of Geography, Research Paper No. 75 (1960). The latter was studied by V. C. Finch and R. S. Platt, *Geographic Surveys*, Geographic Society of Chicago, Bulletin No. 9, (1933).

[17] *Op cit.*

[18] Six hundred sixty feet was chosen as an average spacing because, as will be seen in Fig. 8, a grid of that density was placed over the land-use map. However, such a spacing approximates the 1000 feet suggested as somewhere near the optimum for soil surveys by Youden and Mehlich, *op. cit.*

[19] *Op. cit.*

4

STATISTICAL ANALYSIS
OF GEOGRAPHICAL SERIES

ROBERTO BACHI

GEOGRAPHICAL SERIES

Geographical series constitute a substantial portion of official statistics, and are widely utilized in scientific research. Nevertheless the methods of treatment of such series are less developed than those of other types of statistical series and have not yet been systematically included in current statistical textbooks. Some elementary methods for the treatment of geographical series are illustrated in this paper,[1] but no claim is made that they are completely new or that their list is exhaustive.

We shall separately consider methods for the treatment of the following series: (*a*) series showing the distribution of the cases of a phenomenon over the territory; (*b*) geographical series of frequency distributions of attributes or variables; and (*c*) series showing the average intensity of a phenomenon in each section of the territory; (*d*) series showing movements over the territory.

THE TREATMENT OF SERIES SHOWING THE DISTRIBUTION OF THE CASES OF A PHENOMENON OVER THE TERRITORY

THE DISTRIBUTION OF DISTANCES

Let us consider (1) series showing the exact location of each individual case of a phenomenon (e.g., the address of each case of measles occurring in the course of a given period in a town); or (2) series showing the number of cases of a phenomenon occurring in each place or district (such as the population of each of the inhabited places of a country).

Among the methods of treatment employed in order to synthesize such geographical series, frequent use is made of its arithmetic mean or of its median ("center of gravity" or simply "center" of the phenomenon; "median center").

Reprinted from *Bulletin de l'Institut international de statistique*, **36** (1957), 229–240, by permission of the author and editor.

These values should, however, be supplemented by values measuring the geographical spread or dispersion of the phenomenon. Let us see how such values can be calculated and used.

Let $1, \ldots, i, \ldots, l, \ldots, n$ be the cases of the phenomenon under survey, $x_1, \ldots, x_i, \ldots, x_l, \ldots x_n$ the longitudes of their places or points of occurrence, $y_1, \ldots, y_i, \ldots, y_l, \ldots y_n$ their latitudes, and let d_{il} be the distance between i and l (to be calculated generally by $\sqrt{(x_i - x_l)^2 + (y_i - y_l)^2}$ and sometimes as "road distance," "railroad distance," etc.).

In order to study the spread of the cases over the territory we can, even if the number of cases is large, calculate the distribution of all the $1/2n(n-1)$ distances between them. Table 1 gives some examples of such calculations showing the spread of some urban populations, by means of distributions of "road distances" between inhabitants. Distribution of distances like those given in Table 1 can be used not only for comparing the spread of populations in various towns (or countries), but also for studying the changes over time of the spread of populations or other phenomena, for comparing the spread of various classes of the population, and for appraising the extent of distances covered by migrants over the territory.

THE STANDARD DISTANCE

The distribution of distances may be summarized by taking its median, its arithmetic average (see Table 1), the square root of the

arithmetic average of the squares of distances (or "mean quadratic distance") etc. This last value can be calculated directly from the longitudes and latitudes of the points, without actually measuring each distance.

Mean quadratic distance with repetition[2]

$$(1) \quad {}_R^2 D = \sqrt{\frac{\sum\limits_{i=1}^{s} \sum\limits_{l=1}^{s} f_i f_l d_{il}^2}{n^2}}$$

$$= \sqrt{2 \left[\frac{\sum\limits_{i=1}^{s} f_i x_i^2}{n} - \left(\frac{\sum\limits_{i=1}^{s} f_i x_i}{n} \right)^2 \right.}$$

$$\overline{ \left. + \frac{\sum\limits_{i=1}^{s} f_i y_i^2}{n} - \left(\frac{\sum\limits_{i=1}^{s} f_i y_i}{n} \right)^2 \right] }$$

It is seen from Eq. 1 that the mean quadratic distance with repetition is equal to $\sqrt{2}$ times the quadratic average of the distances of each of the cases from their center. By taking the coordinates of the center as

$$(2) \quad \bar{x} = \frac{\sum f_i x_i}{\sum f_i}, \quad \bar{y} = \frac{\sum f_i y_i}{\sum f_i}$$

it is found that the quadratic average of distances, which can be termed "standard distance" between each of the cases and their center, is:

Standard distance $= d$

$$= \sqrt{\frac{\sum\limits_{i=1}^{s} f_i x_i^2}{n} - \left(\frac{\sum\limits_{i=1}^{s} f_i x_i}{n} \right)^2 + \frac{\sum\limits_{i=1}^{s} f_i y_i^2}{n} - \left(\frac{\sum\limits_{i=1}^{s} f_i y_i}{n} \right)^2}$$

TABLE 1

Road distances (in km) between inhabitants in Rome and Zurich

	0–2	2–4	4–6	6–8	8–11	Total	Average (meters)
(1) Actual distances between inhabitants							
Rome 1925	29,567	43,192	22,921	3668	652	100,000	3123
Zurich 1915	33,575	48,270	18,155	—	—	100,000	2688
1925	32,560	48,563	18,876	—	—	100,000	2717
(2) Distances covered by migrants							
Rome 1924–26	48,468	32,663	15,051	3169	649	100,000	2470
(3) Ratio $\frac{(2)}{(1)} \cdot 100$							
Rome 1924–26	164	76	66	86	100	100	79

$$(3) \quad = \sqrt{\frac{\sum_{i=1}^{s} f_i(x_i - \bar{x})^2}{n} + \frac{\sum_{i=1}^{s} f_i(y_i - \bar{y})^2}{n}}$$

The standard distance can be calculated very quickly by taking the square root of the sum of the variances of longitudes and latitudes of the cases studied. If frequencies are given for a large number of inhabited places or sections of the territory, they can conveniently be rearranged, once according to classes of longitudes, and once according to classes of latitudes. Two frequency distributions are thus obtained, on which the usual calculations for the second moment about the mean are performed.

Standard distance appears to be the simplest measure of geographical dispersion to be associated with the center (considered as an index of location of the phenomenon studied). It enables one, *inter alia*, to describe synthetically the actual dispersion of a phenomenon, to compare it with the dispersion to be expected under certain hypotheses, to appraise its change over time, and to compare it with the dispersion of other phenomena.

EXAMPLES OF APPLICATIONS OF THE STANDARD DISTANCE

The "standard distance" has been applied in order to evaluate the spread of human populations. For instance, by studying the geographical distribution of the population of Israel in 1953, we found that the actual standard distance was 48.5 km as compared to a theoretical value of 105.5 km, which would have been found under the hypothesis of uniform distribution of the population over the territory. This discrepancy was found to be due to the following factors: (1) that inhabited places (having a standard distance of 64.1 km) are actually scattered over part of the territory only; (2) that the population is unevenly distributed among those places (under the hypothesis of random assignation of actual populations to the inhabited places, the standard distance would have been 61.9 km); (3) that larger towns are less spread than smaller settlements.

Other applications of standard distances seem to suggest that the method may be useful in many fields, such as (1) comparative analysis of the distributions of different ethnic, social,

or political groups, or of waves of immigrants over the territory of a country or of a town, and of their changes over time; (2) epidemiological studies; (3) analysis of agricultural and industrial statistics (distributions of cultures, of various branches of production, etc.); (4) analysis of geographical distribution of health, educational, or social services as compared to that of the population served, etc.

APPLICATION TO THE STUDY OF HETEROGENEOUS POPULATIONS AND TO THE SUBDIVISION OF A POPULATION BY GEOGRAPHICAL ZONES

Another application of the method can be mentioned, which is useful for the analysis of the geographical spread of a heterogeneous population, viz., of a population composed of distinct ethnic, social, or economic groups. Let us take again as an example the geographical distribution of the population of Israel. This population can be broken down into two main groups: (*a*) the Jews and (*b*) the Moslems, Christians, and Druzes. The square of the standard distance of the population from the center can be subdivided, as shown by Table 2, into two parts — one which is "explained" by the tendency of each group to concentrate around its own center, and the other which remains "unexplained." The ratio of "explained" to total is in the example considered $e_1 = 11.76$ per cent.

The same method can also be applied to geographical series, which can be divided into subseries by dividing the territory into zones according to historical, economic, sociological, geographical, etc., criteria. For each subseries (included in one zone) the center and the standard distance are calculated and the whole series is described by means of these values.

Sometimes, when the territory is being subdivided into a certain number (s) of zones, the question arises whether the particular frame of division adopted is better than other alternative frames of division into s zones.

Other things being equal, that frame should be preferred which has the highest value of e_1—viz., the frame which renders minimal the aggregate "within zone" squared distance and which renders maximal the aggregate weighted squared distance between the centers of the zones and the general center.

TREATMENT OF GEOGRAPHICAL SERIES SHOWING FREQUENCY DISTRIBUTIONS OR AVERAGES

The method illustrated in Table 2 may be considered as suited to the study of any geographical series of frequency distributions of attributes and variables (e.g., distribution of the population of each district by occupation, by literacy, or by income, etc.). For each attribute (e.g., for each occupation) or for each class of the variable (e.g., for each income group) centers and standard distances are calculated, and these values are compared to those of the entire population.

In the case of variables, some further methods of treatment may sometimes be introduced. For instance, on the basis of data on the distribution of Italian Army recruits by geographical region and height, it has been found that the "centers" of the groups of recruits whose height is respectively "less than 150 cm," "151–155 cm," . . . , "181 and more cm" follow a rather regular line, with the height increasing from South to North and East to West. The standard distance of all recruits within each group is somewhat lower on an average than the standard distance of all recruits, and e_1 is found to be 5.76 per cent. By interpolation, we can obtain estimating equations

$$x = 10.47 - 0.064\,h; \quad y = 27.51 + 0.092\,h$$

of longitudes (x) and latitudes (y) of centers of recruits of height h.

The square of standard distance between the places of residence of the recruits and their general center may be divided into two parts: (1) the average of squares of distance of each case from the estimated center of its class (the center being obtained from the estimating equations given above); (2) the weighted average of squares of distances of the estimated centers of each class from the general center. By calculating $100 \times (2)/(1) + (2)$, a ratio $e_2 = 5.56$ per cent is obtained, which is found to be somewhat lower than ratio e_1.

By the use of a similar method it is sometimes possible to analyze series showing the average intensity of a phenomenon in each section of the territory. For instance, the series showing the percentage of illiteracy in each of the ninety-two provinces of Italy (1931) was analyzed by means of the calculation of centers and standard distances of population of groups of provinces classified according to illiteracy. By joining the centers of the various groups of provinces, a line is obtained which seems to give a useful indication of the geographical direction of increasing illiteracy from North to South and West to East. Standard distances show that the spread is much smaller within each group of provinces than in the country as a whole ($e_1 = 78.2$ per cent). From estimating equations of longitudes (x) and latitudes (y) of centers of provinces with average illiteracy i ($x = 0.151\,i - 3.568$, $y = -0.164i + 46.510$), a value of $e_2 = 73.7$ per cent is found.

TABLE 2

Squares of standard distances of two groups of population in Israel

	Jewish pop.	Moslem, Christian & Druze pop.	Total pop.
1. Number inhabitants included in calculation[a]	1,445,659	148,098	1,593,757
2. Average of squares of distances from center of total population (km)	22,123	37,599	
3. Average of squares of distances from center of own group (km)	21,837	10,578	
4. Square of distance between center of group and center of total population (km)	286	27,021	
5. Ratio of "explained" square distance, per cent	1.29[b]	71.87[b]	11.76[c]

[a] Data for end of 1953. New immigrants' reception centers, Beduin nomadic population, and certain other groups were excluded from calculation.

[b] Ratio (4)/(2).

[c] Ratio $\Sigma(4)\cdot(1)/\Sigma(2)\cdot(1)$ obtained by adding up data for the two population groups.

The Treatment of Series Showing Movements Classified by Places of Departure and Arrival

When studying these series, even the most expert statistician may find himself confused by the intricacies of raw data. In a country subdivided into, say, 200 districts, statistics on internal movements of persons (commodities, trucks, etc.) will yield 40,000 figures, which must be treated and synthesized in some way if any conclusions are to be drawn. Treating the data may help both (1) to describe the phenomenon and (2) to test some hypothesis, which could "explain" certain aspects of the phenomenon.

Three groups of methods for the treatment of series of movements are discussed in the following.

As an example of series of movements we consider data on internal migrations between the various sections of the town of Rome (1925).

INDICES OF PREFERENCE OR DISLIKE FOR EACH DIRECTION OF MOVEMENTS

In order to study directions of internal migrations, it may be useful to compare the actual data with theoretical data which would be obtained under certain hypotheses. Two very simple hypotheses are the following:

(1) Let us assume that internal migrations are not influenced by geographical or other factors differentiating the various sections. Then (a) the number of persons leaving each section and that of persons coming to each section should be proportional to the number of inhabitants of the sections, and (b) migrants from and to each section, as estimated above, should exchange their respective residences at random. Let us indicate the population of section i by P_i; that of the section l by P_l; the population of the whole territory by P; the number of migrants from section i to section l by $_im_l$; the number of migrants originating from section i by $_im$; the number of migrants coming to section l by m_l; and the total number of migrants by m.

The expected number of migrants from i to l in the above hypothesis would then be mP_iP_l/P^2. By calculating the ratios

$$(4) \qquad 100\frac{_im_l}{mP_iP_l/P^2}$$

between the actual and the theoretical numbers of movements from section i to section l for the internal migration between ten sections of the city of Rome (1925), we found that (1) movements occur in all directions; (2) there is a marked tendency of migrants to remain in the section in which they previously resided; (3) migrants who do change section show a preference for sections near that of previous residence; (4) central sections are the least attractive and generally lose to other sections, intermediate sections gain partially from the central ones and lose to the peripheral ones, and the latter generally gain. The centrifugal character of internal migration is thus clear.

(2) A second alternative hypothesis which may be suggested for comparing the actual data with theoretical data is that used in general in the analysis of contingency tables. Let us assume that we have already studied the influence of general tendencies such as those mentioned above . . . to migrate from the center to the periphery, etc. We may now take the marginal totals given by the statistics (viz., the number of people entering and leaving each section) as fixed numbers. If the previous place of residence had no influence upon the selection of the new residence, we may assume that the migrants would have changed their respective residences at random. Under this hypothesis the expected number of persons migrating from i to l should be $_im \cdot m_l/m$. If $_im_l$ exceeds this expected number, an index of attraction in the direction i-l may be calculated by taking

$$(5) \qquad 100\frac{_im_l - {_im} \cdot m_l/m}{_im - {_im} \cdot m_l/m}$$

This index is $+100$ per cent when all persons who formerly resided in section i have their new residence in section l. If $_im_l$ is smaller than the expected number, an index of dislike in the direction i-l may be calculated. Indices calculated in this way for internal migrations in Rome show the attraction toward the previous section of residence and neighboring sections and the dislike for other sections (which grows with the increasing distance from sections of previous residence).

DISTANCES COVERED BY MIGRANTS

Actual and theoretical distributions of migrations can be easily converted into distributions

TABLE 3

Actual and theoretical mean distances[a] covered in internal migrations (meters)

(Rome 1924–26, Zurich 1905–26.)

Town and year	Actual	THEORETICAL		Percentage ratios	
		Hypothesis (i): Migrations proportional to population[b]	Hypothesis (ii): Random distribution of migrants[b]	1/2	1/3
	1	2	3	4	5
Rome 1924–26	2470	3123	3330	79	74
Zurich 1905	1984	2645	2456	75	81
1910	2006	2650	2507	76	80
1915	1766	2688	2520	66	70
1919	1916	?	2528	?	76
1926	1944	2717	?	72	?

[a] Road distances.
[b] For Rome, 1925.

by distance covered by migrants. An example of such distributions is given by Table 1 for internal migrations in Rome (1925). This table shows that the ratios between actual and theoretical numbers decrease from those for short distances to those of up to 6 km, due to the strong tendency of migrants to remain near their previous places of residence. The ratios increase, on the other hand, after the sixth kilometer and reach 100 at the end of the series, thus showing that persons who move to a new home far from their previous one are indifferent to whether they move, say, 8 km or 11 km from it.

Distribution of distances may be summarized by taking averages from them. Various averages can be of use for this purpose:

(1) The arithmetic average of all distances covered by migrants is

$$(6) \qquad D = \frac{\sum\limits_{i=1}^{s} \sum\limits_{l=1}^{s} {}_i m_l d_{il}}{m} = \frac{\sum\limits_{i=1}^{s-1} \sum\limits_{l=i+1}^{s} ({}_i m_l + {}_l m_i) d_{il}}{m}$$

Under the hypothesis...of migrations proportional to population and occurring at random, the mean distance covered by migrants becomes

$$(7) \qquad {}^P D = \frac{2 \sum\limits_{i=1}^{s-1} \sum\limits_{l=i+1}^{s} P_i P_l d_{il}}{P^2} = {}_R D_P$$

i.e., it equals the mean distance with repetition between two inhabitants.

Under . . . the hypothesis of random association of actual places of departure and places of arrival, the arithmetic average of distances covered by migrants becomes

$$(8) \qquad {}^r D = \frac{2 \sum\limits_{i=1}^{s-1} \sum\limits_{l=i+1}^{s} {}_i m \cdot m_l d_{il}}{m^2}$$

Examples of Eqs. 6, 7, 8 are given in Table 3 for Rome and Zurich. The actual mean distances in both cities are found to be shorter than the theoretical ones.

(2) The quadratic average of all distances covered by migrants

$$(9) \qquad {}^2 D = \sqrt{\frac{\sum\limits_{i=1}^{s} \sum\limits_{l=1}^{s} {}_i m_l d_{il}^2}{m}}$$

$$= \sqrt{\frac{\sum\limits_{i=1}^{s-1} \sum\limits_{l=i+1}^{s} ({}_i m_l + {}_l m_i) d_{il}^2}{m}}$$

$$^2 D = \sqrt{\frac{\sum\limits_{i=1}^{s} ({}_i m + m_i)(x_i^2 + y_i^2)}{m}}$$

$$\overline{\qquad\qquad - 2 \sum\limits_{i=1}^{s} \sum\limits_{l=1}^{s} {}_i m_l (x_i x_l + y_i y_l)}{m}$$

$$
(10) \quad = \sqrt{ \frac{\sum\limits_{i=1}^{s} (_i m + m_i)(x_i^2 + y_i^2)}{m} } \\
\frac{ - 2\left(\sum\limits_{i=1}^{s} x_i \sum\limits_{l=1}^{s} {}_i m_l x_l + \sum\limits_{i=1}^{s} y_i \sum\limits_{l=1}^{s} {}_i m_l y_l \right) }{m}
$$

Formula 10 has two very distinct advantages. (*a*) It may be calculated quickly from coordinates of points of departure and arrival without any need to perform the laborious calculations of the distances d_{il}.[3] (*b*) Its square may be split into a few components which are of interest as measures of the main effects of migration, as shown below.

SYNTHETIC MEASURES OF EFFECTS OF MIGRATIONS

Let us first introduce these measures and then show their relationship with ^2D.

Let us consider the places or points of departure of the migrants. As any other set of points, they can be summarized by the methods indicated . . . by calculating their center

$$
\bar{x}_D = \frac{\sum\limits_{i=1}^{s} {}_i m x_i}{m}, \quad \bar{y}_D = \frac{\sum\limits_{i=1}^{s} {}_i m y_i}{m}
$$

and standard distance from their center

$$
d_D = \sqrt{ \frac{\sum\limits_{i=1}^{s} {}_i m (x_i^2 + y_i^2)}{m} - (\bar{x}_D^2 + \bar{y}_D^2) }
$$

Similarly, we can calculate the center of points of arrival

$$
\bar{x}_A = \frac{\sum\limits_{l=1}^{s} m_l x_l}{m}, \quad \bar{y}_A = \frac{\sum\limits_{l=1}^{s} m_l y_l}{m}
$$

and their standard distance

$$
d_A = \sqrt{ \frac{\sum\limits_{l=1}^{s} m_l (x_l^2 + y_l^2)}{m} - (\bar{x}_A^2 + \bar{y}_A^2) }
$$

from their center.

These data enable us to measure the main effects of migrations as follows:

(1) The migrations have caused a shift of $\sqrt{(\bar{x}_D - \bar{x}_A)^2 + (\bar{y}_D - \bar{y}_A)^2}$ in the center of places of residence of the migrants.

(2) The migrations have caused a shift in the center of the population[4] during the period under survey, which can be evaluated by multiplying the shift in the place of residence of migrants, as given under (1), by the ratio of the number of migrants to population m/p.

(3) The migrations have caused a change in the spread of places of residence of the migrants, which can be measured by comparing d_D and d_A. In the case of the migrations in Rome we found that the standard distance of places of arrival is larger than the standard distance of places of departure, thus showing the centrifugal character of these migrations.

(4) This change in the spread of places of residence of migrants has brought about some change in the spread of the whole population.[5]

If migrants had exchanged their places of residence at random, the square of quadratic average of distances covered by them would be equal to

$$
(11) \quad {}^{r,2}D^2 = [(\bar{x}_D - \bar{x}_A)^2 + (\bar{y}_D - \bar{y}_A)^2] \\
+ d_D^2 + d_A^2
$$

This could be roughly interpreted as follows:

The average of squares of distances may be split into three components arising from three sets of "journeys," viz., (*a*) from points of departure to their center; (*b*) from this center to the center of points of arrival; (*c*) from the center of points of arrival to these points.

Generally, however, points of arrival are not associated at random with points of departure. The actual value of the square of quadratic averages covered by migrants is

$$
(12) \quad {}^2D^2 = [(\bar{x}_A - \bar{x}_D)^2 + (\bar{y}_A - \bar{y}_D)^2] + d_D^2 + d_A^2 - \\
- 2\left[\left(\frac{\sum\limits_{l=1}^{s} x_l \sum\limits_{i=1}^{s} {}_i m_l x_i}{m} - \bar{x}_D \bar{x}_A \right) \right. \\
\left. + \left(\frac{\sum\limits_{l=1}^{s} y_l \sum\limits_{i=1}^{s} {}_i m_l y_i}{m} - \bar{y}_A \bar{y}_D \right) \right]
$$

The difference between $^{r,2}D^2$ and $^2D^2$ is equal to twice the sum of (*a*) the covariance of longitudes of points of departure and arrival and (*b*) the covariance of latitudes of points of departure and arrival.

If we indicate by $r_{D,A,x}$ the coefficient of correlation between longitudes of points of departure and arrival, by $r_{D,A,y}$ the corresponding coefficient of correlation for latitudes, and by $\sigma_{D,x}$, $\sigma_{D,y}$, $\sigma_{A,x}$, $\sigma_{A,y}$ the standard deviation of longitudes (and latitudes) of points of departure (and arrival), we can write Eq. 12 in a different way:

$$(13) \qquad {}^2D^2 = [(\bar{x}_A - \bar{x}_D)^2 + (\bar{y}_A - \bar{y}_D)^2]$$
$$+ d_D^2 + d_A^2 - 2(r_{D,A,x}\sigma_{D,x}\sigma_{A,x}$$
$$+ r_{D,A,y}\sigma_{D,y}\sigma_{A,y})$$

This formula enables us to find (1) a lower bound to the minimal value of the square of quadratic average of distances $({}^{2,\min}D^2)$ by assuming that both $r_{D,A,x}$ and $r_{D,A,y}$ are equal to 1; (2) an upper bound to the maximal value $({}^{2,\max}D^2)$, by assuming $r_{D,A,x} = r_{D,A,y} = -1$; (3) the value in case of random association of points of departure and arrival, by assuming

$$r_{D,A,x} = r_{D,A,y} = 0$$

The above values enable us to calculate an index which measures nonrandomness in association of points of departure and points of arrival of migrants. The index is obtained by calculating the ratio of (a) the excess[6] of the squared quadratic average of distances in case of random association over the squared quadratic average of actual distances, to (b) the maximum possible value of this excess. This index varies between 0 and +1.

$$(14) \qquad \frac{{}^{r,2}D^2 - {}^2D^2}{{}^{r,2}D^2 - {}^{2,\min}D^2}$$
$$= \frac{r_{D,A,x}\sigma_{D,x}\sigma_{A,x} + r_{D,A,y}\sigma_{D,y}\sigma_{A,y}}{\sigma_{D,x}\sigma_{A,x} + \sigma_{D,y}\sigma_{A,y}} = r_{D,A}$$

In the case of internal migrations in Rome this index is 0.4042.

An even more synthetic value than ${}^2D^2$ may sometimes be introduced, viz., ${}^2D^2_{p_0,p_t}$ measuring the square of the mean quadratic distance between the place of residence at time 0 and place of residence at time t for all inhabitants—both migrants and nonmigrants.[7] It can be shown that this value can be split either into its components with regard to parameters of population at time 0 and time t, or into a larger number of components, concerning, separately, nonmigrants, departing migrants, and arriving migrants.

FOOTNOTES

[1] This paper is a summary of a larger article now in preparation, in which details of calculations and proofs of various formulae are given.

[2] The formula is given here for quadratic mean distances "with repetition" (viz., including distances between each case and itself) and for data grouped in s classes (sections of the territory, districts, places, etc.).

[3] In the following examples distances are expressed in arbitrary units of measurement, as straight distances between coordinates of centers of sections as drawn in maps used for calculations.

[4] Let us assume that the distribution of the population is influenced only by internal migrations. Let us indicate the center of population at the beginning of the period considered by $(\bar{x}_{p_0}, \bar{y}_{p_0})$ and the center of population at the end of the period considered by $(\bar{x}_{p_t}, \bar{y}_{p_t})$. The distance between the two centers is

$$\sqrt{(\bar{x}_{p_t} - \bar{x}_{p_0})^2 + (\bar{y}_{p_t} - \bar{y}_{p_0})^2}$$
$$= \frac{m}{p}\sqrt{(\bar{x}_D - \bar{x}_A)^2 + (\bar{y}_D - \bar{y}_A)^2}$$

Shifts in the center of population due to other factors such as births, deaths, external migrations, might be measured separately.

[5] Let us start again from the hypothesis considered in the previous footnote, that only internal migrations cause changes in the geographical distribution of the population. Under this hypothesis we find that the square of standard distance of population changed, from the beginning to the end of the period considered, by

$$d_{p_t}^2 - d_{p_0}^2$$

By splitting this difference into its various components it is actually found that the most important component in our example is

$$\frac{m}{p}(d_A^2 - d_D^2)$$

This is equal to the difference between the square of standard distance of points of arrival and the square of standard distance of points of departure, multiplied by the ratio of number of migrants to population.

[6] We assume $^{r,2}D^2 > {}^2D^2$. "Nonrandomness" can be interpreted as due to the tendency to select new places of residence nearer to the former ones than under the random hypothesis. In the most unlikely case, that $^{r,2}D^2 < {}^2D^2$, a ratio $({}^2D^2 - {}^{r,2}D^2)/({}^{2,\max}D^2 - {}^{r,2}D^2)$ might be calculated.

[7] The knowledge of such distances is sometimes obtained from censuses or samples in which inhabitants are requested to give, besides their present place of residence, the place of residence at a certain past date. An analogous formula can also be applied to distance between "place of residence" and "place of work."

5

TEMPERATURE EXTREMES
IN THE UNITED STATES

ARNOLD COURT

Extremes of temperature, like extremes of many other climatic elements, are of continuing interest to the public as well as to meteorologists and geographers. They are often cited uncritically, without regard to accuracy or the probability of recurrence. Yet it is axiomatic that as more and more years of observation accumulate at a place, greater and greater extremes will be observed, so that the magnitude of the recorded extreme depends on the length of the record.

Until recently, no valid means for comparing extremes based on different periods has been available, and observed extremes could only be tabulated without analysis. Development in the last decade of the statistical theory of extreme values has provided a means of estimating the *most probable extreme value* likely in any given period of time, on the basis of all the extremes that have been observed. Application of the theory to rather short series, not necessarily of equal length, for different places yields values that may be compared directly.

In this paper the theory has been applied to the highest and lowest air temperatures of each year at 100 places in the United States, obtaining the extremes expected to occur once in a century. These highest and lowest temperatures, estimated on the basis of the annual extremes recorded between 1901 and 1930, are shown on two maps, and are compared to the extreme temperatures actually recorded during the entire meteorological history of these and other places. The study is part of a continuing investigation being carried out by the Environmental Protection Section of the Office of the Quartermaster General. The objective is to define the probable extremes of various climatic elements, so that equipment may be designed and tested for satisfactory operation under all conditions likely to be encountered.

THE THEORY

The statistical theory of extreme values, as developed largely by E. J. Gumbel,[1] is applicable to a set of extreme values, each of which is independent of the others and is itself the extreme of a sample from a distribution of the exponential type, like the normal one—continuous and unlimited (at least within the realm

Reprinted from *Geographical Review*, **43** (1953), 40–49, by permission of the author and editor.

of observation), and decreasing toward zero for very large and very small values.

Adapted by tables and diagrams to ready computation, the theory may be used for routine analyses of extremes that fit the basic requirements. It has been applied with notable success to two widely differing types of extremes—material-breaking strengths (considered as those of the weakest links or elements of the material) and climatic extremes.

According to the theory, the frequency distribution of a set of extreme values is not symmetrical, though the original observations from which the extremes are extracted may be symmetrical. Instead, the distribution of extremes is "skewed" toward the more extreme values. For example, most of the highest temperatures of many years cluster near the lower end of the range of the extremes, and the few very high extremes are not counter-balanced by as many very low ones.

The relation between a set of extreme values and the observations from which they are derived is shown in Fig. 1, which also illustrates the symmetry of the original observations and the skewness or distortion of the extremes. The large histogram, to which a "normal" curve has been fitted, shows the frequency of occurrence of the highest temperature of each summer day (June–August) at Washington, D. C., during seventy-four years—a total of 6808 daily observations.[2] In the lower right a solid histogram shows the frequency of occurrence of the highest temperatures in each of the seventy-four summers, with a smooth curve representing the extreme-value theory fitted to it. Since the daily values are by 5° groups, the ordinate for the seasonal values has been multiplied by five to make the two curves comparable.

The highest daily temperatures are not fitted too well by a normal curve; they are skewed somewhat to the left, but not as much as would be the case if they were independent values and thus subject to the theory of extreme values. Incidentally, the analysis of the extremes applies only to summer; in five of the seventy-four years, the highest temperature of the year came outside the three summer months, once in May and four times in September.

In applying the theory of extreme values to temperatures, it is assumed that the highest (or lowest) temperature attained in any one year at a given place is independent of the corresponding value in the previous or following year. While it is possible that hot years and cold years may run in cycles, no such interdependence has been established. Although there is a physical lower limit to air temperature (absolute zero) and possibly an upper limit, neither is close enough to the range of observed temperatures to negate the assumption.

The most questionable assumption in applying the theory of extreme values to annual temperature extremes is the implication that the temperatures of each year represent separate samples from the same population, that is, that the climate is not changing. Since climate undoubtedly has changed since the ice ages, and apparently has changed since the last glacier maximum of the late eighteenth century, it may be changing somewhat from decade to decade, if not from year to year. However, such changes are so slight that, for practical purposes, climate may be considered as constant over a thirty-year period. Any extrapolation to 100 years, such as may be inferred from the present analy-

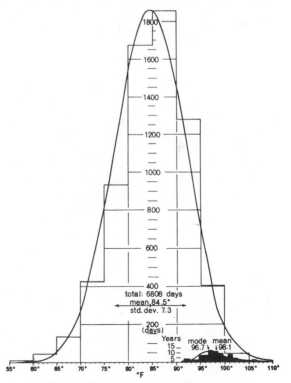

FIGURE 1. Frequencies of highest temperatures of each summer day and year, Washington, D. C., 1872–1945, June-July-August.

sis, must be qualified by explaining that it assumes no material change from conditions during the period on which it is based.

SIGNIFICANCE OF THE THEORY

Basically, the theory of extreme values gives the probability of occurrence in any trial of an extreme of given value. Conversely, it may be used to determine the extreme which has a given probability of not being equaled or exceeded in any one trial; for example, a year. For climatic comparisons, the second use is preferable; extremes with less than some given probability of not being equaled or exceeded are computed for various places. For such comparisons a convenient probability is 0.99, that is, one chance in a hundred that the extreme in any year will be as great as, or greater than, the computed value. This probability is used here.

An event which has a probability of 0.99 of not occurring has a probability of 0.01 of occurring; in this case, the event is the occurrence of an extreme equal to, or greater than, the computed value. An event with this probability is expected to occur about 10,000 times in a million years, assuming no change in conditions. Consequently, the average of all the intervals between occurrences of this event is 100 years, but according to the probability theory, half of these intervals will be less than seventy years, and about one in a hundred will be zero; that is, the event will occur in consecutive years. In general, for an event expected to occur on the average once in t years, the probability is $e^{-n/t}$ that it will not occur or be exceeded in less than n years.

The extreme value with a given probability of occurrence in any sample (year) may be computed, according to the theory of extreme values, from the following formula: $x = \bar{x} \pm K s_x$, where $\bar{x}$ and s_x are the mean and standard deviation of a set of extreme values (as defined), and K depends only on the given probability and the size of the set of known

extremes, n. The plus sign is used for largest extremes, the minus for smallest. For probabilities of 0.01 and 0.20 (one in 100 and one in five, respectively), values for K for various sample sizes are shown below.

The formula shows that extremes to be expected with equal probability at various places depend on the average and standard deviation of the extremes already observed. Even though the mean annual extreme temperatures (average of the highest temperatures of each year) at two places are the same, the expected 100-year extremes may be different, unless the variability of the highest temperatures from year to year is the same; the place with the greater variability has a higher 100-year value.

Any value computed by this formula is an estimate; there are two chances in three (specifically, 0.68269) that the highest value actually occurring in thirty samples (years) will not differ from the computed value by more than 1.026 s_x. Thus both the magnitude and the reliability of the expected extreme depend on the standard deviation of the observed values —that is, on the variability from sample to sample. This reliability is not identical with that mentioned earlier for the probability that the extreme, which occurs on the average once in a century, will recur after a shorter interval. The figure applies to the probable magnitude of the largest value observed within a fixed period of 100 years; the earlier figures were for a fixed value and a variable period.

For Washington, D. C., the highest temperature likely to be reached in a century is 110° F.; the probability is 0.68 that the highest temperatures actually occurring in any 100-year period will be within 0.946 × 3.03 of this figure, or between 107.1° and 112.9°. On the other hand, for any value that occurs on the average only once in 100 years, the probability is 0.63 that it will occur or be exceeded in less than any given 100 years, 0.50 that it will occur or be exceeded within the first seventy years of any 100-year period, and 0.40 that it will occur or be exceeded within the first fifty years.

Sample size, n:	*15*	*20*	*25*	*30*	*40*	*50*	*70*	*100*	*200*
K for prob. 0.01:	4.005	3.836	3.728	3.653	3.554	3.491	3.413	3.349	3.263
K for prob. 0.20:	0.967	0.919	0.888	0.866	0.838	0.820	0.797	0.779	0.755

APPLICATION OF THE THEORY

To apply the theory of extreme values, a set of independent extremes is required; for the present purpose, such a set is the highest or lowest temperature during each of many years. For simplicity the analysis was confined (with one exception, mentioned later) to data presented in *Climatic Summary of the United States*,[3] which contains data through 1930; no comparable summary has been published since. This summary lists data for all Weather Bureau stations and for thousands of cooperative observers, but gives year-by-year values for only 190 stations, almost all of them first order, that is, operated by Weather Bureau employees.

A standard period, 1901 to 1930, was chosen for the analysis, since this period has long been accepted as the basis for international climatic "normals." Of the 190 stations for which annual extremes were published, only 150 had data for the chosen thirty years; of these, 100 were selected to give adequate geographic coverage of the United States.

For each of the 100 stations, the highest and lowest temperatures of each year from 1901 to 1930 were analyzed and the probable highest and lowest temperature likely in ten, thirty, and 100 years were computed and tabulated.[4] For comparison, the highest and lowest temperatures actually observed during the thirty-year period were also tabulated, and the highest and lowest of record as given in the Weather Bureau's *Local Climatological Summary* for 1949; in a few cases such extremes were compiled from other published sources. Station histories and climatic notes in the 1950 summaries were consulted; some of them are quoted below.

Maximum and minimum temperatures during the thirty-year period at the 100 stations were generally in good agreement with the theoretical thirty-year values: only six of the observed maximums and nine of the observed minimums departed from the expected values by more than $1.026 \, s_x$, and of these departures only four of the minimums were more than half a degree beyond this limit. None of the observation series extended over 100 years, but at three places the highest temperature recorded from the start of observations through 1949 exceeded the theoretical 100-year value by more than the 68 per cent probability limit $(0.946 s_x)$, although only one did so by more than half a degree. Three all-time minimums were lower than $0.946 \, s_x$ of the theoretical 100-year values, all by more than half a degree.

Some of these differences, however, are due to questionable data. At Boise, Ida., for example, a record of 121° F. is credited to 1871, with 113° in 1870 and 108° in 1872 and 1874. These observations were made under the supervision of the Office of the Army Post Surgeon, Boise Barracks, with unknown instrumental exposure; between 1877 and 1880 thermometers were in a "standard window shelter" in a north window. No figure higher than 109° (in 1940) has been recorded since then, in good agreement with the 111° expected, on the basis of the 1901–1930 data, to occur once in a century. At Portland, M., the record lowest temperature of −39°, which is 11° colder than the 100-year value expected on the basis of the 1901–1930 data, occurred in February, 1943, in the third winter of official observations at the city airport, where "temperatures are considerably lower . . . than in the city on calm cold mornings." From 1873 to 1940, the lowest temperature observed in downtown Portland, in 1917, was −21°, only 1° higher than the expected thirty-year value and 7° higher than the expected 100-year value. This discrepancy emphasizes that the analyses apply only to the places of observation, and that marked changes in instrument exposure affect the all-time record values. Likewise, at Roseburg, Ore., the only subzero reading was −6° in 1888, when the thermometer shelter was on the roof of a downtown building, fifty-four feet above the ground; this value is 14° lower than the 100-year extreme based on a thirty-year record during which the lowest temperature was 11°.

At several places the lowest or second-lowest reading during the thirty years on which the analysis was based occurred twice, so that the expected thirty-year minimum is significantly colder than the lowest observed during the period. For example, at Helena, Mont., temperatures of −30° or colder occurred seven times during the thirty years, and the lowest during that period, −32°, occurred three times; thus the analysis indicates an expected thirty-year value of −42°, 10° colder than the observed and the same as the seventy-one year record set in 1893; the expected 100-year value is $-51°$. Local influences may in effect limit the temperature at Helena, so that the annual minimums there do not follow the theory of extreme values. At four other places in Montana, temperatures of $-60°$ or colder have been recorded, and many places have observed readings below $-50°$. Similarly, at Spokane the lowest temperature during the thirty years was $-17°$, the second lowest was $-16°$, and $-15°$ occurred twice; thus the analysis indicates that the lowest temperature expected in thirty years is $-25°$, $8°$ colder than observed. But both before and after this period, invasions of extremely cold Canadian air caused severe winters in 1887–88, 1889–90, 1936–37, 1948–49, and 1949–50, and the lowest temperature recorded in seventy years, $-30°$ in 1888, is within $4°$ of the expected 100-year value. At Cheyenne, Wyo., the lowest temperature during the thirty years, $-30°$, occurred twice, as did the second lowest, $-28°$, making the expected thirty-year value $-37°$, $10°$ colder than the observed. In 1875, however, $-38°$ was recorded, within $6°$ of the expected 100-year value.

Other discrepancies between observed and theoretical values can be ascribed to chance. At Sacramento, "the lowest temperature recorded here during a century of available record, including Weather Bureau and private records," in December, 1932, was $17°$, $4°$ lower than the expected 100-year value. At San Diego, temperatures below freezing have occurred only five times since 1871, but one of these, $25°$ in 1913, was $4°$ lower than the expected thirty-year value and $2°$ lower than the 100-year value.

In addition to the 100 stations, one other is shown on Fig. 2: $130°$ for Greenland Ranch, Death Valley, Calif., the hottest place in North America. Although $134°$ was recorded there in 1913, detailed study[5] has shown this observation to be questionable; $127°$ is the highest reliable temperature recorded since observations began in 1911.

THE MAPS

The maps (Figs. 2–3) of the highest and lowest temperatures to be expected once in a century in the United States are similar in general outline to the available maps of the observed temperature extremes. There are, however, significant differences in detail. Despite the general interest in extreme temperatures, relatively few detailed maps of them exist. The most recent maps for the United States were prepared in 1939, under the supervision of W. A. Mattice of the Weather Bureau, for the volume *Climate and Man*.[6] These maps, based on records of some 5000 first-order and cooperative Weather Bureau stations during a forty-year period, 1899–1938, show "Highest Temperatures Ever Observed," by $5°$ isotherms, and "Lowest Temperatures Ever Observed," by $10°$ isotherms. Maps of the highest and lowest temperatures ever observed in each month, "based upon the records of 200 first-line Weather Bureau stations over a period of fifty years," were prepared in 1947 by J. L. Baldwin and others of the Weather Bureau, and have since appeared in the appropriate month of each year on the reverse of the Daily Weather Map published in Washington. No annual maps were prepared; hence several winter or summer maps must be combined for comparison with Fig. 2 and 3.

The chief difference between maps of expected extremes and those of observed extremes is that the former appear much less complex: the isotherms are more regular, and in general the maps resemble those of average minimum and maximum temperatures. Part of this smoothness may be due to the use of only 100 stations instead of the 200 or 5000 mentioned above. To compensate in part for the sparseness of plotted points, the isotherms were drawn roughly in accordance with topography, but no temperature data were considered apart from the 100 expected values, the Death Valley maximum, and the fact[7] that five of the ten occurrences of temperatures of $-60°$ or colder occurred in and near Yellowstone Park. Ten-degree isotherms have been used on both maps, and a $115°$ isotherm was added to Fig. 2 to emphasize the hotter areas.

Much of the smoothness can apparently be attributed to the method of analysis, which in effect provides corrected extremes based on thirty observed values rather than reliance on only one isolated observation. Many wide differences in observed extremes at near-by places with comparable climates are reduced markedly by this method. For example, the highest recorded temperatures at Topeka and Dodge City, Kans., are $114°$ and $109°$, respectively, but the expected 100-year value at both

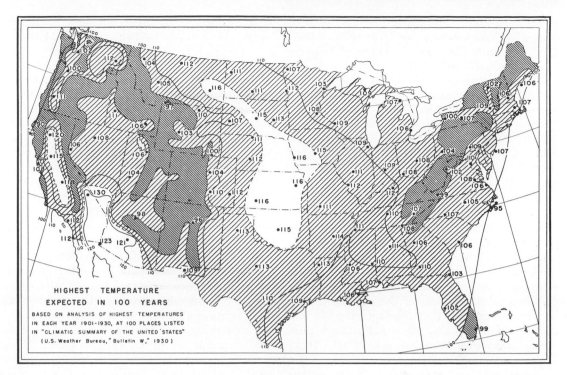

HIGHEST TEMPERATURE
EXPECTED IN 100 YEARS

BASED ON ANALYSIS OF HIGHEST TEMPERATURES
IN EACH YEAR 1901-1930, AT 100 PLACES LISTED
IN "CLIMATIC SUMMARY OF THE UNITED STATES"
(U.S. Weather Bureau," Bulletin W," 1930)

FIGURE 2

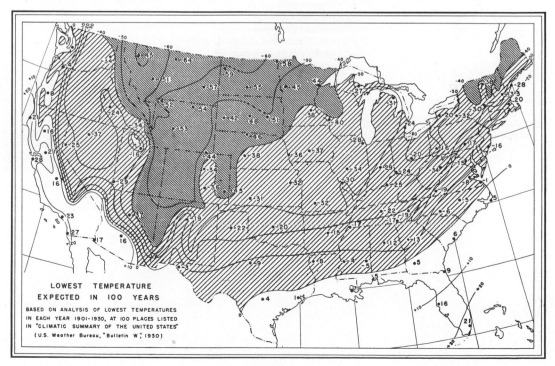

LOWEST TEMPERATURE
EXPECTED IN 100 YEARS

BASED ON ANALYSIS OF LOWEST TEMPERATURES
IN EACH YEAR 1901-1930, AT 100 PLACES LISTED
IN "CLIMATIC SUMMARY OF THE UNITED STATES"
(U.S. Weather Bureau," Bulletin W," 1930)

FIGURE 3

is 116°. Similarly, the lowest recorded temperatures at Chattanooga and Knoxville, Tenn., are −10° and −16°, but the expected 100-year values are −17° and −19°.

The only part of the United States likely to record temperatures of −60° or colder during a century is in Montana, Idaho, and Wyoming, though such readings have occurred also in North Dakota and Colorado. The expected minimums are highest on the California coast (San Francisco, 28°; Los Angeles, 23°; San Diego, 27°).

The most significant feature of the two maps is the delineation of the area of the Great Plains in which temperatures of 115° or higher may be expected once in a century. No 115° isotherm appears in this area on any of the monthly maps of observed extremes, but fifteen pockets of 115° temperatures are indicated on the map in *Climate and Man*. Most of the all-time records in this region were established during the hot, dry summer of 1936, when 121°, the highest temperature ever recorded east of the Rocky Mountains, was registered at Steele, N. D., and Fredonia and Alton, Kans. Temperatures of 120° were recorded during July and August of 1936 at nine other places in the Plains states: Wishek, N. D.; Gannvalley, S. D.; Eureka and Wellington, Kans.; Ozark, Ark.; Alva, Altus, and Poteau, Okla.; and Seymour, Tex. The only other record of a temperature of 120° east of the Rockies was at Tishomingo, Okla., in July, 1943.

In the Central Valley of California somewhat higher temperatures are likely once in a century, and in the California–Arizona desert, Yuma is likely to experience 123° and Death Valley 130°. The extreme heat of the two areas is also pronounced on maps of mean maximum and of mean daily temperatures; the likelihood of very high readings on the Great Plains, however, is not indicated by any other map. Average temperatures, even average extremes, are lower in the Dakotas than in Texas, but readings of more than 115° are more likely in the central and northern Great Plains than in the southern.

Study of the two maps presented here may yield other information of interest and value. However, their chief purpose is to demonstrate the results of a method of climatic analysis that permits ready and rational comparison of extreme temperatures at various places. Even more important, the method as outlined permits an estimate of the extreme temperature (or other condition) likely to occur in a given period, and thus permits realistic use of the available data on temperature and other extremes.

FOOTNOTES

[1] E. J. Gumbel, "The Return Period of Flood Flows," *Annals of Mathematical Statistics*, **12** (1941), 163–190; "On the Frequency Distribution of Extreme Values in Meteorological Data," *Bulletin of the American Meteorological Society*, **23** (1942), 95–105; "Simplified Plotting of Statistical Observations," *Transactions of the American Geophysical Union*, **26** (1945), 69–82; *The Statistical Forecast of Floods* (Columbus: Ohio Water Resources Board, 1948).

[2] *The Climatic Handbook for Washington, D. C.*, U. S. Weather Bureau, Technical Paper No. 8, (1949).

[3] *Climatic Summary of the United States*, U. S. Weather Bureau Bulletin W, (1930).

[4] This table is on file at the Society's building. Photostat copies may be obtained.

[5] A. Court, "How Hot is Death Valley?" *Geographical Review*, **39** (1949), 214–220.

[6] *Climate and Man, Yearbook of Agriculture 1941*, U. S. Dept. of Agriculture (Washington: U.S.G.P.O., 1941), pp. 708–709 (maps).

[7] A. Court, "Coldest Temperatures in the United States," *Weatherwise*, **4** (1951), 136–139.

6

ASPECTS OF THE MORPHOMETRY OF A "POLYCYCLIC" DRAINAGE BASIN

RICHARD J. CHORLEY

The drainage basin of the river Heddon in north Devon (Ordnance Survey 1: 25,000, sheet 21/64) is an excellent example of what is conventionally termed "polycyclic landscape." The higher parts of the basin are made up of a gently sloping surface which contrasts strikingly with the steep-sided valley which forms the lower part of the stream system (Fig. 1). This separation of the surface into distinct slope elements is also reflected in the profile of the river Heddon (Fig. 2), which exhibits two "graded" reaches, with a possible third in the most headward part, separated by a marked break of slope at about 520 feet. The curve of the second graded reach has been extended until it attains zero slope at about 460 feet. These data, like the rest here employed (measured with chartometer and compensating polar planimeter), were obtained from the Ordnance Survey map of the area on a scale of 1: 25,000, and form the basis of what is a short essay on technique, rather than a contribution to the detailed denudation chronology of Exmoor.

The mathematical form which best approximates to the graded reach of a stream has long been a subject for debate. British workers have found the best fit to be empirically given by a logarithmic curve, whereas American geologists have been more impressed with the exponential relationships between distance downstream and the postulated factors which theoretically control stream bed slope.[1] Thus Krumbein, Shulits, and Holmes, for example, have stressed the connection between the particle size of bed material and the slope of the stream bed, and a mathematical model has been constructed on this basis.[2] One author, however, recognizes a greater complexity in the interaction of factors which control the longitudinal profile of a graded stream and believes that the changes of these controlling factors ". . . are usually such as to decrease slope requirements in a downstream direction but, because none of them is systematic, the graded

Reprinted from *Geographical Journal*, **124** (1958), 370–374, by permission of the author and editor.

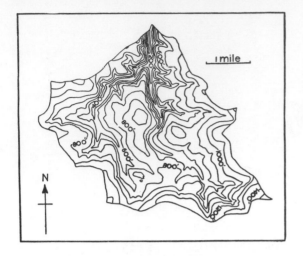

FIGURE 1. Heddon river basin

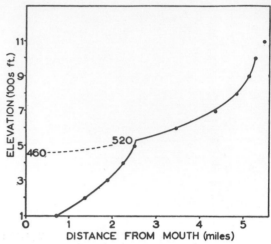

FIGURE 2. Longitudinal profiles of R. Heddon

profile cannot be a simple mathematical curve in anything more than a loose or superficial sense."[3]

A different method of dealing with longitudinal profiles is to treat the elevations along them as an ordinary statistical sample. The characteristic upward concavity of the profile will obviously skew the frequency distribution of the elevations very strongly toward the right, inasmuch as a majority of points on the profile lie at the lower elevations. Such a "skewness" suggests some similarity with a typical logarithmic normal distribution. Fig. 3 illustrates the characteristics of arithmetic and logarithmic normal frequency distributions, and it is of note that when the typically right-skewed frequency distribution of the logarithmic kind (A) is plotted against a logarithmic scale (B) it assumed the symmetrical, bell-shaped form of the normal distribution. Normal distributions, when plotted as cumulative frequencies on probability paper (C and D), employing the appropriate arithmetic or logarithmic scale on the abscissa, appear as straight lines, whereas skewed distributions produce curves. Thus when the percentage of the total length of the river Heddon below a corresponding elevation is plotted on logarithmic normal probability paper (Fig. 4), each of the reaches is sharply defined as a linear plot, in this instance giving a break of slope at about 530 feet. Such a method of identifying graded reaches might prove valuable for profiles which contain many complicated breaks of slope and for which very detailed surveys are available.

One feature, however, of recent attempts at developing denudation chronologies has been the uncritical acceptance of many breaks of stream slope as records of relative uplift; this is so despite the growing recognition that such breaks can result from relatively minor lithologic variations, from the sudden addition of discharge or load at a tributary junction, or from variations in composition and attrition of bed material.[4] Only when breaks of stream slope, particularly minor ones, can be demonstrated to be unrelated to any of the above possible causes can they be employed in any wider sense. The correlation of different breaks of slope, and of hypothetical base levels obtained by extrapolation, also give some source for dissatisfaction; statistical testing would give a much more objective and quantitative correlation probability than the subjective methods currently in use.

The distribution of elevations in the Heddon basin as a whole, represented by the hypsometric curve (Fig. 5), is also capable of more standard statistical treatment.[5] The typical form of the hypsometric curve for individual, one-cycle drainage basins suggests that the elevations of the whole basin surface are normally distributed.[6] This was tested for the Heddon basin by plotting the percentage area of the basin below corresponding elevations on arithmetic probability paper (Fig. 6), and this revealed, rather surprisingly, a linearity indicative of a normal distribution. The chi-square test provides an alternative quantitative method of testing normality of distribution, and provides a measure of the probability that a given fre-

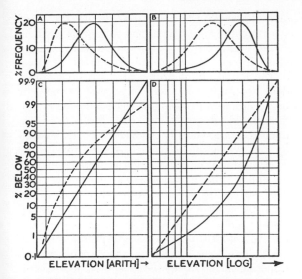

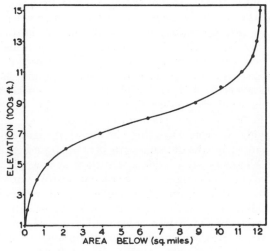

FIGURE 3. Frequency distributions of arithmetic normal (solid line) and of logarithmic normal (broken line) distributions, refered to (A) arithmetic and (B) logarithmic scales. Same distributions plotted below in cumulative form on (C) arithmetric and (D) logarithmic probability paper.

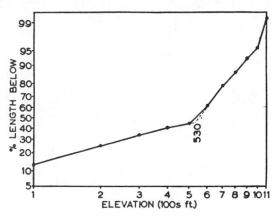

FIGURE 4. Logarithmic normal probability plot of percentage elevations, R. Heddon

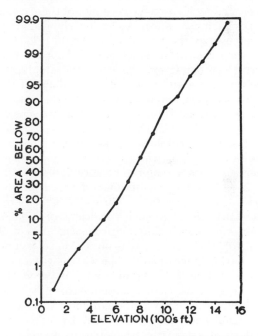

FIGURE 5. Hypsometric curve for Heddon basin

FIGURE 6. Arithmetic probability plot of percentage elevations in Heddon basin

quency distribution is representative of a normal distribution.[7] This normality, presented by the distribution of elevations within the Heddon basin, despite the fact that its surface is manifestly composed of two very different slope elements, can be explained in that each surface composes about half the total basin area and that the break of surface slope at about 720 feet

(Fig. 7) lies at about the midpoint of the present total relief of the basin. Where the formation of a lower surface at the expense of an upper one has progressed much more, or much less, completely, the frequency distribution of the elevations shows a characteristic "skewness."[8] In any event, the hypsometric curve as here employed is incapable of doing more than to

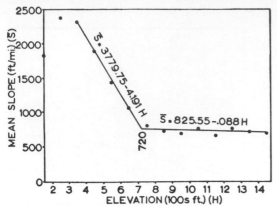

FIGURE 7. Plot of mean land slope versus elevation in Heddon basin

suggest the existence of a break of slope within the basin, without assisting much in its exact location.

If, however, the mean slope of each 100-foot contour strip is obtained, using the method suggested by Hanson-Lowe, a plot of these mean slopes against mean elevation immediately differentiates the two slope elements (Fig. 7).[9] Ignoring the mean slopes obtained for the two lowest contour strips, the least accurate due to the small area and to the elongate shape of the strips, two regressions were fitted by the method of least squares. These show that below a general elevation of 720 feet there is a decrease of mean land slope with increasing elevation; whereas, above this height, the surface of the drainage basin exhibits a uniform slope of 729 feet/mile (7°52′). A test of significance of trend for the mean land slopes above 720 feet (Fig. 7) indicates that the regression coefficient of -0.088 is not significantly different from zero ($0.30 < P < 0.40$); therefore, there is no reason to assume a variation in mean land slope with height above this elevation.[10] If the difference between the two regressions, each representative of a separate slope element, was less graphically obvious, its significance could be tested by using the analysis of covariance, which is a test to indicate whether a given plot of points on a graph can best be described by a single regression equation, or whether more than one is preferable.[11] It is not the purpose of this paper to discuss the operation of erosional mechanisms, but to describe some useful techniques which may be employed—in this instance with map data—to recognize and isolate some significant features of landscape geometry. The apparent discrep-

ancy between the elevation of the break of stream slope and that of the surface as a whole cannot, however, be passed over. It is commonly allowed that the existence of a break of slope in the longitudinal profile of a stream channel does not imply that any important changes of bed gradient will occur to the headward of the break; indeed, this assumption forms the basis upon which ancient base levels are extrapolated by the projection of graded stream curves. No such assumption regarding the inviolability of an upper subaerial surface can be made, however, when it is intersected and encroached upon by a lower surface of greater slope. Creep always tends to blur such an angle of junction, and to replace it by a convex profile much of which has been formed at the expense of the upper surface. One of the most striking features of the upper parts of the Exmoor slopes is their broad convexity of quite considerable radius; it is therefore not too surprising if this study of technique should imply that rounding action by creep should have destroyed the upper surface to an average level of over 700 feet, and should have extended the erosional effect of the cutting of the inner valley some 1400 feet in mean width beyond the hypothetical position of the break in land slope in cases where creep was not operative, and where such a break could be maintained as a sharp feature. This discrepancy between the elevations down to which the earlier elevated stream profile is maintained, and to which the earlier surface as a whole is preserved, perhaps explains why difficulties have been often encountered in trying to correlate the elevations of stream channel breaks of slope with breaks of gradient of the associated landscape surface as a whole.

What inferences on erosional history one tries to draw from the morphometry of regions exhibiting features such as those statistically expressed above is a matter of personal preference. However, such elaborate erosional time-sequences have been constructed, often based upon very subjective and uncritical treatments of the geometry of the landscape involved, that any attempt to place the initial analysis and description of the geometry of poly-cyclic landscapes on a more precise basis cannot but add authority to future attempts at developing denudation chronologies. Particularly is this so when such attempts depend on the conservative techniques of mathematical statistics.

FOOTNOTES

[1] J. F. N. Green, "The River Mole: Its Physiography and Superficial Deposits," *Proceedings of the Geological Association of London*, **45** (1934), 35–69. O. T. Jones, "The Upper Towy Drainage System," *Quarterly Journal of the Geological Society of London*, **80** (1924), 568–609.

[2] C. D. Holmes, "Stream Competence and the Graded Stream Profile," *American Journal of Science*, **250** (1952), 899–906; W. C. Krumbein, "Sediments and Exponential Curves," *Journal of Geology*, **45** (1937), 577–601; S. Shulits, "Rational Equation of River-Bed Profile," *Transactions of the American Geophysical Union*, **22** (1941), 622–630; A. N. Strahler, "Dynamic Basis of Geomorphology," *Bulletin of the Geological Society of America*, **63** (1952), 923–938.

[3] J. H. Mackin, "Concept of the Graded River," *Bulletin of the Geological Society of America*, **59** (1948), 463–512.

[4] A. O. Woodford, "Stream Gradients and Monterey Sea Valley," *Bulletin of the Geological Society of America*, **62** (1951), 799–852; E. Yatsu, "On the Longitudinal Profile of a Graded River," *Transactions of the American Geophysical Union*, **36** (1955), 655.

[5] S. W. Wooldridge, "The 200 foot Platform in the London Basin," *Proceedings of the Geological Society of London*, **39** (1928), 1.

[6] A. N. Strahler, "Hypsometric (Area-Altitude) Analysis of Erosional Topography," *Bulletin of the Geological Society of America*, **63** (1952), 1117–1142.

[7] F. E. Croxton and D. J. Cowden, *Applied General Statistics* (Englewood Cliffs, N.J.: Prentice-Hall, Inc., 1939). A. N. Strahler, "Statistical Analysis in Geomorphic Research," *Journal of Geology*, **62** (1954), 1–25.

[8] A. N. Strahler, "Hypsometric Analysis," *op. cit.*

[9] J. Hanson-Lowe, "The Clinographic Curve," *Geological Magazine*, **72** (1935), 180.

[10] P. A. Chenoweth, "Statistical Methods Applied to the Trentonian Stratigraphy in New York," *Bulletin of the Geological Society of America*, **63** (1952), 521–560.

[11] H. M. Walker, and J. Lev, *Statistical Inference* (New York: Holt, Rinehart & Winston, Inc., 1953).

7

THE INTERACTANCE HYPOTHESIS
AND BOUNDARIES IN CANADA:
A PRELIMINARY STUDY

J. ROSS MACKAY

In the study of geographic regions, boundaries are usually drawn even though it is recognized that they may be zonal to indeterminate. If there is any validity to a boundary, then it must separate regions that differ according to some specified criterion, such as terrain or language. The inhabitants separated by a boundary do not, except in very unusual circumstances, live in complete isolation from each other. On the contrary, a constant stream of human interactions flows back and forth across a boundary. People travel, visit, migrate, intermarry, telephone, telegraph, attend schools, send letters, export raw materials, and import finished products across boundaries. If we can estimate, with reasonable precision, the effect of physical and cultural boundaries (e.g., a river or political boundary) upon each type of interaction, we will possess a powerful tool for regional analysis and boundary studies. We might like to know, for example, how a long, un-bridged portion of the Ottawa River separates or unites the settlements on opposite shores when we specify, or wish to alter, a set of conditions. We can neither remove nor bridge the river, nor can we increase or decrease the size of the settlements, but we can do so in a statistical sense by means of an interactance model and thus compare before and after effects. We may find, for example, that a mile width of river has the same barrier effect for travel as a land distance of 100 miles. We know that the international boundary restricts free movement of peoples and goods between Windsor and Detroit, but we do not know just how effective the barrier is, since we cannot duplicate the conditions without a boundary. Perhaps for many types of human activities Windsor is, in geographical terms, nearer to Vancouver than

Reprinted from *The Canadian Geographer*; 11 (1958), 1–8, by permission of the author and editor.

to Detroit. The interactance hypothesis provides us with one approach to such boundary studies. It is the purpose of this paper to suggest the use of the interactance hypothesis in boundary studies in Canada and to discuss a nonlinear form of the interactance model.

THE INTERACTANCE HYPOTHESIS

The interactance hypothesis has been defined most fully by S. C. Dodd, whose model is shown in Eq. 1.[1]

$$(1) \qquad I = \frac{KTP_A P_B A_A A_B}{D}$$

I stands for interaction. It is nearly as varied in type as are the activities of man. Interactions may be economic, social, educational, recreational, and so forth. Trade between two cities is an economic interaction; migration between two cities is a social interaction; attendance at a university is an educational interaction, or so we are prone to think; and the visit of a tourist to a park is a recreational interaction. Interactions are measured in the appropriate units, such as dollars or number of people. K is a constant. It is the reciprocal of the total number of interactions of the groups concerned. T is the time element, such as a day or a week, over which interactions are measured. P_A and P_B are the populations of the two interacting groups. Population is used in the statistical sense where it refers to an aggregation of elementary units, such as number of people employed in manufacturing or volume of trade, and not in the restrictive sense of the total number of people within a given area. A_A and A_B are the specific indices of per capita activity of the populations P_A and P_B; examples would be average income per person or acreage of wheat per farm. D is a space dimension. It expresses distance or nearness and might be measured in miles, cost per mile, ease of access, time of travel, and so forth. The space dimension is particularly geographic, because it involves the concept of distribution.

In order to construct and test an interactance model, it is desirable to have at least ten to fifteen observed interactions. A group of five populations can combine in ten different ways to give ten interactions; a group of six can give fifteen interactions. Interactions among a minimum of five to six population groups should therefore be investigated before a statistically valid model can be constructed.

The interactance hypothesis is based upon the observational fact that groups of people tend to interact more as they become larger, and more "intense" in their activities. To illustrate with a familiar example, if other things are equal, we would normally expect to have more automobile traffic (i.e., interaction) between large cities (i.e., large P_A and P_B) than between small cities; between cities with a high percentage of automobiles per capita (i.e., high values of A_A and A_B) than with a small percentage of automobiles per capita, and between cities connected by paved highways (small D) rather than dirt roads. The interactance hypothesis enables us to study such interactions by means of a theoretical model that expresses the relationships existing among the variables of the types just mentioned. The hypothesis, in modified form, has been used in theoretical and applied studies in several disciplines, examples being: Stewart's potential of population;[2] Reilly's law of retail gravitation;[3] Ravenstein's laws of migration;[4] and Zipf's $P_1 P_2/D$ element.[5]

Interaction as given in Eq. 1 is assumed to vary directly with time, population, and activity, but inversely with distance. If population is doubled, interaction is doubled; if distance is doubled, interaction is halved. However, this may not be the case. It is quite possible that a population of 10,000 might generate more or less than twice the number of interactions of a population of 5,000. Likewise, a separation of 100 miles might exercise more or less than twice the effect of a separation of 200 miles. These possibilities should be examined. F. C. Iklé has tested an equation in which the exponent of P was 1.0. He then solved for the exponent of D, obtaining values of from .689 to 2.57 for certain airline and automobile traffic in the United States.[6] In a study of intercity travel desire recently completed at the University of Washington, various *predetermined* combinations of exponents for P and D were tested to see which gave the highest coefficient of correlation.[7] It was found that the square root of the population and the square of the distance yielded the highest coefficient of correlation for the several combinations tested. Swedish studies on migration have given values of the exponent of D of from 0.4

to 3.0.[8] There is good evidence, therefore, to show that the exponent of D might range considerably above or below 1.0. Less attention has been paid to the exponent of P, but there is also the possibility that it too might vary appreciably from 1.0. If the exponents of P and D can both vary from 1.0, Eq. 2 will represent the general case, of which Eq. 1 is a special case.

$$(2) \qquad I = \frac{KTP_A^M P_B^M A_A A_B}{D^N}$$

Iklé has discussed a method of solving for the exponent of D with 1.0 as the exponent of P.[9] His solution may be extended to cover the more general case of Eq. 2 by taking logarithms of both sides and then fitting a linear regression to the logarithms of the values by the least squares method. The unknowns, namely M and N, may then be determined. It needs hardly be emphasized that the derived values of M and N are not necessarily correct. There should be rational grounds for accepting the statistical results obtained before they are applied in further studies.

For a great many interactions, a simplification of Eq. 1 is quite adequate. By measuring interactions over unit time for areas with similar intensities of activities, T, A_A, and A_B may be disregarded and Eq. 1 reduced to Eq. 3.

$$(3) \qquad I = \frac{KP_A P_B}{D}$$

The Interactance Model and Boundary Study

In order to demonstrate the use of the interactance hypothesis in boundary studies, let us assume: (1) that equation 1 has been computed for a given interaction between pairs of Quebec cities; and (2) that the observed interactions between pairs of Quebec-Ontario cities comprise about 20 per cent of the interactions that would be obtained if both cities were in Quebec. The drop in interaction of 80 per cent is then a measure of the interaction differential between Quebec and Ontario. The reduced level of interaction across the interprovincial boundary might result from several factors acting singly or in combination. For example, only a portion of the population of each Quebec-Ontario city might

interact with the other; the activity of each Quebec-Ontario city might be reduced when they interact; or the distance factor might be increased in crossing the Quebec-Ontario cultural boundary. The interactance hypothesis does not identify which variables contribute to the lessened activity; more information is required to identify the model.[10] Even though the causative factor is unknown, the fall-off in interaction between Quebec-Ontario cities, as compared to Quebec-Quebec cities can be expressed in terms of the distance factor D. In the present example, an Ontario city interacts with a Quebec city as if it were five times as far away as it really is by comparison with a Quebec city of the same population and separation.

Boundary effects for two types of interactions are shown in Figs. 1–5. The interactions which have been used are volume of long-distance telephone traffic and marriages. These particular interactions were chosen because: other studies have shown that they follow, in general, the $P_A P_B / D$ relationship;[11] the raw data was obtainable; and the data linked places that were geographically far apart, such as Vancouver and Quebec city.

Long distance telephone traffic was obtained through the courtesy of the telephone companies concerned. Only traffic originating at Montreal, Quebec, and Sherbrooke has been plotted in the accompanying graphs, but similar results were also obtained in studying the flow patterns for Toronto, Vancouver, and Winnipeg. In most cases, destination data [were] obtained for at least fifty of the largest cities in Canada and twenty of the largest in the United States. Ideally, it would have been desirable to have separated long distance telephone traffic first into day and night calls, and then according to the purpose of the calls, e.g., business, personal, and administrative, but the data [were] unobtainable. In addition, the populations served by toll centers could not be precisely determined, but evidently city and toll center populations are numerically similar. Not all of the stations for which destination data [were] obtained appear in Fig. 1–5, because the volume of traffic to some cities was too small to plot on the scales that have been used. In order to have the figures as unencumbered as possible, no "units" are shown for the x-axis, because any unit system is purely arbitrary, depending upon the measures used for P and D. What is important is the pattern or scatter of the points and the slope of the trend, these being independent of the system of units used.

Long-distance telephone traffic originating at Montreal, Quebec, and Sherbrooke for the same ten-day period in 1956 is shown in Fig. 1. Total number of calls is plotted on the ordinate; $P_A P_B/D$ along the abscissa. P_A is the city of origin, namely Montreal, Quebec, or Sherbrooke. P_B is the city of destination; these are the seventeen largest cities in Quebec (excluding the city of origin) and the ten largest cities in Ontario. Straight-line distance in miles was used for D. Attempts were made to introduce cost factors for D, but since traffic was not separable into day and night calls, which vary in rate, cost factors were unsatisfactory. Despite the generalization introduced by using origin-destination straight-line distance for D, the agreement in results indicates that it is a reasonably satisfactory approximation to the true distance factor, whatever it may be. The points in Fig. 1 show two obvious trends, one of Quebec

cities, the other of Ontario cities. The range in population from Montreal to Grand'Mère, the smallest city plotted, is about 100 to 1, and yet the origin-destination data give a remarkably consistent pattern. Not only do Montreal's origin-destination data form a pattern by [themselves], but [they are] basically the same as that of Sherbrooke and Quebec. This agreement in interaction for cities so diverse in size and function as Montreal, Quebec, and Sherbrooke suggests that long distance telephone traffic tends to integrate overall conditions rather than to reflect a particular interest, such as business or administration. The Ontario cities also show a consistent pattern, but their trend line lies well below that of the Quebec cities. On the average, an Ontario city receives roughly a fifth to a tenth the telephone traffic of a Quebec city with the same $P_A P_B/D$ value. This may be interpreted as a measure of the Quebec-Ontario boundary. The cause of the drop in traffic cannot be determined at present, so it is premature to try to identify the elements in the equation. The fall-off might be due, for

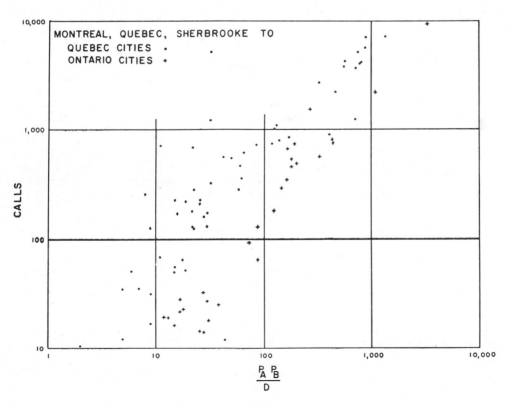

FIGURE 1

example, to a decline in A_A or A_B in crossing the boundary (e.g., some Quebec-Ontario traffic might be carried over teletype lines rather than telephone lines); to the fact that only a portion of P_A reacts with P_B (e.g., administrative calls are not exchanged between Quebec-Ontario); and so forth. Whatever the cause, an Ontario city reacts as if it were five to ten times as distant as a Quebec city of the same size.

In Fig. 2, traffic originating at Montreal for a ten-day period in 1954 is plotted against P_B/D for twenty-two of the largest cities in Quebec, twenty-nine in the rest of Canada, and eighteen in the United States. P_A (Montreal) is common to all, so it has been omitted. Clearly, traffic from Montreal to Quebec cities forms one pattern; traffic to cities in the English speaking provinces a second; and traffic to cities in the United States a third pattern. Traffic from Montreal to nearby English-speaking cities like Toronto behaves in the same general way as that for distant cities like Edmonton and Vancouver. The "boundary" between French/English-speaking cities may be equated to an

increased distance factor of 5 to 10; that of the international boundary to about 50. Thus the French-English boundary is relatively small compared to that of the international boundary, when both are expressed in terms of distance.

In Fig. 3, a regression line has been fitted to the Quebec cities shown in Fig. 2 on the assumption that the relationship is of the $P_A^M P_B^M / D^N$ form. P_A^M (Montreal) has been omitted, as it is common to all points. The equation reduces then to:

$$(4) \qquad I = \frac{K P_B^M}{D^N}$$

By taking logarithms of both sides we obtain:

$$(5) \quad \log I = \log K + M \log P_B - N \log D$$

This is the equation of a straight line so that K, M, and N can be solved by the least squares method. The values which concern us, namely M and N, are 1.1 and 0.9. These values differ little from the values of 1.0 used in Fig. 2.

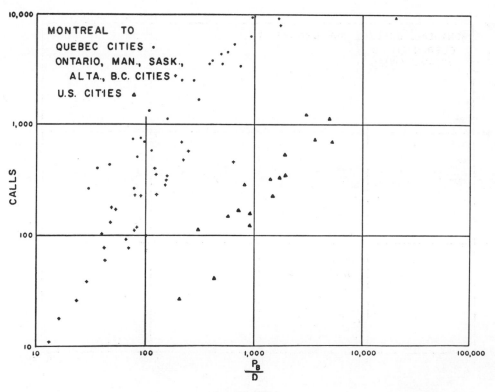

FIGURE 2

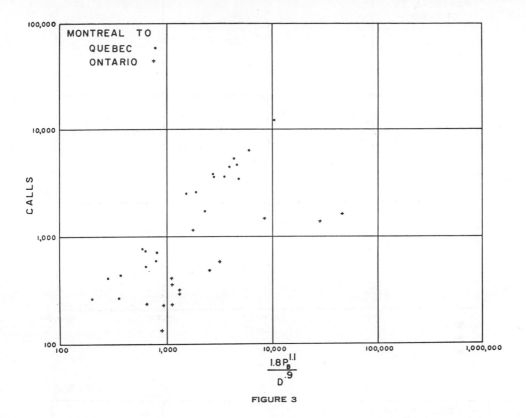

FIGURE 3

They suggest that the P_B/D relationship is quite adequate for traffic involving only Quebec cities. The Ontario cities were *not* used in calculating the regression line, but their positions have been plotted upon the basis of the $P_B^{1.1}/D^{.9}$ model obtained for the Quebec cities. The scatter of the Ontario cities is much greater than for the Quebec cities, since the model was derived for the latter.

A regression line calculated for the Ontario cities is shown in Fig. 4, the method of calculation being identical to that for the Quebec cities in Fig. 3. Exponents of 0.9 and 1.7 were obtained for P and D, respectively, that for D differing significantly from 1.0, thus suggesting a nonlinear relationship.

In Fig. 5, the number of marriages registered in Vancouver, with brides resident in Vancouver and grooms resident in other cities, has been plotted for the three years of 1952 to 1954.[12] The data for the three years has been combined, in order to give larger and more representative totals. Despite the scatter pattern of the cities, marriages of Vancouver brides to grooms res-

ident in British Columbia lie within one band; the cities of Toronto and Winnipeg lie slightly below the British Columbia band; the American cities of Seattle, Tacoma, and Bellingham also lie below the British Columbia band; and the predominantly French-speaking city of Montreal lies well below the British Columbia band. The trends in marriage data show a greater scatter than for telephone traffic, but this is not unexpected, because relatively small numbers of marriages (e.g., six to ten) are involved for many of the places plotted despite the three-year total used. Even so, boundary effects are obvious, although the interpretation is another matter, because it involves factors such as language. religion, migration, and age groups.

As the preceding examples illustrate, the interactance hypothesis may be used to give an expression of boundaries in terms of distance. If many more interactions were used, new meanings could be assigned to the boundaries. The interactance hypothesis provides, of course, only one of many quantitative approaches to boundary studies. Others, such as variance

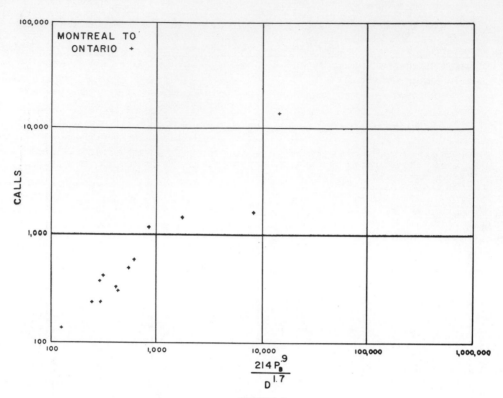

FIGURE 4

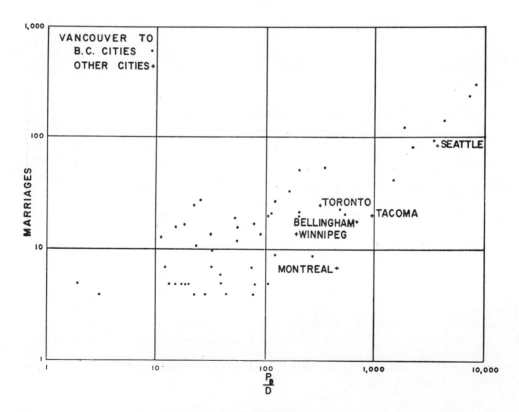

FIGURE 5

analysis, factor analysis, discriminant functions, and reflexiveness have their unique contributions to make to boundary studies.

CONCLUSIONS

These preliminary investigations show that the interactance hypothesis can be used to study some boundaries in Canada. A number of general conclusions can be drawn as a result of the investigations so far conducted. (1) Since Montreal, Quebec, and Sherbrooke differ greatly in size and urban function, yet show similar patterns in long-distance telephone traffic, such traffic seems to sum up the life of the cities, and not one facet of it (e.g., business or administration). (2) The drop in traffic from Montreal, Quebec, and Sherbrooke to the largest English-speaking cities in Canada is about a fifth to a tenth that of Quebec cities; it is about a fiftieth for cities in the United States. Thus the English-speaking Canadian cities behave as if they were five to ten times as far away as Quebec cities of the same size and separation and those in the United States as if they were fifty times distant. (3) Traffic among Quebec cities seems accurately expressed by the $P_A P_B/D$ model. (4) A nonlinear form of the model seems best for Quebec-Ontario cities (5) Marriage data for Vancouver give trends similar to long-distance telephone traffic.

FOOTNOTES

[1] S. C. Dodd, "The Interactance Hypothesis: A Gravity Model Fitting Physical Masses and Human Groups," *American Sociological Review*, **15** (1950), 245–256.

[2] J. Q. Stewart, "Empirical Mathematical Rules Concerning the Distribution and Equilibrium of Population," *Geographical Review*, **37** (1947), 461–485.

[3] W. J. Reilly, "Methods for the Study of Retail Relationships," *University of Texas Bulletin*, No. 2944 (1929).

[4] E. G. Ravenstein, "The Laws of Migration," *Journal of the Royal Statistical Society*, **43** (1885), 167–235; and **52** (1889), 241–305.

[5] G. K. Zipf, "The $P_1 P_2/D$ Hypothesis: The Case of Railway Express," *Journal of Psychology*, **22** (1946), 3–8.

[6] F. C. Iklé, "Sociological Relationship of Traffic to Population and Distance," *Traffic Quarterly* (1954), 123–136.

[7] Washington State Council for Highway Research, *State Interest in Highways*, (1952), 2.1–2.24.

[8] D. Hannerberg, T. Hägerstrand, and B. Odeving, *Migration in Sweden: A Symposium*, Lund Studies in Geography, Series B, No. 13 (1957), 112–120.

[9] Iklé, *op. cit.*, 129.

[10] The problem of identification is frequently encountered in similar studies, e.g., L. R. Klein, *Econometrics* (New York: Harper & Row, Publishers, 1953), pp. 17–18.

[11] For example, see: J.H.S. Bossard, "Residential Propinquity as a Factor in Marriage Selection," *American Journal of Sociology*, **38** (1932), 210–224; J. A. Cavanaugh, *Formulation, Analysis and Testing the Interactance Hypothesis*, unpublished Ph. D. thesis, University of Washington (1950); M. R. Davie and R. J. Reeves, "Propinquity of Residence Before Marriage," *American Journal of Sociology*, **44** (1939), 510–517; H. L. Green, *The Reach of New York City and Boston into Southern New England*, Cambridge, Massachusetts, unpublished Ph. D. thesis, Harvard University, (1952); R. C. Klove, "The Definition of Standard Metropolitan Areas," *Economic Geography*, **28** (1952), 95–104; G. A. Miller, "Population, Distance and the Circulation of Information," *American Journal of Psychology*, **60** (1947), 276–284; and G. K. Zipf, "Some Determinants of the Circulation of Information," *American Journal of Psychology*, **59** (1946), 401–421.

[12] The data [were] obtained through the cooperation of the Vancouver District Registrar's Office.

8

PHYSICS
OF POPULATION
DISTRIBUTION

JOHN Q. STEWART and WILLIAM WARNTZ

This report describes on-the-average regularities which have been proved to exist in the distribution of people within cities and in rural areas and across countries as a whole. A review is included of a good deal of previously published work, but new data are presented as well. In particular, none of the tables and figures has appeared in print before, although many of the tables are assembled from social physics notebooks of eight or ten years ago—when this sort of approach had not achieved its current degree of acceptability.

The "social mechanics" principles indicated in the present paper are necessarily inadequate to deal with other wide areas of human behavior which also have significance for social science. But then mechanics is only one aspect of physics. Space here is not available to describe how, by developing ideas about "social energies," the approach becomes powerfully broadened.

POPULATION DENSITIES WITHIN A CITY

Every city tends to conform to a common pattern of internal population distribution, although a variety of local disturbing factors may in individual cities obscure or severely modify it. Not a single city exists which would be so free from these as to exhibit exactly the standard pattern. The standard city is circular in shape. The density of population, D, within it is maximum at the center where it is D_o. The density drops radially from the peak in all directions, according to the exponential formula:

$$D = D_o \, 2^{-r/b}$$

where r is the distance from the center, and b

Reprinted from *Journal of Regional Science*, **1** (1958), 99–123, by permission of the authors and editor.

is a short distance which is a constant for the given city.

We call b the "halving distance," because every increase in r by that amount carries to a ring where the density is cut in half. Thus contours of equal density are concentric circles. Their common center is the center of the "residential city." (In the next section we shall consider the "occupational city.")

In 1940 and earlier, the standard city had a definite edge at some radius, a, where the edge density, D', was

$$D' = D_o\, 2^{-a/b}$$

D' being constant for all cities in the United States, and equal to about 2000 persons per square mile. The city's total population, P_c, is the integral of the density, D, taken over the whole area out to the boundary radius, a, successive ring by ring from center to edge. The area, A, of course is πa^2

The first indication of this pattern of concentric rings decreasing exponentially in population density followed from the observation that on the average the area, A, of a city was proportional to the three-fourths power of the population, P_c.[1] Table 1 presents the original statistics. The only reasonable mathematical formula for internal density distribution which can yield such a relation between area and a power of the population is the exponential one for D as a function of r which is given above.

Then study of 1940 census data for all tracted United States cities, as well as inspection of several actual cities, indicated the value of D'. To fit the three-fourths power rule, the halving distance, b, has to increase very slowly with the population P_c. In addition, examination of density variation within several tracted cities confirmed directly the tendency to the law of exponential decrease outward. That law independently has been published by the economist Colin Clark.[2] See also a note by Stewart.[3]

Table 2 gives further confirmation and clarification of the pattern, showing how the central density, D_o, depended on the population, P_c, in 1940. These data suggest that the halving distance, b, increases from about a third of a mile for the smallest cities, of 2500 population, to perhaps four miles for the largest ones. Note that D_o is roughly proportional to the square root of P_c. As population increases, the increased

"attraction" (demographic gravitation) between

TABLE 1

Evidence for the relation of the area to the population of U.S. cities, 1940

Rank of city	Log C	Rank of city	Log C	Rank of city	Log C
1	2.67	31–35	2.44	151–165	2.61
2	2.59	36–40	2.48	166–180	2.60
3	2.62	41–45	2.41	181–195	2.55
4	2.47	46–50	2.45	196–210	2.65
5	1.98	51–55	2.54	211–225	2.54
6	2.60	56–60	2.41	226–240	2.56
7	2.55	61–65	2.58	241–255	2.56
8	2.64	66–70	2.54	256–270	2.61
9	2.76	71–75	2.59	271–285	2.48
10	2.65	76–80	2.51	286–300	2.57
11	2.58	81–85	2.63	301–315	2.52
12	2.70	86–90	2.64	316–330	2.53
13	2.70	91–95	2.48	331–345	2.63
14	2.73	96–100	2.62	346–360	2.48
15	1.98	101–105	2.69	361–375	2.52
16–20	2.49	106–120	2.58	376–390	2.51
21–25	2.37	121–135	2.55	391–405	2.46
26–30	2.52	136–150	2.68	406–412	2.55

Log C is the logarithm to base 10 of C, where $C = P^{3/4}/A$, P being the population of any city and A the land area in square miles within its political limits (census of 1940). The rank in the first column is the order of their population size, New York being rank 1, Chicago 2, etc. Los Angeles, rank 5, is notorious for the excessive area within its city limits. The largest fifteen cities are listed individually. After that only medians are listed—of groups of five cities each to rank 105, then of groups of fifteen for the smaller cities (84,323 to 25,087). Where medians are tabulated, P is the median population of the group and A the median land area; as a rule these values do not then refer to the same city.

The same rule, the proportionality of area to the three-fourths power of population, held for the 140 metropolitan districts (listed in the 1940 census for all cities above 50,000); but for these the value of C in the formula is only 45 instead of 357.

In addition, five more values of log C were computed for medians of five groups of, respectively, 11, 11, 11, 41, 41 small cities each. These have median populations of 11,087, 8186, 6253, 4134, 2577, and median land areas of 3.9, 2.3, 1.8, 1.3, 1.2 square miles. For the five groups, log C was found to be, respectively, 2.44, 2.57, 2.59, 2.60, 2.48. This shows satisfactory agreement with the formula for cities as small as 2500. With the inclusion of these five, fifty-nine values of log C are listed. Their average is 2.553, corresponding to $C = 357$, and $A = P^{3/4}/357$. (Data compiled by Catherine Kennelly.)

TABLE 2

Peak densities for tracted cities, 1940

Number of cities	Median population	Median peak density
1	7,455,000	264,000
3	1,931,000	71,000
5	859,000	90,000
7	587,000	48,000
11	368,000	32,000
13	282,000	28,000
13	152,000	35,000
7	86,000	29,000

From city maps published by the Census for the sixty cities for which population by census tracts was listed in 1940, the tract of highest population density in each city was determined from estimation of tract areas. These densities are presented in the form of medians for small groups of cities arranged by size of city. The sixty individual cities ranged in size from that of New York to that of Macon, Ga. (pop. 58,000). The median densities of the densest tracts are given in people per square mile of the tract area (areas of streets not deducted). Scales of miles published with the census maps of cities were in some instances suspect —indeed the computed density for the peak tract of Atlantic City, N. J., was at first so out of line with the general relation that the published scale was checked on the ground and found to be in error. The resultant correction eliminated the discrepancy.

Other scattered inspections on the ground in the 1940's indicated that the peak densities for typical smaller cities likewise tended to decrease regularly with population, to about 4000 per square mile for cities of 2500, the census lower limit. Thus United States cities in 1940 tended to conform to a common pattern of internal population distribution, with peak density (in units of persons per square mile) roughly equal to seventy-five times the square root of a city's total population. But see also Table 4.

people weighs down on and compresses the central population.

Evidence for the proportionality of the area, A, to the three-fourths power of P_c for cities in the United States and Europe was found to extend back at least to 1890, and there can be little doubt that cities were so structured a long time ago. Table 3 and Fig. 1, compiled recently by Warntz, exhibit the same rule for British cities in 1951. Table 4 shows that cities in areas where general potential of population[4] is low tend to have larger areas than others of the same size class located where the base potential (i.e., potential in the adjoining rural district produced by the remainder of the country) is high. This confirmed also in the British study.

Full data as to the effect of base potential of population in changing D_o, D', and b have not been compiled. It must be emphasized that the center of population density is not the business center except in the smallest cities. Of interest is the slow increase in the number of stories in dwellings in the central region of peak density from the smallest to the largest cities. Their height rises from one or two stories in cities of a few thousand people to six or seven stories in walk-up tenements in New York's Lower East Side.

To explain the sharp-edge density of a city —a fall in a few hundred feet from 2000 people per square mile to rural densities of less than 200—one resorts to the concept of "cohesion" among city dwellers. The provision of the urban facilities which convert farm acreage into city lots requires joint cooperation supported by the inhabitants. Similarly, the molecules within a water drop stick together, and their mutual cohesional energy supports the "surface tension" of their boundary. Molecules cannot freely "evaporate" across the boundary—unless by addition of heat the temperature is raised to the boiling point, when cohesion is overcome and the surface tension and the boundary itself disappear. Molecules in a gas have independent careers and do not so stick together.

Over and above the capital energy released in any region, rural or urban, by demographic gravitation, additional energy is released from cohesion in a city. This shows itself in increased activities of various sorts—more local motor traffic, more local telephone calls. In large cities demographic gravitation is relatively more important, and cohesion in small ones.

We can also speak of "adhesion," a clinging of people to desirable land (or, negatively, their repulsion from unfavorable sites). A main transportation route running out of a city is an example of desirable land, and despite the gravitational attraction of the city, residences "rise" along it as water rises in a capillary tube (because of adhesion to the glass). But glass repels mercury (relative to the force of cohesion of liquid mercury particles for one another), so a surface of mercury is depressed within an inserted capillary tube. Similarly, people tend to avoid areas naturally or artificially "unattractive."

TABLE 3

Areas and populations of cities in England and Wales, 1951

Rank	City	Population (in thousands)	Area (in thousands of acres) Actual	Expected
1	London	3,348	74.8	105
2	Birmingham	1,112	51.1	46
3	Liverpool	790	27.3	35
4	Manchester	703	27.3	32
5	Sheffield	513	39.6	26
6	Leeds	505	38.3	25
7	Bristol	442	26.4	23
8	Nottingham	306	16.2	17
9	Kingston-upon-Hull	299	14.1	16
10	Bradford	292	25.5	16
11	Newcastle-upon-Tyne	292	11.1	16
12	Leicester	285	17.0	16
13	Stoke-on-Trent	275	21.2	15
14	Coventry	258	19.1	15
15	Croydon	250	12.7	14
16	Cardiff	244	15.1	14
17	Portsmouth	233	9.2	14
18	Harrow	219	12.6	13
19	Plymouth	209	13.1	13
20	Ealing	187	8.8	12
21–25	—	180	8.4	11
26–30	—	163	12.5	10
31–35	—	147	10.3	9.5
36–40	—	141	8.1	9
41–45	—	121	4.3	8
46–50	—	115	6.6	8
51–55	—	110	8.0	7.5
56–60	—	106	7.0	7.5
61–70	—	103	6.5	7
71–80	—	85	8.1	6.5
81–90	—	81	7.0	6
91–100	—	73	4.7	5.5
101–110	—	68	8.2	5
111–125	—	66	5.2	5
126–140	—	58	5.8	4.5
141–157	—	53	6.0	4.5

Our lakefront cities are not circular, but are drawn out as semiellipses as the result of adhesion to the shore. Population density in the Pine Barrens of New Jersey has been below that in neighboring fertile land in every census from 1790 on. A small city in a narrow valley is elongated—although the demographic gravitation usually is strong enough to crowd houses on steep slopes near the center.

While we have no adequate explanation as yet for the causes of the standard city pattern, cohesion must play a major role, along with demographic gravitation—and adhesion can account for some of the observed distortions.

The daily, even hourly, movings about of people increase with technological and economic advancement—just as the kinetic energy of molecules in the physical world increases with temperature. One's daily observations show how the automobile (much more effectively than the older forms of transport) operates to lower the boundary tension of cities. Widespread electric power networks, consolidated rural schools, state police protection of rural residents, and so

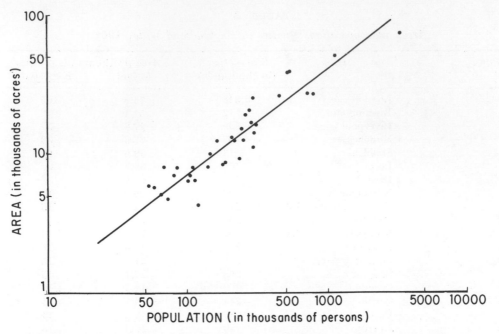

FIGURE 1. Relation of area to population for English and Welsh cities, 1951

In Figure 1 land area in acres has been plotted against population on log-log paper for the 157 English and Welsh cities of over 50,000 persons in 1951. Land areas are in statute acres for the official political units (including inland water) as reported in the General Register Office's Census 1951, England and Wales, Preliminary Report, London, 1951. The leading twenty cities are shown individually. The next forty cities are indicated by means of medians of area and population for groups of five each. Groups of ten are employed for the next fifty cities. Following are two groups of fifteen each and finally one of seventeen. The above line indicates that the area of a city varies directly as the three-fourths power of the population. The equation relating area and population and used to compute "expected" values in Table 3 was found by a linear least squares solution of the logarithmic values of the variables for the first twenty cities. Stated in the power form this equation is: Area (in acres) equals 1.33 times population to the three-fourths power. If areas are to be stated in square miles, then the formula becomes: Area equals population to the three-fourths power divided by 481. (The coefficient of correlation, r, was found to be 0.87.) Compare this value of 481 to the ones similarly obtained in the United States of 357 in 1940 and 400 in 1890. In each of these cases the exponent of population was found to be three-fourths. Grouped data for the remaining 137 cities were also plotted in Figure 1 and indicate that the same relationship holds. The strong and well defined relationship of area to population is demonstrated.

Such scatter around the lines as exists can be further reduced by recourse to the macroscopic variable, base

potential of population. Examination of the data clearly reveals that high potentials tend to constrict the area whereas at low potentials cities of a given population tend to occupy a larger area than indicated by the relationship of population alone. The effect of base potential is more pronounced for the less populous cities. (Potentials for the United Kingdom are mapped in Figure 2.) In the final analysis, each city is a unique case and a complete explanation would entail a complex of microscopic factors such as local topography, a multitude of personal decisions, and the like. The point to be stressed is that social scientists must learn the value of first approximations and develop the abilities to make them. Of course the local planner whose job is an engineering one must learn to appreciate both the general and the particular.

on, have the same effect. Very important also is the fan of good highways extending out from every city, built and maintained at general expense rather than by direct assessment of those who choose to live along them. The combination of increased real incomes per capita with state and federal subsidies for local improvements and for rural amenities is breaking down the old constant high-edge density. In "star" patterns along the highways each city now in effect extends out well beyond the old bounding radius that was set by the high D'.

TABLE 4

Area of cities: Variation with base potential and size

Population	Potentials of population				
	170,000	260,000	370,000	520,000	730,000
1,000,000+	—	—	172	127	299
500,000	—	—	61	46	—
200,000	45	53	38	18	19
100,000	50	38	20	19	10
50,000	13	14	10	10	5
33,000	11	12	9	7	6
25,000	7	9	6	6	4

All the 412 United States cities over 25,000 population in 1940 are represented. Their areas in square miles are presented in terms of median areas for groups of cities classified by population and by "base potential of population." The latter is the potential of population produced in the neighborhood of a city by all other people in the country, excluding those in the city itself. The rows refer to cities of the indicated population classes: namely, over 1,000,000, 500,000 to 1,000,000, . . . 25,000 to 33,000. The columns run according to base potentials, with median values 170,000, 260,000, 370,000, 520,000, 730,000—in 1940.

Evidently, deviations in city areas from the one-variable relation of Table 1 are in part systematic, being well correlated with base potential as a second variable. Higher values of the latter are associated with a "compression" in city areas (related no doubt to greater land values of surrounding rural acreage). Warntz's examination of a number of British cities indicates the same effect (Table 3).

The edge density now has perhaps fallen until it is almost indistinguishable from the rural density of the general countryside.

Plausibly, the standard city pattern is not otherwise changed. But many millions of people are listed now in the census as rural, nonfarm dwellers who might more properly be listed as urban. If this is so, the 1960 count of the urban fraction will, by former standards, be low by as much as 10 per cent.

Already in 1950, when the total population of the United States was 150,700,000, and there were 4284 cities, empirical regularities which had held from the first census[5] would have suggested an urban fraction of 64 per cent, instead of the tabulated 58.8. The reduction in the edge density of cities has changed the old balance of city and country. Further investigation is needed to arrive at a full theoretical explanation of the intraurban equilibrium—the density pattern outlined above and the changing rural-urban equilibrium. "Microscopic" studies of cities one at a time emphasize local distortions and necessarily have failed to reveal the existence of the standard city pattern.[6]

"Natural law" has been demonstrated to hold in social science as in physical science. City and regional planners who ignore tendencies of mass behavior do so at peril of serious failure in their designs.

REMARKS ON OTHER CHARACTERISTICS OF CITIES

The residential city pattern has impressed itself also upon urban statistics other than those for population distribution. A correlation of urban rents with population and base potential existed in 1940 (before rent controls were effective as another influence).[7] Table 5, having the same sort of arrangement as Table 4, reveals the same two-variable dependence for municipal taxes per capita as for areas upon population and base potential—although where high values of the latter reduce the area they tend to increase the tax. Table 6 shows a like dependence in the excess of urban births over deaths per 1000 people.

Thus it is clear that the customary grouping of city statistics by size class alone, regardless of base potential, can obscure significant regularities. Base potential is a macroscopic variable, which no amount of microscopic study can reveal.

The density pattern discussed in the first section is for the residential city, as has been

TABLE 5

Municipal taxes per capita: By city size class and base potential

| Population | Potentials of population | | | | |
	170,000	260,000	370,000	520,000	730,000
1,000,000+	—	—	36	38	73
500,000	—	—	37	72	—
200,000	19	29	18	54	70
100,000	19	16	16	41	52
50,000	17	15	15	57	50
33,000	14	22	14	37	51
25,000	14	19	14	38	39

The form is identical with that of Table 4, but with medians of municipal taxes, in dollars per year per capita in 1940, presented for the same 412 United States cities. Whereas higher base potential compressed the areas, it increased the city taxes.

TABLE 6

Excess of urban births over deaths: By city size class and base potential

| Population | Potentials of population | | | | |
	170,000	260,000	370,000	500,000	730,000
1,000,000+	—	—	6.2	2.4	3.5
500,000	—	—	4.6	2.8	—
200,000	9.2	5.8	4.3	3.1	3.4
100,000	6.0	7.1	6.4	2.5	4.2
50,000	8.4	4.9	6.0	3.2	3.2
33,000	11.1	4.8	6.7	4.9	5.0
25,000	9.7	7.6	5.8	5.5	4.9

Same 412 cities as in Tables 4 and 5 (1940). Listed are medians of the excess of urban births over deaths (per 1000 total population annually). Here base potential was even more effective than city size in reducing the excess.

stated. Before the advent of modern rapid transit, the "occupational city"—the spatial distribution of people at their jobs within cities —necessarily closely coincided with the residential city. Nowadays it seems that proper census statistics—which should be taken on a sampling basis—would define the occupational city, superimposed upon the residential one.

We may guess that the mathematical equations for the two would be the same, and that the two "cities" would differ only in the numerical values of the parameters, P_c, A, a, D_o, b, D'. (From discussion above it is clear that these six represent only two independent variables, P_c and D'—providing we ignore the effect of base potential, which is a third independent variable.)

Observations as one travels about the country indicate that the same factors which have reduced edge density, D', for the residential city

have likewise reduced it for the occupational city. We shall return to this point below.

Hitherto unpublished data compiled from the 1940 United States census by Catherine Kennelly relate to the distribution among leading cities of a few sample occupations. Just as the city residential populations conform to the well-known "rank-size," or Pareto, rule,[8] so also do the special sub-populations of residents listed city by city in specified occupations.

The rank-size rule states that, R being the rank of a given city in the list, the population for it equals MR^{-n}, M being the population of the largest city of rank 1, and n an exponent constant for the sequence of all cities. When P_c is thus ranked, n for United States cities has long been unity, with New York at rank 1. If now "authors" are counted, New York again in 1940 had the largest contingent, 2765 of them, and the exponent n remained unity. Los Angeles ranked 2, whereas in the total population list it was 5. Denver was 7 instead of 24; Cambridge, Mass., 26 instead of 78; and Buffalo 42 instead of 14.

For real estate agents and brokers, n was again unity. New York led with 10,884; Miami ranked 17 instead of 48; Pittsburgh 22 instead of 10. For operatives making automobiles and auto equipment, n was roughly 3/2; Detroit ranked 1 instead of 4; Flint was 2 instead of 56; New York was 12. This sort of statistic is a useful addition to the methodology of classifying cities with respect to their assumed special roles—a tricky business.[9]

What would one mean by the population, P_e, of the occupational city? It would be the number of individuals whose places of employment lie within the boundary of a given city. Walter Isard emphasizes three factors which relate to the concentration or dispersal of places of employment.[10]

The first of these, economy of scale, is related in part to the technological factors in a given industry and to the limited divisibility of certain factors of production. For certain kinds of manufacturing, low per unit costs of output can be achieved when many units per time period are produced at one location by a single firm. Thus mass production economies up to a certain level of output tend to concentrate a large output at a given geographical point.

In the second place, economies of localization may be experienced when several similar firms in an industry cluster around a given geographical point in close proximity to one another.

Third, urban economies which depend upon city utilities and facilities, local labor supply, etc., have brought the plants into actual cities.

Today ample observable evidence makes it clear that the lowering of a city's edge density for industry is becoming even more pronounced than for residences. No large-scale "decentralization" is resulting. Our once tightly bound cities surround themselves with "evaporated" dwellings and plants—but the escape is only from local urban cohesion and not from the major national demographic gravitation. Only if the level of real national income increases tremendously will the high-density concentrations of residence and industry in the existing "manu-facturing belt" thin out by removals to outlying situations of low population potential. To maintain the level of sociological intensity when people move farther apart demands that genuinely new and adequately profitable resources be tapped thereby.[11] Even then an associated increase in the birth rate probably would tend to maintain existing peaks of potential.

RURAL DENSITY: INTERPENETRATING REGIONS

Figure 2 is a hitherto unpublished map of population potentials for the United Kingdom, 1951. It permits testing there the relation of rural population density to the potential of population (produced by all the people). Results

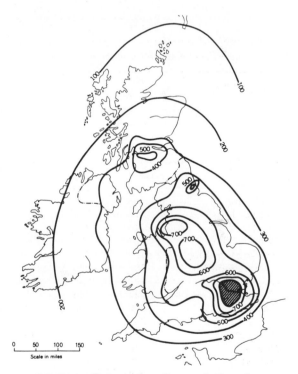

FIGURE 2. Potentials of population in thousands of persons per mile in the United Kingdom, 1951

Contours of the "potentials of population" for the United Kingdom, 1951. Potential is a measure of the propinquity of people in the aggregate. Each individual contributes to the total potential at any place by an amount equal to the reciprocal of his distance away. This map of lines of equipotential of population in the

United Kingdom, presented here for the first time, was drawn by means of logical contouring from values computed for 99 control points including the geographic centers of counties in England, Scotland, Wales, the Isle of Man, Northern Ireland, and the Irish Free State. The contours shown portray the base potentials from which each local city peak rises. The values of potential range from less than 100,000 persons per mile in the Shetland Islands to more than 1,900,000 persons per mile in the London Basin. If the influence at a distance of the rest of Europe's population were included in the computation of U. K. potentials, these potentials of course would be everywhere higher. The effect would be most pronounced in the southeast declining toward the northwest. Examination of the general European map in John Q. Stewart, *Coast, Waves and Weather*, Boston, 1945, p. 166, shows that the general pattern of the contours over the United Kingdom would be little changed however. Special thanks are owed to David Neft, Christopher Warntz, and Francis Barkoczy for assistance in computing and drafting this map.

TABLE 7

Potentials of population and rural population densities, England and Wales, 1951

County	Potential of population (in thousands of persons per mile)	Rural densities (in persons per square mile) Actual	Expected
Surrey	1,040	383	620
Derbyshire	786	386	350
Lancashire	780	298	345
Hertfordshire	775	364	340
Bedfordshire	745	235	315
Warwickshire	737	232	305
Nottinghamshire	723	234	295
Buckinghamshire	709	286	285
Staffordshire	703	234	280
Yorkshire (W. R.)	694	233	270
Essex	689	208	265
Leicestershire	665	257	250
Cheshire	661	251	245
Durham	636	378	225
Oxfordshire	628	183	220
Kent	626	262	215
Worcestershire	604	202	205
Northamptonshire	573	146	180
Gamorganshire	569	453	180
Denbighshire	563	149	175
Gloucestershire	561	246	175
Berkshire	558	285	170
Sussex	557	233	170
Shropshire	550	120	165
Rutlandshire	542	126	160
Monmouthshire	541	119	160
Hampshire	536	215	160
Flintshire	533	332	155
Cambridgeshire	526	163	150
Herefordshire	516	93	145
Huntingdonshire	506	122	140
Suffolk	501	142	137
Wiltshire	499	163	135
Somersetshire	483	162	130
Lincolnshire	482	122	128
Radnorshire	481	30	127
Norfolk	450	155	111
Yorkshire (N. and E. R.)	449	91	110
Breconshire	443	55	107
Northumberland	440	54	106
Dorsetshire	432	122	103
Caernarvonshire	422	102	97
Merionethshire	412	40	92
Westmorland	404	51	89
Montgomeryshire	402	38	88
Anglesey	397	121	86
Cardiganshire	395	53	85
Cumberland	394	89	85
Carmarthenshire	381	112	79
Pembrokeshire	335	79	60
Devonshire	333	104	60
Cornwall	301	131	49

Presented here in tabular form are the data of Fig. 3. Fifty-two counties in England and Wales are shown. (London and Middlesex counties had no rural population in 1951.) The potential of population values (given above in thousands of persons per mile) are the ones computed as control point values for the drawing of the map in Fig. 2. Actual density of population in rural districts (averaged by county) was obtained from the 1951 census data. The "expected" rural density was computed in the following way: Let D = rural density in persons per square mile and V = potential of population in persons per mile, then $D = 5.55 \times 10^{-10} V^2$.

Of course potential of population does not give final accuracy. It is, however, a single macroscopic integrative index which introduces a powerful unifying first approximation into the study of the geographical variation of sociological phenomena. Its effects must be supplemented by local factors in individual cases. The ruggedness of the terrain in such Welsh counties as Radnor, Montgomery, and Merion presumably offers a strong deterrent to rural settlement, whereas the gentler slopes and more fertile soils in certain other places encourage it.

are given in Fig. 3 and Table 7. Once again the rural density, D_R (in persons per square mile) is found to vary as the square of the potential, V (in persons per mile). We have

$$D_R = kV^2$$

where k (with the units stated) is determined for England and Wales as roughly 5.55×10^{-10}

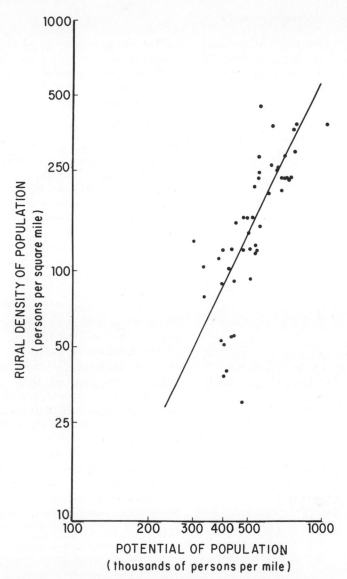

FIGURE 3. Density of population in rural districts and potential of population, English and Welsh Counties, 1951

The density of population in rural districts (averaged by counties) in England and Wales (in persons per square mile) for the 1951 census was found to be equal to 5.55×10^{-10} times potential of population (in persons per mile) to the second power. (The least squares coefficient of correlation, r, is 0.70.) The same exponent of potential has been found in the observation of various other groupings of people. Therefore potential of population at a point as a macroscopic factor serves to provide a means of first approximation of the rural density over the area around that point. This estimate makes possible a better understanding of the significance of local or microscopic factors. (See also Table 7.)

Table 8 compares with this other values of k found as multipliers in the same proportionality of D_R to V^2 in the United States at different dates, in Europe, and in Mexico. Respective total populations, P_T are listed, along with corresponding rural populations, P_R, and the ratio, w, of rural to total population. Tabulated also for each case is the computed value of a certain pure number, q, derived as follows:

Let A be the total area over which the populations P_T and P_R are dispersed. Therefore

$$P_R = \int D_R dA = K \int V^2 dA$$

where k, being constant throughout the area, can be written outside the integral sign. The integration is over the entire area. Let there be a pure number q, where

$$q = \frac{P_T^2}{\int V^2 dA}$$

then

$$k = \frac{P_R}{P_T^2} \cdot q$$

and, since

$$w = \frac{P_R}{P_T}$$

$$k = \frac{wq}{P_T} \text{ or } q = \frac{P_T \cdot k}{w}$$

Inasmuch as the potential V is that produced at any point by the whole population, P_T, divided by distance, while area always has the dimension of the square of distance, $\int V^2 dA$ has the dimension P_T^2, and q comes out dimensionless, a pure number, as is w.

Table 8 shows that q is remarkably stable from case to case. For a population uniformly distributed over a circular disk (Table 10), q is readily computed as about 0.11.

The listed values of k in Table 8 were obtained by fitting a median straight line of slope 2, on log-log graph paper, to plotted values of observed D_R at various points of known potential, V. Then q was computed from the said k in each case. Now q could have been determined directly by summing terms $V^2 dA$.

It can be shown that $\int V^2 dA$ computed over an assigned area for a fixed total population, P_T, is larger if the population is strongly concentrated near the center of the area — and smaller if instead most of the people are placed near the boundary rim of the area. Hence a small value of q indicates central concentration of the population; a medium value of q indicates roughly uniform distribution; and a larger q means boundary concentration.

So we have in q, thus computed, a new general index of distribution.

If, in computing V, people are assigned different weights, it is required to take P_T not as the sum of the actual people, but as the sum of the product of people by their respective weights. None of the cases listed in Table 8 involved weights other than unity throughout. But weights suggested in different sections of the United States in 1940 would have increased the effective value of P_T by about 11,000,000 standard people.

The tendency of rural density to be proportional to the square of the potential, across a great country, is a well-established fact. This indicates that such a country as the United States possesses demographic unity of a certain type. The applicability of the rank-size rule for

TABLE 8

Parameters for rural population density

Region	P_T (millions)	P_R (millions)	$10^{12}k$	w	q
United States 1900	76.0	45.8	880	0.603	0.111
1930	122.8	53.8	425	0.438	0.119
1940	131.7	57.2	351	0.435	0.106
Europe, 1930's	499.7	321.8	149	0.644	0.116
Mexico, 1930	16.4	11.0	3820	0.671	0.093
England & Wales, 1951	43.7	8.4	555	0.192	0.126

The columns listed, respectively, for six different cases studied, total population, rural population, the value of k (multiplied by a million million), the numerical ratio, w, of rural population to total population, and, finally, another pure number, q, defined as equal to $P_T k/w$ (see text). In each case D_R, the rural density anywhere in the country, was approximately kV^2, V being the potential of population at the point, and k a parameter constant over the country at the time. The value of k as listed was determined by a median fit to the observed values of D_R, without any regard to the later computation of q. The greatest relative concentration of population near the center is indicated for Mexico, because q comes out smallest there.

cities also indicates a unity. Therefore we conclude that any subdivision into separated "regions" can have only special sorts of meaning —there are no unique regions.

The fact that there are no unique regions has already been recognized in the wide use by regional analysts of two classes of regions: the "homogeneous" and the "nodal." As an example of the homogeneous, there are regions where the rural density runs rather consistently high or low—the Pine Barrens of New Jersey being an example of low density of population in every census from 1790 on. This is a kind of homogeneous region which is identifiable by its systematic deviation from a general regularity. Besides the proportionality of rural density to the square of the potential, other demographic or economic terms are known to vary as the square or as some other power of potential. For each such relation across the country, systematic deviations of actual from expected values may define a different set of regions.

Examples of nodal regions are the campus of a seasoned, privately endowed, "national" university and the dispersed residences of its students, a metropolitan newspaper and its territory, a seaport and its hinterland. They are all very special: the hinterland of a given port may differ for different commodities. The competition of nodal regions of a given sort may be "interpenetrating," as for colleges, or "all-or-none," as for newspapers in different great cities. Thus sales of the old St. Louis *Star Times* by counties around the city were proportional to the respective potentials of population there of the counties, but only out to where that newspaper's territory was rather sharply bounded by competition of papers in Kansas City, Chicago, Memphis. In contrast, leading colleges each draw students from every part of the country.

Even where subdivision into regions is for administrative purposes, as into states, counties, Federal Reserve districts, relations to population potential (or to income potential) make themselves evident, again confirming the general sociological unity of the country.[12]

Some Fundamentals of the Gravity Model

The recent rapid increase in the number of papers and articles employing the so-called "gravity models," while attesting (however belatedly) to the fact that distance is truly a dimension of social systems, has unfortunately brought with it much confusion concerning the exponent of distance to be employed. Whereas the "weights" assigned to people must be adjusted to fit observations, the function of distance is not such an arbitrarily adjustable parameter.

It appears that at present, potential of population, V, is the most widely known aspect of the gravity model. Knowledge of numbers of people, P, and their distances apart, r, are at once necessary and sufficient for the computation of potentials and the ultimate plotting of lines of equipotential on a map. Other demographic measures which can also be derived from these primitive quantities or "dimensions," and which are consistent with potential of population, include density, D, energy, E, and gradient, g. Time and velocity and acceleration are also consistent with the above, but will not be considered here. Time is another primitive.

Potential of population is a "scalar" quantity (having no direction in space) and is equal to number of people divided by their distance away. The potential which a given population concentration creates at a distant point Q is:

$$V_Q = \frac{P}{r}$$

But the total potential at any point is produced by all groups of people. If the distribution may be regarded as continuous over a surface, the following formula applies:

$$V_Q = \int \frac{1}{r} D \, dA$$

where dA signifies an infinitesimal element of the area over which the integration is extended.

Since density of population has the dimensions of persons per unit area, and area has the dimension of distance squared, the derived potential of population has the dimensions of number of people per unit distance.

If the values of potential have been computed for a sufficiently large number of appropriately spaced "control points," then a map such as Fig. 2 can be drawn to exhibit lines of equipotential or "contours."

If a constant contour interval is maintained throughout the map, the gradient of potential varies inversely as the spacing of the contours —gradient being the rate of change of potential with distance. Whereas potential is a scalar quantity, gradient is a vector directed at right angles to the equipotential contour at any place. Thus the unit of gradient has the dimensions of persons per mile squared. It should be noted that gradient and density thus have the same dimensions.

Although much analysis has centered upon the relation of the potential field to the geographical variation in certain sociological and economic phenomena, gradient has been shown to be important with regard to location theory.[13]

If only two separated groups of people are considered, their mutual "demographic energy" can be computed as:

$$E = \frac{P_1 P_2}{r}$$

The unit of energy therefore is persons squared per mile. The energy alternatively can be interpreted as the product of the population of either group times the potential contributed there by the other group. If one wishes to compute the energy of any group of people, say a city population, in relation to the total population, this can be found by multiplying the population of the city by the total potential contributed there by all people. Again the unit of energy is persons squared per mile.

Thus a rigorous and consistent set of measures exists of a population as it is distributed spatially. It should in particular be noted that the above formulae include without disagreement the case of W. J. Reilly's "breakpoint" between competing market cities.[14] He published the rule of inverse square of distance because he investigated gradients, not potentials.

Both Reilly and Stewart found their respective exponents as empirical regularities without any a priori postulates.

REMARKS AND FORMULAE IN RELATION TO POTENTIAL THEORY

Mathematical statisticians have seldom blazed the difficult trail which leads from observations of the world to new branches of science. Their convention-bound methods come into play only after discovery of the leading concepts and relations of the new field. Statistics necessarily is microscopic. It deals with the data of special cases, and can work with broad data only if the cases already have been put together by connections discovered in studies in the field in question. The operation of a principle may be obscured by the simultaneous effects of other principles, and mere statistics cannot, in complete ignorance of conditions, sort out the principles.

Very wide ramifications are possessed by the formula for the influence of people at a distance —as directly proportional to the number of people (weighted in whatever numerical ratio may be necessary) and inversely to the first power of the distance. The present paper indicates many of the ramifications, and in addition suggests some of the other factors which can add their own peculiar effects.

Naturally, a mathematics-statistics hopper, however recondite and busy, which lumps confusedly together all these factors will be incapable of closely verifying the law of inverse distance. This description, we suggest, applies to the recent study by Hammer and Iklé of long-distance telephone calls and airplane trips between certain cities.[15] When in their study people were weighted equally, the formula for "mutual energy" of the two city populations (their product divided by the distance apart) was roughly verified. But when the machine was allowed (subject only to the hidden conventions of mathematical statistics) to select the weights assigned to the people of each city, the exponent of distance came out as something like the negative three-halves power.

No comparative test was made with the approximate weights previously published by others—namely, 2, 1, and 0.8 for different sections of the United States, nor, alternatively, per capita income. The actual observations of telephone calls and travel [were] not tabulated. One would not expect that airline trips among the given cities in the single month of March, 1950, would furnish a stable sample. Nor have experts of the American Telephone and Telegraph Company complied or released a broad table of phone calls among cities of all sizes. (Likewise, the Federal Reserve System has made no adequate compilation of the interdistrict flow of bank checks.)

It can be mathematically fallacious to assume

a scalar "potential," or index, equal to population divided by distance to the nth power, where n is any exponent. For example, if n is greater than 2, the index would have infinite values for finite distributions of population density. This is because $\pi r^2 D / r^n$ equals $\pi D / r^{n-2}$, and, if n is greater than 2, approaches infinity as r approaches zero. The same objection applies with the gradient if n is greater than 1 in the potential. Consequently, it is a misnomer to use the name "gravity model" unless potential and gradient are defined as in the present paper. In three-dimensional space there are not gravity models, only the gravity model. People are distributed in three-dimensional space, although for convenience demography often can neglect the third dimension.

The published observational evidence for the usefulness of a scalar index operating to the inverse first power of distance is direct, varied, and remarkably strong as social science evidence goes. Mathematical statistics can be a good servant; but only a weak social science, intent on becoming weaker, will welcome it as a master.

LOCAL PEAKS OF POTENTIAL

Suppose a small city lies in a rural district where, apart from the city's own contribution, the contours of equipotential are, nearly enough, parallel straight lines, equally spaced. In "Some Fundamentals of the Gravity Model" (above), gradient is defined as the rate of change of potential with the distance at right angles to the contours of equipotential. So here the general gradient, g, is uniform. The small city, if all alone, would be surrounded by contours more or less circular, sloped "downhill" radially outward. Superposition of these two sets of contours results in the single system illustrated schematically in Fig. 4.

If instead of a city we had only a village, the hatched contour in the figure, and the circular ones included within its closed loop, would not come into existence. There would only be a short, downhill ridge raised above the general level across the village. No local peak would then be formed, and no closed contours around the town. The condition that there be a local peak is roughly this: within the loop of the hatched contour the density of the local population must exceed the uniform gradient, g— the latter being measured at a distance away, outside the local influence. (As stated above,

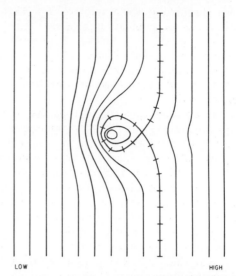

LOW   HIGH

FIGURE 4. Schematic representation of contours of potential near a small city

Far to the right the hatched contour would close around the main concentration of the country's population, forming thus the other, much larger, loop of a distorted figure eight. Its self-crossing marks a "saddle" or "pass." The "local peak" of the small city rises to the left, and the main massif of the nation to the right. On both sides of this axis the slope from the saddle is gently downhill. Farther to the left the city peak slopes sharply down. In general the slope or gradient at any point is perpendicular to the equipotential there, and, as this direction is ambiguous at the self-crossing, the gradient there is necessarily zero.

gradient and population density have the same dimensions.)

The phenomenon of "urban sprawl" is well known near great cities. The gradient away from the central city is so large that even fairly sizable concentrations of local population do not match or exceed it. Local closed contours of potential are not achieved, and unless its internal cohesion is very great, the would-be small city can have no independent demographic existence. As with the planet Saturn, the powerful gravitation of the central metropolis tears apart satellite towns. Is it possible for planners to provide the high cohesion which would preserve the character of such precariously perched neighborhoods?

A THEOREM OF TOPOLOGY

The contours of potential are mathematically determined when the density of population is known throughout the whole country. Certain distributions of population produce "pits" as well as "peaks" of potential. Of course the bottom of a pit may itself be at a high potential; the requirement merely is that the slope be upward in all directions in the immediate neighborhood.

An interesting theorem of topology applies within any closed contour of equipotential on a surface, as first stated scores of years ago by the great physicist Clerk Maxwell, and later by the well-known mathematician Marston Morse. The number of peaks plus the number of pits minus the number of passes equals 1, always. Thus in the situation of Fig. 4 a second and major peak is necessarily implied, far to the right (e.g., for the United States at New York City), and the portrayed parallel straight line contours really are parts of great sweeping arcs concave toward the major peak. In general, each separate city peak on the general massif is accompanied by its own neighboring pass on the New York side. Three otherwise isolated cities near together and forming a triangle would be separated by three passes on its three sides, and a pit would exist within the triangle.[16]

POTENTIAL NEAR THE CENTER OF A SMALL POPULATED AREA

If a circular disk of radius r has uniform population density, $\bar{D}$, throughout, then the total population, P, is $\pi r^2 D$. The increment of potential at the center produced by a ring of radius r and infinitesimal width dr is $2\pi \bar{D} \, dr$. Hence the total central potential is

$$V_c = 2\pi \bar{D} r = \frac{P}{(r/2)}$$

For an irregular area, A, not too different in shape from a circle, the same formula approximately applies, if by r we understand the value determined by setting $\pi r^2 = A$, again even though A be irregular. But if some actual area, A, is elongated, an ellipse will approximate it better. Mere inspection of the map will suggest a plausible approximation to α/β, the numerical ratio of the semimajor to the semiminor axis. The area of the chosen ellipse would be $\pi \, \alpha/\beta$. However, Table 9 requires only estimation of the ratio α/β. One computes r as before, as though the assigned area A belonged to a circle. The potential near its center approximates

$$V_c = \frac{P}{fr/2}$$

where f is the number read from Table 9 as a function of α/β.

By these means it is easy to approximate the potential of a given population "on itself," inasmuch as if the area, A, is small the assumption of uniform density, $\bar{D}$, is nearly always moderately good.

Table 10 shows how the potential within the uniform circular disk falls off with increasing distance out from the center.

ADDITIONAL FORMULAE FOR THE "STANDARD CITY"

In "Population Densities Within a City" (above), we had

TABLE 9
Table for computing the potential at the center of an elliptical disk

Ratio of axes α/β	Eccentricity	Value of f
1.0	0.000	1.00
1.5	0.745	1.01
2.0	0.866	1.02
2.5	0.917	1.06
3.0	0.943	1.09
4.0	0.968	1.12
5.0	0.980	1.15
6.0	0.986	1.20
8.0	0.992	1.27
10.0	0.995	1.33

For a uniformly distributed population over a circular disk (i.e., an ellipse with eccentricity zero), the potential at the center is equal to the population divided by half the radius, r. Values of f in the table (computed using elliptic integrals) permit ready computation of the potential at the center of an elliptical disk having a uniform distribution of population, as equal to the population divided by the quantity, half the equivalent radius times f. By equivalent radius we mean the radius of a circle which would have just the area of the chosen ellipse. The central potential of the elliptical disk is less than that of this circular disk (with the same population) in the ratio of 1 to f. This is because of the elongation of the ellipse, which puts the population farther away from the center. The first column gives the ratio of the semimajor axis, α, to the semiminor one, β. The text describes the procedure when this table is used to approximate the potential "on itself" of a small populated area.

$$D = D_o \, 2^{-r/b}$$

which we now rewrite,

$$D = D_o \, e^{-r/b'}$$

where $b' = b/\log 2$, the logarithm being to base e. The population of an infinitesimal ring of radius r and width dr is

$$dP_c = 2\pi \, D_o r \, e^{-r/b'} \, dr$$

Hence the potential at the center is

$$V_o = 2\pi b'(D_o - D')$$

D_o being as before the central density, and D' the edge density, with

$$D' = D_o e^{-a/b'}$$

Now

TABLE 10

Potential within a uniform circular disc, as a function of the distance from the cener

Ratio c/r	Relative potential
0.00	1.00
0.05	1.00
0.15	0.99
0.25	0.98
0.35	0.97
0.45	0.95
0.55	0.92
0.65	0.88
0.75	0.84
0.85	0.78
0.95	0.70
1.00	0.65

If a population, P, [is] distributed uniformly over a circular disk of radius r, the potential at the center is $2P/r$. This value is written in the table as, relatively, 1.00. The relative potential falls as shown with increasing distance c from the center, reaching only 0.65 at the edge (where c is equal to r). At a considerable distance beyond the edge, where the ratio c/r is large, the relative potential is approximately $r/2c$; thus at a distance of five radii from the center, where c/r is 5, it is 0.10, about. For at a distance the entire population P can be considered as though concentrated at the center, and the potential there is about P/c. Note that even at the very edge this approximate formula would give 0.50 for the relative potential, as compared with the accurate value of 0.65 tabulated.

$$\int r \, e^{-r/b'} dr = -b'(r - b')e^{-r/b'}$$

so we see that the whole population out to the bounding radius a is

$$P_c = 2\pi \left[b'^2 D_o - b'(a + b')D'\right]$$

Empirically it was shown that the radius a increases in proportion to the three-eighth power of the population, P_c; and that D_o is proportional to the square root of P_c. The constants of the two proportions are invariant for all the cities at a given time (if we ignore the effect of base potential), but are expected to change from census to census, slowly. The edge density also was constant for the sequence of cities in 1940, ideally.

Hence the above equation determines b' as a function of P_c, at any rate for 1940 when we have all the empirical constants. Solutions can be tabulated; a/b' is a useful parameter.

WORLD MAP OF POPULATION POTENTIAL

Inasmuch as the inverse distance formula for potential is good in three dimensions, potentials at representative points all over the earth can be computed once population densities everywhere are known. Distances must be measured not as arcs on the surface of the globe, but as straight-line chords direct from point to point. (For one thing, the arc distance is ambiguous because it can be measured either way around the great circle through any two points.) Obviously, populations of the various regions must be weighted. Per capita income weightings are perhaps available. "Social mass" per person would be better—perhaps 3000 tons in the United States, only a few hundred pounds for Australian aborigines on their native deserts.

SOCIOLOGICAL INTENSITY

In a quasi-equilibrium, the contours of population potential are observed in the simplest situations to outline coinciding "isotherms" of human social activity of various sorts. For instance, in the United States in 1950 the number of cities per 100,000 square miles of populations 25,000 to 35,000 varied about as the cube of the income potential.

However, other factors, as indicated in

"Remarks on Other Characteristics of Cities" (above), may combine with the potential to raise or depress social activity in a region. It is suggested that the indicated isotherms depict levels of "sociological intensity," and that this, rather than potential of population, is the active operating agent in bringing about such correlations as the one just stated for small cities. It corresponds to the statistical concept of temperature in physics.

While potential is objectively defined, the problem of an equally objective definition of sociological intensity or "social temperature," is still being studied. The relation for small cities refers to one type of combination of man-with-land or income-with-land. Dr. J. D. Hamilton, one of our associates in the social physics group, has suggested a close relationship between rules governing such combinations and the rules of physical chemistry governing molecular compounds.

FOOTNOTES

[1] J. Q. Stewart, "Suggested Principles of Social Physics," *Science*, **106** (1947), 179–180.

[2] C. Clark, "Urban Population Densities," *Journal of the Royal Statistical Society* Series A, **114** (1951), 490–496.

[3] J. Q. Stewart, "Urban Population Densities," *Geographical Review*, **43** (1953), 575.

[4] For a recent discussion of demographic gravitation and potentials of population see J. Q. Stewart and W. Warntz, "Macrogeography and Social Science," *Geographical Review*, **48** (1958), 167–184. See also "Some Fundamentals of the Gravity Model," below.

[5] J. Q. Stewart, "Empirical Mathematical Rules Concerning the Distribution and Equilibrium of Population," *Geographical Review*, **47** (1947), 461–485.

[6] H. Hoyt, *The Structure and Growth of Residential Neighborhoods in American Cities* (Washington: Federal Housing Administration, 1939).

[7] J. Q. Stewart, Chap. 2 in R. Cox and W. Alderson, *Theory in Marketing*, (Homewood, Ill.: Richard D. Irwin, Inc., 1949).

[8] J. Q. Stewart, "Urban Population Densities," *op. cit.*, 464.

[9] Cf. an excellent and broadly stimulating paper by O. D. Duncan, "Population Distribution and Community Structure," *Cold Spring Harbor Symposia on Quantitative Biology*, **22** (1957), 357–371.

[10] W. Isard, *Location and Space Economy* (New York: John Wiley & Sons, Inc., 1956), p. 172.

[11] J. Q. Stewart and W. Warntz, "Macrogeography and Social Science," *op. cit.*, 178.

[12] *Ibid.*, 173.

[13] For example, *ibid.*, 178.

[14] W. J. Reilly, "Method for the Study of Retail Relationships," *University of Texas Bulletin*, No. 2944 (1929).

[15] C. Hammer and F. C. Iklé, "Intercity Telephone and Airborne Traffic Related to Distance and the 'Propensity to Interact,'" *Sociometry*, **20** (1957), 306–316.

[16] For four cities at the corners of a square, with a pit inside, see J. Q. Stewart, "Urban Population Densities," *op. cit.*, 475.

IV

ANALYSIS
OF SPATIAL DISTRIBUTIONS

1

STATISTICAL STUDY OF THE DISTRIBUTION OF SCATTERED VILLAGES IN TWO REGIONS OF THE TONAMI PLAIN, TOYAMA PREFECTURE

ISAMU MATUI

The Tonami Plain, which constitutes the datum area for this study, is celebrated for its scattered villages. This plain is one of the small alluvial areas situated at the northwestern part of Toyama Prefecture, hemmed in by mountains on all sides except where it faces Toyama Bay in the Japan Sea. Irrigated paddy fields make up the greater part of this alluvial plain. Widely scattered rural settlements, with several large and small towns interspersed among them, [are] the characteristic feature of this plain. Several Japanese geographers have recently studied this habitation problem from the point of view of geography and history. Dr. T. Ogawa[1] of the Kyoto Imperial University, who was the first to study this region, investigated some of the climatic and historic influences upon the distribution of these villages. An investigation in greater detail from the historical side has been made by S. Makino,[2] while quite recently the same has been made on the geographical side by S. Ishii.[3] Recently T. Murata[4] has studied the extent to which the isolated farms are scattered by a new method

of his own, selecting the Tonami Plain especially for his subject. The geographical investigations of R. Tôki[5] constitute also an important research covering this district.

The short statistical investigation of the problem of disseminated villages here presented is restricted to that of map-study, without any attempt to cover the various questions that might have to be considered in a complete geographical interpretation of the problem. In fact, from the standpoint of pure geography, the value of such a discussion is a debatable one.

The two areas that have been arbitrarily selected and considered here are rectangular. The former is situated eastward of Hukuno town and is 4 km in length and 3 km in width, while the latter, which is north of Demati town, is 3.9 km in length and 3.25 km in width (Fig. 1, 2). The first-named district is divided into 1200 squares, each side being 100 meters long. There are 910 houses here, uniformly

Reprinted from *Japanese Journal of Geology and Geography*, **9** (1932), 251–266, by permission of the author and editor.

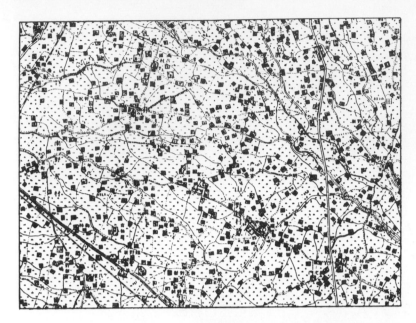

FIGURE 1. A section of topographic map (1 : 20,000 Military Land Survey) showing the western part of Hukuno town

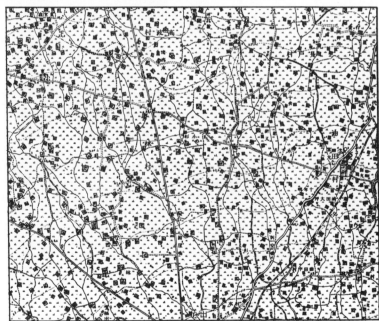

FIGURE 2. A section of topographic map (1 : 20,000) showing the northern part of Demati town

distributed. The number of houses in each of these small squares was observed and tabulated (see Table 1 and Fig. 3). A theoretical discussion follows.

When n points are taken at random within a given area, consisting of m small areas equal in size, the probability $P(r)$ that r points will fall into a small area as mentioned above, can be written:

$$(1) \qquad P(r) = \frac{e^{-\nu}\nu^r}{r!} \qquad \text{(Poisson's formula)}$$

where[6]

$$\nu = \frac{n}{m}$$

Returning to our present question, the values of n and m are 910 and 1200, respectively.

TABLE 1

```
2 2 2 1 0 1 0 0 1 2 0 0 0 0 1 2 0 1 0 1 0 2 2 0 1 1 2 0 1 1 1 1 2 1 1 2 0 1 2 0 2
0 2 0 1 2 0 1 1 1 2 2 0 1 1 0 0 0 1 0 1 0 2 2 0 1 2 2 1 2 1 0 0 1 0 1 0 2 0 1 2
1 0 1 1 0 0 1 0 1 1 1 0 1 0 1 1 0 1 2 0 2 0 0 1 3 0 1 2 1 0 2 1 1 2 0 0 1 0 2 2
0 1 1 1 0 2 0 1 2 0 0 0 2 2 0 0 0 1 0 0 1 2 0 0 0 1 0 0 0 1 0 9 0 0 0 1 1 1 1 1
1 2 0 0 0 0 0 0 0 0 1 0 2 0 2 2 0 1 2 1 0 1 1 1 0 3 0 1 2 0 1 1 1 1 0 0 1 0 3 1
1 3 1 0 1 0 1 0 0 0 0 2 2 0 2 0 0 1 0 0 1 0 0 0 0 1 2 1 1 1 2 1 0 2 1 3 1 1 1
0 1 0 0 0 1 0 1 0 1 2 0 1 3 1 1 4 1 3 1 0 1 1 0 0 0 0 0 0 2 2 2 0 1 2 0 3 0 1
0 0 1 0 1 0 0 1 0 0 1 3 0 0 1 0 0 1 0 0 1 0 2 2 0 2 0 0 1 2 1 2 2 0 0 1 1 0 0 1
0 1 1 0 1 1 0 1 1 3 1 1 3 0 1 0 2 0 1 0 0 0 0 1 3 3 2 0 0 0 0 1 0 1 0 1 0 0 0 1 0
0 0 0 0 0 1 1 2 0 0 1 5 2 0 0 0 0 2 0 0 2 1 0 1 0 0 2 0 0 0 1 0 0 1 0 0 0 1 2 0
0 2 0 0 1 1 1 0 1 1 1 0 2 1 4 2 1 0 1 2 2 0 1 1 2 1 0 0 0 0 1 2 2 0 0 0 0 0 0
0 0 0 1 1 0 1 0 0 0 0 1 2 2 2 0 0 0 1 0 1 3 1 2 0 0 0 0 0 2 1 2 0 0 0 2 0 1 1 1
0 1 0 0 1 2 0 0 0 0 0 0 0 1 1 0 1 1 1 1 2 1 1 1 3 0 1 0 1 1 0 1 4 1 1 2 0 1 0 2
0 0 0 1 1 1 1 0 1 1 0 0 0 0 1 2 0 1 1 1 1 3 0 2 1 0 0 0 0 2 0 0 0 3 0 2 0 1 1 2
0 1 1 0 0 0 1 1 2 0 0 1 0 0 1 0 0 2 0 0 0 1 1 0 0 0 1 1 1 0 0 0 0 2 0 0 2 1 0 0
3 4 1 1 0 3 1 0 0 0 2 0 0 0 1 0 1 2 1 0 0 1 4 1 0 0 2 2 0 0 0 1 0 1 1 1 0 4 4 0
0 0 1 0 0 1 1 1 1 1 1 0 0 1 0 2 0 3 2 0 2 2 3 1 0 0 1 1 0 1 3 0 0 1 1 0 1 1 1 0
1 1 0 1 0 1 0 0 2 1 0 0 2 2 0 0 2 1 5 2 0 0 0 0 0 0 0 0 1 0 0 1 2 2 0 0 2 1 0 1
0 3 0 1 0 0 0 2 0 0 0 2 0 0 0 0 0 1 0 2 0 0 0 0 1 1 0 0 2 0 0 0 0 0 0 1 3 0 0 1
0 1 1 0 2 0 1 0 0 0 0 0 1 1 0 0 1 0 1 0 0 0 1 1 2 1 1 0 0 0 0 1 1 0 1 0 0 2 1 2
1 0 0 0 1 1 0 0 1 1 1 0 0 2 1 0 0 0 0 1 3 0 2 2 1 4 0 1 0 0 1 0 3 0 0 1 1 0 1 0
0 2 1 1 0 1 1 0 0 0 1 1 0 0 3 1 1 0 0 1 0 1 0 2 5 2 1 1 0 1 2 0 0 1 1 0 1 2 0 0
0 0 0 0 0 2 0 1 1 1 2 0 0 1 1 2 1 0 1 0 0 3 2 1 4 5 0 2 1 1 1 1 2 0 2 0 0 1 0 1
0 0 1 1 2 0 0 0 1 0 0 1 1 0 0 0 0 0 2 0 0 1 2 2 1 0 0 3 3 1 1 0 1 0 0 0 0 0 1 0
1 0 1 1 0 0 1 1 2 2 1 1 0 0 0 0 0 1 0 0 2 1 1 0 0 0 0 0 1 1 0 0 1 1 0 0 2 0 0 2
0 0 1 1 1 1 1 0 0 0 2 2 1 2 0 0 0 2 1 0 0 0 0 0 1 1 0 3 0 0 1 2 0 7 1 0 2 0 0 2
0 1 1 1 1 2 2 2 0 0 2 0 3 1 0 1 0 1 0 0 1 0 0 0 1 1 1 3 1 0 1 0 2 1 2 1 0 0 0 1
0 2 1 0 0 0 2 1 2 0 0 0 0 0 1 0 3 0 1 1 0 0 0 1 0 0 1 0 0 0 2 2 1 1 0 1 0 1 1 0
0 0 0 0 1 0 0 2 0 0 0 0 0 0 0 0 1 1 0 0 1 1 0 1 0 0 1 1 0 1 1 1 2 0 1 0 2 1 0 1 1
2 0 0 1 2 0 0 0 0 0 1 0 0 1 1 2 1 3 2 0 0 0 0 0 0 0 0 0 1 0 0 0 1 1 1 1 0 2 1 0
```

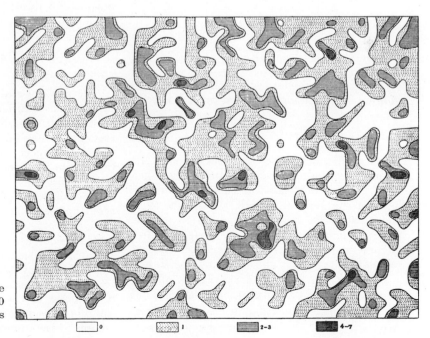

FIGURE 3. Map showing the density of houses per 100 m² in the same part as Fig. 1

| | 0 | | 1 | | 2–3 | | 4–7 |

Thus the probability that r houses shall be in a small section can be calculated from Eq. 1. The results are shown in Table 2.

In order to compare the results of observation with those of calculation, the author computed the frequency of houses (ranging from 0 to 9) in each square from Table 1 and placed it in Table 3 with the values calculated from Table 2. The calculated values agree well with the observed values.

Now consider a quantity δ, defined as

$$\delta = \frac{r - \nu}{\nu}$$

which measures the deviation from the mean value. The observed value of $|\bar{\delta}|$ found from Table 3,[7] is $|\bar{\delta}|$ (obs.) $= 0.98$, while the calculated value of $|\bar{\delta}|$ is

$$|\bar{\delta}| = \frac{2e^{-\nu}\nu^{\lambda}}{\lambda!}$$

where λ is the greatest positive integer (including zero), not greater than ν. Thus in our case $\lambda = 0$, since $\nu = 0.76$. Accordingly

$$|\bar{\delta}| \text{ (cal.)} = 0.95$$

Similarly we have

$$\bar{\delta}^{2}(\text{obs.}) = 1.58$$

$$\bar{\delta}^{2}(\text{cal.}) = \frac{1}{\nu} = 1.32$$

Next we proceed to study the distribution of houses in direction from west to east. Let

$$\Delta = r_{1} - r_{2}$$

where r_1 and r_2 are successive values of r. The frequencies of all successive r_1 and r_2 are taken from Table 1 and placed in Table 4, where the head of the vertical column corresponds to r_1 and that of the horizontal column to r_2. The upper figures in each column show the frequency of observation and the lower that of calculation.

Now we can easily find the values of $\bar{\Delta}(r)$ from Table 4 and compare them with those of $\bar{\Delta}(r)$, which are calculated from the formula, $\bar{\Delta}(r_1) = r_1 - \nu$. The results are given in Table

5, and also graphically in Fig. 4. These show that the straight line as calculated theoretically agrees well with that observed. In the same way the observed value of $\bar{\Delta}^2$ is easily found from Table 4, namely,

$$\bar{\Delta}^{2}(\text{obs.}) = 1.67$$

while the calculated value is

$$\bar{\Delta}^{2}(\text{cal.}) = 2\nu = 1.52$$

From the above study it is evident that the distribution of houses in direction from west to east is similar to that of points taken at random, to which latter the analyses of Fig. 5 and Tables 6 and 7 show that the distribution of houses in north-south direction is also similar.

The present author observed next the duration of the same value of r both in sense west-east and north-south, the results being shown in Tables 8–11, where H_1 and H_2 show the respective observed values for the west-east and north-south directions, and H the value from calculation. The tables show good agreement between observation and calculation. The average duration of the same value of r can easily be calculated from these tables. These results are shown in Table 12, where T_1 and T_2 correspond to the values of the west-east and north-south directions, respectively, while the calculated value (T) is given by

$$T = \frac{1}{1 - P(r)}$$

The point of real interest in our comparison between observation and calculation, as stated above, is that the distribution of houses in the rectangular area taken for our purpose is similar in every respect to those of points taken at random in the same area. On the other hand, however, it does not necessarily follow from mere coincidence of their superficial characters that the two phenomena have also the same causes.

The second district is divided into 750 equal squares, each side being 130 meters long. The total number of isolated farms (not houses) in this region amounts to 846. At first sight, the distribution of these farms seems to be quite uniform throughout the whole area. The author computed the number of farms in each of these small squares and listed them in Table 13. Similar observations and theoretical calculations, as stated above, were made from this table and also from the probability formulae. These results are given in Tables 14–24 and also in Figs. 6 and 7. The reader may notice slight discrepancies between observation and calculation, but on the whole these are not great.

The object of this paper is to draw attention to the subject discussed herein for future consideration rather than to solve the problem of the distribution of scattered dwellings.

TABLE 2
Numerical value (P) of r

r	$P(r)$
0	0.473
1	0.355
2	0.133
3	0.033
4	0.006
5	0.001
6	0.0001
7	0.00001
8	0.000001
9	0.0000001

TABLE 3
Frequency of r

r	Obs.	Cal.
0	584	567
1	398	426
2	168	159
3	35	40
4	9	7
5	4	1
6	0	0
7	1	0
8	0	0
9	1	0
Sum	1200	1200

TABLE 4
Frequency of successive r_1, r_2 in west-east direction

r_1 \ r_2	0	1	2	3	4	5	6	7	8	9
0	290	197	69	14	1	0	0	1	0	1
	262	197	74	18	3	1	0	0	0	0
1	170	132	60	17	6	2	0	0	0	0
	197	148	55	14	3	0	0	0	0	0
2	84	45	29	1	0	1	0	0	0	0
	74	55	24	5	1	0	0	0	0	0
3	15	13	4	2	1	0	0	0	0	0
	18	14	5	1	0	0	0	0	0	0
4	2	4	1	0	1	1	0	0	0	0
	3	3	1	0	0	0	0	0	0	0
5	1	0	3	0	0	0	0	0	0	0
	1	0	0	0	0	0	0	0	0	0
6	0	0	0	0	0	0	0	0	0	0
	0	0	0	0	0	0	0	0	0	0
7	0	1	0	0	0	0	0	0	0	0
	0	0	0	0	0	0	0	0	0	0
8	0	0	0	0	0	0	0	0	0	0
	0	0	0	0	0	0	0	0	0	0
9	1	0	0	0	0	0	0	0	0	0
	0	0	0	0	0	0	0	0	0	0

TABLE 5

Numerical values of $\bar{\Delta}(r_1)$ in west-east direction

r_1	$\bar{\Delta}$(obs.)	$\bar{\Delta}$(cal.)	r_1	$\bar{\Delta}$(obs.)	$\bar{\Delta}$(cal.)
0	−0.68	−0.75	5	+3.50	+4.25
1	+0.13	+0.25	6	—	+5.25
2	+1.23	+1.25	7	+6.00	+6.25
3	+2.03	+2.25	8	—	+7.25
4	+2.33	+3.25	9	+9.00	+8.25

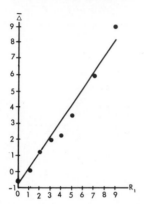

FIGURE 4. Relation between r_1 and $\bar{\Delta}X$: observed value west-east direction

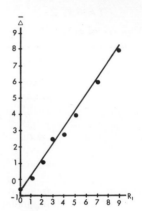

FIGURE 5. Relation between r_1 and $\bar{\Delta}X$: observed value north-south direction

TABLE 6

Frequency of successive r_1, r_2 in north-south direction

r_1 \ r_2	0	1	2	3	4	5	6	7	8	9
0	279	200	65	13	4	0	0	0	0	0
	260	195	73	18	3	1	0	0	0	0
1	189	118	58	14	4	2	0	1	0	1
	195	146	55	14	3	0	0	0	0	0
2	80	46	29	6	0	2	0	0	0	0
	73	55	23	5	1	0	0	0	0	0
3	17	14	2	1	0	0	0	0	0	0
	18	14	5	1	0	0	0	0	0	0
4	3	3	2	1	0	0	0	0	0	0
	3	3	1	0	0	0	0	0	0	0
5	3	0	0	0	1	0	0	0	0	0
	1	0	0	0	0	0	0	0	0	0
6	0	0	0	0	0	0	0	0	0	0
	0	0	0	0	0	0	0	0	0	0
7	0	1	0	0	0	0	0	0	0	0
	0	0	0	0	0	0	0	0	0	0
8	0	0	0	0	0	0	0	0	0	0
	0	0	0	0	0	0	0	0	0	0
9	0	1	0	0	0	0	0	0	0	0
	0	0	0	0	0	0	0	0	0	0

TABLE 7
Numerical values of $\bar{\Delta}(r_1)$ and $\bar{\Delta}^2$ in north-south direction

r_1	$\bar{\Delta}$(obs.)	$\bar{\Delta}$(cal.)	r_1	$\bar{\Delta}$(obs.)	$\bar{\Delta}$(cal.)
0	-0.69	-0.75	6	....	$+5.25$
1	$+0.18$	$+0.25$	7	$+6.00$	$+6.25$
2	$+1.19$	$+1.25$	8	....	$+7.25$
3	$+2.38$	$+2.25$	9	$+8.00$	$+8.25$
4	$+2.78$	$+3.25$	$\bar{\Delta}^2$	1.71	1.50
5	$+4.00$	$+4.25$			

TABLE 8
Duration of $r = 0$

Duration	H_1	H_2	H
1	148	164	158
2	76	69	75
3	36	37	35
4	13	19	17
5	13	9	8
6	1	2	4
7	4	3	2
8	2	1	1
9	1	1	0

TABLE 10
Duration of $r = 2$

Duration	H_1	H_2	H
1	114	115	120
2	21	19	16
3	4	5	2
4	0	0	1

TABLE 9
Duration of $r = 1$

Duration	H_1	H_2	H
1	177	206	177
2	61	48	63
3	17	12	22
4	8	10	8
5	2	4	3
6	1	0	1
7	0	0	0

TABLE 11
Duration of $r = 3$

Duration	H_1	H_2	H
1	31	33	37
2	2	1	1
3	0	6	0

TABLE 12
Average duration of r

r	T_1	T_2	T
0	1.99	1.91	1.90
1	1.50	1.42	1.55
2	1.21	1.21	1.15
3	1.06	1.03	1.03
4	1.13	1.00	1.00
5	1.00	1.00	1.00
6	—	—	1.00
7	1.00	1.00	1.00
8	—	—	1.00
9	1.00	1.00	1.00

TABLE 13

```
2 2 1 3 1 1 1 2 1 3 0 4 0 1 1 4 1 2 0 1 1 1 1 1 1 1 1 2 1 0
0 1 1 3 0 1 1 1 0 0 1 1 2 1 1 2 1 2 1 1 0 2 1 1 0 2 1 1 1 0
1 2 1 1 0 1 0 2 1 1 1 3 0 0 0 1 2 1 3 1 0 3 1 0 1 3 1 2 2 2
3 2 1 2 2 0 0 1 4 1 3 1 1 2 0 1 1 1 0 1 1 1 0 2 1 3 2 1 0 2
2 2 1 0 1 1 2 0 1 1 0 1 1 0 1 1 1 2 0 0 1 1 3 0 1 0 0 1 2 0
4 3 2 2 1 2 0 2 1 0 1 2 1 1 1 1 2 1 1 1 2 1 0 1 2 2 1 1 0 2
2 3 2 2 2 1 1 2 1 2 1 3 1 2 1 1 0 0 1 1 2 3 2 1 1 1 2 1 1 2
1 2 4 1 3 1 1 1 2 2 0 1 0 2 1 2 0 1 1 2 1 2 2 1 2 0 0 2 1 1
2 0 1 0 1 0 1 3 1 0 2 3 2 1 0 1 1 2 1 1 0 2 1 0 1 0 2 0 2 2
0 0 1 0 0 1 0 1 0 0 1 2 1 1 2 2 2 0 0 0 3 1 3 1 2 1 0 3 2 0
0 1 1 2 0 0 1 2 1 2 0 1 0 1 1 1 2 0 2 1 1 1 1 0 1 4 0 1 0 0
0 1 1 1 0 0 1 1 1 3 1 1 1 2 0 2 1 1 4 0 2 2 1 1 1 1 1 1 2 2
2 0 1 1 2 0 0 3 1 1 0 0 0 2 1 1 0 1 2 0 0 1 2 2 0 1 3 0 2 3
1 1 1 0 0 0 0 0 1 2 1 1 2 1 1 1 1 2 1 2 1 0 1 0 0 1 1 2 2 2
1 2 0 1 1 0 1 0 3 0 1 1 0 1 0 0 1 1 1 0 2 0 2 1 1 5 2 1 2 2
4 2 0 0 1 1 2 0 2 1 1 0 0 1 0 1 1 0 2 1 0 0 1 1 3 0 1 3 1 0
2 1 0 0 0 1 3 2 4 0 1 1 0 2 2 1 2 1 1 0 0 0 0 1 1 3 0 1 1 3
1 3 1 1 0 1 1 1 1 2 1 0 0 2 1 0 1 0 1 0 0 2 1 1 1 0 0 2 2 1
0 0 1 1 1 0 0 2 2 1 1 2 3 2 2 0 0 2 2 1 2 0 0 0 1 0 2 1 2 2
0 0 1 1 1 0 0 1 0 0 1 1 4 1 0 0 1 1 3 1 1 0 1 0 1 1 0 3 0 2
0 1 2 0 0 0 1 3 0 1 0 1 2 0 0 1 0 3 2 3 1 4 0 1 1 3 0 2 2 1
1 0 0 1 1 0 0 2 1 1 1 0 0 1 2 1 1 0 1 2 2 3 1 1 2 1 1 2 2 1
3 1 1 0 2 0 0 1 2 1 0 2 2 0 0 0 0 3 3 1 0 1 3 3 1 1 1 3 2 2
1 0 1 1 1 1 1 0 1 2 1 1 1 2 0 1 2 3 2 2 0 0 0 2 2 0 0 1 1 2
1 2 0 0 2 2 0 1 1 1 0 2 1 2 1 0 1 4 1 2 3 0 0 2 0 0 1 1 3 2
```

TABLE 14

Numerical value of P(r)

r	P(r)	r	P(r)
0	0.324	4	0.022
1	0.365	5	0.005
2	0.206	6	0.001
3	0.078		

TABLE 15

Frequency of r

r	Obs.	Cal.
0	206	243
1	318	274
2	164	154
3	49	58
4	12	16
5	1	4
6	0	1
Sum	750	750

TABLE 16

$|\bar{\delta}|$ (obs.)	0.73
$|\bar{\delta}|$ (cal.)	0.73
$\overline{\delta^2}$ (obs.)	0.90
$\overline{\delta^2}$ (cal.)	0.89

TABLE 17

Frequency of successive r_1, r_2
in west-east direction

r_1 \ r_2	0	1	2	3	4	5
0	62	90	38	9	1	0
	76	86	48	18	5	1
1	81	126	72	27	7	1
	86	97	55	21	6	1
2	39	69	33	8	2	0
	48	54	31	12	3	1
3	12	20	13	2	0	0
	18	21	12	4	1	0
4	5	5	1	1	0	0
	5	6	3	1	0	0
5	0	0	1	0	0	0
	1	1	1	0	0	0

TABLE 18

*Frequency of successive r_1, r_2
in north-south direction*

r_1 \ r_2	0	1	2	3	4	5
0	65	83	40	8	1	0
	76	85	48	18	5	1
1	86	126	68	24	3	1
	85	96	54	20	6	1
2	38	69	35	10	4	0
	48	54	30	12	3	1
3	11	18	12	4	2	0
	18	20	12	4	1	0
4	1	5	4	1	0	0
	5	6	3	1	0	0
5	1	0	0	0	0	0
	1	1	1	0	0	0

TABLE 19

Numerical values of $\bar{\Delta}(r_1)$ and $\bar{\Delta}^2$

r_1	$\bar{\Delta}$ (obs. WE)	$\bar{\Delta}$ (obs. NS)	$\bar{\Delta}$ (cal.)
0	-0.71	-0.93	-1.13
1	-0.22	-0.14	-0.13
2	$+0.82$	$+0.77$	$+0.87$
3	$+1.81$	$+1.61$	$+1.87$
4	$+3.16$	$+2.34$	$+2.87$
5	$+3.00$	$+5.00$	$+3.87$
$\bar{\Delta}^2$	1.65	1.53	2.26

TABLE 20

Duration of $r = 0$

Duration	H_1	H_2	H
	96	95	111
2	38	35	36
3	7	6	12
4	2	2	4
5	1	3	1
6	0	0	0

TABLE 21

Duration of $r = 1$

Duration	H_1	H_2	H
1	109	118	111
2	53	45	40
3	23	15	15
4	4	8	5
5	2	4	2
6	0	1	1
7	0	1	0
8	1	0	0

TABLE 22

Duration of $r = 2$

Duration	H_1	H_2	H
1	102	99	97
2	25	25	20
3	4	5	4
4	0	4	1

TABLE 23

Duration of $r = 3$

Duration	H_1	H_2	H
1	45	41	50
2	2	4	4
3	0	0	0

TABLE 24

Average duration of r

r	T_1	T_2	T
0	1.43	1.46	1.48
1	1.66	1.66	1.57
2	1.25	1.27	1.26
3	1.04	1.09	1.08
4	1.00	1.00	1.02
5	1.00	1.00	1.00

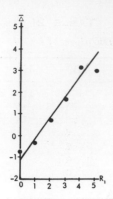

FIGURE 6. Relation between r_1 and $\bar{\Delta}X$: observed value west-east direction

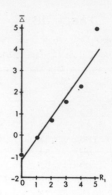

FIGURE 7. Relation between r_1 and $\bar{\Delta}X$: observed value north-south direction

FOOTNOTES

[1] T. Ogawa, "On the Homesteads in the Western Part of Etchu Province," *Japanese Journal of Geography*, **26** (1914), 895–905.

[2] S. Makino, "On the Village System in the Provinces of Kaga, Noto, and Etchu Under the Old Feudal Administration," *ibid.*, **27** (1915), 684–692; Makino, "Scattered Dwellings and Villages Surrounded by Moats," *History and Geography*, 180–202.

[3] H. Ishii, "Habitations in the Etchu Plain, "*Geographical Review of Japan*, **6** (1930), 573–584.

[4] T. Murata, "The Extent to Which Isolated Farms Are Scattered," *ibid.*, **6** (1930), 1744–1753.

[5] R. Tôki, *Chorology* (Tokyo, 1931).

[6] Here both n and m are assumed to be very large.

[7] $|\bar{\delta}|$: mean value of $|\delta|$.

2

A QUANTITATIVE EXPRESSION
OF THE PATTERN OF URBAN SETTLEMENTS
IN SELECTED AREAS OF THE UNITED STATES

LESLIE J. KING

The agglomerated settlement in which there is a concentration of nonfarm activities is a ubiquitous feature of the American landscape. Throughout the country these urban settlements range in population size from that of the small lowly hamlet of 100 or so inhabitants up to the large metropolitan area of several million people. Functionally they also vary in character, although the majority of them might be considered to have basically the same *raison d'être* in that they provide some form of service to the inhabitants of the surrounding rural areas. However, the demand for goods and services originating within the farming sector of any large area can seldom be satisfied by a single urban center. On the contrary, the physical and economic limitations to movement over the surface of the earth generally necessitate the existence of several urban settlements within any large area. Furthermore, the fact that these limitations are not constant in their effects throughout the continent is reflected in the character of the distribution pattern of urban settlements from one area to

another. The widely spaced, irregular pattern of settlements characteristic of much of the semiarid West, for example, contrasts strongly with the more compact and rectangular arrangement of settlements to be found in the Midwest. Many comparisons and contrasts along these lines have already been pointed up within the body of geographic literature.[1] However, the greater part of this descriptive work to date has been characterized by an almost unquestioning reliance upon [such] qualitative terms as "sparse," "dispersed," "agglomerated," or "dense." While these terms have meaning with reference to the context in which they are used, they lack objectivity for more extended comparative purposes. It appears desirable, therefore, that a more precise connotation be given to these descriptive terms as a means of facilitating comparative analysis and the discovery of more universal generalizations concerning the nature of settlement patterns.

Reprinted from *Tijdschrift Voor Econ. en Soc. Geographie*, **53** (1962), 1–7, by permission of the author and editor.

The problem of deriving a mathematical expression of the pattern of settlement distribution has already received considerable attention from European geographers. In this regard, the works of Bernard,[2] Colas,[3] Debouverie[4] Demangeon[5] Meynier,[6] and Zierhoffer[7] are especially worthy of mention.

However, these earlier formulations were based on certain critical ratios—for example, the average area per dwelling or the number of settlements in the commune—and generally no analysis was made of the actual linear distances separating the settlements within an area.[8] These attempts at quantitative analysis have therefore been criticized for their generality and for the fact that they are frequently insensitive to important variations in settlement pattern.[9]

In this study there is outlined a new approach to the problem of expressing the character of settlement patterns in mathematical terms. The approach is based upon modern statistical theory and the notions of probability. In contrast to earlier work in this field, greater emphasis is given to the actual distance separating settlements, and the statistical techniques which are used in this study are in fact known as the "near-neighbor analysis."

Statistical analysis of the near-neighbor measure, which is, as the name suggests, a straight-line measurement of the distance separating any phenomenon and its nearest neighbor in space, was originally developed by plant ecologists who were concerned with the distribution patterns of various plant species over the surface of the earth.[10] Near-neighbor analysis indicates the degree to which any observed distribution of points deviates from what might be expected if the points were distributed in a random manner within the same area. A random distribution of points is defined as a set of points on a given area for which "any point has had the same chance of occurring on any subarea as any other point; that any subarea of specified size has had the same chance of receiving a point as any other subarea of that size, and that the placement of each point has not been influenced by that of any other point."[11] While this is essentially a mathematical concept, it is possible by use of a square grid with numbered intersections and a random numbers table to construct an artificial random distribution (Fig. 1b). From the laws of mathematical probability[12] it can then be demonstrated that the mean distance (rE) between each point and its nearest neighbor which could be expected in such a random distribution is equal to $\frac{1}{2}p^{-1/2}$, where p is the observed density of points in the area under consideration. The ratio of the observed mean distance (rA) to this expected value (rE), is termed the near-neighbor statistic (R). This ratio has a range in value from zero, when there is maximum aggregation of all the points at one location (Fig. 1a), through 1, which represents a random distribution, up to 2.15^{13} which is expressive of a pattern of maximum spacing analogous to the hexagonal arrangement discussed by Christaller and others[14] (Fig. 1c). In this sense the statistic R provides a meaningful and precise expression of the distribution pattern of points within any area. Furthermore, the ratios for different areas can be compared directly with one another, and the significance of the differences between them can be assessed by standard statistical procedures.[15] For any single area it is possible to test not only the significance of the departure of the observed mean distance (rA) from that expected in a random distribution (rE), but also the significance of the deviation of the observed mean distance from that which would be expected if the points within the area were either aggregated at one location or dispersed in a hexagonal pattern. In the first of these two hypothetical cases the expected value of rA would be zero, while in the second it would be equal to $2^{1/2}/(3^{1/4}p^{1/2})$, where p is defined as before.[16]

In this study an attempt is made, using the techniques outlined above, to describe some of the empirical characteristics of the distribution of urban settlements in different areas of the United States. Whereas in the preceding discussion the emphasis has been on a set of points distributed in space, the focal point of attention now becomes a number of urban places which are distributed over the surface of the earth. It is assumed that within each area selected for study there is an equal chance that an urban settlement will be located on any one unit area of ground as on any other area, and conversely, that every location has an equal chance of receiving an urban center. Location theory suggests that these assumptions are quite unrealistic, but as a theoretical norm or model they have considerable value.

The sample areas for this study were chosen

THEORETICAL   SETTLEMENT   PATTERNS

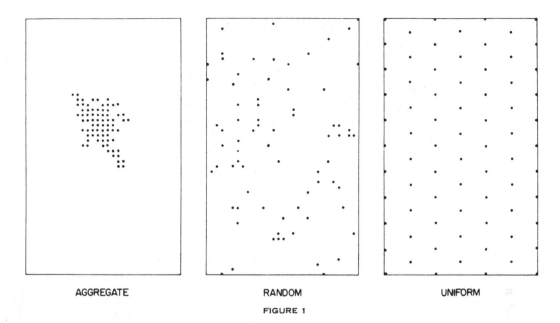

AGGREGATE   RANDOM   UNIFORM

FIGURE 1

in such a way as to insure a representative cross section of as many of the physical and economic regions within the United States as was practicable. The locations of the twenty areas which were selected are shown in Fig. 2. Within each area the term "urban settlement" was taken to include all settlements listed in the United States census[17] together with any smaller communities shown on the United States Department of Commerce Transportation Maps,[18] and published road atlases.[19]

For each area a series of straight-line measurements were taken between the urban centers and their respective nearest neighbors.[20] There was no consideration given to the population size of the towns concerned, since the emphasis was upon urban settlement as an attributal phenomenon, and while it is highly desirable that the variable, population size, should eventually be incorporated into the analysis, for the time being it is disregarded.

In many cases the nearest neighbor of a given town lay outside of the sample area. The distances to these neighbors were measured and included in the computations, but no town lying outside of the sample area was ever used as a center of measurement. In addition, it was often the case that two towns within an

area were located closer to one another than they were to any other town, in which case the same distance was measured twice.

The obtained values of the near-neighbor statistic R are presented in Table 1. Intuitively it was expected that these values would vary in magnitude from one area to another, for it would seem as though variations in the physical geography, the economic base, transportation facilities, and land-occupance history are likely to influence the spacing of urban settlements in any area. An examination of Table 1 reveals that the expected range in value for the near-neighbor statistic R did occur, and it is apparent that the tendencies toward aggregated, random, and uniform spacing of towns vary considerably throughout the country.

On the one hand, the most marked tendency toward an aggregated-settlement pattern appears in two of the areas within the western Cordillera system, namely, Washington and Utah, for which the R values are .71 and .70, respectively. These low values here reflect an almost linear arrangement of pairs of towns along major rivers, the Yakima River in Washington and the Duchesne River and its tributaries in Utah (Fig. 3). In each case settlement is associated with irrigated "oases," while

LOCATION OF SAMPLE AREAS

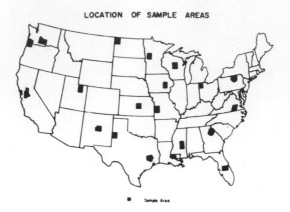

■ Sample Area

FIGURE 2

TABLE 1

Near-neighbor statistics

Sample Area	Number of towns	Density of towns per square mile	Mean observed distance (miles) rA	Expected mean distance in random distribution (miles) rE	Near-neighbor statistic R	Nature of pattern
California	96	.0243	3.46	3.21	1.08	Random
Florida	64	.0200	3.32	3.53	.94	"
Georgia	132	.0350	3.52	2.67	1.32	Approaching uniform
Iowa	82	.0307	3.86	2.85	1.35	" "
Kansas	51	.0166	5.16	3.88	1.33	" "
Louisiana	140	.0437	2.57	2.39	1.08	Random
Minnesota	55	.0169	5.32	3.85	1.38	Approaching uniform
Mississippi	104	.0280	3.84	2.99	1.28	" "
Missouri	80	.0219	4.67	3.38	1.38	" "
New Mexico	23	.0065	6.82	6.20	1.10	Random
North Dakota	28	.0082	6.13	5.52	1.11	"
Ohio	131	.0512	2.80	2.21	1.27	Approaching uniform
Oregon	128	.0317	2.86	2.81	1.02	Random
Pennsylvania	177	.0466	2.28	2.32	1.22	Approaching uniform
Texas (N.W.)	38	.0104	6.03	4.90	1.23	" "
Texas (S.E.)	61	.0182	4.29	3.70	1.16	" "
Utah	20	.0061	4.49	6.40	.70	Aggregated
Virginia	122	.0363	3.20	2.62	1.22	Approaching uniform
Washington	32	.0073	4.14	5.85	.71	Aggregated
Wisconsin	97	.0299	3.58	2.89	1.24	Approaching uniform

the greater part of both areas remains virtually uninhabited. With such an arrangement of pairs of settlements, the observed mean distance between towns and their nearest neighbors tends toward zero, and as a result the obtained value of R approaches that which would be characteristic of a more aggregated grouping.

At the other extreme, a tendency toward uniform spacing was apparent in twelve of the areas studied, most notably in Minnesota and Missouri ($R = 1.38$), and in Iowa ($R = 1.35$). At the same time, however, additional statistical tests concerning the magnitude of the rA values revealed that in no area could the distribution of towns be described as a truly uniform one (Table 2). Nevertheless, the fact that the tendency toward uniform spacing is most marked in the midwestern states of Minnesota, Missouri, and Iowa (Fig. 4), emphasizes the descriptive value of the near-neighbor statistic R, since the general uniformity of relief, the method of original subdivision of the land based upon the quarter section, the rectangular road pattern, and the generally even spread of population associated with a relatively intensive feed-grain/livestock economy are characteristic

AGGREGATED PATTERNS

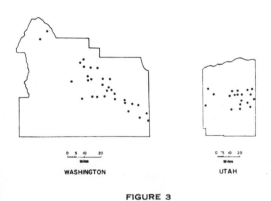

WASHINGTON   UTAH

FIGURE 3

TENDENCY TOWARDS UNIFORM SPACING

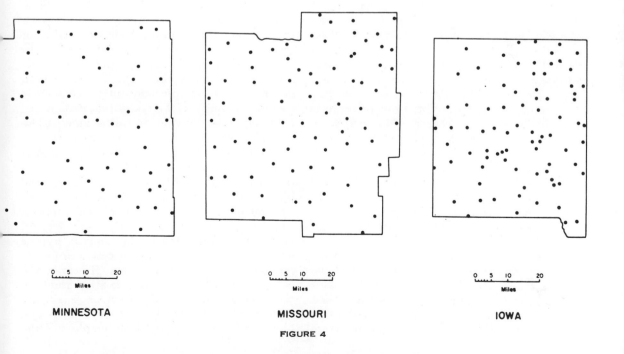

MINNESOTA   MISSOURI   IOWA

FIGURE 4

TABLE 2

Tests for uniform spacing

Area	Density of towns per square mile	Mean observed distance rA (miles)	Expected mean distance in uniform distribution of given density ru	Difference between rA and ru Significant?
California	.0243	3.46	6.90	Yes
Florida	.0200	3.32	7.59	*"*
Georgia	.0350	3.52	5.74	*"*
Iowa	.0307	3.86	6.13	*"*
Kansas	.0166	5.16	8.34	*"*
Louisiana	.0437	2.57	5.13	*"*
Minnesota	.0169	5.32	8.27	*"*
Mississippi	.0280	3.84	6.42	*"*
Missouri	.0219	4.67	7.27	*"*
New Mexico	.0065	6.82	13.28	*"*
North Dakota	.0082	6.13	11.86	*"*
Ohio	.0512	2.80	4.75	*"*
Oregon	.0317	2.86	6.03	*"*
Pennsylvania	.0466	2.82	4.98	*"*
Texas (NW)	.0104	6.03	10.55	*"*
Texas (SE)	.0182	4.29	7.97	*"*
Utah	.0061	4.49	13.74	*"*
Virginia	.0363	3.20	5.64	*"*
Washington	.0073	4.14	12.57	*"*
Wisconsin	.0299	3.58	6.22	*"*

features of these areas which would favor a more even spacing of towns. That even in these areas there is not apparent a more marked tendency toward a hexagonal arrangement of towns can in part be attributed to adverse physical features, such as the glacial lake-strewn surfaces of Minnesota; to the linear and dendritic patterns associated with the transportation routes of rivers, highways, or railways; to original site features, such as river fords, power sites, forestry and mining centers; and finally to mere chance. The pattern of settlements in Wisconsin ($R = 1.24$) appears to reflect the importance of these factors to an even greater extent, for in this area the tendency toward uniform spacing is even less pronounced than in the other midwestern areas, notwithstanding the fact that it is very akin to these same areas in its broad physical, economic, and social characteristics.

Elsewhere throughout the United States the tendency toward a uniform spacing of settlements is most marked in Kansas and Georgia and is of varying importance in a further six areas. Kansas might well be considered to be part of the Midwest, although in terms of climate and land use it is significantly different from the other midwestern areas. A general east-west linearity in the arrangement of many of the towns within this area reflects the direction of the major transportation routes which traverse the area (Fig. 5). A similar control of settlement patterns by transportation networks is apparent in the Mississippi area and on the Staked Plains of northwestern Texas. In both of these areas a predominantly rectangular pattern of major highways is reflected in the relatively close spacing of towns along these routes, while in the interstitial areas towns are spaced further apart. These conflicting patterns within the areas have tended to lower the obtained values of R. By contrast, in Georgia the pattern of transportation routes is in very close agreement with the arrangement characteristic of a hexagonal pattern of settlements (Fig. 5). Many of the larger towns, for example, appear to be associated with the intersection of five or six radial transportation routes. However, the comparatively low value of R is attributable to the irregular spacing of numerous small settlements along and between the major highways. Considerations such as these emphasize the

SETTLEMENTS AND ROAD NETWORKS

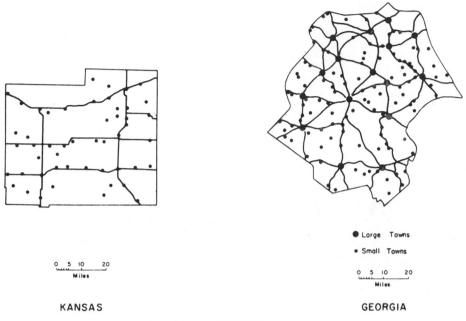

KANSAS   GEORGIA

FIGURE 5

desirability of incorporating the population-size variable into the analysis. In many areas the tendency toward either aggregation or uniformity would undoubtedly be more pronounced if the distribution patterns of only certain size towns were to be analyzed. A further inadequacy of the study design is pointed up by a consideration of the pattern of settlements in Ohio (Fig. 6). In the northwestern half of this area, that is, to the north and northwest of the Maumee River, the pattern of settlements appears more uniform than it does to the south of the river, where there is considerable linearity in the arrangement of the settlements. Possibly this is related to the fact that in the northwest the terrain is slightly more hilly in association with old morainic deposits, whereas to the south and southeast a lacustrine plain surface predominates. Considerable care should obviously be exercised in the choice of sample areas, since, as in this case, two distinct patterns within an area may tend to contradict one another and thereby render the statistical results largely meaningless.

In the remaining areas of southeastern Texas, Virginia, and Pennsylvania, in which the tendency toward a uniform spacing of settlements is also statistically significant, the results are more difficult to interpret. In each case the observed mean distance (rA) is greatly exceeded by that which would be expected of a uniform distribution. In Pennsylvania this discrepancy stems in part from the fact that there were many closely spaced settlements in the northeast-southwest trending valleys, while the ridges and interfluves were frequently devoid of settlements. Similarly, on the Virginia Piedmont and the Texas Coastal Prairies, a close spacing of settlements along the major transportation routes with wide areas of intervening territory in which nucleated settlements are few in number, resulted in comparatively low values for the observed mean distance.

What of the six areas in which the distribution of settlements is apparently random (Table 1)? These anomalies are easily explained away in terms of the mathematics of the near-neighbor measure. For example, the compara-

OHIO SAMPLE TOWNS

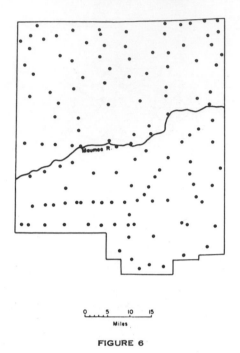

0   5   10   15
Miles

FIGURE 6

RANDOM PATTERN

0   5   10   20
Miles

NORTH DAKOTA

FIGURE 7

tively low value of R for North Dakota is a function of, on the one hand, the low density of towns per square mile which accounts for a large value of rE, and, on the other hand, a large value of rA resulting from the fact that there are only a few widely spaced towns within the area (Fig. 7). However, the more important consideration is whether or not a random distribution of settlements has any real geographic significance. In the North Dakota area, for example, the critical fact appears to be that the settlements are located along three major transportation axes which have an approximate east-west orientation, rather than that the distribution is statistically random. Indeed, the concept of randomness with respect to settlement patterns might well be disregarded, except for the fact that the value of $R = 1$ is a convenient and useful origin from which to measure the tendencies toward an aggregation or uniform spacing of settlements. As the value of R decreases and approaches zero, so the tendency toward an aggregation of settlements might be presumed to be greater, and, conversely, as the value of R increases from 1, then the tendency toward

a uniform spacing of settlements becomes more pronounced.

The discussion up to this point has been focused upon the validity of the near-neighbor statistic as a descriptive statistic of the manner in which urban settlements are distributed over portions of the earth's surface. Considerable emphasis has been given to the interpretation of the various obtained values of R, and it is evident that the statistic is sufficiently sensitive in character to point up the differences which do exist between various distribution patterns. Whether or not the hypothetical norms of aggregation, randomness, and uniform spacing are accepted as meaningful reference points, the near-neighbor statistic provides a logically acceptable and precise expression of the character of a distribution pattern of settlements. Furthermore, inasmuch as the statistic ranges in value from 0 to 2.15, within which limits any value is possible, it is logically consistent to consider the near-neighbor statistic as a continuous variable over this range. Accepting this to be the case, then a number of powerful, sophisticated, statistical techniques, such as correlation and regression analysis, can be brought to bear on the more fundamental and important problem of providing an explanation of the variation in the magnitude of the obtained values of R. Some tentative hypotheses relevant to this problem have already been suggested in this study, but the degree to which these hypotheses are valid with respect to all of the areas has yet to be determined. While an extended analysis along these lines falls outside of the scope of this paper, it might be noted that the value of R appears to be related in a positive direction with the variables *percentage of an area in cropland, percentage of land area in farms*, and *percentage of total population classed as rural farm*.[21] That is to say, the tendency toward a uniform spacing of settlements appears to be more pronounced in those areas in which the amount of cropland is high, or the percentage of total area in farms is high, or, finally, the percentage of the total population classed as rural farm population is high. Conversely, the tendency toward an aggregation of settlements will be greater as the magnitude of these same variables decreases. It should be stressed that the amount of explained variation in the values of R which is accounted for by the relationship of these variables is not particularly high, and there are obviously a number of additional relevant variables which must be incorporated into the analysis before a satisfactory level of explanation is achieved. The problem awaits further investigation.

FOOTNOTES

[1] See, for example, J. Garland, ed., *The North American Midwest* (New York: John Wiley & Sons, Inc., 1955), pp. 28–39. Also, H.H. McCarty, *The Geographic Basis of American Economic Life* (New York: Harper & Row, Publishers, 1940). In his discussion of the Great Plains area, for example, McCarty states: "Cities and towns are widely spaced, since their frequency necessarily varies with the density of the open-country population" (p. 237).

[2] J. Bernard, "Une Formule pour la cartographie de l'habitat rural avec application au département de l'Yonne," *Comptes Rendus du Congrès International de Géographie*, **3** (1931), 108–117.

[3] M. R. Colas, "Répartition de l'habitat rural," *Bulletin de l'Association Géographique Français* (1945), 51–56.

[4] A. H. Debouverie, "Une Méthode à base numérique pour la cartographie de l'habitat, spécialement applicable à la Belgique," *Bulletin de la Société Belge d'Etudes Géographiques*, **13** (1943), 146–196.

[5] A. Demangeon, "Une Carte de l'habitat," *Annales de Géographie*, **42** (1933), 225–232.

[6] A. Meynier, "L'Habitat rural dans les Ségalas," *Comptes Rendus du Congrès International de Géographie*, **3** (1931), 99–102.

[7] A. Zierhoffer, "Sur une Formule servant à exprimer la dispersion et la concentration absolue de l'habitat rural," *Comptes Rendus du Congrès International de Géographie*, **3** (1934), 410–415.

[8] In a sense this judgment is not entirely correct. For example, Zierhoffer considered dwellings to be dispersed if more than 150 to 200 meters separated them. Debouverie, in his study of Belgium, regarded the distance of 100 meters between dwellings as the limit of dispersion. However, no attempt was ever made to analyze these distances and to provide an explanation for the variation in them. In effect, the distance between dwellings (or towns) was always regarded as a constant and not as a variable.

[9] See J.M.A. Houston, *Social Geography of Europe* (London: Gerald Duckworth & Co., Ltd., 1953), pp. 81–85; and J. Tricart, *Cours de géographie humaine*, Vol. I: L'Habitat rural (Paris: Centre de Documentation Universitaire, 1959), pp. 72–75.

[10] See P. J. Clark and F. C. Evans, "Distance to Nearest Neighbour as a Measure of Spatial Relationships in Populations," *Ecology*, **35** (1954), 445–453.

[11] *Ibid.*, 446.

[12] The derivation of the rE values involves consideration of the Poisson exponential function. The mathematical derivation of the formulae used in this study is presented in *ibid.*, 451–452.

[13] It is true that the mean distance between nearest neighbors is maximized in a hexagonal distribution where each point has six equidistant nearest neighbors. In this case it can be shown that the maximum value for rA is $2^1/_2/(3^1/_4 \ p \ ^1/_2)$ and that $R = 2.15$.

[14] W. Christaller, *Die zentralen Orte in Süddeutschland* (Jena, 1933); A. Lösch, *Die rämuliche Ordnung der Wirtschaft* (Jena, 1944); J. E. Brush, "The Hierarchy of Central Places in Southwestern Wisconsin," *Geographical Review*, **43** (1953), 380–402.

[15] An analysis of variance is sufficient. For the necessary transformations see Clark and Evans, *op. cit.*, 452.

[16] *Ibid.*, 452.

[17] U. S. Bureau of the Census, *Seventeenth Decennial Census of the United States: Census of Population*, 1950, Vol. I: Number of Inhabitants (Washington: U.S.G.P.O., 1952).

[18] U. S. Department of Commerce, *United States Transportation Maps* (Washington: U.S.G.P.O., 1938–49).

[19] Principally: *Road Atlas* (Chicago: Rand McNally & Co., 1959).

[20] The distances, measured in miles, represent the direct airline distances between the approximate geographic centers of the towns concerned.

[21] These tentative conclusions were presented in L. J. King, "Consideration of the Spatial Distribution of Urban Places in Selected Areas of the United States," unpublished manuscript, Department of Geography, State University of Iowa (1958).

3

A FAMILY OF DENSITY FUNCTIONS
FOR LÖSCH'S MEASUREMENTS
ON TOWN DISTRIBUTION

MICHAEL F. DACEY

Lösch[1] measured the minimum distances separating towns in several midwestern parts of the United States and published the frequency distribution of distances. The importance of these urban distributions is evidently indicated by the frequent reproduction of his histographs. He obtained, in his words, "clear-cut frequency curves." Neither he nor other students have yet identified the necessary descriptive function; in this note it is shown that the gamma distribution may be fitted to each observed distribution. Table 1 recapitulates Lösch's frequency distributions for midwestern areas in the United States containing fifty or more towns, while Table 2 summarizes the frequency distribution for English towns. Lösch's tables contain areas of fewer than fifty towns, and we cannot adequately estimate frequency curves for them.

At least for the first approximation it may be anticipated that the location of a nearest neighbor is the outcome of a chance event. Because the event takes place in an essentially two-dimensional space, this chance event may be considered subject to circular convolutions. Under this hypothesis, the distribution of distances between nearest-neighbor towns is a gamma variate. It is known that in a random distribution of points in two-dimensional space the distribution of the squares of distances between nearest neighbors is a $\gamma(1)$ variate with scale parameter $\beta = \pi d$, d evidently being the density of points per unit area.[2]

Tables 1 and 2 present data which may be fitted to this gamma function. For a continuous variable x the probability density for a gamma variate with parameter α is defined by:

$$(1) \qquad f(x; \alpha, \beta) = \frac{x^{\alpha-1}e^{-x/\beta}}{\beta^{\alpha}\Gamma(\alpha)}$$

$$(\alpha > 0,\ \beta > 0,\ 0 \leq x \leq \infty)$$

The β is a scale parameter.

Reprinted from *The Professional Geographer*, **16** (1964), 5–7, by permission of the author and editor.

TABLE 1

Frequency distributions of distances to nearest larger town

Distance in miles	Population class in thousandths and area							
	.3–1		1–4			4–20		20–100
	Iowa	*Ill. Ind. Ohio*	*Iowa*	*Iowa Miss.*	*East Texas*	*Ill. Ind. Ohio*	*Iowa Miss.*	*Ill. Ind. Ohio*
0–	1	150	0	7	11	28	0	{ 8
2–	11	171	0	103	39	70	8	
4–	13	24	5	82	45	68	9	{ 20
6–	36	2	2	11	23	42	22	
8–	97		0		8	5	8	{ 23
10–	107		2		3		1	
12–	69		8		1		3	{ 9
14–	30		11		1			
16–	20		16					{ 1
18–	5		28					
20–	2		22					
22–	1		12					
24–			19					
26–			7					
28–			7					
30–			4					
32–			4					
34–			2					
36–			2					
38–40			1					
Total	392	347	152	203	131	213	51	61

Adapted from Lösch, pp. 391–392.

One geometric interpretation of the gamma variate with shape parameter α is that the distribution is formed by convolution of α variables, which are independent and identically random. Each variable has the exponential density function e^{-z}. In the data under consideration, this may be taken to mean that the location of the nearest neighbor of a town is a circular function of the density of towns. Furthermore, the neighborhood relationship for each town constitutes an independent event. The geometrical interpretation for differing values of α is obscure; however, the consequence is known, for as α increases the gamma distribution approaches the normal distribution and for α larger than 10 the approximation to the normal is for most practical purposes very good.

Table 3 presents the results obtained by fitting the gamma function to the distances from a town to the nearest town of the same or

TABLE 2

Distances separating English towns

Distance in miles	Population Class	
	10,000	20,000–100,000
0–	117	150
2–	28	46
4–	14	25
6–	3	9
8–		6
10–12		

Adapted from Lösch, p. 394

larger size. The estimated parameters do not necessarily constitute either minimum variance or most efficient estimates of the true parameters. In most cases it was possible to establish approximate parameters simply by comparing the ratios of the .1, .5, and .9 fractiles of

TABLE 3

*Description and analysis of gamma functions**

Area	Population Class	Variable	Shape Parameter	Scale Parameter	χ^2	Degrees of Freedom
Iowa	300–1,000	r^2	$\Gamma(2.1)$	$\dfrac{.01375}{3.1^{1/2}}$	8.833	7
Iowa	1,000–4,000	r^2	$\Gamma(1.2)$	$\dfrac{.00294}{2.2^{1/2}}$	.116	2
Illinois Indiana Ohio	1,000–4,000	r^2	$\Gamma(0.2)$	$\dfrac{.17000}{1.2^{1/2}}$	7.163	6
Iowa Missouri	1,000–4,000	r^2	$\Gamma(1.3)$	$\dfrac{.08915}{2.3^{1/2}}$	3.934	6
East Texas	1,000–4,000	r^2	$\Gamma(0)$	.03436	1.365	3
Illinois Indiana Ohio	4,000–20,000	r^2	$\Gamma(0.3)$	$\dfrac{.04773}{1.3^{1/2}}$	1.471†	2
Iowa Missouri	4,000–20,000	r^2	$\Gamma(2.2)$	$\dfrac{.03606}{3.2^{1/2}}$	1.721	1
England	10,000–20,000	r	$\Gamma(0.1)$	$\dfrac{.63}{1.1^{1/2}}$	1.417	4
England	20,000–100,000	r	$\Gamma(0)$	.50000	5.139	5

*Gamma functions were fitted to the frequency distributions of Tables 1 and 2. The scale parameter was estimated from density of places. Because the scale parameter cannot be accurately determined, it was altered in some cases to improve the fit. However, for counting degrees of freedom, it was accepted that this parameter was estimated from the data. So degrees of freedom equal the number of classes minus three.

†The tail of the observed frequency distribution was smoothed.

each observed distribution with fractiles of the incomplete gamma function. This procedure for estimating parameters is described by Hold.[3] We have taken this easy way wherever possible, instead of the laborious computation of maximum-likelihood estimates because our purpose is not to obtain accurate estimates of the gamma parameter, but simply to demonstrate that this distribution is adequate to describe the frequency distributions given by Lösch. The computed χ^2 values are all significant at the .1 or higher probability level; most are significant at the .5 or higher probability level. A typical level of correspondence between observed and calculated frequency distributions is shown in Table 4.

The difference between midwestern United States and England is conspicuous. Using r to denote nearest-neighbor measurements the variable r^2 has been fitted to the midwestern areas, while for English towns the variable is r. The reason for this difference is not known.

TABLE 4

Distance r	Observed frequency f_0	Calculated frequency f_c	$f_0 - f_c$	$\dfrac{(f_0 - f_c)^2}{f_c}$
0.	92	92.86	− .86	.008
1.	58	56.32	+1.68	.050
2.	33	34.16	−1.16	.039
3.	13	20.72	−7.72	2.876
4.	16	12.57	+3.43	.936
5.	9	7.62	+1.38	.250
6.	7	4.62	+2.38	} .336
7.	2	2.80	− .80	
8.	4	1.70	+2.30	} .644
9.	2	1.03	+ .97	
10.	–	1.60	−1.60	
Total	236	236		$(\chi^2 \equiv)$ 5.139

Observed and calculated frequency distributions for English towns with a population of 20,000–100,000 are given in Table 2. For a chi-square test of goodness of fit the degrees of freedom are 5, and the tabulated probability for obtaining a χ^2 as large as 5.139 is approximately .4.

Lösch attempts an explanation which may or may not prove acceptable:

In England, ... where the towns cluster in the five coal districts and around London, the distances are much less, practically insignificant, especially between smaller and medium-sized towns. Towns are not evenly distributed over a uniformly fertile plain, as in the American Middlewest, but cluster about the few places where natural resources are to be found.[4]

FOOTNOTES

[1] A. Lösch, *The Economics of Location* (New Haven: Yale University Press, 1954).

[2] M. F. Dacey, "Order Neighbor Statistics for a Class of Random Patterns in Multidimensional Space" (mimeographed, 1963).

[3] A. Hold, *Statistical Theory with Engineering Applications* (New York: John Wiley & Sons, Inc., 1952).

[4] Lösch, *op. cit.*, p. 438

4

MODIFIED POISSON PROBABILITY LAW
FOR POINT PATTERN
MORE REGULAR THAN RANDOM

MICHAEL F. DACEY

Mapping, and using map evidence, for incisive, descriptive statements about spatial distributions is a fundamental operation in geographic research. In terms of their abstract properties, map distributions exist in one of the three lowest geometric dimensions—the use of points, lines, and areas to represent a distribution. Map analysis is the description of the density and pattern of this geometry. The map itself may serve as the descriptive statement, or the many subtleties of map distributions may be summarized into symbols, words, or numbers. Highly regular or obviously systematic patterns are found infrequently in geographic investigations. Usually the patterns display no obvious order or system. In interpreting such patterns, there is a temptation to dismiss analysis with the statement that the distribution is irregular or, possibly, to say that it is a random distribution. To say that a distribution is irregular neither effectively describes it nor suggests cause. To say that a distribution is random, in a nontechnical sense, is to say that

the pattern has no discernible order and that cause is undeterminable. In the terminology of mathematical statistics, the term "random" has a precise meaning which refers to the process generating a pattern, and the random pattern is the realization of a theoretical random process. A random process is synonymous with pure chance because each event has an equal probability of occurrence. In terms of a map pattern, pure chance means that each map location has an equal probability of receiving a symbol. Since it is highly unlikely that geographic distributions, particularly locational patterns involving human decisions, are the result of equally probable events, it is expected that most map patterns reflect some system or order. It is for this reason that map patterns are examined for evidence of a spatial process. The search for a process may take many different

Reprinted from *Annals of the Association of American Geographers*, **54** (1964), 559–565, by permission of the author and editor.

paths. One procedure is to obtain a probability law that, on one hand, accurately describes properties of the map pattern and, on the other hand, suggests properties of the underlying spatial process.

This report describes a probability law and shows its application to map analysis. The class of patterns to be studied may be represented on a map by point symbols. A point pattern may be described, for many analytical purposes, by three types of spatial processes: the random or stochastic process, clustering or contagious processes, and regular or geometric processes. The theoretical, random-point pattern has been extensively examined, and a recent study by Dacey summarizes many properties of stochastic-point processes on the plane.[1] Processes of spatial clustering have been formulated for stellar and ecological models and are characterized by the negative binomial, Neyman Type A, and similar contagious probability distributions. Properties of contagious distributions are summarized by Feller and by Gurland.[2] In contrast, there has been little, if any, interest in more regular than random-point patterns. Processes generating spatial regularity in the arrangement of activities are an integral feature of geographic theory. Central place theory, for example, states that, in the uniform plane, market and service centers are regularly distributed in a honeycomb pattern, and that a dispersed pattern of towns and cities has been observed in a number of study regions.

This report considers a probability law that describes one type of spatial pattern having a more regular or systematic arrangement of points than produced by a random process. First, properties of this probability law are stated and an urn model with an obvious spatial analog is constructed. Second, applications of this probability law are illustrated and numerical examples are drawn from the distribution of farms on the Tonami Plain, Japan, and of towns and cities in Iowa.

PROBABILITY LAW FOR MORE REGULAR THAN RANDOM PATTERN

The discrete probability law studied in this report has two parameters: a positive real number γ and a probability p lying between zero and 1. This law is defined for a random variable x that takes on nonnegative, integer values only. The probability mass function is

$$(1) \quad p(x) = (q\gamma^x e^{-\gamma}/x!) +$$
$$(p x \gamma^{x-1} e^{-\gamma}/x!) \quad x = 0, 1, \ldots$$
$$= 0 \qquad \text{otherwise}$$

where
$$\gamma > 0$$
$$0 \le p \le 1$$
$$q = 1 - p$$

I can find no previous statement of Eq. 1.

PROPERTIES

The z crude moment of Eq. 1 is

$$v_z(x) = \sum_{x=0}^{\infty} x^z p(x) \quad z = 0, 1, \ldots$$

This summation is evaluated easily in terms of its moment-generating function

$$\Psi(t) = \sum_{x=0}^{\infty} e^{tx} p(x)$$
$$= q e^{-\gamma} \sum_{x=0}^{\infty} (\gamma e^t)^x / x! +$$
$$p e^{t-\gamma} \sum_{x=0}^{\infty} (\gamma e^t)^{x-1} / (x-1)!$$
$$= q e^{\gamma(e^t - 1)} + p e^{\gamma(e^t - 1) + t}$$

The $p(x)$ is a probability-density function because it has the properties (a) the probabilities sum to unity and (b) no negative probabilities:

(a) $\qquad \Psi(0) = q + p = 1$
(b) $\qquad$ it is easy to show that

for the first term of Eq. 1

$$q\gamma^x e^{-\gamma}/x! > 0 \qquad x = 0, 1, 2, \ldots$$

and for the second term of Eq. 1

$$p\gamma^{-1} e^{-\gamma}/(-1)! = 0 \qquad x = 0$$
$$p\gamma^{x-1} e^{-\gamma}/(x-1)! > 0 \qquad x = 1, 2, \ldots$$

The z crude moment of $p(x)$ is given by the z derivative of $\Psi(t)$ and evaluating the result for $t = 0$. It may be shown that the expected value of $p(x)$ is

$$(2) \qquad \Psi'(0) = E(x) = \gamma + p = \mu$$

The second moment is

$$\Psi''(0) = v_2(x) = \gamma(1 + \gamma + 2p) + p$$

So the variance is

$$(3) \qquad V(x) = \Psi''(0) - \Psi'^2(0) = \mu - p^2$$

A common index of dispersion is the quantity $D = V/E$. A random distribution is denoted by $D = 1$, because the mean and variance of the Poisson distribution have the same value. A contagious, or more dispersed than random, distribution is denoted by $D > 1$, and a systematic, or less dispersed than random, distribution is denoted by $D < 1$. The distribution under consideration is always less dispersed than random because

$$D(x) = \frac{\mu - p^2}{\mu} < 1. \qquad p > 0$$

ESTIMATION OF PARAMETERS

The distribution (Eq. 1) may be fit to observed data by the method of moments. Let $m_1(x)$ and $m_2(x)$ denote estimates from empirical data of the expectation and second central moment, respectively. The estimates of p and γ, written $\hat{p}$ and $\hat{\gamma}$, are obtained by substituting in Eqs. 2–3, $m_1(x)$ for $E(x)$, $m_2(x)$ for $V(x)$, $\hat{p}$ for p, and $\hat{\gamma}$ for γ. One obtains

$$m_1(x) = \hat{\gamma} + \hat{p}$$

and

$$m_2(x) = \hat{\gamma} + \hat{p} - \hat{p}^2 = m_1(x) - \hat{p}^2$$

So

$$(4) \qquad \hat{p} = \{m_1(x) - m_2(x)\}^{1/2}$$

$$\hat{\gamma} = m_1(x) - \hat{p}$$

and

$$\hat{q} = 1 - \hat{p}$$

Alternatively, the p and γ may be estimated from the mean and proportion of zeros.

URN INTERPRETATION

An urn interpretation is described for $p(x)$. Two independent samples are drawn from urns. The first urn contains N balls, labeled 1, 2, ..., N. It is assumed that N is large. From this urn n balls are drawn *without replacement*. Then the n balls are returned to the urn and m balls are drawn *with replacement*. Let $p_1(y)$ denote the probability that any i^{th} label is drawn y times in the first sample, and let $p_2(z)$ denote the probability that any i^{th} label is drawn z times in the second sample. The probability $p(x)$ that the ith label is drawn x times in both samples is to be found. Clearly, $x = y + z$.

Put $p = n/N$. In the first sample, a label is drawn at most once and is drawn with probability p. Hence,

$$(5) \qquad p_1(y) = p \qquad\qquad y = 1$$
$$= q = 1 - p \qquad y = 0$$
$$= 0 \qquad\qquad \text{otherwise}$$

Put $\gamma = m/N$. The second sample follows the binomial distribution. For N large it is satisfactory for most purposes to use the Poisson approximation to the binomial distribution. Using the Poisson distribution gives

$$(6) \qquad p_2(z) = \gamma^z e^{-\gamma}/z! \quad z = 0, 1, 2, \ldots$$
$$= 0 \qquad\qquad \text{otherwise}$$

The ith label is drawn once in the first sample with probability p and, in this case, the probability that in both drawings it occurs x times is the probability $y = 1$ and $z = (x - 1)$. Since the samples are independent, the probability is

$$(7) \qquad p_1(1)p_2(x - 1) = pp_2(x - 1)$$

The ith label is not drawn in the first sample with probability q, and in this case, the probability that in both drawings it occurs x times is the probability that $y = 0$ and $z = x$. Since the samples are independent, the probability is

(8) $$p_1(0)p_2(x) = qp_2(x)$$

The ith label is drawn once or not drawn in the first sample. So the probability of drawing a label x times in both samples is simply the sum of Eqs. 7–8

$$p(x) = qp_2(x) + pp_2(x - 1)$$

Substituting Eq. 6 for $p_2(\cdot)$ and writing $x/x!$ for $1/(x - 1)!$ gives

$$p(x) = (q\gamma^x e^{-\gamma}/x!) +$$
$$(px\gamma^{x-1}e^{-\gamma}/x!) \qquad x = 0, 1, \ldots$$

SPATIAL INTERPRETATION

A spatial analog of the urn model is obtained by considering a large map partitioned into N regions of equal area. Objects are assigned to regions by two different sample methods. (1) A systematic sample is used to assign one individual to each of pN different regions. (2) A random sample is used to assign m individuals to the N regions; a convenient procedure is to lay a rectangular coordinate system on the map and locate each individual by ordered pairs of random numbers. The probability that a region receives x individuals is $p(x)$.

EFFECT OF PARAMETER P

In the urn formulation the $(n + m)$ objects are partitioned into two classes. pN of the objects are randomly assigned to urns with the restriction that no urn contains more than one such object, and γN objects are randomly assigned to urns without restrictions. The parameter p is a measure of the bias toward evenness in an otherwise random assignment of objects.

For $p = 0$ the assignment is entirely random, and $p(x)$ is simply the Poisson probability law with parameter γ.

For $p = 1$ Eq. 1 may be written

$$p(x) = 0 + \frac{x\gamma^{x-1}e^{-\gamma}}{x!} = \frac{\gamma^{x-1}e^{-\gamma}}{(x - 1)!}$$

Since $$(-1)! = \infty$$

and $$\gamma = \mu - 1$$

then $$p(0) = 0$$

and $$p(x) = p_2(x - 1) \quad x = 1, 2, \ldots$$

This means that where $p = 1$, at least one event occurs in each urn and the probability that $x (= 1, 2, \ldots)$ events occur is the Poisson probability, with parameter $(\mu - 1)$, that $(x - 1)$ events occur.

ILLUSTRATIONS OF THE PROBABILITY LAW

Computation of the probability $p(x)$ and application of the probability model to map patterns are illustrated. The probability law is used to describe patterns formed by (1) the distribution of farms in a homogeneous agricultural region, and (2) the distribution of larger towns and cities in the highly uniform state of Iowa. The analysis of these data contains a brief discussion of reasons for predicting a map pattern more regular than random. In addition to this analysis, the first study includes numerical examples showing estimation of parameters and the computation of expected frequencies.

THE DISTRIBUTION OF ISOLATED FARMS IN THE TONAMI PLAIN

According to Matui, the Tonami Plain, Toyama Prefecture, Japan, is celebrated for its scattered villages.[3] This alluvial plain contains several large and small towns interspersed among widely scattered rural settlements.

For one small region in this plain, Matui conducted a map analysis of the distribution of houses and isolated farms. He presented considerable evidence that the distribution of houses conforms to a random pattern. The evidence for randomness in the arrangement of farms is less convincing.

To study isolated farms, the study region was divided into 750 squares, each measuring 130 square meters. The region contained 846 isolated farms, and Matui counted the number of farms in each of the small squares; the pattern of cell frequencies and the summary frequency distribution are given on page 151 (above).

Matui tested the hypothesis of a random distribution of farms. Under the assumption of a random arrangement, the frequency distribution of farms per cell evidently is given by the Poisson distribution. The calculated frequencies are listed in Table 1. A chi-square test may be used to examine the hypothesis of randomness. The calculated $\chi^2 = 18.6$; with four degrees of freedom, there is little evidence of randomness in the observed spatial arrangement.

Rejection of the hypothesis of randomness is not surprising. Matui described the region as a highly homogeneous agricultural area characterized by uniform patterns. Under these conditions, if the spatial arrangement is determined by an essentially random process, an underlying bias toward a systematic distribution, such as Eq. 1, is expected.

TABLE 1

Observed and calculated frequency distributions for the number of isolated farms in small square subregions of an arbitrary study region in the Tonami Plain, Japan

Number of farms per cell x	Observed number of cells Ob	Calculated number of cells	
		Poisson Law $N \cdot p_2(x)$	Equation (1) $N \cdot p(x)$
0	206	243	205
1	318	274	318
2	164	154	165
3	49	58	50
4	12	16	10
5	1	4	2
6	0	1	0

Source: Observed data from Matui.

ESTIMATION OF PARAMETERS BY METHOD OF MOMENTS

The model was fit to the farm-pattern data by the method of moments. The calculated mean and variance are

$$m_1(x) = \sum xf(x)/N = 1.128$$

$$m_2(x) = \sum [x - \bar{x}]^2 f(x)/N = 0.904$$

Using the equations in Eq. 4

$$\hat{p} = [m_1(x) - m_2(x)]^{1/2} = [1.128 - 0.094]^{1/2}$$
$$\doteq 0.473$$

$$\hat{\gamma} = m_1(x) - \hat{p} = 1.128 - 0.473 = 0.655$$

For the analysis of the farm pattern the parameters with 2 decimal-place accuracy are $\hat{p} = 0.47$, $\hat{\gamma} = 0.66$, $\hat{q} = 0.53$, and $\hat{\mu} = 1.13$.

COMPUTATION OF EXPECTED FREQUENCIES

The probabilities $p(x)$ are easily computed from a table of individual terms of the Poisson distribution. Poisson probabilities are extensively tabulated (see Molina).[4] Calculation of $p(x)$ from individual terms of the Poisson distribution is illustrated for the observed data in Table 1.

The probability terms of Eq. 1 are computed directly from probabilities of the Poisson distribution with parameter γ, and let $p_2(x; \gamma)$ denote the Poisson probability that x events occur. Next compute $q[p_2(x; \gamma)]$ and $p[p_2(x; \gamma)]$. The required probabilities are given by

$$p(0) = q[p_2(0; \gamma)]$$

$$p(1) = q[p_2(1; \gamma)] + p[p_2(0; \gamma)]$$

$$p(2) = q[p_2(2; \gamma)] + p[p_2(1; \gamma)]$$

and in general

$$p(x) = q[p_2(x; \gamma)] + p[p_2(x - 1; \gamma)] \quad x = 0, 1, \ldots$$

For the farm data $\gamma = 0.66$, and column 2 of Table 2 gives the Poisson probabilities $p_2(x; 0.66)$. The estimated probabilities are $q = 0.53$ and $p = 0.47$ and columns 3 and 4 list $0.53[p_2(x; 0.66)]$ and $0.47[p_2(x; 0.66)]$. The probability $p(x)$ is obtained by adding the value for x in column 3 to the value for $(x - 1)$ in column 4; that is,

$$p(x) = qp_2(x) + pp_2(x - 1)$$

as listed in column 5.

Expected frequencies are given by $p(x)N$, where N is the total number of observations. The farm pattern was divided into 750 cells, so expected frequencies are given by $750p(x)$ (Table 1).

ANALYSIS OF PATTERN

The correspondence of Eq. 1 to the farm data is evidence that the distribution of farms is more regular than random. This conclusion is, however, solely in terms of the distribution

TABLE 2

Example of calculation of probabilities (Eq. 1) from probabilities of the Poisson Distribution

(1)	(2)	(3)	(4)	(5)
x	$p_2(x; 0.66)$	$0.53 \cdot$ $[p_2(x; 0.66)]$	$0.47 \cdot$ $[p_2(x; 0.66)]$	$p(x)$
0	0.51685	0.27393	0.24292	0.27393
1	0.34112	0.18079	0.16033	0.42371
2	0.11257	0.05966	0.05291	0.21999
3	0.02476	0.01312	0.01164	0.06603
4	0.00409	0.00217	0.00192	0.01381
5	0.00054	0.00029	0.00025	0.00221
6	0.00006	0.00003	0.00003	0.00028
7	0.00001	0.00001	0.00000	0.00004
8	0.00000	0.00000	0.00000	0.00000
Total	1.00000	0.53000	0.47000	1.00000

Notes: Column 2 gives Poisson probabilities, Eq. 6, with parameter $\gamma = 0.66$. Column 5 gives Eq. 1 for parameters $\gamma = 0.66$ and $p = 0.47$.

of farms per cell. This test does not take into account the two-dimensional pattern of cell frequencies. For example, if the same set of cells were distributed in the study region so that all vacant cells were in one part of the region, and the cells with three, four, and five farms were in a different part of the region, the results of the preceding analysis would not be changed. Accordingly, the study of cell frequencies alone is an inadequate basis for establishing the type of pattern formed by the arrangement of farms.

One approach to the pattern of cell frequencies is to test for independence in cell frequencies between adjacent cells. In general, consider a study region divided into N rectangular cells. Adjacent cells are combined into blocks of two cells, four cells, eight cells, . . . , and in general into blocks of 2^k cells. Largely to simplify this discussion, it is assumed that $N/2^k$ is not small. Let $p(x, 1) = p(x)$. Then if cell frequencies are independent events, it is a matter of elementary probability theory to obtain the recursive formula

$$(9) \quad p(x; 2^k) =$$

$$\sum_{y=0}^{x} p(y, 2^{k-1}) p(x - y, 2^{k-1}) \quad k = 1, 2, \ldots$$

Under the assumption of independence, this relation holds no matter how cells are combined.

To analyze the pattern in the cell frequencies of Matui's data, cells were combined into blocks of two and four. The two-cell blocks were obtained by combining adjacent west—east cells, and the four-cell blocks were obtained by combining squares of four cells. The observed frequency distributions are shown in Table 3. The calculated frequencies were obtained by applying Eq. 9 to Eq. 1. There is considerable evidence of independence in the frequencies of adjacent cells. A more extensive test may be conducted by considering other combinations of cells and blocks containing larger numbers of cells. Further tests were not conducted because there is no basis for suspecting that cell frequencies are not independent.

PATTERN SUMMARY

These tests present substantial evidence that the pattern of isolated farms is more regular than random. This conclusion agrees with Matui's verbal description of the Tonami Plain as a homogeneous area characterized by uniform patterns. It is stressed, however, that this result is contingent upon the size of cell defined by Matui. Selection of a smaller size of cell might yield a different interpretation of the map pattern.

EXAMPLES FROM THE ARRANGEMENT OF PLACES IN IOWA

Equation 1 was initially formulated for a study, by Dacey, of the spacing between larger places in the state of Iowa.[5] The domain

TABLE 3

Observed and calculated frequency distributions for the number of isolated farms in blocks of small square subregions of an arbitrary study region in the Tonami Plain, Japan

Number of farms per block x	Blocks of one cell		Blocks of two cells		Blocks of four cells	
	Ob	Ex	Ob	Ex	Ob	Ex
0	206	205	30	28	2	1
1	318	318	88	87	9	6
2	164	165	105	112	15	18
3	49	50	86	84	26	31
4	12	10	45	42	43	38
5	1	2	17	16	35	35
6			3	5	25	25
7			1	1	14	15
8					6	7
9					3	3
10					1	1
11					0	0
12					1	0
Total	750	750	375	375	180	180

Sources: Ob: Matui. For blocks of four cells the top row of cells was not used.

Ex: Table 1 and Eq. 9.

of that study was the ninety-nine most populous places in 1950, and the size 99 was chosen because Iowa is divided into ninety-nine counties. So the mean number of places per county was $\mu = 1$. For these ninety-nine places, the number of places in each county was obtained, and the frequency distribution is given in Table 4. Frequencies calculated from the Poisson distribution (Table 4) are an extremely poor fit, grossly overestimating the number of counties with a single place. Equation 1 was formulated to produce in an essentially random process a bias in the occurrence of single events. Table 4 gives frequencies calculated from Eq. 1 for $p = 0.77$ and $\gamma = 0.23$.

The degree of correspondence between observed and calculated frequencies is suspiciously close. To test more completely the application of Eq. 1, the distribution of urban places (places with 2500 or larger population) among Iowa counties was obtained for each census. The model was fit to each series by estimating μ from the mean number of places per county and p by the method of moments. Highly accurate estimates, comparable with the goodness-of-fit in Table 4, were obtained for each series. Further analysis of the time-series data displayed a very simple relation between the two independent parameters. Table

TABLE 4

Observed and calculated frequency distributions of 99 largest Iowa cities among the 99 Iowa counties, 1950

Number of cities per county x	Observed number of counties Ob	Calculated number of counties	
		Equation (1) $N \cdot p(x)$	Poisson Law $N \cdot p_2(x; 1)$
0	18	18	36
1	65	65	36
2	14	14	18
3	2	2	6
$\geqslant 4$	0	0	3

Source: Ob: U.S. Bureau of the Census: *U.S. Census of the Population: 1950*, Vol. I: Number of Inhabitants (Washington: U.S.G.P.O., 1952).

5 compares observed distributions with expected frequencies computed from the rule $p = 0.79\mu$. The 1960 fit alone is not acceptable. However, for $p = 0.745$, the calculated frequencies correspond closely to the observed 1960 frequencies. Reasons for the apparent shift in the structural relation between p and μ in the decade from 1950 to 1960 have not been established.

This spatial process is not limited to urban places and counties. A 10 per cent sample of

TABLE 5

Observed and calculated frequency distributions
of urban places per county
in Iowa: 1840–1960

x	1840 Ob	1840 Ex	1850 Ob	1850 Ex	1860 Ob	1860 Ex	1870 Ob	1870 Ex
0	98	98	96	96	88	87	80	78
1	1	1	3	3	10	12	16	20
2					1	0	3	1
3								
μ	0.010		0.030		0.121		0.222	
p	0.008		0.024		0.096		0.175	
q	0.992		0.976		0.904		0.825	
γ	0.002		0.006		0.025		0.047	

x	1880 Ob	1880 Ex	1890 Ob	1890 Ex	1900 Ob	1900 Ex	1910 Ob	1910 Ex
0	69	68	58	57	35	38	39	38
1	27	29	36	39	58	53	51	53
2	3	2	5	3	6	7	9	7
3					0	1	0	1
μ	0.333		0.465		0.707		0.697	
p	0.263		0.367		0.559		0.551	
q	0.737		0.633		0.441		0.449	
γ	0.070		0.098		0.148		0.146	

x	1920 Ob	1920 Ex	1930 Ob	1930 Ex	1940 Ob	1940 Ex	1950 Ob	1950 Ex*	1960 Ob	1960 Ex
0	31	29	30	29	23	24	21	21	20	13
1	55	59	57	59	63	63	64	64	60	69
2	13	10	12	10	13	11	13	12	15	15
3	0	1	0	1	0	1	1	1	3	2
4									0	0
5									1	0
μ	0.818		0.818		0.899		0.939		1.051	
p	0.646		0.646		0.710		0.742		0.830	
q	0.354		0.354		0.290		0.258		0.170	
γ	0.172		0.172		0.189		0.197		0.221	

Sources: Ob: U.S. Bureau of the Census: *U.S. Census of the Population: 1960,* Vol. I: Number of Inhabitants (Washington: U.S.G.P.O., 1962).

Ex: Calculated from Eq. 1, with $p = 0.79 \mu$.
* Owing to rounding, Ex values total 98.

townships in Iowa was drawn from the 1950 census, and the number of incorporated places (regardless of population) in each sample township was obtained. A place in two or more townships was assigned to the one township having the largest proportion of the place's population. Table 6 gives the observed frequency distribution of places per township and the expected frequencies calculated from Eq. 1 with parameters estimated by the method of moments.

The data in Tables 4–6 indicate substantial regularity in the distribution of places in Iowa.

TABLE 6

Observed and calculated frequency distributions
of places per township for a ten per cent
sample of townships, Iowa, 1950

Number of places per township x	Observed number of townships Ob	Caclulated number of townships Ex
0	86	85
1	69	71
2	12	10
3	0	1
$\geqslant 4$	0	0

Sources: Ob: U.S. Bureau of the Census: *U.S. Census of the Population: 1950,* Vol. I: Number of Inhabitants (Washington: U.S.G.P.O., 1952).

Ex: Calculated from Eq. 1, with parameters $\gamma = 0.149$ and $p = 0.408$.

FOOTNOTES

[1] M. F. Dacey, "Two-Dimensional Random-Point Patterns: A Review and an Interpretation," *Papers and Proceedings of the Regional Science Association,* 13 (1964), 41–58.

[2] W. Feller, "On a General Class of Contagious Distributions," *Annals of Mathematical Statistics,* 14 (1943), 389–400; J. Gurland, "A Generalized Class of Contagious Distributions," *Biometrics,* 14 (1958), 229–249.

[3] I. Matui, above, pp. 149–158.

[4] E. C. Molina, *Tables of Poisson's Exponential Limit* (Princeton: D. Van Nostrand Co., Inc., 1942).

[5] M. F. Dacey, "Imperfections in the Uniform Plane," *Michigan Inter-University Community of Mathematical Geographers,* No. 4 (1964).

5

MAPS BASED ON PROBABILITIES

MIECZYSLAW CHOYNOWSKI

While studying the distribution of brain tumors in a part of Poland[1] I had occasion to employ a type of statistical map which, so far as I know, has not previously been used and which seems potentially useful in a variety of applications. The method is so simple that there is no need to present it in detail. Everybody who finds it likely to be useful in his work will be able to use it and to improve upon it, having read this suggestion.

Statistical maps as presently used show, mostly by hatching or shading, the distribution of some phenomenon over a geographical area in terms of absolute frequencies or percentages.[2] While this method is useful as a simple description of the data, it may have shortcomings when one wants to make inferences based on the spatial distribution of the phenomenon, as was the case in my study of brain tumors.

Having constructed a map which showed the rates of brain tumors in sixty counties (*poviat*) of southern Poland (a part of this map is shown in Fig. 1), I found that some of the rates were very high or very low in comparison with the average for the whole area, this average being 5.17 per 100,000 inhabitants (see the third column of Table 1, containing data for seventeen counties). As these marked geographic irregularities were very surprising, I studied the data further and noticed that the counties deviating without any clear explanation (such as quality of medical care, differences in age composition, etc.) had small populations. Consequently, even a small difference in absolute frequencies created a substantial difference in rates. To put it differently, the deviations might well be attributable to sampling variations.

It then occurred to me to construct a map showing not the incidence of tumors, but the probability of these incidences if in fact the true incidence were the same for the whole area.

Reprinted from *Journal of the American Statistical Association*, **54** (1959), 385–388, by permission of the author and editor.

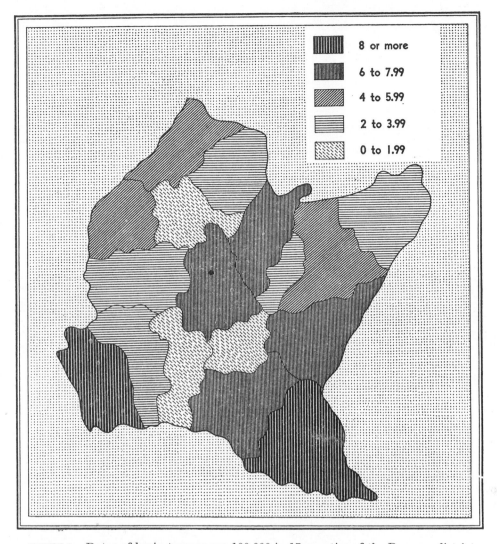

FIGURE 1.   Rates of brain tumors per 100,000 in 17 counties of the Rzeszow district

Since brain tumors are comparatively rare (12 per 100,000 persons in a period of seven years in the county having the largest incidence), the Poisson distribution should be satisfactory for calculating the probability of any given number of tumors. Table 1 shows the data and the resulting probabilities for seventeen counties. These probabilities are either upper- or lower-tail probabilities, depending upon whether the observed rate is above or below the mean rate. Table 1 shows that though [the] one county with the low and the one with the high rate have probabilities less than 0.05 (and in the whole area there were some with even less than 0.01),

some of the rates that are most striking and difficult to explain have comparatively high probabilities. Gorlice, which has excellent medical care, thanks to which tumors are well diagnosed, had a very high rate, which significantly exceeded the average for all sixty counties. Lesko had a very high rate, which appeared not to deviate significantly from the average. Brzozow, which is a rather backward county with less adequate medical care, had a very low rate, which was significantly less than the average, while Kolbuszowa and Krosno had very low rates, which did not produce unusually low probabilities.

A map with hatching corresponding to the probabilities of Table 1 is shown in Fig. 2. Such a map makes it possible to study the spatial distribution of a phenomenon without danger of basing one's conclusions on nonsignificant random variations. This method may be used for any phenomena distributed geographically, for example, in medicine zoology, ecology, botany, sociology, economics, etc.

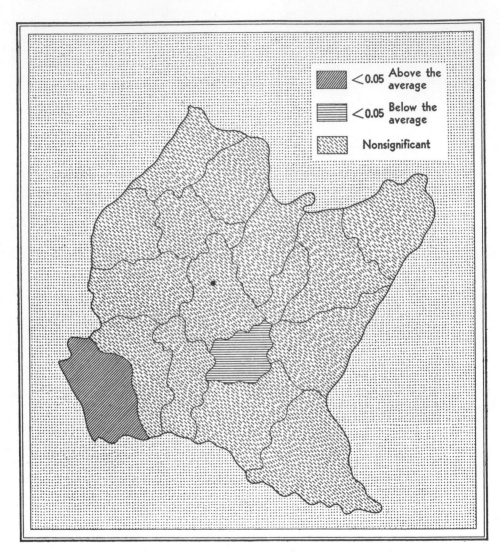

FIGURE 2. Probabilities of observed numbers of tumors in 17 counties

TABLE 1

Number of brain tumors and resulting probabilities in seventeen counties
of the Rzeszow District chosen for illustration

County	Population in thousands	No. of tumors for 100,000	Number of tumors		Probability
			Expected	Observed	
Brzozow	70	0.000	3.619	0	0.0264
Debica	110	3.636	5.687	4	0.3292
Gorlice	83	10.843	4.291	9	0.0314
Jaroslaw	102	5.882	5.273	6	0.4318
Jaslo	101	3.960	5.222	4	0.4025
Kolbuszowa	60	1.667	3.102	1	0.1844
Krosno	101	1.980	5.222	2	0.1072
Lesko	17	11.765	0.879	2	0.2199
Lubaczow	40	2.500	2.068	1	0.3881
Lancut	91	6.593	4.705	6	0.3324
Mielec	73	5.479	3.774	4	0.5211
Nisko	67	2.985	3.464	2	0.3277
Przemysl	88	6.818	4.550	6	0.3057
Przeworsk	57	3.509	2.947	2	0.4330
Rzeszow	182	7.143	9.409	13	0.1560
Sanok	56	7.143	2.895	4	0.3293
Tarnobrzeg	67	4.478	3.464	3	0.5227

FOOTNOTES

[1] M. Choynowski and A. Maciejak, "Nowotwory śródczaszkowe w świetle cyfr [Intracranial Tumors: A Statistical Analysis]," *Nowotwory,* **5** (1955), 284–314.

[2] F. E. Croxton and D. J. Cowden, *Applied General Statistics* (Englewood Cliffs, N. J.: Prentice-Hall, Inc., 1946), Chap. 6.

6

CLIMATIC CHANGE AS
A RANDOM SERIES

LESLIE CURRY

Fate, Time, Occasion, Chance and Change?—
　　To these All things are subject . . .
　　　　　—SHELLEY, *Prometheus Unbound*

Methods of representing various phenomena of nature and speculation about their inter-relationships are closely tied together. It is too often forgotten that geographical studies are not descriptions of the real world, but rather perceptions passed through the double filter of the author's mind and his available tools of argument and representation. We cannot know reality; we can have only an abstract picture of aspects of it. All our descriptions of relation or process are theories or, when formalized, better called models. Thus explicit model building as used in this paper is no innovation, but rather a frank recognition of human frailty.

In the study of climate, as elsewhere, mean values of variable quantities are used as representations of the changing phenomena of nature. This is an enormous step away from the real world, but unfortunately there is a widespread belief that certain traditionally defined means have physical reality, that they faithfully depict the real world rather than provide a highly abstract picture useful in certain contexts. Average values are taken over particular space-time dimensions and have meaning only for these dimensions. They are formed to exclude unwanted detail, so that only firm theory can decide which are the relevant facts to be included.

As soon as one lapses into believing that traditionally defined mean values are aspects of the real world and can be used in each and every context, reasoning takes a curious course. (This misuse of the mean is also found in qualitative arguments.) For example, mean monthly resultant winds, apparently specifically designed to remove the largest and most obvious features of the weather, have been computed and then used, until recently, to "explain" the pattern of that weather.

Reprinted from *Annals of the Association of American Geographers*, **52** (1962), 21–31, by permission of the author and editor.

Mean monthly rainfall is consistently used as a measure of moisture supply to plants in disregard of the time dimensions of water storage and its removal.

Even worse is the practice, when discussing processes or relationships, of assuming that the equalities specified for means defined over particular space-time coordinates may be carried over into different dimensions. If, for example, an insurance company has its mean income over a number of years equal to its mean payments and consequently argues that since it is in equilibrium it does not need reserve funds in hand, the firm will soon be out of business.[1] Equally, as will be shown, equations written for short-period means may not be carried over into long periods.

Two problems are considered in this paper: vegetation change and climatic change. New interpretations are possible when climatic calculations are made in terms of random variations operating within "natural" periods derived from functionally related phenomena. First, it is proposed that a climatically determined vegetation cover may undergo change due to variations concealed within the usual climatic mean and so lead to false hypotheses. The second argument, which occupies most attention, is that climate is varying continuously and randomly solely because of endogenous processes, of which the fluctuations that produced the Ice Ages are spectacular manifestations. It is shown that, if the tropical oceans have a 50 per cent chance of acting as a net source or as a net sink of atmospheric heat in a year, they can, because of their large storage capacity, impose fluctuations of the magnitude and periodicity of the Ice Ages. The small residual of total energy exchanged in the earth and atmosphere each year which affects oceanic storage has legitimately been neglected in weather analysis. However, it cannot be ignored over long spans of time because of its unexpected cumulative effect. Finally, a naïve but plausible physical interpretation is made of the probabilistic models used.

CLIMATIC CHANGE BY DEFINITION

The official international definition of climatic variation (i.e., change) is that the difference between nonoverlapping ten-year period means is greater than a value depend-

ing on the dispersion of individual values. In other words, there is a strong probability that the values are samples from different populations. But as Campbell has asked: What are the populations of which the decades being compared are samples?[2] To answer, as do Levy and Roth, that the two records must be regarded as samples of a varying population begs the question, since we want to know if the population is varying.[3] This conundrum is not hair splitting; we really do need an operational definition of climatic change.

A short-rooted grass would regard as highly variable rainfall which a long-rooted tree would find uniform. Each would have different periods of calculation since they have different lengths of "memory"; the grass would be crying "change" when the tree was noting only the usual dispersion of values. To define the official length of memory of climatology as ten years is confusing. The period of calculation must surely have some more objective basis than official decree.

There is no statistical technique which will allow an objective definition of the population to be described; this has to be inserted into the machine by the investigator. We assert climatic change because of landscape evidence of different weather conditions in the past; thus the individual features of the landscape should provide us with clues as to the period of calculation involved. In each case, there is some specific period of calculation appropriate to each phenomenon because of its "memory," e.g., its storage system or life span. The relevance of these ideas to a problem of landscape change will now be examined.

VEGETATION BOUNDARIES: A RECURRENT EVENTS MODEL

We are all familiar with statements of this form: "The limit of a particular vegetation is defined by, say, a mean annual rainfall of so many inches." Such statements can be useful, but are always inaccurate and may be quite misleading. It is feasible for a place experiencing an unvarying mean rainfall to have numerous changes of vegetation, none of which are cyclic in a genetic sense. The natural biotic landscape is not in a uniquely determined equilibrium with climate.

Take, for example, Canterbury on the South

Island of New Zealand, although many other parts of the world could be chosen. When Europeans arrived, tussock grassland occurred on the plains, but there were many evidences of totara forest occupation in a previous era: strewn logs, overage trees on rocky outcrops, and so on. At present, totara forest exists in areas having an annual rainfall of about forty inches or more. Since the Canterbury Plains have less than this, ergo, the climate has changed. If it is thought that there is a climax vegetation corresponding to a given climate as defined by mean values, it is necessary to invoke external factors, such as man, river capture, and so on, or a changing mean rainfall to provide causal explanations of vegetation change.

Nobody really believes that forty inches of rain per year in itself determines the vegetation of a place. It is more likely to be some specific requirement, such as, say, the absence of a period of two weeks with soil moisture reduced to wilting point during the germination and seedling stage of the first five years of a tree's life. Let us assume this to be the situation for the totara and that after this period it will continue to maturity and eventual death at a hundred years, regardless of the prevailing moisture conditions. Let there be nine places on a traverse with a decreasing probability of the occurrence of successful establishment conditions in any one year as shown in Table 1. We want to know how likely it is that totara will occupy the soil, the age distribution of trees, and so on.

From the theory of recurrent events[4] the mean of the recurrence times of success runs (i.e., of satisfactory moisture conditions) of length r is

$$\mu = (1 - p^r)/(qp^r)$$

with p as the probability of success in a year, and $q = 1 - p$ as the probability of a failure. The variance of these recurrence times is

$$\Sigma^2 = [1/(qp^r)^2] - [(2r + 1)/(qp^r)] - (p/q^2)$$

The number of successful runs is approximately normally distributed.

Table 1 gives the results of these calculations. The recurrence interval must be less than the 100 years mean expectation of life for totara to reproduce; at values near this

figure, stands of trees are likely to be of a single age. The remarkable feature emerges that even at I, with only a 10 per cent chance of favorable conditions occurring in any one year and an expectation for the recurrence interval of over 100,000 years, there is a 10 per cent chance of there being a recurrence interval which would allow the successful establishment of a reproducing forest, depending, of course, on the diffusion parameters for seeding. Along the traverse, this probability increases so that in the area A to D, forest will occur at all levels of probability. At E, with a mean expectation of forest conditions, there is nevertheless a 20 per cent chance of conditions not being favorable.

We learn here an important lesson: The vegetation of a place depending on climate can be considered as existing only with a certain degree of probability and that vegetational change does not imply climatic change. Note that the improbable event may have been happening since the history of the place was first recorded. It has been shown that phenomena related to climate may show change, although climate is being viewed as a stationary time series. We now take up the question of whether the nonstationary condition of climate, as displayed by the glacial epochs, may be derived from random fluctuations.

CLIMATIC CHANGE AS A RANDOM STORAGE BALANCE

When one considers the enormous literature on climatic change, it is surprising that there do not appear to have been any investigations of these variations as the results of a random process.[5] Presumably the reason is that intuitively it seems impossible that such large fluctuations as the Ice Ages could result from random variation. But intuition may not be a good guide. To paraphrase Professor Hare, our choice of logic in climatology appears to be chosen more from the length of our life span than from the various time spans involved.[6] As a justification for offering yet another hypothesis on climatic change, it should be understood that an adequate theory has not yet been developed. Either we have theories contributing to our understanding of the physical processes involved in fluctuations

TABLE 1

Maximum intervals between success runs for given probabilities

Places	A	B	C	D	E	F	G	H	I
p	0.9	0.8	0.7	0.6	0.5	0.4	0.3	0.2	0.1
μ	7.0	10.3	16.5	29.6	62.0	161.0	586.5	3,907.0	111,120.0
σ	14.0	14.5	19.6	32.0	63.9	162.6	587.9	3,908.0	111,100.0
$P_{0.1}$	0	0	0	0	0	0	0	0	0
0.2	0	0	0	2.7	8.3	24.4	92.7	624.0	17,796.0
0.3	0	2.8	6.3	13.0	28.8	76.5	280.8	1,925.0	53,348.0
0.7	14.3	17.8	26.7	46.2	95.2	245.5	892.2	5,939.0	168,892.0
0.8	18.8	22.5	33.0	56.5	115.7	297.6	1,080.0	7,190.0	204,444.0
0.9	24.9	28.9	41.6	70.6	143.8	369.1	1,339.0	8,909.0	253,328.0
0.99	39.6	44.1	62.2	74.6	148.9	378.9	1,370.0	9,916.0	258,863.0
0.999	50.4	55.2	77.3	99.2	198.1	504.1	1,822.0	12,115.0	344,410.0

p = Probability of success in a year.
P = Probability of the recurrence interval being less than the stated number of years for five successes in a row.

occurring in very recent times, but which can be extrapolated back in time only by the crudest assertions, or we have theories which are elegant in the periodicities they produce but which are weak in physical reasoning.

All the theories so far developed are deterministic in their phrasing; that is, given B, a cause A is looked for. Since climatology has followed its short-term sister science in regarding the atmosphere as a system which achieves equilibrium within a short period, i.e., a set of simultaneous equations, it is natural that some factor external to the atmosphere is looked for as a cause—volcanic activity or sunspots, to mention the most popular.[7] Volcanoes or sunspots may well produce changes in the general circulation, but there is no evidence for believing that their fluctuations coincide with or are of the scale demanded by the glacial epochs. Perhaps we should banish our causes to remote regions only after looking closer to home.

Defant first advanced the idea that the large-scale eddies of the westerlies could be regarded as turbulence elements in a quasi-horizontal flow.[8] Thus the individual, closed circulations or particular features of these may be regarded as random events which can usefully be studied via probability theory. We may take the net meridional flow of heat or moisture across a latitude circle within a year as a random event. We would expect any marked deviation from the "equilibrium" condition to result in a feedback of energy which

would restore the situation—to use short-term concepts. But what if the energy be stored so that it is removed completely from the circulation? A new equilibrium might be established, rather than the former one perpetuated by feedback. If this addition to storage goes on long enough, the new equilibrium may be sufficiently different from the original to speak of a "climatic change." To use a partial analogy from Keynesian economics: if for some reason mass unemployment occurs, the economic system may achieve a new equilibrium neglecting these people rather than return to the original full employment via feedback processes.

The two main long-term storage compartments for atmospheric energy are the tropical oceans and the polar glaciers. We shall attempt to show that fluctuations in storage there, resulting purely from random events, can be of the magnitude and duration of the Ice Ages. However, that change is not suggested as occurring to any greater extent relatively for the fluctuations of the Ice Ages than for totaras in New Zealand or short-rooted grass. The only difference is that the length of memory, and thus the period of calculation to define change, is in millions of years compared to a hundred years and a few days. While changes in the ice caps and oceans are associated with changes in the general circulation, this means only that the circulation is not in a uniquely defined equilibrium and that the true mean circulation would have to be defined over glacial and nonglacial epochs combined—if one wished to engage in such pointless labors.

MODEL 1: COIN TOSSING

Without referring at this stage to atmospheric processes, let there be a storage system of extremely large, perhaps infinite, capacity and let there be a fifty-fifty chance of storage gaining or losing one unit in a unit period. Intuitively we regard this as an equilibrium condition in which there would be fluctuation in size around the mean position, but there certainly would not be gains or losses at the scale of the glacial-interglacial advances and retreats. But recent research in probability theory has shown that intuition here is quite unreliable. In fact, no matter how long the period for which the system is watched, it is more likely that storage will never return to its original size or will return only once than that any other course of events will occur.

The model used here is analogous to two persons with unlimited funds tossing a coin. Feller shows that the lead in this game will remain on one side practically all the time with a very high probability; that is, measured from the starting point, the most likely course of events is that the system will show secular change, either gaining or losing.[9]

For each fixed $\alpha > 0$ the probability that up to and including time $2n$ the amount stored will return to its original value fewer than $\alpha(2n)^{0.5}$ times tends, as $n \rightarrow \infty$, to

$$f(\alpha) = (2/\pi)^{0.5} \int_0^{\alpha} e^{-0.5s^2}\, ds$$

In practice, a close approximation is provided for even small values of n. The right-hand side of this equation is a truncated normal cumulative distribution function so that standard tables may be used with $f(\alpha) = 2\Phi(\alpha) - 1$; s and ds are the usual terms of the standardized normal distribution.

Some features of this theorem should be noted. As the length of the period studied is increased, the number of returns to the initial value is not increased proportionately. For a given probability, returns are proportional to the square root of the length of period under investigation. This feature is in accord with what we know of the increase in wave length

of the oscillations of climate the further back in time we look. Table 2 provides an estimate of the probabilities of various numbers of complete cycles within the last 600,000 years— one estimate of the period since the beginning of the Pleistocene. Although the number of cycles is remarkably small, it is nevertheless larger than the hypothesized cycles as displayed, for example, by Brooks.[10] However, these "empirical" cycles are, by the nature of the evidence, extremely smoothed series and will show only major advances. Feller indicates that the average time between consecutive returns to the original value will increase roughly linearly for each additional return. Thus it is evident that many of these advances would not be noted. This model reveals that the correct number of cycles of the right order of periodicity could be obtained with a fair degree of probability. The implication of this model will not be pursued further, because the assumption of equal unit exchanges of energy can be replaced by more realistic notions.

MODEL 2: QUEUING, TIME INDEPENDENT

Let us assume a storage system of extremely large capacity and allow that the input and output should vary in random fashion. This situation is analogous to people arriving at intervals at a service counter and waiting in line to be served, the time needed for any one person being random. The method for answering such questions as how long the waiting line will be is known as "queue theory." It is a remarkable fact that if mean input equals mean output, the queue is likely to grow out of all bounds. For this reason, mean input is taken to be slightly less than mean output, i.e., a model allowing infinite storage is not realistic.

When the system has settled down to its normal working, so that it does not depend on the original state when first observed and thus its states are independent of time, the probability of n or more units being in the system is

$$Q_n = (\text{mean input/mean output})^n = \rho^n$$

And with $\rho = 0.999$, then

$n = 1000$	2000	3000
$Q_n = 0.368$	0.135	0.050

TABLE 2

Returns to origin and numbers of cycles for given probabilities, with 2n = 600,000

$f(\alpha)$	0.08	0.16	0.24	0.38	0.52	0.63	0.73	0.81	0.91
$\alpha(2n)^{0.5}$	77	155	232	387	542	697	851	1006	1316
"Cycles"	18	39	58	97	135	174	213	251	329

The mean number in the system $L = \rho/(1 - \rho) = 999$. As ρ approaches unity, the probabilities of large values in storage increase very rapidly.

Consider the Pleistocene European ice cap and assume that mean precipitation was much the same as at present, say one meter, and follow Charlesworth in believing that the maximum thickness of the ice was about 3000 meters.[11] Then if input is slightly less than output, the probabilities of reasonable magnitudes are high: there is an 8.5 per cent chance of having storage of between 2000 and 3000 meters. However, it must be admitted that the time needed for the system to settle down to its steady state, i.e., the relaxation time, is enormous. Consequently, it is doubtful if a statement of the probabilities of the possible states of the system which is independent of the duration of the system is valid.[12] The relaxation time is $\cong$ (input$^{0.5}$ + output$^{0.5}$)^2 / (output − input)^2. And with $\rho = 0.999$, it is $\cong$ 14,000,000 years.

MODEL 3: QUEUING, TIME DEPENDENT

In this model we assume infinite storage, random inputs, outputs of equal mean, and also that storage is never empty.[13] Let $i =$ mean input per annum, and $t =$ number of years. The probability of storage not being greater in size than N is[14]

$$P \cong (2N + 1)/(4\pi \ it)^{0.5}$$

To obtain a change of the order of 3000 meters with an input (i) of one meter, the length of time (t) which must be considered is 4,000,000 years. When $i = 1$ and $t = 4 \times 10^6$, then

$P =$ 0.01	0.1	0.5	0.9	1.0
$N =$ 35	354	1772	3190	3544

To reach an absolute maximum of 3000 meters with an input of one meter, the length of time to be considered is 3×10^6 years. Assuming the period of time since the Alpine orogeny to be 70×10^6 years, an absolute maximum of 15,000 meters could be reached in this time, and there is an 80 per cent chance of 3000 meters being obtained.

Although it is difficult to devise a statistical model which exactly portrays the features of the period under review, sufficient information has been obtained to suggest strongly that changes of the order of those known to have occurred could have been the result of random events.

RANDOMNESS AND CAUSATION

The notion of random variation can be interpreted in two ways. It might be that the aggregate effect of a number of cycles of differing but wholly determinate periodicities would appear as a random series.[15] Thus the hypothesized sunspot cycles of various periods could produce a random variation in the corpuscular component of solar radiation and so affect the atmospheric circulation. In this sense, randomness is simply a convenient method of describing the aggregate effect of deterministic processes which can be described eventually.

On the other hand, randomness can be thought of as the result of numerous causes of variable intensity, operating in unmeasurable and unknowable interaction. From this point of view, forecasting would never be possible, and it would hardly be valid to speak of causes: "only the event will teach us in its hour."

THERMAL FEEDBACK RECONSIDERED

The assumption that one zone of the earth can cool or warm relative to another without compensating changes occurring is likely to be questioned. However, the atmosphere does not redistribute all "surplus" energy within a short period, since considerable storage does occur in the oceans and in the polar caps during certain seasons. Consequently, it is reasonable to believe that an identical amount will not be released in a later season. But, it may be argued, warmer oceans will increase their output of long-wave radiation or of latent heat of condensation causing opposing cooling. To the extent that this energy is advected, feedback would be operative.

In applying the physical laws of instantaneous states to the atmosphere, care must be taken to consider their applicability. As was stressed earlier, our data are always means measured over particular areas of space and time; insofar as turbulent motion affects the overall motion, a correction factor has to be applied to the thermodynamic laws. There must be a point beyond which these laws, while still valid, are not useful.

This is surely the essence of recent theory concerning the general circulation. In the classical theory, differences in the radiational balance of the various latitudes produce an ordered wind arrangement which transports energy to provide the temperature gradients of the climatic map. Thermal differences are the cardinal feature from which all else follows. Using this approach, changes in the heat balance would produce changes in circulation which would tend to restore (at least in part) the original balance. But present ideas do not accord thermal factors this predominant role and, indeed, were developed largely because of the inadequacy of direct thermal drives as explanations of reality.[16] Purely dynamic factors are now thought to determine the order to be found in the wind system, while transport of heat is a secondary and largely incidental task. Thus it must be accepted that energy balance and circulation should be considered separately; at least they do not stand in one-to-one correspondence, which is all that the present argument requires.

It would have been relatively easy to allow feedback in the first model by replacing the unrestricted random walk in one dimension, which is another name for the coin-tossing analogy, by a random walk with elastic barriers. Here, instead of the probability of moving to the left or to the right remaining constant (i.e., of there being a 50 per cent chance of winning or losing at each toss of the coin), the further that the walker is from his starting point, the greater are his chances at each step of moving back toward this point. This would correspond to feedback, but not to a fully compensating effect, which does not appear to be physically justified. In such a walk there is an outer limit to the distance traveled from the center which would be approached asymptotically. This modification of the model would not affect the results substantially, provided that the limit was placed far enough away to allow fluctuations of the magnitude of the Ice Ages to occur. Since any limits or feedback which we might impose would be sheer guesses, and since our models are designed to suggest that Ice Ages could be the result of random processes, the simpler formulation is preferred.

A PHYSICAL INTERPRETATION

In attempting to invest these abstract notions with physical plausibility, it must be admitted that this could be done with greater conviction were even the simplest facts of ice cap development known. Obviously, surface temperatures need to be lower to have glaciation in, say, Western Europe, but whether this would be accompanied by higher or lower temperatures in the middle troposphere is not known. Ignoring some evidence to the contrary,[17] it is assumed here that temperature trends at the ground and at the 500 mb. level would be the same.

To comply with the reasoning so far, any secular change in circulation must not violate the condition of unchanging mean input and output. Thus it is difficult to transpose short-term circulation changes between zonal and meridional flow into the long period. At any stage of an Ice Age there must be virtually as much energy being transferred between tropics and poles as now and for the same reasons as now.

Although the zonal-meridional classification is retained, it is interpreted rather differently from its short-term meaning. It appears that the mean meridional or zonal components of flow could only change in response to a greater or lesser degree of anchoring of waves in the westerlies. Zonal motion is thus associ-

MIDDLE TROPOSPHERE CIRCULATION, SURFACE TEMPERATURES AND THEIR RECENT CHANGE, NORTHERN HEMISPHERE

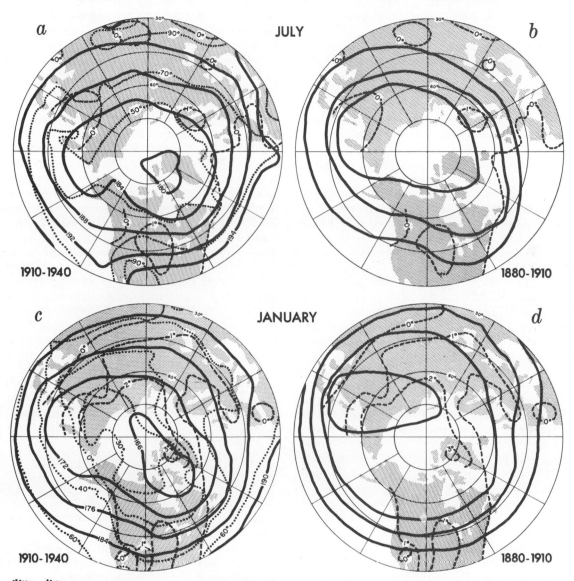

a

JULY

b

1910-1940

1880-1910

c

JANUARY

d

1910-1940

1880-1910

·········· Mean surface temperatures in °F, from Willett,
H.C., and Sanders, F., Descriptive Meteorology, 2nd ed.,
New York, 1959

⌒⌒⌒ Elevation of mean
500 mb. surface in hundreds of
feet; 1880-1910 contours are
hypothesized, 1910-1940 contours
are from Willett and Sanders
op. cit.

— — — Increase in mean temperature from period 1880-1910
to 1910-1940, from Lysgaard,
Leo., op. cit., quoted in Wexler, H.,
op. cit.

FIGURE 1

ated with less anchoring and a more regular progression of eddies in a mean flow which is more westerly. Meridional flow allows more northerly or more southerly mean flow in particular areas due to greater anchoring and thus a greater intensity of the various "centers of action."

The disposition of the quasi-permanent cyclones and anticyclones is related to relative surface temperature conditions and to mountain barriers. Only the former are capable of producing change since the Alpine orogeny. If the relative surface temperatures of continents and oceans are capable of independent change, then the degree of anchoring of westerly waves should be affected and thus the extent of meridional motion.

The map of surface mean temperatures for the northern hemisphere in July shows isotherms bulging southward over the eastern sides of the continents and the western sides of the oceans. The isotherms are reasonably paralleled by the geostrophic flow at 500 mb. (Fig. 1a). Assuming this picture to be representative of the period 1910–40, the change in the 500 mb. mean flow which would be associated with surface mean temperature changes from the 1880–1910 period as depicted by Lysgaard[18] is sketched in Fig. 1b. Areas experiencing more mean southerly winds in this earlier period would be warmer and those having winds of a more northerly track would be cooler. To produce these changes, the circumpolar track of the westerlies would need to be more elliptical, implying that the northern centers of action were of greater import and thus a more meridional mean flow would occur. More intense cyclonic conditions over land and anticyclonic conditions over the oceans could reflect cooler oceans.

In January, surface isotherms also roughly parallel the strongly elliptical westerlies at 500 mb. with their intense cyclonic curvature over the continents (Fig. 1c). To produce the trend of the surface isotherms of the 1880–1910 period a more zonal flow would be required (Fig. 1d). Europe and eastern North America would be cooler; eastern Asia and western North America would be warmer. A reduction in the significance of the centers of action could again be the result of cooler oceans. Note that cooler oceans, because of the smaller quantities of energy they are likely to supply

to higher latitudes, could produce generally lower temperatures in the polar area, as in fact was the case.

In summary, Lysgaard's findings can be interpreted as a change to more meridional flow in the winter of the recent period and to more zonal flow in summer, changes which have been associated with reduced glaciers. Presumably, increasing ice caps could be produced by reverse trends and could be brought about by cooler oceans.

Changes in heat storage of the oceans are thus suggested as producing "secular changes" in the atmospheric circulation and thus in glacier size. Consequently, the probability models should be applied to the oceans and reasoning concerning glacier size interpreted as changes in heat storage of the oceans, with glaciers appearing as dependent variables. This formulation has the virtue of allowing the northern and southern ice advances to be in phase. Note, however, that the northern hemisphere, being more differentiated into land and sea, will be more quickly affected by anchoring and to a greater degree than will be the southern hemisphere. Thus a whole "cycle" experienced north of the equator could be missing in the south, although presumably not one of the size of the major glacial advances. We shall now examine the validity of our hypothesis on the basis of the more detailed evidence of atmospheric changes in the recent past afforded by studies made of old weather maps.

THE SYNOPTIC EVIDENCE

The best-attested facts concerning change during the period of synoptic charts are Scandinavia's experience of more southerly winds, higher temperatures, less storminess, and higher pressures in winter.[19] Greater anchoring of waves in the westerlies, producing a more anticyclonic flow over northern Europe, would bring warmer winds from the south, storms would pass to the north, and pressures would be increased. Sea ice would decline, as reported, and the temperature gradient in the lower half of the troposphere to North Africa would be reduced. The increase in temperature over eastern North America and the increase temperature gradient from the Caribbean to the ice limit[20] may be interpreted as a shift in mean winds from the north, that is, a more zonal flow, following from less anchoring associated with a more cyclonic flow over the continent, a feature which would produce falling pressures and increased storminess, as recorded.

The increased intensity of the surface circulation, although widely reported,[21] does not follow naturally from these ideas, although the greater meridional temperature gradient in the western Atlantic could provide a limited zone of faster westerlies.

We may turn to the findings of Lamb and Johnson, who investigated all the available records of circulation over the Atlantic and its bordering continents.[22] In summary, they note that periods of strong circulation in winter over the ocean are associated with southerly flow dominance over the Atlantic and western Europe, with the Atlantic cyclone track far to the north over Spitzbergen, and with the sea ice off Iceland and Greenland reduced. In periods of weaker circulation, depression tracks are further south, pressures are low in the eastern Atlantic, and cold winters occur over Canada and Asia. If strong circulation be interpreted as greater anchoring and weak circulation as less anchoring, these results are readily understandable in terms of the present model. Why faster westerlies should be associated with more meridional flow—the reverse of short-period conditions—is difficult to understand; nor is the cause of the well-attested increased precipitation in the present subtropical desert areas during periods of advanced glaciation apparent. Perhaps these problems might yield to a more rigorous analysis.

CONCLUSION

The notion of random change may not be satisfying intellectually to those unaccustomed to think in probabilistic terms. Nevertheless it does appear to be able to produce changes of the required magnitude and periodicity. Whether it should be interpreted as an aggregate effect of determinate cyclic processes, and thus a demonstration of the relevance of sunspots to climatic change, is an open question. The alternative view, preferred by the writer, is of an indeterminate process working through the heat storage of the oceans rather than directly on the ice caps of the continents. It may be that some of the various postulated periodicities of climate, as well as the more certain index cycle of weather, will be understood in terms of other, smaller energy storage compartments of the earth and its atmosphere. Whatever the correct answer may be, it is hoped that it has been demonstrated that useful knowledge can be gained of the operation of indeterminate processes. That there are dynamic processes operating in space to produce changing areal differences, and thus qualifying as a legitimate field of geographic inquiry, can hardly be questioned. In this sense, the reasoning involved should be of interest to all students of geography faced as they often are with the problem of estimating the effects of chance.

FOOTNOTES

[1] See L. Curry, "The Climatic Resources of Intensive Grassland Farming: The Waikato, New Zealand," *Geographical Review*, **52** (1962), 174–194.

[2] N. Campbell, "The Statistical Theory of Errors," *Proceedings of the Physical Society*, **47** (1935), 800–809.

[3] H. Levy and L. Roth, *Elements of Probability* (London: Oxford University Press, 1936), p. 108.

[4] W. Feller, *An Introduction to Probability Theory and Its Applications* (New York: John Wiley & Sons, Inc., 1950), p. 300.

[5] A random process is a series of events to each of which there correspond appropriate probabilities of particular outcomes.

[6] F. K. Hare, "The Westerlies," *Geographical Review*, **50** (1960), 345–367.

[7] H. Wexler, "Radiation Balance of the Earth as a Factor in Climatic Change," in Harlow Shapley, ed., *Climatic Change* (Cambridge: Harvard University Press, 1953), pp. 73–105; R. A. Craig and H. C. Willett, "Solar Energy Variations as a Possible Cause of Anomalous Weather Changes," *Compendium of Meteorology* (Boston: American Meteorological Society, 1951), pp. 379–390.

[8] A. Defant, "Die Zirkulation der Atmosphäre in den gemässigten Breiten der Erde," *Geografiska Annaler*, **3** (1921), 209–266.

[9] Feller, *op. cit.*, p. 83.

[10] C. E. P. Brooks, "Geological and Historical Aspects of Climatic Change," in *Compendium of Meteorology, op. cit.*, pp. 1004–1018.

[11] J. K. Charlesworth, *The Quaternary Era* (London: [Edward] Arnold [Publishers], Ltd., 1957), II, 44.

[12] P. M. Morse, *Queues, Inventories and Maintenance* (New York: John Wiley & Sons, Inc., 1958), p. 67.

[13] This assumption is made to allow easy mathematical formulation; later reasoning shows it to be valid.

[14] D. G. Kendall, "Some Problems in the Theory of Queues," *Journal of the Royal Statistical Society*, Series B, **13** (1951), 151–161.

[15] A. J. Lotka, *Elements of Mathematical Biology* (New York: Dover Publications, Inc., 1956), pp. 30–34.

[16] C. G. Rossby, "On the Nature of the General Circulation of the Lower Atmosphere," in G. P. Kuiper, ed., *The Atmosphere of the Earth and Planets*, 2nd ed. (Chicago: University of Chicago Press, 1952), and references therein.

[17] V. P. Starr, "The Physical Basis for the General Circulation," in *Compendium of Meteorology, op. cit.*, pp. 541–550.

[18] L. Lysgaard, "On the Present Climatic Variation," *Royal Meteorological Society Centennial Proceedings* (1950), 206–211.

[19] S. Petterssen, "Changes in the General Circulation," *Geografiska Annaler*, **31** (1949), 212–221; and H. H. Lamb and A. I. Johnson, "Climatic Variation and Observed Changes in the General Circulation," *ibid.*, **41** (1959), 94–133.

[20] J. H. Conover, "Climatic Changes as Intepreted from Meteorological Data," in Shapley, *op. cit.*, pp. 221–230; Lamb and Johnson, *op. cit.;* and F. Bello, "Climate: The Heat May Be Off," *Fortune* (Aug. 1954).

[21] H. C. Willett, "Atmospheric and Oceanic Circulation as Factors in Glacial-Interglacial Changes of Climate," in Shapley, *op. cit.*, pp. 51–71.

[22] Lamb and Johnson, *op. cit.*

7

TREND-SURFACE MAPPING IN GEOGRAPHICAL RESEARCH

R. J. CHORLEY and P. HAGGETT

Although geographers are traditionally concerned with the description, analysis, and explanation of areal distributions of phenomena, much of the most vigorous development of new techniques in this field has come from outside geography. The harnessing of the vast potential of computer systems to mapping problems has been pressed forward both in subjects like meteorology, where mechanical graph plotters, line printers, and cathode-ray tube displays are being used to map directly the output of digital computers,[1] and in botany, where field information on the occurrence of vascular plants is being rapidly processed and printed out (for example, the 1623 maps of the *Atlas of the British Flora*).[2] The most striking adaptations of computer technology to traditional mapping problems are being employed in the earth sciences, however; for example, in geophysical prospecting, structural mapping, and sedimentary petrology.[3] Here the most fundamental developments in mapping techniques lie less in the automation of traditional

techniques (a field reviewed for geographers by Tobler),[4] but in the evolution of new ways of extracting more information from map data. This paper reviews developments in one of the most promising of these techniques, trend-surface mapping, and attempts to assess its significance for, and applications in, the wider field of geographical research.

THE NATURE OF TREND-SURFACE MODELS

Considerable insight into mapping techniques has come from the mathematical theory of information, originally developed in the late 1940's by American workers such as C. E. Shannon in relation to communications engineering. In terms of information theory we may

Reprinted from *Transactions and Papers of the Institute of British Geographers*, Publication No. 37 (1965), 47–67, by permission of the authors and the Institute.

regard the map as a "communications channel" into which bits of information are fed (for example, height values for individual control points). The information is then coded (for example, by contours) and transmitted in the form of an isarithmic map. Because geographical problems, like those of geology, are characterized by areal sampling restrictions, by a multiplicity of variables, and by the interaction and simultaneous variation of most of the variables,[5] we cannot be certain how much of the information transmitted by a map may be regarded as a "signal" and how much as random variations, or "noise."

Areal data always present such ambiguities (for example, those of definition),[6] and the most obvious manner in which to treat them is to attempt to disentangle the smooth, broader regional patterns of variation from the nonsystematic, local, and chance variations,[7] and then to ascribe mechanisms or causes to the different components. Thus the regional effect is commonly viewed as a smooth, regular distribution of effects, termed a "trend surface" or "trend component",[8] which are too deep, too broad, and too great in "relief" to admit of the purely local explanation which is reserved for the residuals, or deviations.[9]

Trend surfaces can thus be considered as response surfaces,[10] from which aspects of origin, dynamics, or process can be inferred, wherein variations in form may be thought of as responses to corresponding areal variations in the strength and balance of the controlling factors. As will be shown later, on this level, trend-surface mapping represents an attempt to build up some generalized picture of areal variability in order to test some process-response model, in which an attempt is made to explain distributions in terms of sets of process factors.[11]

Although the discussion throughout this paper is confined to isarithmic maps describing continuous surfaces, this does not mean that trend-surface models are restricted to such conventional isarithmic surfaces as terrain elevation or isobaric pressure. Bunge has suggested that only "pure hideboundness" keeps cartography from applying isarithmic techniques to a wide range of geographical phenomena.[12] Population, like light, may be profitably regarded either as a series of discontin-uous quanta or as a continuum. The choice is largely a matter of scale, convention, and convenience; and over thirty years ago, Jones urged the more general use of ratio-type maps in studies of land use and agricultural geography.[13] Isarithmic maps represent, in cartographic terms, the highest level of the four-stage measurement sequence—nominal, ordinal, interval, and ratio—and the great flexibility and utility of the ratio scale for both mapping and statistical analysis are strong arguments for converting the largest possible amount of appropriate geographical data into this form.

CONSTRUCTION OF TREND SURFACES

The information from which trend surfaces may be derived is contained within the original input (that is, control-point data), and such surfaces are ultimately controlled as to their accuracy by the quality of this original data.[14] However, trend-surface mapping differs from conventional contour mapping in the use it makes of the data.[15] Figure 1 shows a series of maps derived from the same control-point data from central Portugal with a representative cross section of control-point values.[16] In conventional isarithmic mapping (Fig. 1a), each control point contributes information only for the area immediately adjacent to it, in the sense that contour lines are drawn between a control point and its immediate neighbors, but it does not affect values outside the polygon formed by joining the control points which immediately surround it. In the two types of trend-surface mapping illustrated, this restriction is not maintained. In Fig. 1b a method of "moving means" has been adopted by which a series of control points is averaged to give a series of new values. Depending on the number of points averaged (that is, analogous to the grid size used), each control point is allowed to contribute information over a wider area. The effect of this, as shown in the two accompanying maps, is (1) to damp down local irregularities to give a clearer picture of the regional trend and (2) to allow the separation of local "residuals." Figure 1c shows the logical development of this information-generalization sequence in which, by using best-fit regression analysis, each control point contributes information to the *whole* of the area being mapped,

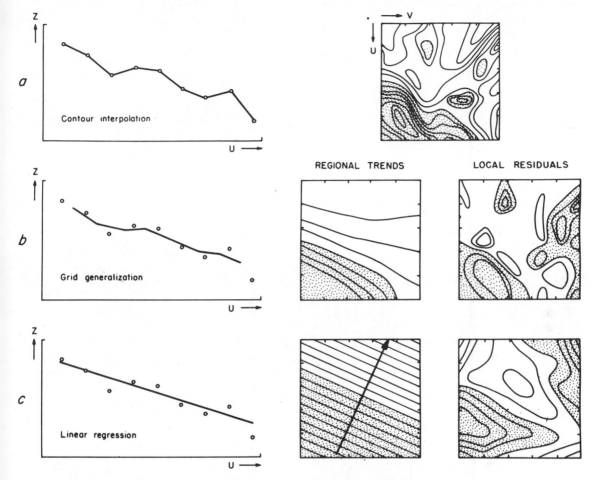

FIGURE 1. Analysis of forest distribution in a 10,000 square kilometer section of the Tagus-Sado basin, central Portugal through (*a*) contour interpolation, (*b*) grid generalization, and (*c*) linear regression. The cross sections are drawn orthogonal to the dominant regional trend in the area.

individual local values being sacrificed to the overall trend.

Inspection of the three graphs shows that, while at different levels of sophistication, contour interpolation (Fig. 1*a*) and regression analysis (Fig. 1*c*) are relatively objective methods, the derivation of the intermediate type of surface leans heavily on the scale of grid selected. The construction of trend-surface maps from areal data may thus be broadly divided into those which are primarily selective and those which are more, but not exclusively objective in character. This division also broadly separates, as Fig. 2 shows, (1) the

graphical and the grid methods from (2) the computation methods.

SELECTIVE METHODS

Nettleton has discussed the ambiguity of areal data, when one is to identify regional trends, by pointing to the common lack of clear criteria for separating the whole field into its supposed component parts.[17] Added to this, any graphical method depends to some extent on subjective decisions on the part of the operator.[18] The first group of the graphical-selective methods falls conveniently into the

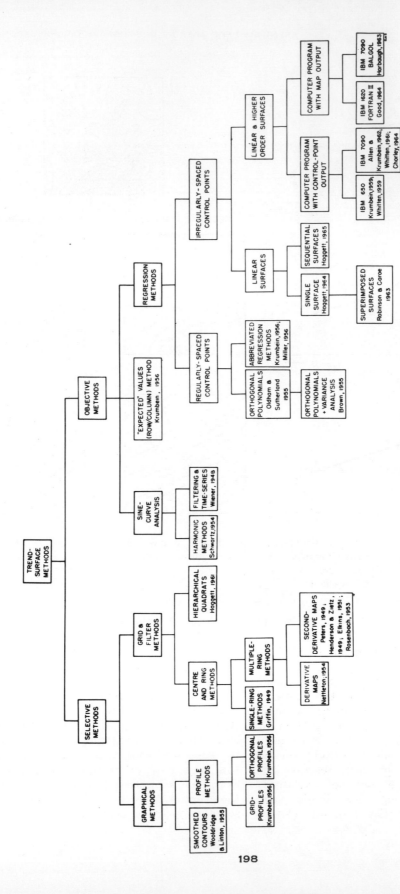

FIGURE 2. Schematic table of alternative methods of trend-surface analysis. Details of papers included in this table are given in the list of references at the end of this article.

"eyeball" method of drawing smoothed contours (for example, those on the Chiltern Pliocene bench drawn by Wooldridge and Linton)[19] and the various profile methods. The simplest of these is the "parallel-profile" method, in which equally spaced parallel profiles are constructed, smoothed out by eye, and used as the basis for the production of a three-dimensional map.[20] A grid of "intersecting profiles," adjusted at their intersections, can also be used to obtain a set of internally consistent values on a rectangular grid, the vertices of which form the control points for a contoured map. Krumbein has also described a matrix method for the construction of "orthogonal profiles."[21]

The second group of selective methods, the "grid-filter" type, are largely restricted to center-point and ring constructions. In the simplest form of these, a circle of unit radius is centered on each grid point and the values obtained by interpolation on the circumference are averaged to give the central grid-point value.[22] More complex multiple-ring methods involving first- and second-derivative maps have also been devised and widely applied to geophysical prospecting.[23]

Haggett has used a variant of the ring method, the "hierarchical quadrat" method, in which a series of square cells (quadrats) of increasing area were drawn around each control point.[24] Figure 3 shows the values obtained for a survey of forest distribution in central Portugal in which 960 control points were established at the vertices of a rectangular grid system with four sizes of quadrat (2500 square kilometers, 625 square kilometers, 156 square kilometers, and 39 square kilometers). Comparison of the four maps indicates the way in which the regional trend is closely related to the size

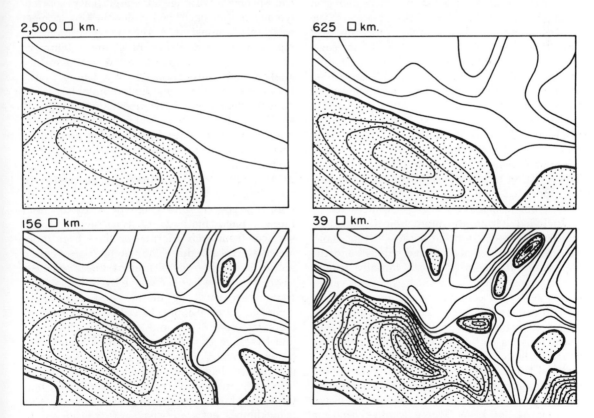

FIGURE 3. Analysis of forest distribution in a 15,000 square kilometer section of the Tagus-Sado basin, central Portugal through a hierarchy of quadrat sizes: (*a*) 2500 square kilometers, (*b*) 625 square kilometers, (*c*) 156 square kilometers, and (*d*) 39 square kilometers. Contours are given at intervals of ten angular units and areas above the mean are shaded (from Haggett [see note 24]).

of the grid, the "2500 filter" allowing only broad regional swells to be transmitted, whereas the "39 filter" allows considerably greater detail.

OBJECTIVE METHODS

The so-called objective methods are also anomalous in a number of respects. Obviously the selection of the number and spacing of the control-point array vitally influences the form of the resulting map, and Merriam and Harbaugh have demonstrated the effects of areal extent and control-point density for five nested areas in Kansas, varying from the whole state to a locality of about thirteen miles square.[25] Even allowing for a high density and even scatter of control points, however, there are two other problems involving selective anomalies—grid spacing and the mathematical families of surfaces employed.

Where the areal array is in rectangular grid form, Nettleton has shown that many of the results hinge on their spacing, for the grid acts like an electric filter which will pass components of certain frequencies while excluding others.[26] Indeed, Holloway views all smoothing attempts as forms of filtering, and points out that on hemispherical meteorological maps a grid-point spacing of 500 miles completely attenuates features on a scale of about 1500 miles, whereas 4000-mile features are retained at about 75 per cent of their original amplitude.[27] The question of the choice of the mathematical form of fitted surface will be returned to in the subsequent discussion of regression methods.

Included within the more objective mathematical methods of trend-surface fitting, both the use of matrices of expected values[28] and the fitting of sine curves[29] were initially useful. In the expected-values method, the mean values of the rows and columns of rectangular arrays of control points are used to compute the expected value of a point in terms of the characteristics of both the row and column in which it lies. These computed values give the regional trend surface, which may be compared with the original values at each intersection to give maps of local residuals. Although the use of sine curves has been largely confined to time series where a linear sequence of values may be "decomposed" into constituent parts (for example, into the diurnal curves of meteorological observations or the business cycles of economet-

ric observations), it can be extended to areal distributions. Using Fourier series, the isarithmic map may similarly be broken down into a series of waves of varying harmonic characteristics. These methods, however, have been found to be too cumbersome and restrictive and are being replaced.

Of all the methods described, that of "fitted regressions" is by far the most flexible and promising from the geographical viewpoint. In the same manner as two-dimensional regressions are fitted to graph data, so it is possible to calculate best-fit three-dimensional regressions related to areally distributed data. Similarly, the degree of "fit," or "explanation," can be expressed in conventional terms—the percentage reduction in the total sum of squares (Fig. 4).[30] The choice of the family of mathematical surfaces to be so fitted rests upon the versatile orthogonal polynomials, which have the special advantage of adaptability to electronic computing. Their value in this respect was first demonstrated some ten years ago for regularly spaced control points,[31] and a definitive paper on their application to trend-surface analysis was later prepared by Grant.[32] Abbreviated regression methods employing polynomials were used by Krumbein and by Miller,[33] the latter fitting first- and second-order polynomials to areal data by a graphic method of successive approximations, as earlier described by Ezekiel.[34]

Although Grant was mainly concerned with rectangular grid data, he indicated how irregularly spaced data could be utilized,[35] and more refined methods of constructing trend surfaces from such information have been more recently described.[36] The simplest regression methods involve the fitting of linear surfaces to areal data, as has been done by Robinson and Bryson to rural population and rainfall in Nebraska,[37] by Lippitt to sedimentary parameters in New York and Southern Ontario,[38] and by Haggett to forest distribution in southeastern Brazil.[39] This method of simplified areal description has been carried a stage further into the analytical realm by Robinson and Caroe,[40] who attempted to test correlations or coincidences between what were considered to be superimposed surfaces, and by Haggett, who mapped successive residuals from linear surfaces to obtain sequential surfaces, each representing the areal activity of progressively

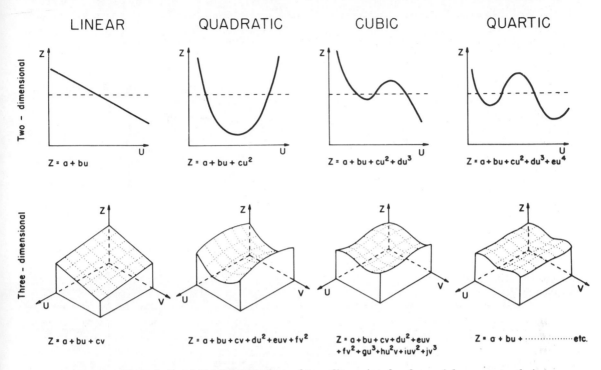

FIGURE 4. The relationship of four orders of two-dimensional polynomial curves to their three-dimensional counterparts. The latter are based on Krumbein's findings in the West Brock area, Carter County, Okla. (see note 7).

less regionally significant controls.[41] However, such work brings us into the field of the exploitation of trend surfaces which is the subject of the last part of this paper.

Obviously the descriptive restrictions imposed by having only linear surfaces to fit to complex distributions has, despite their relatively simple computation, required that more complex trend surfaces be fitted involving the use of high-speed electric computers.[42] For this purpose, progressive expansions of linear, quadratic, and cubic polynomial functions have been used, of the general form:

$$Z = a + bU + cV + dU^2 + eUV + fV^2 \\ + gU^3 + hU^2V + iUV^2 + jV^3$$

where Z is the areally distributed variable, and U and V are the locational rectangular coordinates. The general forms of these surfaces are indicated by Fig. 4, although considerable variation is possible within this versatile family (for example, Fig. 15) and, indeed, attempts are being made to introduce higher degree functions

into geological work.[43] Broadly, it is possible to separate those computer programs which give a control-point output only, from those which also supply some form of printed contour map, although mathematically there is no difference between them. In the former group is the FORTRAN program prepared for the IBM 7090,[44] which (1) computes linear plus quadratic plus cubic polynomial surfaces by least squares, (2) gives the reduction in sums of squares achieved by each surface, and (3) produces an output matrix of up to 35×35 point values for each surface, together with the residuals. In the latter group are the FORTRAN II program for the IBM 1620[45] and the more elaborate BALGOL program for the IBM 7090.[46] This latter produces linear plus quadratic plus cubic polynomial surfaces both as equations and contour maps, residuals for each surface, and certain properties of the trend and residual surfaces (for example, an error measure, reductions in the sums of squares, the volume beneath the surface, spatially weighted averages, and the arithmetic mean). The computations for

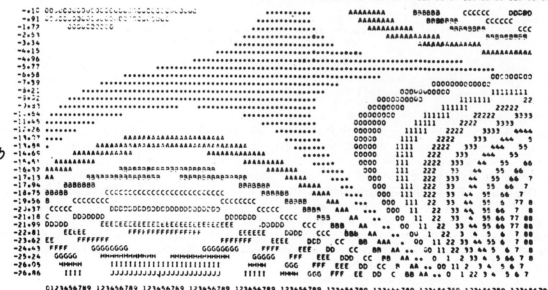

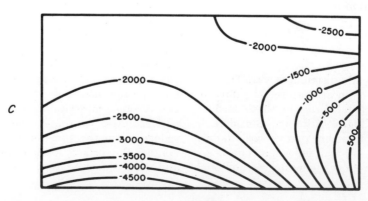

a program involving 200 data points (excluding the printing of the map) takes some forty-eight seconds at a computer cost of three dollars, and is approximately equivalent to about 100 hours of work by a skilled desk calculator operator. An example of a printed map, which commonly measures up to sixty square inches, in given in Fig. 5.

INFORMATION OUTPUT FROM TREND-SURFACE ANALYSIS

Figure 6 exemplifies a more formal analysis of the information output from the trend-surface program which, for both regional surfaces and residuals falls broadly into descriptive and interpretative information.

Descriptive information relating to regional trend surfaces includes details of their morphometry and accuracy in relation to the original data. For linear surfaces, morphometry includes the equation giving the dip and strike of the plane and, for higher-order surfaces, the equation and volume beneath, together with some spatially averaged values. Examples of the value of generalizations obtained by the use of regional trend-surface analysis in terms of the composition of granite massifs have been given by Whitten.[47] In addition to the morphometry, however, it is necessary to relate these best-fit trend surfaces to the original data from which they were derived. Besides the reduction in the total sum of squares effected by the surface, some indication of confidence limits is required.[48] It is necessary to inquire whether the fitted surface is a valid expression of large-scale variations in the mapped variable, or whether it may have arisen purely by chance from the sample of map points used, and to what extent the residuals may "contain locally important signals." As Krumbein has stressed, mappable data contain variations at several geographic levels. Just as tests of significance of

trend are applied to two-dimensional best-fit regressions, so Krumbein has described a three-dimensional test of significance of trend for fitted surfaces, giving levels of confidence that the improvement of fit offered by the regional surface is due to a real trend and not to chance alone (Fig. 7). Even where the fit of the surface (that is, the reduction in the sum of squares effected by it) is poor, the form of the bounding confidence surfaces may demonstrate that the trend of the surface is "real"—in other words "having some flexibility in its angle and direction of dip, but without sufficient freedom so that its direction of inclination could be completely reversed."[49]

The interpretation of regional trend surfaces resolves itself into three main considerations—the major trend, discrete trends, and interlocking trends. Little more need be said here regarding the obvious advantages of identifying the sort of major regional trends referred to above, but the other two types of interpretation also have considerable geographical potential. Figure 8 shows the general isopleths of the color index for the Lacorne granite massif in Quebec, to which single trend surfaces of low explanation have been fitted.[50] When the region is divided into two areas, however, two sets of concentric surfaces of much higher explanation appear, supporting the idea of discrete multiple granitic intrusion. It is readily apparent that such a test involves the same reasoning as the covariance analysis commonly applied to two-dimensional regressions. Allen and Krumbein have also used trend-surface analysis in an attempt to disentangle interlocking trends of facies components in the Top Ashdown Pebble Bed of the Weald (Fig. 9).[51] A surface fitted to the garnet content of the bed (sum of squares reduction 21.8 per cent) suggests a deltaic source in the northeast, with the residuals appearing as protochannels in the delta front, whereas other regional components indicate a second interlocking and contemporaneous deltaic source in the northwest.

It is however, to the interpretation of residuals that most effort has been directed. Simpson discussed the general construction of residual maps,[52] and Swartz considered some of their geometrical properties.[53] Thomas has examined the geographical implications of maps of residuals from conventional regression analysis, but their value in outlining oil structures has been the primary stimulus for their

◁ **FIGURE 5.** Trend-surface analysis applied to the top of the Arbuckle Group (Cambrian-Ordovician) for the whole state of Kansas by the Fortran II program for the IBM 1620 computer: (*a*) Plot of the original data (elevations in feet). (*b*) Printout of the contour map for the best-fit cubic surface (contour interval 150 feet; reference contour [. . . .] at minus 2000 feet). (*c*) Contours produced from printout (*b*) (see note 45).

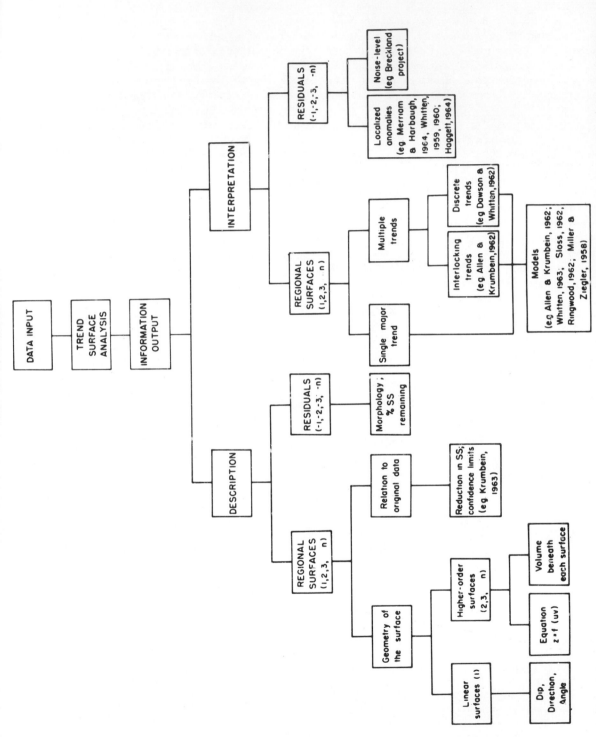

FIGURE 6. Schematic table of the types of information output from trend-surface analysis of a geographical distribution

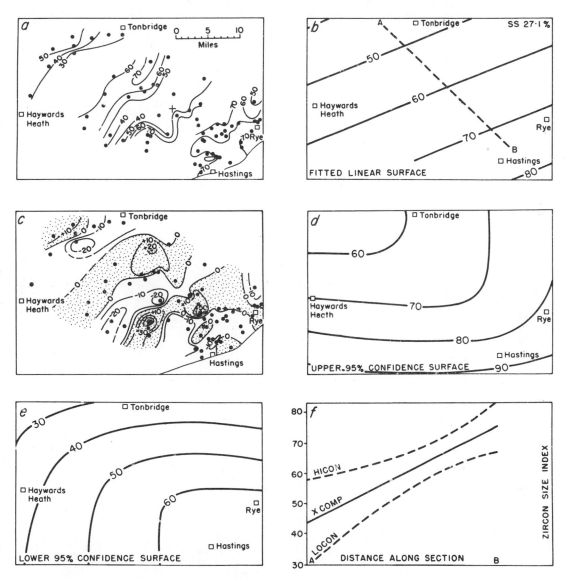

FIGURE 7. Trend-surface analysis and confidence intervals applied to the zircon size index (in microns) of the Top Ashdown pebble bed, south-eastern England (from Allen and Krumbein [see note 51] and Krumbein [see note 48]). (*a*) Sampling points and generalized isopleths (ten-micron intervals). The cross indicates the areal center of gravity of the sampling points. (*b*) Best-fit linear surface fitted to the data, effecting a reduction in the sum of squares of 27.1 per cent. (*c*) Deviations (in microns) from the best-fit linear surface, with positive deviations stippled. (*d*) The upper 95 per cent confidence surface. (*e*) The lower 95 per cent confidence surface. (*f*) Cross sections of the linear surface (X comp.) and of the upper (hicon) and lower (locon) 95 per cent confidence surfaces along the line AB (Fig. 7*b*). The form of the bounding confidence limits indicates that, although the linear surface has considerable flexibility, it is very improbable that the indicated trend could be completely reversed.

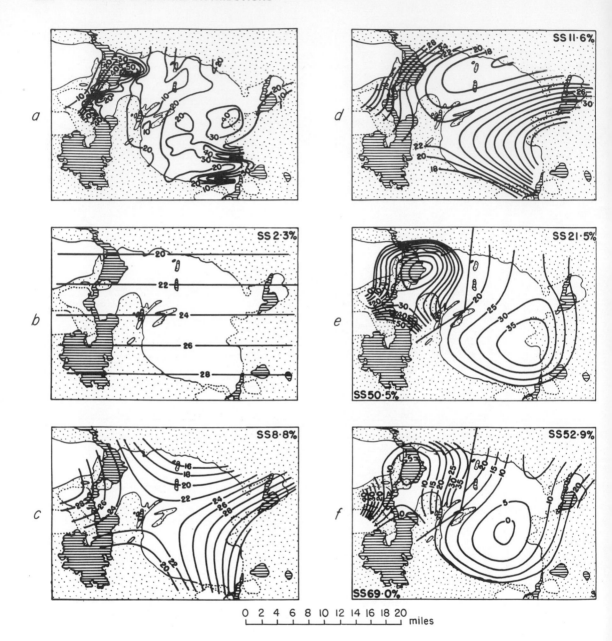

FIGURE 8. Trend-surface analysis applied to the composition of the Lacorne granitic massif, Quebec (from Whitten [see "A Surface-Fitting Program," note 11]). (*a*) Isopleths applied to colour index data. (*b*) Best-fit linear surface fitted to the data in (*a*). (*c*) Best-fit quadratic surface fitted to the data in (*a*). (*d*) Best-fit cubic surface fitted to the data in (*a*). (*e*) Two areally separated best-fit cubic surfaces fitted to the data in (*a*). These give marked improvements in the sums of squares so effected (SS), and suggest two separate circular intrusions. (*f*) Two similarly areally-separated best-fit cubic surfaces fitted to quartz percentages of the Lacorne granitic massif, supporting the multiple-intrusion hypothesis suggested by (*e*).

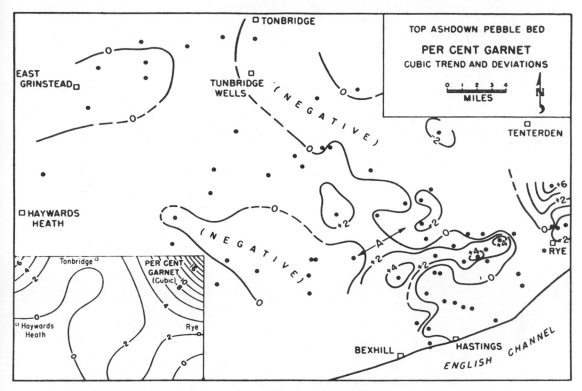

FIGURE 9. Cubic trend surface fitted to garnet percentages sampled in the area of south-eastern England shown in Fig. 7 (reduction in sum of squares 21.8 per cent), together with deviations from it. The former suggests a garnet-rich north-eastern source and the latter proto-channels in the delta front. Analysis of the garnet component enables the separation of a medium-grained, arenaceous, garnet-rich north-eastern source from a north-western source of chert pebbles with silt and clay (from Allen and Krumbein, 1962).

development.[54] Merriam, and Harbaugh and Merriam have, for example, depicted the more local structures in Kansas by means of residuals from the Arbuckle Group regional trend (Fig. 10) and have shown how the Lost Springs oilfield is associated with a gentle local flattening or structural terrace on a westward regional dip (Fig. 11).[55] Another productive field wherein interpretation has been assisted by means of the identification of residuals is in the character of granitic intrusives; and Whitten has shown how deviations in the composition of the Thorr granite of Donegal appear as a "palimpsestic ghost stratigraphy" probably related to Precambrian metasedimentary rocks preserved throughout this granite in their "pregranite positions."[56] This gives some evidence regarding the manner of formation of the mass (Fig. 12). Chorley has also used this residual technique to distinguish possible glacial admixtures from

the *in situ* Lower Greensand soil facies of east-central England (Fig. 13);[57] while Haggett has attempted an explanation of the distribution of residuals of forest distribution in south-eastern Brazil.[58] It is thus readily apparent that both the geometry and the areal associations of residuals often give valuable clues as to their controlling factors and mechanisms.

Haggett has suggested that there may be hierarchies both of regional components and of different orders of residuals present in any single pattern of areal distribution.[59] However, there always remains, even after the most complete "areal filtering," a randomly distributed, unexplained component commonly termed "noise." Noise itself emanates from a number of different sources, such as errors of identification and measurement, but in most geographical distributions there is a real random element the existence of which must be recognized. What

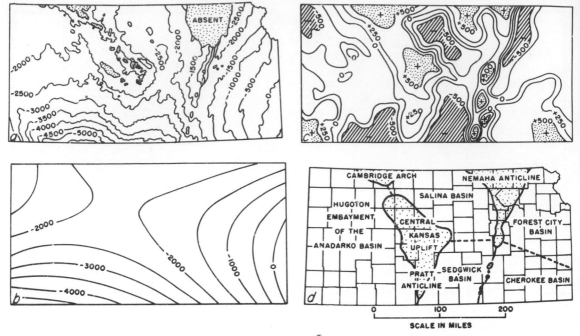

FIGURE 10.   The geological structure of Kansas illustrated by the trend-surface analysis of the top of the Arbuckle Group (from Merriam and Harbaugh [see note 25]). (*a*) Isopleths drawn on the top of the Arbuckle Group. (*b*) Quadratic trend surface fitted to the elevations of the top of the Arbuckle Group. (*c*) Deviations from the trend surface shown in (*b*). (*d*) The major structural features of Kansas deriving both from (*b*) and (*c*).

might be thought of as noise on one level, however, may be subsequently identified as partly explicable local components on another level. The high proportion of unexplained residuals (78.49 per cent) from the third-degree regional surface fitted to the distribution of Breckland surface-sand size facies (Fig. 14) contains an explainable local variation, due perhaps to periglacial sorting processes.[60]

FURTHER EXPLOITATION OF TREND-SURFACE ANALYSIS

Although there have been, as yet, comparatively few applications of trend-surface analysis to conventional geographical problems, the foregoing discussion suggests a number of possible utilizations. These may be summarized under four headings: (1) improved isarithmic mapping, (2) simplified description and comparison of complex geographical patterns, (3) comparative areal analysis, and (4) construction of process-response models.

(1) The speed and objectivity of contour-type mapping by computers has already led to its widespread use in meteorology and geophysics, and its adaptation to geography would seem to be only a matter of time. Like the cartographer, the computer carries out simple linear interpolation between control points, and is subject, in certain cases, to the same indeterminacy to which Mackay has drawn attention.[61] This problem of indeterminacy may be overcome by rearranging the pattern of control points into a triangular lattice, which has the advantage over square systems in that "linear interpolation is unambiguous in extending isarithms, since only one single plane can go through three points in space."[62] Nordbeck has derived a computer program (NORKI) which transforms the square network into a triangular one. In the NORKI program, however, there is some loss of detail, in that it takes four control points arranged in a square to give one control point in the triangular system. Ojakangas and Basham have overcome this problem with their INGRID program written in FORTRAN for an IBM 7090 computer.[63] In this program the input consists of

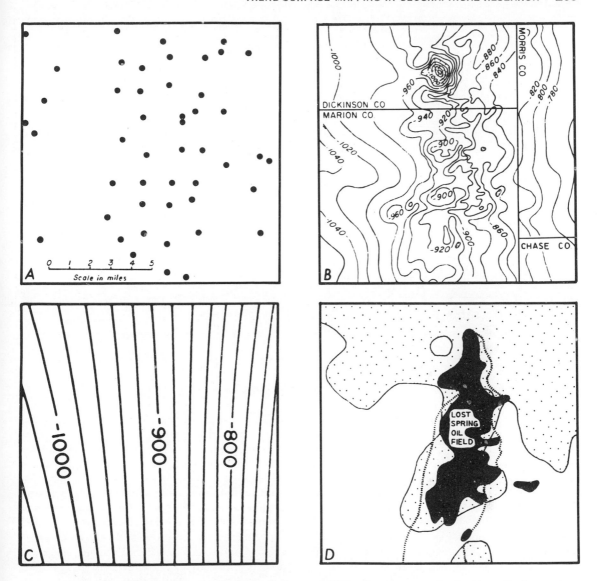

FIGURE 11.   Trend-surface analysis applied to an oil-bearing structure in the Lost Spring area of Dickinson and Marion Counties, east-central Kansas (from Merriam and Harbaugh [see note 25]). (*a*) Location of control wells. (*b*) Isopleths drawn on top of the 'Mississippi chat' formation. (*c*) Quadratic trend surface fitted to elevations on top of the Mississippi chat formation. (*d*) Positive deviations (stippled) from the quadratic trend surface, surface, associated with the oil-producing area (black).

a series of control points (up to a maximum of 4000) given in terms of their UV coordinates (for example, National Grid reference numbers) and Z values (for example, elevation). Since the control points may be irregularly distributed over the area, the first stage of the INGRID program is to interpolate values for the grid intersections of any specified grid size to give

a square network of control points. This stage is followed by contouring in which a quadratic surface of the form:

$$Z = a_0 + a_1 U + a_2 V + a_3 UV$$

is fitted to the four corners of *each* grid square: the Z value of each unit cell within the square

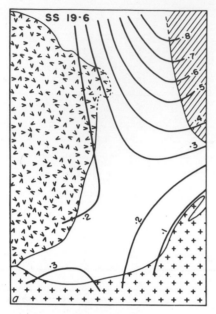

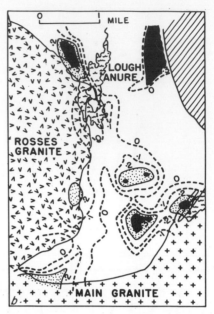

FIGURE 12.   Trend-surface analysis and deviations applied to the microcline-plagioclase ratios of the "older granite" of the Thorr district, Co. Donegal (Whitten [see "Quantitative Areal Model Analysis," note 47]). (*a*) Best-fit quadratic trend surface. (*b*) Positive deviations (0–0.2 isopleths; 0.2–0.3 shaded; greater than 0.3 black) from the quadratic trend surface, suggesting a "ghost stratigraphy" of metasedimentary relics.

is then computed from this surface and printed out as a contour map on an IBM 1403 printer. By using the quadratic surface, Ojakangas and Basham have outflanked Mackay's indeterminacy problem and insured consistency of contours over the whole map area. The program was tested on geophysical data over the West Los Angeles basin, California with 200 original control points, and compared with the hand-contoured U.S. Geological Survey maps of the same area. The number of contours in the computer maps was limited by the number of symbols available (thirty-eight) and by the size of the print-out unit, so that some contour lines were lost in high-gradient areas, where contours were closer together than the printed characters allowed. Moreover, all lines were plotted as continuous contours while the hand-contoured map showed breaks, for example, along the Palos Verdes fault line. Against this, the speed of the system (the whole computation from the input of original data to the final maps took 255 seconds), the relatively low cost ($25.00), and the greater accuracy suggest that isarithmic mapping with contour interpolation by quadratic trend surfaces might be of con-

siderable use in the rapid first-stage investigation of trends in an area.

As in geophysics, so in geography there are many fields of investigation in which the distribution of control points is "spotty" in character, and the individual Z values may be of very variable accuracy.[64] For example, in historical geography Henderson has shown how the 1801 crop returns are abundant in some areas of England and scarce in others.[65] In such instances there is much to be said for fitting regression surfaces to the whole distribution. By this device the errors of individual control points are distributed over the whole map rather than violently distorting a small area, and regional trends of a given level of significance may be culled from the data.

(2) Progressive reduction of complex isarithmic maps to a series of simpler components is being often carried out at present to assist both teaching and research. Thus we may talk of "ridges" of high population density in the northeastern United States or of "gradients" in agricultural intensity in the Middle West. Trend surfaces lend themselves readily to the relatively simple description of regional characteristics.

LINEAR + QUADRATIC + CUBIC $X_1 = \cdot25688 - \cdot07996U + \cdot01968V + \cdot01175U^2 + \cdot0013UV - \cdot00053V^2 - \cdot00052U^3 - \cdot00007U^2V + \cdot0001UV^2 + \cdot00004V^3$

(38·03 % EXPLAINED)

DEVIATIONS FROM A

0 1 2 3 4 5 miles

FIGURE 13. Trend-surface analysis and deviations applied to median grain sizes (mm) of the surface soils of the Lower Greensand outcrop between Ely (E) and Leighton Buzzard (LB) east-central England (from Chorley [see note 57]). (a) Best-fit cubic trend surface (SS 38.03 per cent). (b) Negative deviations from the cubic trend surface (stippled). Dots indicate soil sampling points. Solid dots show where transported flints were encountered, suggesting that glacial drift admixtures might be generally associated with the localities where abnormally fine-grained contaminations occur, so confusing the regional soil grain-size pattern which is broadly related to the bedrock facies of the Lower Greensand.

211

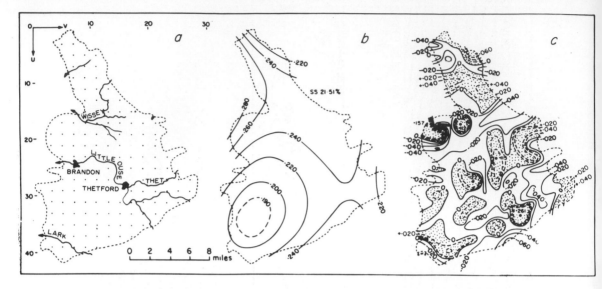

FIGURE 14. Trend-surface analysis and deviations applied to median grain sizes (mm) of the surface sands of the Breckland, eastern England (Chorley *et al.* [see note 60]). (*a*) Rectangular grid (2 km. intervals) of the 149 sampling points. (*b*) Best-fit cubic trend surface. (*c*) Deviations from the cubic trend surface (positive deviations stippled), indicating a high local "noise level."

Thus, using linear surfaces, Haggett was able to describe the distribution of forest in south-eastern Brazil in terms of a simple "shed-roof" gradient dipping inland at right angles to the coastline.[66] Such a description might be readily compared in terms of dip and strike with environmental gradients in the same areas, or with forest gradients in other areas. Using scarcely more complex quadratic surfaces, Davies showed the four main types of system that might be generated by such second-degree equations, viz., a maximum, stationary ridge, a rising ridge, and a minimax (Fig. 15).[67] Since each of these surfaces may be inverted (the maximum to a minimum, the ridge to a trough, and so on), there are eight basic forms which may be identified and compared. Even though any single quadratic trend map may show only part of one of the basic eight forms, some useful yardstick for describing geographical patterns is clearly provided.

Again trend surfaces may be used in research to test prevailing descriptions of physiographic and other forms. Thus Svensson suggested that the application of trend-surface techniques to the mapping and separation of possible erosion surfaces should be further explored.[68] In view of the wide range of alternative forms which have

been recognized by different workers in areas like Wales, it would be profitable to subject such disputed areas to successively more complex trend-surface analyses.

Description of distributions leads inevitably to a recognition of the anomalous problem areas which depart from the overall trend. While in the case of first-order analysis we might expect such anomalies to be widespread, local pockets, which persist after higher-order analysis, may suggest the location of more significant anomalies. Thus the trend surface may act, by its filtering effect, so as to identify or "sieve out" areas for special study.

(3) Trend-surface analysis has already been used as an adjunct to forms of areal multivariate analysis,[69] in attempts to apportion out "explanation for residuals" and to explain the regional variability of one areal feature by means of corresponding areal variations in assumed controlling factors.[70] All these methods, however, simply use the trend surfaces to generate data which are treated by the conventional multivariate techniques; and there is need for the development of direct methods by which trend surfaces themselves can be correlated and the features of one surface explained directly in terms of others. First steps in this

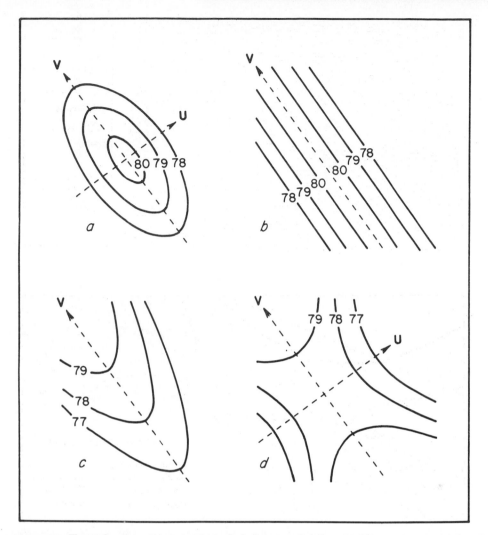

FIGURE 15. Four basic patterns generated by quadratic equations: (*a*) maximum, (*b*) stationary ridge, (*c*) rising ridge, and (*d*) minimax (from Davies [see note 67]).

direction have been provided by Robinson and Caroe,[71] who developed a correlation technique between linear trend surfaces based upon a comparison of vectors, and by Miller, who has used certain properties of the best-fit polynomial surfaces in the comparison of contour maps.[72]

(4) Finally, it is possible to view the formalized description afforded by trend-surface analysis not merely as an aid to the comparison of different areal patterns, but also to adapt the response-surface concept in the building of process-response models. These represent actual or conceptual frameworks with reference to which information is related, or "structured,"

as an aid to generalization in an attempt to explain areal distribution in terms of sets of process factors, and perhaps as a basis for prediction.[73] These models attempt to embrace the broad outlines of the interrelationships of areal-process factors,[74] and have been constructed for the analysis of beach phenomena,[75] stratigraphic units,[76] granite plutons,[77] and the earth's mantle.[78]

Figure 16 shows two such process-response models evolved on the basis of trend-surface analysis. The first, developed by Allen and Krumbein,[79] shows the general sedimentary processes which may explain the stratigraphic sequence revealed by trend-surface analyses of

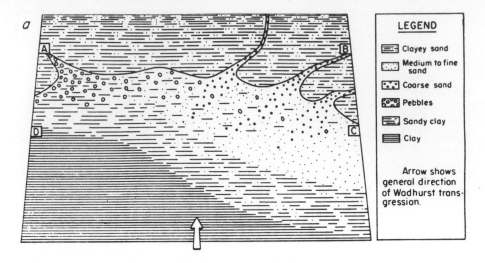

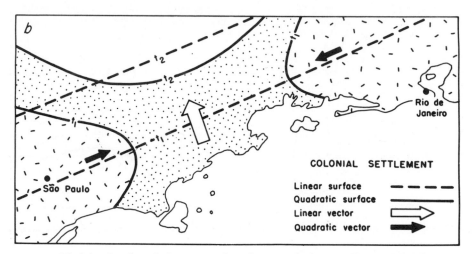

FIGURE 16. Models developed from trend-surface analysis. (*a*) Facies model showing. a perspective view northward across the Wealden basin shortly before the Wadhurst (Lower Cretaceous) transgression. The area ABCD is that treated in Figs. 7 and 9. This model depicts a northwestern pebble source with much silt and clay, and a north-western source of medium-grained arenaceous detritus (with garnets) (from Allen and Krumbein [see note 51]). (*b*) Diachronic model of settlement of the Brazilian *Sudeste* between 1500 and 1850 A.D. Contours describe the linear and quadratic forms of the foundation dates of county towns (*sedes municipiais*).

the Top Ashdown Pebble Bed, southeastern England. The second, developed by Haggett, shows the general settlement processes of Portuguese colonization in southeastern Brazil as a function of a simple linear surface dipping inland and of a quadratic "minimax" form of surface.[80] In this quadratic case there appear to be two main source areas (the Tiête basin around Sao Paulo and the Baixada Fluminense around Rio de Janeiro), with negative areas between

and to the north. Although the two models are elementary, they suggest possible diffusion processes (respectively of sediments and population) that can be further tested by conventional statistical analysis.

CONCLUSION

Striking developments in trend-surface mapping have been made in disciplines like meteorology and geophysics, where the demand for generalization, interpolation, and prediction have provided major financial incentives for research and development, and where the establishment of quantification and rapid computational aids have provided a receptive environment for experimentation. This paper has reviewed some of the more successful experiments that have been made in trend-surface mapping which, with their concern for regional trends and local anomalies, promise to throw new light on long-standing geographical problems both of teaching and research. Both very simple graphical or grid techniques and also very complex computer programs are now available and there seems no reason, other than convention and lethargy, why they should not be very widely adapted for use in all branches of geography, both physical and human, in the immediate future.

FOOTNOTES

[1] J. S. Sawyer, "Graphical Output from Computers and the Production of Numerically Forecast or Analysed Synoptic Charts," *Meteorological Magazine*, **89** (1960), 187–190; F. Wippermann, "Kartenmassige Dartellung Atmosphärischer Felder auf dem Schirm einer Kathodenstrahlrohe," *Tellus*, **11** (1959), 253.

[2] F. H. Perring and S. M. Walters, *Atlas of the British Flora* (Oxford: University Press, 1962).

[3] W. C. Krumbein, "Measurement and Error in Regional Statigraphic Analysis," *Journal of Sedimentary Petrology*, **28** (1958), 175–185.

[4] W. R. Tobler, "Automation and Cartography," *Geographical Review*, **49** (1959), 526–534.

[5] E. H. T. Whitten, "Process-Response Models in Geology," *Bulletin of the Geological Society of America*, **75** (1964), 455–464.

[6] F. Chayes and Y. Suzuki, "Geological Contours and Trend Surfaces: Discussion," *Journal of Petrology*, **4** (1962), 307–312.

[7] W. C. Krumbein, "Regional and Local Components in Facies Maps," *Bulletin of the American Association of Petroleum Geologists*, **40** (1956), 2163–2194.

[8] E. H. T. Whitten, "Composition Trends in a Granite: Modal Variation and Ghost Stratigraphy in Part of the Donegal Granite, Eire," *Journal of Geophysical Research*, **64** (1959), 835–846.

[9] L. L. Nettleton, "Regionals, Residuals and Structures," *Geophysics*, **19** (1954), 1–22.

[10] G. E. P. Box, "The Exploration and Exploitation of Response Surfaces: Some General Considerations and Examples," *Biometrics*, **10** (1954), 16–60. Also: Krumbein, "Regional and Local Components," *op. cit.*

[11] E. H. T. Whitten, *A Surface-Fitting Program Suitable for Testing Geological Models which Involve Areally-Distributed Data*, U. S. Office of Naval Research, Contract NONR 1228–26, Technical Report No. 2 (Evanston: Department of Geology, Northwestern University, 1963). Whitten, "A Reply to Chayes & Suzuki," *Journal of Petrology*, **4** (1963), 313–316; Whitten, "Process-Response Models," *op. cit.*

[12] W. Bunge, *Theoretical Geography*, Lund Studies in Geography, Series C, **1** (1962).

[13] W. D. Jones, "Ratios and Isopleth Maps in Regional Investigations of Agricultural Land Occupance," *Annals of the Association of American Geographers*, **20** (1930), 177–195.

[14] E. H. T. Whitten, "Sampling and Trend-Surface Analysis of Granites: A Reply, "*Bulletin of the Geological Society of America*, **73** (1962), 415–418.

[15] A. H. Robinson, *Elements of Cartography*, 2nd ed. (New York: John Wiley & Sons, Inc., 1960).

[16] P. Haggett, *Locational Analysis in Human Geography* (London: [Edward] Arnold [Publishers], Ltd., 1965), Chap. 9.

[17] Nettleton, *op. cit.*

[18] D. C. Skeels, "Ambiguity in Gravity Interpretation," *Geophysics*, **12** (1947), 43–56.

[19] S. W. Wooldridge and D. L. Linton, *Structure, Surface, and Drainage in Southeast England* (London: George Philip & Son, Ltd., 1955).

[20] Nettleton, *op. cit.*, and Krumbein, "Regional and Local Components," *op. cit.*

[21] Krumbein, *ibid.*

[22] W. R. Griffin, "Residual Gravity in Theory and Practice," *Geophysics*, **14** (1949), 39–56; and Krumbein, "Regional and Local Components," *op. cit.*

[23] T. A. Elkins, "The Second Derivative Method of Gravity Interpretation," *Geophysics*, **16** (1951), 29–50; R. A. Henderson and I. Zietz, "Computation of Second Vertical Derivatives of Geomagnetic Fields," *ibid.*, **14** (1949), 517–534; L. J. Peters, "The Direct Approach to Magnetic Interpretation and Its Practical Application," *ibid.*, **14** (1949), 290–320; O. Rosenbach, "A Contribution to the Computation of the 'Second Derivative' from Gravity Data," *ibid.*, **18** (1953), 894–912; and Nettleton, *op. cit.*

[24] P. Haggett, "Multilevel Variance Analysis of Sobreiro Distribution in the Tagus-Sado Basin, Central Portugal." (unpublished manuscript, University of Cambridge, 1961), pp. 1–25.

[25] D. F. Merriam and J. W. Harbaugh, "Computer Helps Map Oil Structures," *Oil and Gas Journal*, **61** (1964), 158–159, 161–163.

[26] Nettleton, *op. cit.*

[27] J. L. Holloway, "Smoothing and Filtering of Time Series and Space Fields," *Advances in Geophysics*, **4** (1958), 351–389.

[28] Krumbein, "Regional and Local Components," *op. cit.*

[29] C. H. Swartz, "Some Geometrical Properties of Residual Maps," *Geophysics*, **19** (1954), 46–70: N. Wiener, *Cybernetics* (Paris, 1948).

[30] W. C. Krumbein, "Trend-Surface Analysis of Contour-Type Maps with Irregular Control-Point Spacing," *Journal of Geophysical Research*, **64** (1959), 823–834.

[31] S. M. Simpson, "Least-Squares Polynomial Fitting to Gravitational Data and Density Plotting by Digital Computer," *Geophysics*, **19** (1954), 255–269; C. H. G. Oldham and D. B. Sutherland, "Orthogonal Polynomials: Their Use in Estimating the Regional Effect," *Geophysics*, **20** (1955), 295–306; W. F. Brown, "Minimum Variance in Gravity Analysis, Part 1: One-Dimensional," *Geophysics* **20** (1955), 807–828.

[32] F. Grant, "A Problem in the Analysis of Geophysical Data," *Geophysics*, **22** (1957), 309–344.

[33] Krumbein, "Regional and Local Components," *op. cit.;* R. L. Miller, "Trend Surfaces: Their Application to Analysis and Description of Environments of Sedimentation," *Journal of Geology*, **64** (1956), 425–446.

[34] M. Ezekiel, *Methods of Correlation Analysis* (New York: John Wiley & Sons, Inc., 1930).

[35] Grant, *op. cit.*

[36] Krumbein, "Trend-Surface Analysis," *op. cit.;* Whitten, "Sampling and Trend-Surface Analysis," *op. cit.;* Whitten, "A Surface-Fitting Program," *op. cit.;* J. W. Harbaugh, *BAGOL Program for Trend-Surface Mapping Using an IBM 7090 Computer*, Kansas State Geological Survey, Special Distribution Publication No. 3 (1963).

[37] A. H. Robinson and R. A. Bryson, "A Method for Describing Quantitatively the Correspondence of Geographical Distributions," *Annals of the Association of American Geographers*, **47** (1957), 379–391.

[38] L. Lippitt, "Statistical Analysis of Regional Facies Change in Ordovician Coburg Limestone in Northwestern New York and Southern Ontario," *Bulletin of the American Association of Petroleum Geologists*, **43** (1959), 807–816.

[39] P. Haggett, "Regional and Local Components in the Distribution of Forested Areas in Southeast Brazil: A Multivariate Approach," *Geographical Journal*, **130** (1964), 367–378.

[40] A. H. Robinson and L. Caroe, in W. L. Garrison, ed., *Quantitative Geography* (Evanston: Northwestern University Press, 1966) (Evanston: Department of Geography, Northwestern University, 1966).

[41] Haggett, *Locational Analysis in Human Geography*, *op. cit.*, Chap. 9.

[42] W. C. Krumbein, "The Computer in Geology, *Science*, **136** (1962), 1087–1092; Krumbein, "Computer Analysis of Statigraphic Maps," *Bulletin of the American Association of Petroleum Geologists*, **46** (1962), 270; J. M. Forgotson, "How Computers Find Oil," *Oil and Gas Journal*, **61** (1963), 100–109.

[43] A. K. Baird, D. B. McIntyre, and E. E. Welday, "Trend Surfaces of High Order," *Geological Society of America*, **76** (1963), 1880; D. B. McIntyre, *Program for Computation of Trend Surfaces and Residuals for Degree 1 Through 8*, Pomona College, Department of Geology, U. S. Office of Naval Research Report, (Claremont, Calif.), 1–24; J. J. Conner and A. T. Miesch, "Application of Trend Analysis to Geochemical Prospecting Data from Beaver Co., Utah," *Stanford University Publications in the Geological Sciences*, 9 (1964), 110–125.

[44] Whitten, "A Surface-Fitting Program," *op. cit.;* E. W. Peikert, *IBM 709 Program for Least-Squares Analysis of Three-Dimensional Geological and Geophysical Observations*, U.S. Office of Naval Research, Geography Branch, Contract NONR 1228–26, Technical Report No. 4, (Evanston: Department of Geology, Northwestern University, 1964).

[45] D. I. Good, *Trend-Surface Fitting Program for the IBM 1620*, Kausas State Geological Survey, Special Distribution Publication No. 14 (1964).

[46] Harbaugh, *op. cit.*

[47] Whitten, "Composition Trends in a Granite, *op. cit.;* Whitten, "Quantitative Areal Model Analysis of Granitic Complexes," *Bulletin of the Geological Society of America*, **72** (1961), 1331–1359; Whitten, "A New Method for Determination of the Average Composition of a Granite Massif," *Geochimica et Cosmochimica Acta*, **26** (1962), 545–560.

[48] W. C. Krumbein, "Confidence Intervals in Low-Order Polynomial Trend Surfaces," *Journal of Geophysical Research*, **68** (1963), 5869–5878.

[49] *Ibid.*, 5874.

[50] K. R. Dawson and E. H. T. Whitten, "The Quantitative Mineralogical Composition and Variation of the Lacorne, La Motte, and Preissac Granite Complex, Quebec, Canada," *Journal of Petrology*, **3** (1962), 1–37; Whitten, "A Surface-Fitting Program," *op. cit.*

[51] P. Allen and W. C. Krumbein, "Secondary Trend Components on the Top Ashdown Pebble Bed: A Case History," *Journal of Geology*, **70** (1962), 507–538.

[52] Simpson, *op. cit.*

[53] Swartz, *op. cit.*

[54] E. N. Thomas, "Maps of Residuals from Regression: Their Classification and Uses in Geographic Research," State University of Iowa, Department of Geography, Report No. 2 (1960).

[55] Merriam and Harbaugh, *op. cit.;* D. F. Merriam, "Use of Trend Surface Residuals in Interpreting Geological Structure," *Stanford University Publications in the Geological Sciences*, **9** (1964), 686–692.

[56] Whitten, "Composition Trends in a Granite," *op. cit.;* Whitten, "Quantitative Areal Model Analysis," *op. cit.;* Whitten, "A Surface-Fitting Program," *op. cit.;* Whitten, "A Reply to Chayes and Suzuki," *op. cit.;* Whitten, "A New Method for Determination," *op. cit.*

[57] R. J. Chorley, "An Analysis of the Areal Distribution of Soil Size Facies on the Lower Greensand Rocks of East-Central England by the Use of Trend-Surface Analysis," *Geology Magazine*, **101** (1964), 314–321.

[58] Haggett, "Regional and Local Components," *op. cit.*

[59] Haggett, *Locational Analysis in Human Geography*, *op. cit.*

[60] R. J. Chorley, D. R. Stoddart, P. Haggett, and H. O. Slaymaker, "Regional and Local Components in the Areal Distribution of Surface Sand Facies in the Breckland, Eastern England," *Journal of Sedimentary Petrology*, forthcoming.

[61] J. R. Mackay, "The Alternative Choice in Isopleth Interpretation," *Professional Geographer*, **5** (1953), 2–4.

[62] S. Nordbeck, "Framstallning av kartor med jhalp av siffermaskiner," *Meddelanden från Lunds Universität Geogriska Institutionen* (1964) 97.

[63] D. R. Ojakangas and W. L. Basham, "Simplified Computer Contouring of Exploration Data," *Stanford University Publications in the Geological Sciences*, **9** (1964), 757–770.

[64] D. I. Blumenstock, "The Reliability Factor in

the Drawing of Isarithms," *Annals of the Association of American Geographers*, **43** (1953), 289–304.

[65] H. C. K. Henderson, "Agriculture in England and Wales in 1801," *Geographical Journal*, **118** (1952), 338–345.

[66] Haggett, "Regional and Local Components," *op. cit.*

[67] O. L. Davies, ed., *The Design and Analysis of Industrial Experiments* (New York: Hafner Publishing Company, Inc., 1954), p. 523.

[68] H. Svensson, *Method for Exact Characterizing of Denudation Surfaces, Especially Peneplains, as to the Position in Space*, Lund Studies in Geography, Series A, No. 8 (1956).

[69] W. C. Krumbein and J. Imbrie, "Stratigraphic Factor Maps," *Bulletin of the American Association of Petroleum Geologists*, **47** (1963), 698–701.

[70] Thomas, *op. cit.*; A. H. Robinson, J. B. Lindberg, and L. W. Brinkman, "A Correlation and Regression Analysis Applied to Rural Farm Population Densities in the Great Plains," *Annals of the Association of American Geographers*, **51** (1961), 211–221; Haggett, "Regional and Local Components," *op. cit.*

[71] Robinson and Caroe, *op. cit.*

[72] R. L. Miller, "Comparison Analysis of Trend Maps," *Stanford University Publications in the Geological Sciences*, **9** (1964), 669–685.

[73] W. C. Krumbein and L. L. Sloss, *Stratigraphy and Sedimentation*, 2nd ed. (San Francisco: W. H. Freeman & Company, Publishers, 1963); Whitten, "Process-Response Models," *op. cit.*

[74] W. C. Krumbein, "A Geological Process-Response Model for Analysis of Beach Phenomena, *Annual Bulletin of the Beach Erosion Board*, **17** (1964), 1–15.

[75] *Ibid.;* R. L. Miller and J. M. Ziegler, "A Model Relating Dynamics and Sediment Pattern in Equilibrium in the Region of Shoaling Waves, Breaker Zone, and Foreshore," *Journal of Geology*, **66** (1958), 417–441.

[76] Krumbein, "The Computer in Geology," *op. cit.;* Allen and Krumbein, *op. cit.;* L. L. Sloss, "Stratigraphic Models in Exploration," *Bulletin of the American Association of Petroleum Geologists*, **46** (1962), 1050–1057.

[77] Dawson and Whitten, *op. cit.*

[78] A. E. Ringwood, "A Model for the Upper Mantle," *Journal of Geophysical Research*, **67** (1962), 857–867, 4473–4477.

[79] Allen and Krumbein, *op. cit.*

[80] Haggett, "Regional and Local Components," *op. cit.*

8

FOURIER SERIES ANALYSIS
IN GEOLOGY

JOHN W. HARBAUGH and FLOYD W. PRESTON

This paper deals with use of Fourier series in geology. Fourier series are mathematical series consisting of terms containing sines and cosines. Single Fourier series may be used to analyze data represented by curves, whereas double Fourier series may be used to analyze surfaces.

Fourier series should be useful in portraying or modeling geologic features which vary in a more or less cyclic manner. For example, a topographic profile of an upland area that has been dissected by a dendritic drainage system might be thought of as a complex wave form composed of interacting cycles of various amplitudes and periods. This topographic profile could be approximated to any given accuracy by recording elevations along the profile at a sufficient number of data points and by fitting a single Fourier series to these points. A curve may be obtained whose configuration depends upon the number of terms in the Fourier series and the values of the coefficients of the terms. The coefficients may be thought of as numerical descriptors of the profile or surface being studied, and provide a means of

isolating and identifying the contribution of the various underlying harmonics.

An objective in using Fourier analysis is to determine whether variations in some natural feature can be represented by an oscillatory function. If a Fourier series provides a good representation of observed data, then one would generally suspect that the variations are due to causes which vary in some periodic manner. Conversely, if Fourier series do not represent the data convincingly, other mathematical means of representation might be sought, as, for example, the power series polynomials employed in conventional trend-surface analysis. Trend analysis permits interpolation between data points and, to some extent, extrapolation. The effectiveness of both of these uses depends, however, on careful appraisal of the quality of "fit" of the data to the trend function.[1]

Reprinted from *Short Course and Symposium on Computers and Computer Applications in Mining and Exploration* (School of Mines, University of Arizona, 1966), pp. R1-R46, by permission of the authors and editor.

There are two principal applications of Fourier analysis. Trend-surface analysis is currently used in ore reserve calculations, geochemical prospecting, analysis of geologic structure maps, and analysis of lithofacies maps.

A growing number of investigators are applying polynomial approximation or "trend" surfaces to the description of geological and geophysical measurements. Among these are Miller, Krumbein, Mandelbaum, Connor, Whitten, Merriam and Harbaugh, Harbaugh, and Agterberg[2]. An excellent review of trend-surface methods and the general problem of mapping geological parameters is given by Miller and Kahn.[3] The predominant effort has been to use nonorthogonal polynomials. An exception is the work of Oldham and Sutherland.[4] Up to now however, little use has been made of Fourier series for data representation in geology.

Spectral analysis is concerned with identification of the amplitudes and frequencies of the component cycles that constitute the periodic portion of an oscillatory phenomenon. Techniques for this type of analysis have been developed by Blackman and Tukey, Wiener, and used in geology by Anderson and Koopmans for varve analysis.[5]

This paper is largely concerned with the trend analysis aspects of Fourier series. Both trend analysis and spectral analysis are, however, closely related.

MATHEMATICAL DEVELOPMENT

SINGLE FOURIER SERIES

The single Fourier infinite series can be expressed in several ways.[6] The one chosen for the present work is

$$(1) \quad z = \frac{a_0}{2} + \sum_{n=1}^{n=\infty} \left[a_n \cos \frac{n\pi x}{L} + b_n \sin \frac{n\pi x}{L} \right]$$

This series is frequently used to approximate a known function of the form, $z = f(x)$. Under these circumstances, the coefficients a_0, a_n, and b_n, $n = 1, 2, \ldots, \infty$ are obtained from the expressions:

$$(2) \quad a_n = \frac{1}{L} \int_{-L}^{+L} f(x) \cos \frac{n\pi x}{L} \, dx$$

$$n = 0, 1, 2 \ldots, \infty$$

$$(3) \quad b_n = \frac{1}{L} \int_{-L}^{+L} f(x) \sin \frac{n\pi x}{L} \, dx$$

$$n = 1, 2 \ldots, \infty$$

The general restrictions under which Eq. 1 converges to $f(x)$ as n approaches infinity are well known and are documented in such texts as Gaskell, Churchill, and Wylie covering Fourier series.[7] However, in many physical problems one does not know the form of the function $z = f(x)$, thereby precluding the analytical integration of Eqs. 2–3 to obtain the coefficients. However, if information concerning the function is available as tabulated data (x_i, z_i) representing experimentally obtained points on the unknown function, then the coefficients a_n and b_n may be approximated by numerical integration methods.

If k points are chosen at equal intervals of x_i in the region $-L < x_i < +L$, and if the trapezoidal rule of numerical integration is used, the expressions for a_n and b_n become:

$$(4) \quad a_n = \frac{2}{k} \sum_{i=0}^{i=k-1} z_i \cos \frac{n\pi x_i}{L}$$

$$n = 0, 1, 2, \ldots, \frac{(k-1)}{2}$$

$$(5) \quad b_n = \frac{2}{k} \sum_{i=0}^{i=k-1} z_i \sin \frac{n\pi x_i}{L}$$

$$n = 1, 2, \ldots, \frac{(k-1)}{2}$$

The data set (x_i, z_i) is such that $x_0 = -L$, $(x_{i+1} - x_i)$ is constant, and $x_k = +L$, the value of k being odd. The number of coefficients a_n or b_n that can be extracted from a data set depends upon the number of data points. The restriction on n is such that $0 \leqslant n \leqslant N$.

When $N = (k-1)/2$, the approximating function

$$(6) \quad \begin{aligned} z_i &\cong P_{x_i} \\ &= \frac{a_0}{2} + \sum_{n=1}^{n=N} \left(a_n \cos \frac{n\pi x_i}{L} + b_n \sin \frac{n\pi x_i}{L} \right) \end{aligned}$$

passes through each measured data point (x_i, z_i).

Although the use of the trapezoidal rule would seem to be an unnecessary simplification for the numerical integration of Eqs. 2–3, it is shown by Whittaker and Robinson that the use of Eqs. 4–5 produces coefficients which satisfy the least-squares criterion of a "best" fit to the existing data, that is,

$$(7) \qquad \sum_{i=0}^{i=k-1} (z_i - P_{x_i})^2 = \text{Minimum}$$

where P_{x_i} is the polynomial approximation to the observed value z_i corresponding to the value x_i of the independent variable.[8]

Before the advent of digital computers, many numerical schemes were devised to generate the coefficients a_n and b_n with the least computational effort. Because of the relative ease of expressing the sines and cosines of angles that are multiples of 60°, 30°, or 15°, the computational methods involved data sets of 6, 12, 24, or 48 points. Such numerical schemes are described in detail by Scarborough, Manley, and Gaskell.[9] In addition, various optical and mechanical devices have been built for the determination of the coefficients. These are described by Manley.[10]

Use of a function such as Eq. 6 to represent a set of experimental data is analogous to use of a power series polynomial for trend-surface approximation. The term "trend" is used here in the context defined by Grant as a function that describes the behavior of the measured quantities, independent of any experiment.[11] This meaning for "trend" is different from that usually implied by those working with time-series analysis.

Figure 1 shows the shape of a synthetic single Fourier series which uses the set of coefficients in Table 1. Diagrams in the right-hand column are the series truncated at 2, 3, 4, and 5 harmonics. The pure sine and cosine components of each harmonic are also given.

The availability of digital computers now makes generation of trend surfaces of even a high polynomial order a relatively routine task. This fact underscores the importance of applying statistical methods for determining confidence intervals for these surfaces. Krumbein and Agterberg each develop methods for the conventional power series polynomials.[12] Oldham and Sutherland discuss hypothesis tests for selecting the "best" order for orthogonal polynomial approximations of geophysical measurements.[13] Additional tests for each term in any series, orthogonal or nonorthogonal, are

developed by Brown.[14] These latter tests are applied herein to determine the desirability of including specific terms in the Fourier series.

The particular test used for the coefficients depends upon the nature of the model used to describe variations in the property being measured. One can consider the ith value of the dependent variable z to be

$$(8) \qquad z_i = f(x_i) + \epsilon_i$$

where x_i is the ith value of the independent variable, and the "trend" of z with x is given by the function

$$z = f(x)$$

If it is assumed that ϵ is a random variable, that is ϵ_i is not correlated with ϵ_{i+1}, then, as shown by Brown, a ranking of the polynomial terms according to the values of their associated statistic $S_{n,p}\, c_{n,p}^2$ will reveal a sharp change at the transition from those terms which contribute to the trend to those which do not contribute. The terms $S_{n,p}$ and $c_{n,p}$ are defined as:

$$(10) \qquad S_{n,1} = \sum_{i=0}^{i=k-1} a_n \cos \frac{n\pi x_i}{L}$$

$$(11) \qquad S_{n,2} = \sum_{i=0}^{i=k-1} b_n \sin \frac{n\pi x_i}{L}$$

$$(12) \qquad S_{o,1} = k a_o; \; S_{o,2} = 0$$

$$(13) \qquad h_{n,1} = \sum_{i=0}^{i=k-1} z_i \left(a_n \cos \frac{n\pi x_i}{L} \right)$$

$$(14) \qquad h_{n,2} = \sum_{i=0}^{i=k-1} z_i \left(b_n \sin \frac{n\pi x_i}{L} \right)$$

$$(15) \qquad c_{n,p} = h_{n,p}/S_{n,p}$$

$$(16) \qquad p = 1, 2$$

If, in addition, the random variable ϵ is considered to be normally distributed, then by use of an F-test one can determine the desirability of adding a term to the polynomial. Here F is the ratio s_1^2/s_2^2 where s_1^2 and s_2^2 are taken to be the averaged values of $s_{n,p}\, c_{n,p}^2$ for v_1 terms and v_2 terms, respectively. For this F-test the degrees of freedom are v_1 and v_2.

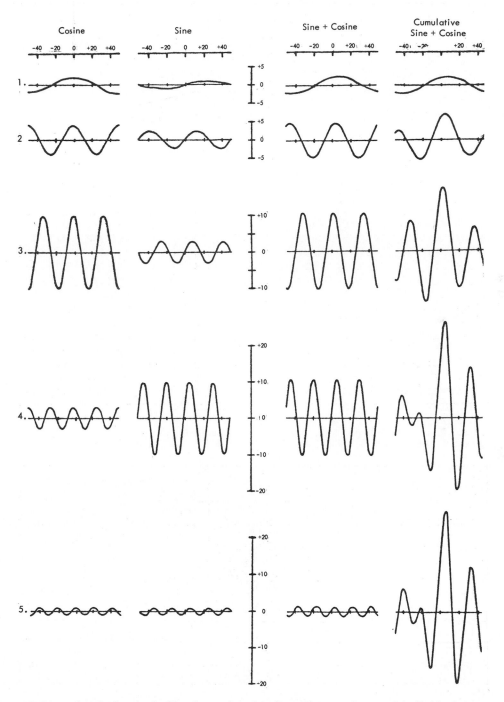

FIGURE 1. Synthetic single Fourier series showing (1) wave forms of individual terms and (2) wave form of series representing the summed individual terms. Coefficients are listed in Table 1. Numbers at left indicate harmonics.

TABLE 1

Coefficients used for generating synthetic Fourier series

Single Fourier series

n	a_n	b_n
0	0.0	—
1	2.0	1.0
2	4.0	2.5
3	10.0	3.0
4	3.0	−10.0
5	1.0	1.0

Double Fourier series

$a_{m,n}$

n \ m	0	1	2	3	4
0	43	54	65	76	87
1	45	56	67	78	89
2	47	58	69	80	91
3	49	60	71	82	93
4	51	62	73	84	95

$b_{m,n}$

n \ m	0	1	2	3	4
0	0	40	48	56	64
1	0	44	52	60	68
2	0	48	56	64	72
3	0	52	60	68	76
4	0	56	64	72	80

$c_{m,n}$

n \ m	0	1	2	3	4
0	0	0	0	0	0
1	27	32	37	42	47
2	33	38	43	48	53
3	39	44	49	54	59
4	45	50	55	60	65

$d_{m,n}$

n \ m	0	1	2	3	4
0	0	0	0	0	0
1	0	22	24	26	28
2	0	27	29	31	33
3	0	32	34	36	38
4	0	37	39	41	43

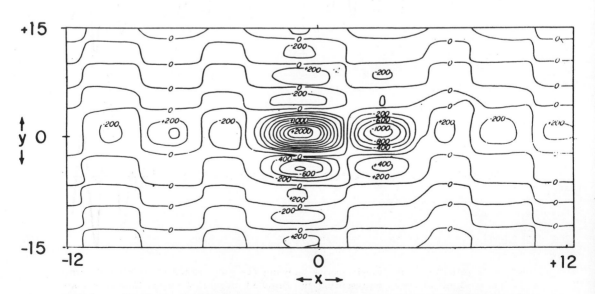

FIGURE 2. Synthetic double Fourier series showing a wave form containing four harmonics in each direction. Coefficients are listed in Table 1.

DOUBLE FOURIER SERIES

The Fourier series may be extended to represent a dependent variable z as a function of two independent variables, x and y.

$$(17) \qquad z = f(x, y)$$

Thus a parameter z may be considered to be oscillatory in two mutually perpendicular directions, such as east-west, and north-south, allowing Eq. 17 to represent the areal variation in z.

Figure 2 shows a contoured surface generated by a double Fourier series using the coefficients of Table 1. The surface shows a high degree of regularity. If many more terms had been used, and if the coefficients had been randomly selected, the surface would show very little regularity.

If we consider a function z to have a fundamental period of $2L$ along the x coordinate and $2H$ in the y coordinate, then the double Fourier series is:

$$
\begin{aligned}
(18) \quad z \cong P_{x,y} &= \sum_{m=0}^{m=M} \sum_{n=0}^{n=N} \lambda_{m,n} \bigg[a_{m,n} \cos \frac{\pi m x}{L} \cos \frac{\pi n y}{H} \\
&+ b_{m,n} \sin \frac{\pi m x}{L} \cos \frac{\pi n y}{H} + c_{m,n} \cos \frac{\pi m x}{L} \\
&\sin \frac{\pi n y}{H} + d_{m,n} \sin \frac{\pi m x}{L} \sin \frac{\pi n y}{H} \bigg]
\end{aligned}
$$

where

$$
(19) \quad
\begin{aligned}
\lambda_{m,n} &= \frac{1}{4} \qquad m = n = 0 \\
\lambda_{m,n} &= \frac{1}{2} \qquad m = 0, n > 0, \\
& \qquad\qquad\quad \text{or } m > 0, n = 0 \\
\lambda_{m,n} &= 1 \qquad m > 0, n > 0
\end{aligned}
$$

If the relation expressed by Eq. 18 can be integrated, the coefficients are determinable from the following relations:

$$
\begin{aligned}
(20) \quad a_{m,n} &= \\
&\frac{1}{LH} \int_{-H}^{+H} \int_{-L}^{+L} f(x,y) \cos \frac{m\pi x}{L} \cos \frac{n\pi y}{H} dx dy
\end{aligned}
$$

$$
\begin{aligned}
(21) \quad b_{m,n} &= \\
&\frac{1}{LH} \int_{-H}^{+H} \int_{-L}^{+L} f(x,y) \sin \frac{m\pi x}{L} \cos \frac{n\pi y}{H} dx dy
\end{aligned}
$$

$$
\begin{aligned}
(22) \quad c_{m,n} &= \\
&\frac{1}{LH} \int_{-H}^{+H} \int_{-L}^{+L} f(x,y) \cos \frac{m\pi x}{L} \sin \frac{n\pi y}{H} dx dy
\end{aligned}
$$

$$
\begin{aligned}
(23) \quad d_{m,n} &= \\
&\frac{1}{LH} \int_{-H}^{+H} \int_{-L}^{+L} f(x,y) \sin \frac{m\pi x}{L} \sin \frac{n\pi y}{H} dx dy
\end{aligned}
$$

For the instances in which the relation among x, y, and z is known only as a tabulated set of data, the equations for $a_{m,n}$, $b_{m,n}$, $c_{m,n}$, and $d_{m,n}$ analogous to Eqs. 4–5 are:

$$
\begin{aligned}
(24) \quad a_{m,n} = \\
\frac{4}{LH} \bigg[&\left(\frac{z_{0,0} + z_{k,0} + z_{0,1} + z_{k,1}}{4} \right) \cos m\pi \cos n\pi \\
&+ \sum_{j=0}^{j=1-1} \left(\frac{z_{0,j} + z_{k,j}}{2} \right) \cos m\pi \cos \frac{n\pi y_j}{H} \\
&+ \sum_{i=0}^{i=k-1} \left(\frac{z_{i,0} + z_{i,1}}{2} \right) \cos \frac{m\pi x_i}{L} \cos n\pi \\
&+ \sum_{j=0}^{j=1-1} \sum_{i=0}^{i=k-1} z_{i,j} \cos \frac{m\pi x_i}{L} \cos \frac{n\pi y_j}{H} \bigg]
\end{aligned}
$$

$$
\begin{aligned}
(25) \quad b_{m,n} = \\
\frac{4}{LH} \bigg[&\sum_{i=0}^{i=k-1} \left(\frac{z_{i,0} + z_{i,1}}{2} \right) \sin \frac{m\pi x_i}{L} \cos n\pi \\
&+ \sum_{j=0}^{j=1-1} \sum_{i=0}^{i=k-1} z_{i,j} \sin \frac{n\pi x_i}{L} \cos \frac{n\pi y_j}{H} \bigg]
\end{aligned}
$$

$$
\begin{aligned}
(26) \quad c_{m,n} = \\
\frac{4}{LH} \bigg[&\sum_{j=0}^{j=1-1} \left(\frac{z_{0,j} + z_{k,j}}{2} \right) \cos m\pi \sin \frac{n\pi y_j}{H} \\
&+ \sum_{j=0}^{j=1-1} \sum_{i=0}^{i=k-1} z_{i,j} \cos \frac{m\pi x_i}{L} \sin \frac{n\pi y_j}{H} \bigg]
\end{aligned}
$$

$$
\begin{aligned}
(27) \quad d_{m,n} = \\
&\frac{1}{LH} \sum_{j=0}^{j=1-1} \sum_{i=0}^{i=k-1} z_{i,j} \sin \frac{\pi m x_i}{L} \sin \frac{\pi n y_j}{H}
\end{aligned}
$$

The data set $(z_{i,j}, x_i, y_j)$ is such that

$$ i = 0, 1, 2, \ldots, k; \quad x_o = -L, x_k = +L $$

$$ j = 0, 1, 2, \ldots, l; \quad y_o = -H, y_l = +H $$

$$ x_{i+1} - x_i = \text{constant} $$

$$ y_{j+1} - y_i = \text{constant} $$

The limiting number of coefficients of all types $a_{m,n}$, $b_{m,n}$, $c_{m,n}$, and $d_{m,n}$ that can be extracted from a set of data is

(28) $4(M + 1)(N + 1) - 2((M + 1) + (N + 1))$

where:

$$N > 0; \quad M > 0$$
$$m = 0, 1, 2, \ldots, M$$
$$n = 0, 1, 2, \ldots, N$$

In a one-dimensional series, the term b_o is always zero. Similarly, the following relation holds for a two-dimensional Fourier series

(29) $\quad b_{0,n} = c_{m,o} = d_{0,n} = d_{m,o} = 0$

For the two-dimensional series, the equations corresponding to $s_{n,p}$, $c_{n,p}$, and $n_{n,p}$ are as follows:

(30)
$$S_{m,n,1} = \sum_{j=0}^{j=l-1} \sum_{i=0}^{i=k-1} \left[\lambda_{m,n} \cos \frac{m\pi x_i}{L} \cos \frac{n\pi y_j}{H} \right]^2$$

(31)
$$S_{m,n,2} = \sum_{j=0}^{j=l-1} \sum_{i=0}^{i=k-1} \left[\lambda_{m,n} \sin \frac{m\pi x_i}{L} \cos \frac{n\pi y_j}{H} \right]^2$$

(32)
$$S_{m,n,3} = \sum_{j=0}^{j=l-1} \sum_{i=0}^{i=k-1} \left[\lambda_{m,n} \cos \frac{m\pi x_i}{L} \sin \frac{n\pi y_j}{H} \right]^2$$

(33)
$$S_{m,n,4} = \sum_{j=0}^{j=l-1} \sum_{i=0}^{i=k-1} \left[\lambda_{m,n} \sin \frac{m\pi x_i}{L} \sin \frac{n\pi y_j}{H} \right]^2$$

(34)
$$h_{m,n,1} = \sum_{j=0}^{j=l-1} \sum_{i=0}^{i=k-1} z_{i,j} \left[\lambda_{m,n} \cos \frac{m\pi x_i}{L} \cos \frac{n\pi y_j}{H} \right]$$

(35)
$$h_{m,n,2} = \sum_{j=0}^{j=l-1} \sum_{i=0}^{i=k-1} z_{i,j} \left[\lambda_{m,n} \sin \frac{m\pi x_i}{L} \cos \frac{n\pi y_j}{H} \right]$$

(36)
$$h_{m,n,3} = \sum_{j=0}^{j=l-1} \sum_{i=0}^{i=k-1} z_{i,j} \left[\lambda_{m,n} \cos \frac{m\pi x_i}{L} \sin \frac{n\pi y_j}{H} \right]$$

(37)
$$h_{m,n,4} = \sum_{j=0}^{j=l-1} \sum_{i=0}^{i=k-1} z_{i,j} \left[\lambda_{m,n} \sin \frac{m\pi x_i}{L} \sin \frac{n\pi y_j}{H} \right]$$

(38) $\qquad c_{m,n,p} = \dfrac{h_{m,n,p}}{S_{m,n,p}}$

The same type of ranking of the double Fourier series coefficients according to the value $S_{m,n,p} \, c^2_{m,n,p}$ can be made to select the most appropriate terms. Likewise, if normality is assumed for the random component, ε, in the expression

(39) $\qquad z_i = f(x_i, y_i) + \epsilon$

then an F-test can be made to determine whether a particular coefficient should be added.

SINGLE FOURIER SERIES ANALYSIS OF SHALE OIL YIELD

Single Fourier series analysis was used to study fluctuations in shale oil yield with respect to depth. Shale oil yield values were measured at approximately one-foot intervals in a vertical core slightly less than 400 feet long penetrating the Green River oil shale. The core was obtained from the National Farmers Union Exploration Company Corehole 9, in SW SW NW, sec. 32, T. 10S, R. 5E, Uintah County, Utah. Shale oil yields in the core were determined by the U.S. Bureau of Mines and are tabulated in the report by Stanfield, Smith, and Trudell.[15] The oil yield values, in gallons of oil per ton of shale, range from 2.2 to 77. When oil yield values vs. depth are plotted (Fig. 3), the resulting curve is complex and irregular. However, casual inspection of the curve suggests that more or less regular "cycles" are present. The question arises as to a means of characterizing this oscillatory behavior and of evaluating the respective contributions of cycles of different wave length.

Results of single Fourier analysis of the data are also shown in Fig. 3. Curves that were obtained by evaluating single Fourier series contain 41, 101, and 161 terms, respectively. The quality of fit is given by the percentage reduction in total sum of squares, which is labeled simply as "per cent fit." A fit of 100 per cent would represent perfect fit of the values obtained by evaluation of the Fourier series to the observed data values.

Contributions of the various terms are given in Table 2, which lists the harmonic number, the cosine coefficients a_n, the sine coefficients,

b_n, and the discrete power spectrum estimates, which are obtained by squaring and adding the coefficients for each harmonic. The wave length of each harmonic is obtained by dividing the total sampling length, 388 feet, by the harmonic number. Thus the wave length corresponding to the first harmonic is 388 feet and to the second harmonic is 194 feet, etc. Terms whose contribution is relatively important correspond to harmonics 1, 2, 3, 4, 6, 11, 14, and 15, as indicated by their power spectrum estimates. However, many of the terms with lower power spectrum values have significance. The interaction of terms, of course, provides

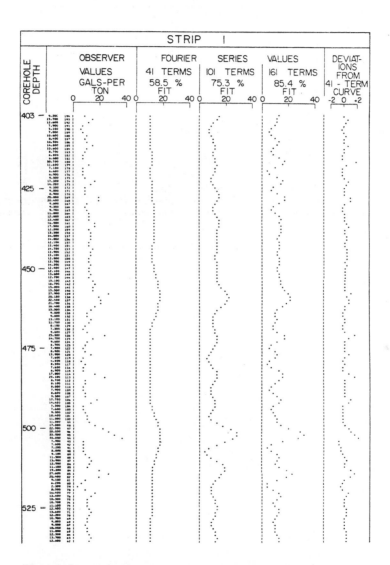

FIGURE 3A. Plot of observed, calculated, and residual values of shale oil yield data from National Farmers Union Exploration Company Corehole 9 in Uintah County, Utah. Because of the length of the core, three successive strips are used to present the data. Figures at extreme left are depth in corehole in feet. MM indicates the position of Mahogany Marker, a widely used stratigraphic datum within the Green River Formations. Shale oil yield values are shown at one-foot intervals. Interpolation was employed at several places to fill in values where observed values were missing. Original data from Stanfield, Smith and Trudell (1964, pp. 69–71).

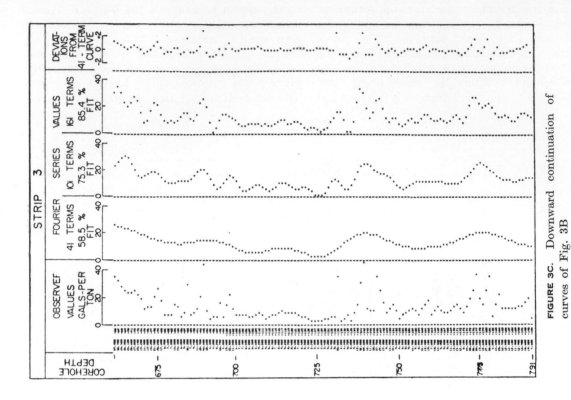

FIGURE 3C. Downward continuation of curves of Fig. 3B

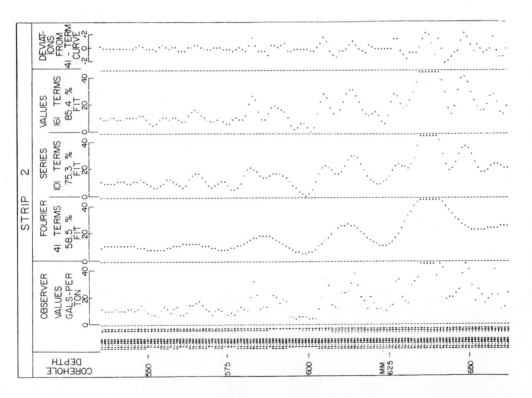

FIGURE 3B. Downward continuation of curves of Fig. 3A

TABLE 2

Fourier coefficients and power-spectrum values of single Fourier series fitted to shale oil yield data. The AZERO/2 value corresponds to an arithmetic mean of 15.318 gallons per ton. Columns headed A(N) are cosine term coefficients whose subscripts (N) pertain to the harmonic number. Columns headed B(N) are sine term coefficients. Power spectrum values represent the sum of the squared coefficient values of each harmonic.

AZERO/2 = 15.318

DEGREE number	A(N)	B(N)	POWER spectrum	DEGREE number	A(N)	B(N)	POWER spectrum
1	3.70952	−3.08208	23.26195	41	−.01045	.02262	.00062
2	1.49276	−5.41977	31.60222	42	−.95580	.39086	1.06632
3	−2.74432	−4.30078	26.02800	43	−1.06806	.44549	1.33922
4	−3.02088	.41361	9.29679	44	.16216	−.03206	.02733
5	−.72282	.81069	1.17968	45	.21260	.00888	.04528
6	−1.07028	2.03220	5.27534	46	.90643	.24978	.88401
7	−.76042	.83164	1.26986	47	.22171	−1.26873	1.65884
8	1.90315	1.27368	5.24424	48	.05032	−.27337	.07726
9	1.08351	−.53227	1.45731	49	.58201	.85081	1.06262
10	−.59251	.54815	.65153	50	1.22200	−.16010	1.51891
11	1.23910	−2.07324	5.83368	51	.43889	−.80347	.83820
12	−1.40983	−1.29937	3.67599	52	.91920	−.03203	.84595
13	−1.10453	−.45392	1.43498	53	.53515	−1.08157	1.45619
14	−2.54833	−.56472	6.81288	54	−.03756	−.65961	.43650
15	−2.83180	1.65968	10.77363	55	.32143	−1.52913	2.44156
16	−.95670	1.68273	3.74684	56	−.77963	−.63184	1.29979
17	−.02259	1.27026	1.61408	57	−.47774	1.05454	1.33987
18	−1.28623	1.02808	2.71132	58	1.18293	.13164	1.41666
19	.22600	.42276	.22980	59	−.10683	−.25972	.07887
20	.54519	−.35407	.42260	60	.08487	−.76772	.59660
21	.03201	.41202	.17078	61	.24279	−.49524	.30421
22	.53217	−1.24118	1.82373	62	.14568	.45534	.22855
23	−.93701	−.87575	1.64492	63	−.00680	1.36897	1.87414
24	.15548	−.44861	.22543	64	−.18605	−1.40958	2.02152
25	−.34770	.38886	1.04934	65	.17148	.02654	.03011
26	−.49849	1.64414	2.95169	66	.26108	.63407	.47021
27	−.15250	−.45346	.22889	67	−.44509	−.15865	.22327
28	1.24169	.94602	2.43674	68	−.93837	.40579	1.04520
29	.93558	.67975	1.33736	69	.54030	−.38915	.44337
30	.20883	−.89660	.84751	70	−.33703	−.39577	.27022
31	−.81312	−1.78467	3.84622	71	.23634	−.64182	.46779
32	−.88840	−.17066	.81837	72	−1.07989	−.24942	1.22838
33	−1.41829	.28975	2.09549	73	−1.28058	−.37979	1.78413
34	−1.30997	1.60069	4.27824	74	.01024	1.02368	1.04802
35	−1.25022	.87448	2.32776	75	.40702	−.08168	.17233
36	−.31736	.03105	.10168	76	−.17398	.10838	.04201
37	.93039	1.63092	3.52551	77	.21292	−.47893	.27471
38	.83444	1.34813	2.51373	78	−.46872	−.34888	.34142
39	.16784	−.52838	.30735	79	.11181	.33166	.12250
40	−.35685	−.75084	.69110	80	.30496	−1.19367	1.51785

the complexity observed in the Fourier series. Inspection of the forty-one-term curve reveals an important wave length of about twenty-five feet, which is substantiated by the relatively large value of the power spectrum of degree 15 (which represents a wave length of 25.8 feet here). Inspection of the 101-term curve reveals an important wave length of about eight to nine feet. This is, of course, superimposed upon the broad period waves emphasized in the curve with forty-one terms. Further study is needed to interpret the geological significance of the different harmonics in Green River oil shale.

DOUBLE FOURIER SERIES ANALYSIS OF CALCIUM CARBONATE VARIATION IN GABBS MAGNESITE DEPOSIT

A double Fourier series was fitted to observed values of per cent calcium carbonate occurring in part of the magnesite deposit at Gabbs, Nev. (Fig. 4). The purpose was to see if the rather large areal variations in calcium carbonate content can be represented as a series of interacting harmonics. The geology of magnesite deposits at Gabbs has been described by Martin.[16] Magnesite occurs as a zone about 400 feet thick within recrystallized dolomite in the Luning Formation of [the] Late Triassic Age. Impurities in the magnesite consist of silica and calcium carbonate. Distribution of calcium carbonate is controlled by a network of intersecting flexures, faults, and joints, which in turn have affected movement of fluids through the magnesite. The magnesite is mined in benches about ten feet thick.

Data used in this study were obtained through the courtesy of Conrad Martin, currently of Stanford University, and formerly of Basic, Incorporated. The data consist of calcium carbonate percentages as determined by chemical analysis of drill cuttings within a ten-foot bench from drill holes spaced about six feet apart. Martin mapped these values over an irregular-shaped area whose dimensions are roughly 350 by 400 feet. Within this area, a smaller rectangular area (Fig. 4) about 220 by 240 feet in extent was chosen for analysis using double Fourier series.

A double Fourier series is capable of effectively representing the general variations in calcium carbonate content within the area of study (Figs. 5–6). A series containing six M-terms and six N-terms has almost reached the maximum degree of complexity attainable with the grid spacing employed; addition of more terms in the series results in only very slight improvement in per cent of total sum of squares.

The usefulness of fitting a double Fourier series to the magnesite data may be assessed as follows: (1) Double Fourier series provides an effective approximation of gross variations but not local fluctuations. (2) Gross variations in calcium carbonate in the part of the Gabbs deposit studied may be effectively represented by as few as six harmonics. Inspection of the power spectrum values reveals that the gross variation may be interpreted in terms of the interactions between two harmonics across the horizontal direction of the map, two harmonics across the vertical direction, and two other harmonics that represent a "cross-product" effect of the two map directions. (3) If a larger area were analyzed by double Fourier series, it might be possible to develop an effective method of predicting calcium carbonate impurities in the magnesite deposits, provided that the network of intersecting flexures, faults, and joints displays a considerable degree of periodicity over a large area. A surface represented by a given Fourier series would, of course, be repeated over and over as it is extended beyond the boundaries of the initial area, permitting some extrapolation.

DOUBLE FOURIER SERIES ANALYSIS OF GEOLOGIC STRUCTURE OF AN AREA IN SOUTH-CENTRAL KANSAS

The geologic structure of the top of the Pennsylvanian Lansing Group was analyzed in an area of about 3500 square miles in south-central Kansas (Fig. 7) to see whether double Fourier series are capable of successfully representing the rather complex shape of the surface (Fig. 8). The structure within the area of study is a southwest-dipping homocline, on which are superimposed many lesser gentle folds.

A surface represented by a double Fourier series is shown in Fig. 9. Except for that part of the map near the long edges of the map, the double Fourier series surface is a fairly good approximation of the actual surface (Fig. 8).

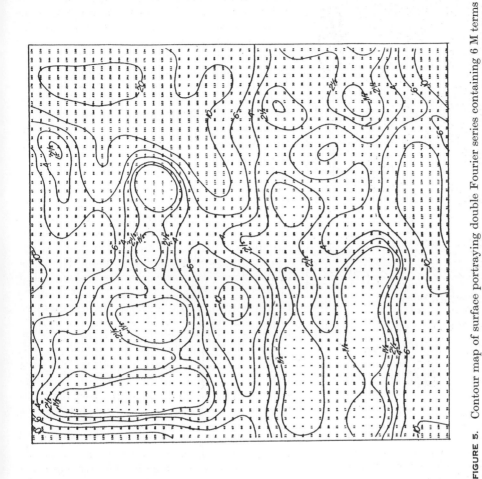

FIGURE 5. Contour map of surface portraying double Fourier series containing 6 M terms fitted to percent calcium carbonate in magnesite deposit (Fig. 4) at Gabbs, Nevada. Numbers on grid represent percent in tenths. Per cent of total sum of squares is 66.46.

FIGURE 4. Map showing distribution of percent calcium carbonate in magnesite deposits at Gabbs, Nevada. The data pertain to part of the 5800–5810 foot bench of the Gloria 5-Betty O'Neal Pit operated by Basic, Incorporated. Patterns portray the range of values within contour bands. Data from Martin (1958).

PERCENT Ca CO₃

0 to 2½

2½ to 6

6 to 20

Greater than 20

North

Scale in feet

0   20   40   60

NEVADA

Gabbs

229

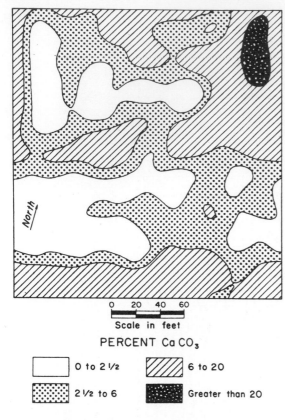

Scale in feet

PERCENT Ca CO₃

0 to 2 1/2	6 to 20
2 1/2 to 6	Greater than 20

FIGURE 6. Map of double Fourier surface representing percent calcium carbonate with contour bands distinguished by same patterns used in Fig. 4. Comparison of Figs. 4 and 6 reveals considerable similarity of broad-scale variations.

Conspicuously absent in the Fourier surface are the relatively small crenulations present in the actual surface. The limit of the ability of this Fourier surface to approximate the actual surface has been reached with six M-terms and six N-terms in the double Fourier series. Incorporation of additional terms does not result in an improvement. Thus the "noise level" has already been reached, and increased complexity of the fitted surface merely interacts at random with data representing the actual surface.

The failure of the Fourier surface of Fig. 8 to provide a good approximation along the long edges of the map is due to the fact that the actual surface was not "leveled" before the Fourier series was fitted. The actual surface has, of course, a pronounced slope toward the southwest (toward left side of map). The effect of this slope is to pose a rather severe constraint on the fitted surface, namely, that it must be the same elevation at corresponding points on either side of the fitted surface, whereas the elevation of the actual surface is quite different on the two long sides of the map. The original surface may be leveled by fitting a least-squares plane to the observed data and subtracting the elevations of this plane at each point. Pierson, *et al.* demonstrate the usefulness of this technique.[17]

The residual map, obtained by subtracting the unleveled Fourier surface from the actual surface, is shown in Fig. 10. The configuration of the residual surface reflects the fact that the

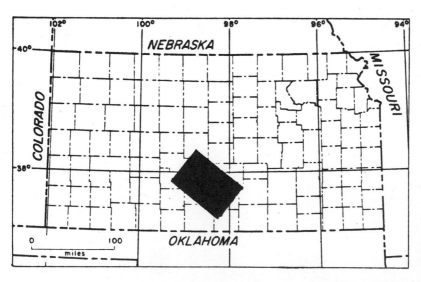

FIGURE 7. Index map showing area in which top of Lansing Group was analyzed

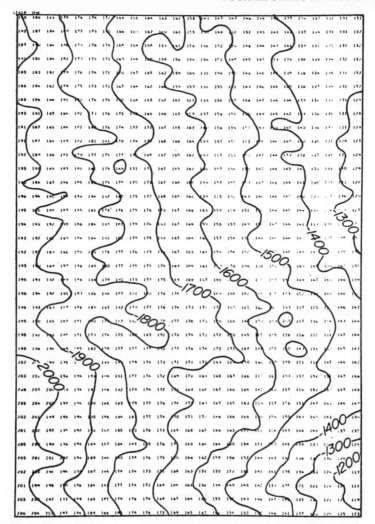

FIGURE 8. Structure contour map based on observed data values of elevations of top of Pennsylvanian Lansing Group in south-central Kansas. See Fig. 7 for location of area and orientation of map. Area is about 48 miles wide and 72 miles long. Data from Merriam, Winchell and Atkinson (1958). Contour values are in feet below sea level. The numbers printed on the grid are in tens of feet and negative signs have been omitted. North is toward the upper right.

small crenulations in the actual surface are not represented by the Fourier surface. The strongly elongate parallel trends of the residuals reflect the interaction between the M harmonic terms (across the short dimension of the map) and data of the actual surface. Furthermore, the elongate residual trends also reflect the orientation of the sampling grid. Different orientations presumably would have an important effect on the configuration of the residuals.

When the original surface is leveled, there is dramatic improvement in the quality of fit of the Fourier surface. To demonstrate the improvement, the original data were leveled by fitting a least-squares plane (Fig. 11), which is, of course, the same process as obtaining the residuals of a first-degree power series polynomial trend surface. When a Fourier surface is fitted to the data of Fig. 11, the fitted surface (Fig. 12) provides a very close approximation. Note that the fitted surface represents a double

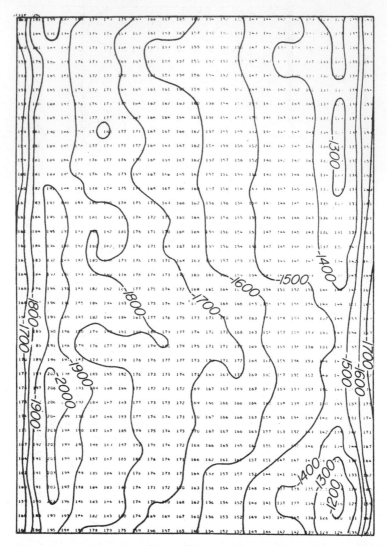

FIGURE 9.   Structure contour map of top of Lansing Group obtained by evaluating double Fourier series containing six M terms and nine N terms. M terms pertain to short dimension of map; N terms to long dimension. Coeffecients of terms have been obtained by analysis of observed data. Percent of total sum of squares is 76.84. Contour of values are in feet below sea level. Numbers printed on the grid are in tens of feet and the negative signs have been omitted. North is toward the upper right (Fig. 7).

Fourier series containing the maximum possible number of terms (12×18) considering the dimensions of the grid (25×37). The per cent of total sum of squares of the fitted surface is 91.3, which represents the highest attainable value utilizing leveled data in this example.

There is an advantage in restoring the "tilt" to the Fourier surface after it has been fitted. This may be done by simply reversing the process by which the leveling was accomplished, namely by adding to the fitted surface the least-squares plane that was subtracted earlier in the leveling process. If the least-squares plane removed in this example is added to the fitted Fourier surface of Fig. 12, the resulting surface is very nearly identical to that of Fig. 8, although it does fail to match in places along the edges.

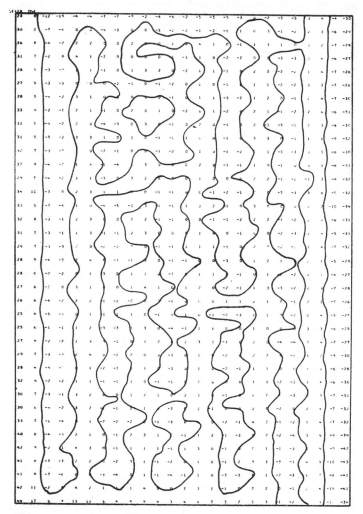

FIGURE 10. Contour map of residual values of structure of top of Lansing Group in south-central Kansas. Counter lines have a value of zero. Printed values pertain to tens of feet.

Figure 13 is an example of a Fourier surface that was fitted to leveled data, and then tilted back. Although the surface is represented by a double Fourier series containing only seven M-terms (horizontal direction) and ten N-terms (vertical direction), the approximation of the original surface (Fig. 8) is fairly good. A measure of the closeness of approximation is given by the residual values (Fig. 14). The pattern of the residual values is of interest, although comparison of the residual highs of Fig. 14 with the locations of oil fields reveals only minor geographic coincidence, and it is concluded that the grid spacing is too coarse to perceive the

structural irregularities that are associated with structurally controlled oil pools.

SUGGESTED USES OF FOURIER ANALYSIS

Fourier series provide a convenient means for interpolation, and limited extrapolation of data that are oscillatory. The use of single Fourier series is analogous to the use of power series in curve fitting, and the use of double Fourier series is analogous to [the] use of power series in trend-surface analysis. Power series are, of course, best applied to nonoscillatory data. Both Fourier series and power series can

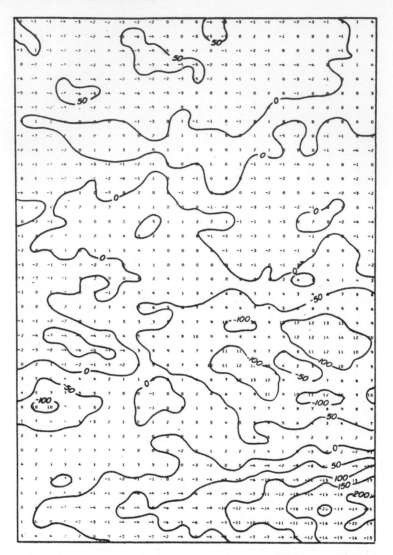

FIGURE 11.   Leveled original Lansing structure data of Fig. 8. The signs have been reversed because the original data were fed in as positive values, although they actually represent feet below sea level. Arithmetic mean of leveled values is approximately zero. Numbers on grid are in tens of feet.

be fitted to satisfy the least-squares criterion, permitting calculation of residuals.

A possible geologic use of single Fourier series would be analysis of rock data encountered in different bore holes. Fourier coefficients from different bore holes could be plotted on maps and contoured. This could provide a mappable index of the geographic variation in oscillatory properties of strata, ore grades, or other features encountered in bore holes.

Double Fourier series may be useful for (1)

"unraveling" cross folding in layered rocks, (2) predicting laterally the intersections of faults or joints in a complex network which exhibits an underlying periodicity, (3) possibly predicting veins in ore deposits, (4) predicting oil field structures, and (5) analyzing the harmonics of topographic surfaces, including those of sand dunes, submerged oölite dunes, and dendritic drainage systems.

Finally, a possible general use of both single and double Fourier series would be to produce

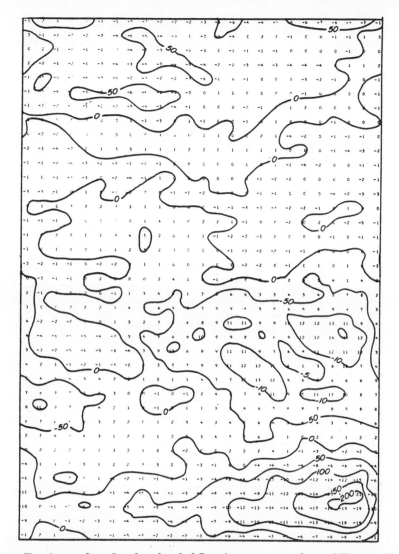

FIGURE 12.   Fourier surface fitted to leveled Lansing structure data of Fig. 11. Note that approximation is very good, except at some places along edge of map. The signs have been reversed because the original data (Fig. 8) were fed in as positive values, whereas they represent feet below sea level. Numbers on grid represent tens of feet.

numerical indices that would be useful in classification. For example, an objective numerical system of classifying the configuration of oil field structures or of landforms could be developed using double Fourier series analysis.

In conclusion, it appears that double Fourier analysis of structural data is useful. However, additional work needs to be done which includes (1) assessment of the desirability of leveling of the data prior to Fourier analysis, (2) finding means of determining how the Fourier sampling grid should be oriented with respect to the structural "grain," (3) establishing guides for grid-point spacing and for the number of columns and rows in the grid, and (4) arriving at suitable guides for determining the "cut-off" point with respect to numbers of M-terms and N-terms to be used in the Fourier series.

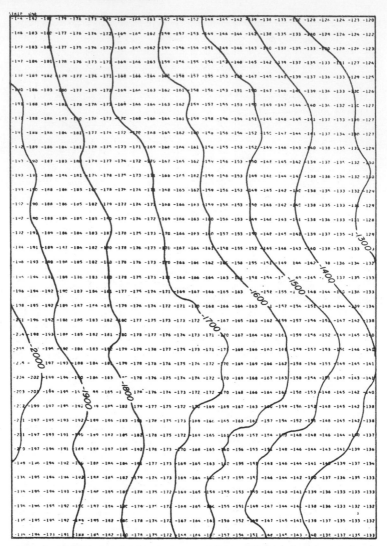

FIGURE 13. Lansing structural surface obtained by tilting Fourier surface represented by double Fourier series containing seven M terms and ten N terms fitted to leveled original data (Fig. 11). Note that signs are all negative on grid and represent tens of feet below sea level.

FOOTNOTES

[1] S. S. Wilks, "Statistical Inference in Geology," in *The Earth Sciences: Problems and Progress in Current Research* (Chicago: University of Chicago Press, 1963), pp. 105–136.

[2] R. L. Miller, "Trend Surfaces: Their Application to Analysis and Description of Environments of Sedimentation," *Journal of Geology*, 64 (1956), 425–446; W. C. Krumbein, "Trend-Surface Analysis of Contour-Type Maps with Irregular Control-Point Spacing," *Journal of Geophysical Research*, 64 (1959), 823–834; Krumbein, "Confidence Intervals on Low-Order Polynomial Trend Surfaces," *ibid.*, 68 (1963), 5869–5878; H. Mandelbaum, "Statistical and Geological Implications of Trend Mapping with Nonorthogonal Polynomials," *Journal of Geophysical Research*, 68 (1963), 505–519; J. J. Connor and A. T. Miesch, "Application of Trend Analysis to Geochemical Prospect Data from Beaver County, Utah," in Stanford University *Publications in the Geological Sciences*, 9 (1964), 110–125; E. H. T. Whitten, "Sampling and Trend-Surface Analysis of Granites, a Reply," *Bulletin of the Geological Society of America*, 73 (1962), 415–

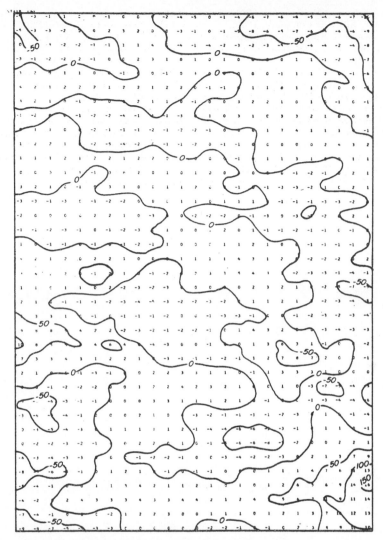

FIGURE 14. Residual map of Lansing structural data obtained by subtracting fitted surface (Fig. 13) from actual surface (Fig. 8). Numbers on grid are in tens of feet above (positive) or below (negative) fitted surface.

418; D. F. Merriam and J. W. Harbaugh, *Trend-Surface Analysis of Regional and Residual Components of Geologic Structure in Kansas*, Kansas State Geological Survey, Special Distribution Publication, No. 11 (1964); J. W. Harbaugh, "A Computer Program for Four-Variable Trend Analysis Illustrated by a Study of Oil Gravity Variations in Southeastern Kansas," *Kansas Geological Survey Bulletin*, **171** (1964); F. P. Agterberg, "Methods of Trend-Surface Analysis," International Symposium on Applications of Statistics, Operation Research, and Computers in the Mineral Industry, *Colorado School of Mines Quarterly*, **59** (1964), 111–130.

[3] R. L. Miller and J. S. Kahn, *Statistical Analysis in the Geological Sciences* (New York: John Wiley & Sons, Inc., 1962), pp. 390–439.

[4] C. H. G. Oldham and D. B. Sutherland, "Orthogonal Polynomials and Their Use in Estimating the Regional Effect," *Geophysics*, **22** (1955), 295–306.

[5] R. B. Blackman and J. W. Tukey, *The Measurement of Power Spectrum* (New York: Dover Publications Inc., 1958); N. Wiener, *The Extrapolation and Smoothing of Stationary Time Series* (New York: John Wiley & Sons, Inc., 1949); R. Y. Anderson and L. H. Koopmans, "Harmonic Analysis of Varve Time Series," *Journal of Geophysical Research*, **68** (1963), 977–993.

[6] J. B. Fourier, *Théorie analytique de la chaleur* (Paris: Gauthier-Villars et Fils, 1822).

[7] R. E. Gaskell, *Engineering Mathematics* (New York: Holt, Rinehart & Winston, Inc., 1958); R. V. Churchill, *Fourier Series and Boundary Value Problems*. (New York: McGraw-Hill Book Company,

1941); C. R. Wylie, *Advanced Engineering Mathematics* (New York: McGraw-Hill Book Company, 1960).

[8] E. T. Whittaker and G. Robinson, *The Calculus of Observations* (Glasgow: Blackie & Son, Ltd., 1924), pp. 264–267.

[9] J. B. Scarborough, *Numerical Mathematical Analysis*, 5th ed. (Baltimore: Johns Hopkins University Press, 1962), pp. 558–573; R. G. Manley, *Waveform Analysis: A Guide to the Interpretation of Periodic Waves, Including Vibration Records* (London: Chapman & Hall, Ltd., 1945); Gaskell, *op. cit.*

[10] Manley, *op. cit.*

[11] F. Grant, "A Problem in the Analysis of Geophysical Data," *Geophysics*, **22** (1957), 309–344.

[12] Krumbein, "Confidence Intervals," *op. cit.;*

Agterberg, *op. cit.*

[13] Oldham and Sutherland, *op. cit.*

[14] W. F. Brown, "Minimum Variance in Gravity Analysis," *Geophysics*, **20** (1955), 807–828.

[15] K. E. Stanfield, J. W. Smith, and L. G. Trudell, *Oil Yields of Sections of Green River Oil Shale in Utah*, U. S. Bureau of Mines, Report of Investigation, No. 6420 (1964), pp. 69–71.

[16] C. Martin, *The Origin of Crystalline Magnesite Deposits*, unpublished report (1958).

[17] W. J. Pierson, *et al.*, "The Directional Spectrum of a Wind-Generated Sea as Determined from Data Obtained by the Stereo Wave Observation Project," New York University, College of Engineering, Meteorological Papers, **2** (1960).

9

CONNECTIVITY OF
THE INTERSTATE HIGHWAY SYSTEM

WILLIAM L. GARRISON

A recent informal survey of two thousand motorists disclosed that less than 2 per cent knew what the National System of Interstate and Defense Highways, or the Interstate Highway System, was. Undoubtedly, this proportion does not apply to the readers of this paper. But readers may not be familiar with certain of the needs for research regarding the Interstate System, so a general discussion precedes presentation of the problem treated in this paper. The problem treated is introduced in the paragraph below. This is followed by the general discussion which gives some characteristics of the Interstate System and the relevance of the research problem. Analyses of the problem and evaluation of results follow.

Everyone knows that the success of an activity is conditioned by its relative location, among other things. The Interstate Highway System is inducing changes in the relative location of urban centers and, thus the success

of activities within these centers. Locations of cities relative to each other are changing, city tributary areas are shifting, and the relative location of sites within cities is changing. General notions stressing locations relative to markets and/or raw materials and in association with compatible activities are available in the literature. However, present concepts of transportation systems are not at this level of generality. Present concepts relate to particular places—such as the head of navigation and break of bulk places—and lack the generality of notions from location theory. Thus they are of little value for the problem of transportation-induced shifts in relative location. What concepts are appropriate? In this paper the Interstate System is treated as a graph, and the

Reprinted from *Papers and Proceedings of the Regional Science Association*, **6** (1960), 121–137, by permission of the author and editor.

usefulness of concepts from the theory of graphs is examined. Examination of the graph yields several measures which may be thought of as indices of connectiveness, status indices, accessibility indices, or indices of relative location. The paper is elementary, both in its use of graph theory and in the analysis of the Interstate System. It reports the results of a pilot study from which it is hoped that more incisive studies will be developed.

The paragraph above is incorrect in one respect. There are certain concepts of transportation systems in the programming literature which are at a high level of generality. The ordinary transportation problem of linear programming is a case in point. The transportation problem may be approached from the theory of graphs, of course. The search in this paper is for a level of approximation which is more elementary than those approximations using programming formats, but which is useful for the consideration of location problems.

THE INTERSTATE SYSTEM

The Interstate System comprises 41,000 miles of high-speed, low transportation cost, limited-access facilities linking many of the major cities of the nation (Fig. 1). The concept of the Interstate System dates back a number of years prior to implementation in 1956.[1] Previous federal highway policy has resulted in the federal aid primary system of about a quarter of a million miles, the federal aid secondary system (the farm-to-market system), and certain national parks and forest roads. The result of this previous policy is a relatively fine-scale network linking urban centers of all classes with each other, and linking urban centers with their tributary areas. The Interstate System is more gross in scale—in a sense it lies on top of previous highway systems, and it emphasizes linkages within and between major cities.

Perhaps two things may be gleaned from this brief statement. First, the Interstate System may be thought of as a large-city or

FIGURE 1. The national system of Interstate Highways, 1957, comprising 41,000 miles of expressway facilities

metropolitan system of highways, since it provides links between (and within) metropolitan areas. This represents a marked shift in federal policy, because previous highway policy might be characterized as catering to rural areas and small urban centers. Another notion is that the Interstate System may be thought of as a new highway network. In many ways it is more comparable to networks of airline and railroad routes than present highway networks.

MAGNITUDE OF CHANGES INDUCED

How far-reaching will be the location shifts following construction of the Interstate Highway System? The writer is inclined to the view that these changes will be as significant as those induced by other major technological changes in transportation systems—railroad developments or paving of rural roads. Many do not share this strong an opinion, and some discussion of points of view is appropriate.

It may be argued that the situation is very different today from what it was when other transportation networks, say railroads, were developed. The railroads opened up large areas to distant markets, especially in the western United States. Consequently, many new industries were developed which produced directly from resources and exported products long distances. Extensive wheat farming is an example of an industry developed in this way. Also, railroads enabled centralization of many manufacturing and service activities from small local establishments to giant national centers. The iron and steel industry serves as an example of this type of change. Production, which was previously highly decentralized, gave way to competition from large centers of production. The key to these changes was a marked reduction in unit transportation cost with the introduction of the railroad. With reduced unit transportation cost, new resources could be brought into the economy and new efficiencies of large-scale production could be realized.

The Interstate Highway System is also markedly reducing unit transportation cost. This is especially true of the portions of the Interstate System within urban centers, where congestion costs are high.[2] It is here that one might look first for changes induced by the Interstate System. What new resources will be brought into the economy? Most striking, perhaps, is the possibility for upgrading to urban land uses resources formerly used for typically rural land uses. Production of amenities from residential sites and recreational amenities are two cases in point. What activities will be centralized from local to larger scale? Perhaps governmental activities in urban centers will be among those most subject to change. Wholesale activities of all types, newspapers, and department stores might be other activities which will change their structure greatly. The Interstate Highway System will induce changes, but most of the changes will relate to different activities and resources than railroad-induced changes.

The tendency to oversimplify previous experience and use it to evaluate the future (which we have been guilty of doing in the paragraphs above) makes it especially difficult to envision the reshaping of the economy that will follow from the continued development of highways. One forgets, for example, that the pattern of railroad routes developed over a long period of time, and during that time many changes went on rather gradually. First, railroads were built in competition with inland waterways and coastal routes. It was probably very difficult to see widespread changes that these original beginnings foretold. At that time, as even now, cost comparisons between transportation media must have presented great difficulties. How difficult it must have been to visualize which of our industries would find great economies of centralization with the availability of railroad transportation. Many probably pointed out that production of buffalo hides hardly warranted building railroads through the arid West. To what extent are we guilty of the same kind of thinking about highways today?

There is some indication of changes that follow highway construction. It is well known that marked changes in rural life were brought about by [the] paving of rural highways.[3] It is now necessary to predict marked changes in urban areas which will follow current developments of highways.

OTHER CONDITIONS

Highways alone are not enough to induce change, of course, just as railroads alone could not remake the face of America. The success of railroads depended upon markets for the products they hauled. Industrialization of Europe and the growth and development of the United States were necessary conditions for the great changes brought about by railroads. Certain conditions are necessary if changes are to be induced by the Interstate System. Continued urbanization and increasing demands for more leisure time at home, amenities, and services are conditions especially pertinent to the changes that will be induced by the Interstate System. Also, governmental conditions, such as the existence of FHA and transportation taxation policy, are important considerations in evaluating highway impact.

SOME RESEARCH QUESTIONS

Decisions on the location of the System and its capacity largely have been made.[4] The Interstate System is limited to 41,000 miles, and the general orientation of these routes is fixed. Decisions about capacity decisions have been made. That is, certain operational methods for forecasting traffic are used to determine traffic demands, and capacity is installed to meet these demands. However, much research on allocation of facilities is needed, in spite of the fact that many of the major decisions have been made. Methods of making capacity decisions on the Interstate System could be improved. Need for investment in highway facilities seems unlimited, and many decisions bearing on location and capacity of facilities similar to those made for the Interstate System will be made in the future.

Certain problems of financing the Interstate System have been recognized. The U.S. Bureau of Public Roads is currently undertaking a highway cost-allocation study designed to deal with these problems at the federal level.[5] Surely this study will not provide all the answers at the federal level, and there is need for work on state and local problems of financing. Also, questions of charges to properly allocate traffic among the several kinds of carriers arise when highway financing is reconsidered, as well as from pressures of problems arising in other sectors of the transportation industry.[6]

THE RELATIVE LOCATION PROBLEM

Answering any one of the questions mentioned above requires some ability to speak intelligently about the influence of the Interstate System on activities. Answering questions of location and capacity obviously requires insights into effects on traffic by location shifts induced by the facility. Resolving questions of tax equity, financing, and the like requires ability to make intelligent estimates of location shifts. Thus relative location is at the heart of these problems. The strategic position of some areas will be enhanced while that of others will be diminished when the highway improvements are made. Questions of how much change and where these changes will take place are inseparable.[7]

THE HIGHWAY SYSTEM AS A GRAPH

Notions from graph theory may be useful in evaluating the relative location problem. In the language of graph theory, the Interstate Highway System is an ordinary graph with 325 edges terminating at 218 vertices. For convenience in this discussion, edges will be termed "routes," vertices will be termed "places," and the graph will be termed "highway system," or "network." An example of a network is given by Fig. 2. Places are marked P_1, P_2, etc., and routes, $L(12)$, $L(23)$, etc. Properties which characterize ordinary graphs and thus transportation systems treated as ordinary graphs are:[8]

1. A network has a finite number of places
2. Each route is a set consisting of two places
3. Each route joins two different places
4. At the most, only one route may join a pair of places
5. No distinctions are made between the

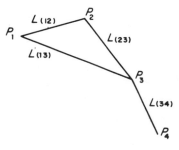

FIGURE 2

"initial" and the "terminal" places of routes; in other words, routes are two-way.

IDENTIFICATION OF PLACES

It was necessary to adopt operational definitions of a place on the Interstate Highway System. All Standard Metropolitan Areas were recognized as places, provided they were on the System. One hundred forty-three SMA's are on the System; twenty-three are not. Each intersection of three or more routes on the System was recognized as a place, regardless of whether or not it was occupied by an urban center which met the size criteria. Also, all ends of routes were recognized as places, e.g., Sweetgrass, Mont. The definition of place was, then, partly topological and partly based on urban size criteria.

These definitions identify a "planar graph"—the intersection of any two routes on the graph is a place on the network. It was decided to use the topological definition of places because these ends of routes and, especially, intersections have locational assets; they are able to ship and receive from several directions. It is worth noting that many intersections on other transportation systems have not developed to the degree that the location at an intersection might seem to warrant. Complicating factors of tariff structures might have contributed to this. In the highway case there is an effect due to presence of demand on a highway which may be important in giving intersections an impetus for development. Heavy streams of traffic create demands for food, lodging, and other goods and services, and these are not supplied by the facility itself. There are no dining rooms, staterooms, or swimming pools on the highway as there are on ships.

Consideration of intersections as major places introduces interesting problems which need to be investigated further. As the transportation network is filled in in an underdeveloped area, for example, intersections on the transportation system are created. These have the effect of introducing new places with strategic locations in the economy and shifting the relative location of places already developed (Fig. 3).

MEASURES OF CONNECTIVITY

DEFINITIONS: A *path* is a collection of routes $P_1 P_2, P_2 P_3, \ldots, P_n P_m$, where all places are different from each other. The *length* of a path is the number of routes in it. The *distance* between two places is the length of the shortest path (or any one of the shortest paths) joining them.

A number of measures have been suggested or may be directly inferred from the concepts of graph theory for measuring the relative cohesiveness of a network or the relative position of places on the network. One such concept is the *associated number* of a place. This number is the maximum of the distances from this place to all other places. In Fig. 2, the associated number of P_1 is 2; of P_3, 1. The *central place* of a network is that place whose associate number is a minimum. P_3 is the central place of Fig. 2. The maximum associated number indicates another characteristic of a network, the *diameter*.

Also, it is known that if there are m places in a network, then the maximum possible number of routes, L^*, in the network is $L^* = m(m-1)/2$. Prihar has suggested that the *degree of connectivity* of a network for which the number of places is known can be expressed:[9]

$$\text{maximum connectivity} = L^*/\left[\frac{m(m-1)}{2}\right] = 1$$

$$\text{minimum connectivity} = L^*/(m-1)$$

$$\text{degree of connectivity} = L^*/\text{observed number of routes}$$

As Prihar suggests, these notions might be very useful in designing networks with several types of cost in mind. If unit over-the-road cost is relatively low and investment cost of facilities high, then the network might take the form of A in Fig. 3. If the reverse is true—investment

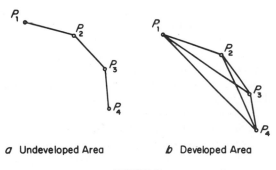

a Undeveloped Area   *b* Developed Area

FIGURE 3

cost low and over-the-road cost high—the network might take the form of B in Fig. 3.

Shimbel has suggested a measure of the *dispersion*, $D(X)$, of a network X, namely:[10]

$$D(X) = \sum_{i=1}^{n} \sum_{j=1}^{n} \text{distance } (ij)$$

He has also suggested a measure of the *accessibility* of the network to the ith place:

$$A(iX) = \sum_{j=1}^{n} \text{distance } (ij)$$

$$i = 1, \ldots, n$$

Also,

$$\sum_{i=1}^{n} (iX) = D(X)$$

An ordinary network corresponds to a matrix $X = \{x_{ij}\}$ when: $x_{ij} = 1$ if, and only if, a route exists between i and j; $x_{ij} = 0$ otherwise. The matrix corresponding to A of Fig. 3 is:

$$X = \begin{matrix} 0 & 1 & 0 & 0 \\ 1 & 0 & 1 & 0 \\ 0 & 1 & 0 & 1 \\ 0 & 0 & 1 & 0 \end{matrix}$$

and the matrix corresponding to B is:

$$X = \begin{matrix} 0 & 1 & 1 & 1 \\ 1 & 0 & 1 & 1 \\ 1 & 1 & 0 & 1 \\ 1 & 1 & 1 & 0 \end{matrix}$$

Examination of the matrix corresponding to a network suggests methods of studying connectiveness. A glance at the ith row or column of the matrix indicates the number of routes associated with the ith place. Examination of the powers of the matrix is also useful. The matrix X^n contains elements indicating the number of ways the ith place may be reached from the jth in n steps. For example, the entry $x_{ij} = C$ indicates that there are C possible ways in the network for place j to be reached from place i in n steps. The sum over the jth column would indicate all of the ways available in n steps for place j to be reached from other places. A

general notion of connectivity may be obtained from the matrix T, where $T = X + X^2 + X^3 + \ldots + X^n$. Shimbel has termed the matrix X^n the *solution matrix*, in the case where powering of the matrix is carried until there are no elements having the value zero. n is the *solution time* of the system. Elements of this matrix show the numbers of ways to reach place j from place i in the n steps. Elements of the matrix T display this information for all routes, and a summation across the columns or down the rows of T will produce a vector of numbers indicating what we might call the *accessibility* of each place on the system.

All of the above properties of a graph and associated matrices X^i and T may be proved by reference to definitions of matrix algebra. Consider, for example, the summation

$$x_{ik}^{(2)} = \sum_{j=1}^{n} c_{ij} c_{jk}$$

The only terms which contribute to this summation are those where $c_{ij} = c_{jk} = 1$. When this is the case, there is a two-length path between i and k via j.[11] By definition $x_{ij}^{(2)}$ is the element in the ith row and k^{th} column of the matrix X^2.

ANALYSES

This regional subsystem formed by the Interstate System in a portion of the southeast United States was selected for exploratory study. This subsystem is shown on the accompanying map (Fig. 4). The subsystem has forty-five places and sixty-four routes. This particular subsystem was selected arbitrarily. The small size of the subsystem made computations relatively simple.

There are at least five types of analysis, not all of which have been made here, which might be applied to this subsystem, namely:

1. Analysis of the connection of the subsystem to the larger highway system

2. Analysis of the subsystem as a whole

3. Analysis of the position of particular places on the subsystem

4. Analysis of details of the subsystem within each urban center or place. A comparison of the within-city connections of the Interstate System will reveal marked differences from city to city.[12] One would expect, then, within-

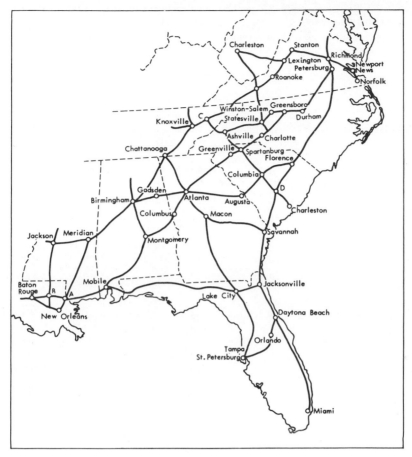

FIGURE 4.   A portion of the Interstate Highway System

city differences from city to city resulting from the construction of the system

5. Comparative analysis of different transportation graphs. These might be undertaken at any one of the four levels of analysis suggested above.

THE REGIONAL SUBSYSTEM

The following statements may be made about the regional subsystem:

1. Its connectivity is

$$L^* = \frac{45(45 - 1)}{2} = 1980$$

$$\text{connectivity} = \frac{L^*}{L} = \frac{1980}{64} = 30.94$$

2. The diameter of the network is 12.

3. The central places of the network are at Atlanta, Columbia, Spartanburg, D, Macon, Savannah, Ashville, and Greenville.

4. The dispersion of the graph is

$$D(X) = \sum_{i=1}^{n} \sum_{j=1}^{n} \text{distance } (ij) = 9292$$

EVALUATION OF PLACES ON THE SUBSYSTEM

It was noted earlier that there were a number of ways the position of a single place on the system might be evaluated. Examples of evaluation of accessibility or status of places follow.

1. The associated number is one indication of how accessible places are to the network. Associated numbers were computed by determining the longest distance for each place. The result is given in Table 1. It must be

remembered that distance by definition is the shortest path between two places.

2. The accessibility index, $A(iX)$, for places on the system is also given in Table 1. This may be thought of as the accessibility of places to the network.

3. An alternate method of measuring accessibility has been made following the method

TABLE 1
Some measures of connectiveness

Place	Associated number	A(i, X) Number	A(i, X) Rank	Shimbel-Katz accessibility Number	Shimbel-Katz accessibility Rank
Atlanta	7	146	$1\frac{1}{2}$	1.88	1
Birmingham	8	173	10	1.37	2
Petersburg	9	189	$16\frac{1}{2}$	1.34	3
Columbia	7	157	3	1.35	4
Spartanburg	7	160	$4\frac{1}{2}$	1.31	5
A	10	213	$24\frac{1}{2}$	1.29	6
Statesville	9	214	26	1.24	7
D	7	168	8	1.22	8
Lake City	8	181	12	1.22	9
B	11	251	38	1.17	10
E	9	218	$29\frac{1}{2}$	1.16	11
Macon	7	160	$4\frac{1}{2}$	1.16	12
Florence	8	173	10	1.12	13
Mobile	9	213	$24\frac{1}{2}$	1.05	14
Meridian	9	199	22	1.01	15
Savannah	7	146	$1\frac{1}{2}$	1.01	16
Chattanooga	8	173	10	.99	17
Montgomery	9	196	20	.99	18
New Orleans	11	252	39	.96	19
Charlotte	8	189	$16\frac{1}{2}$	.96	20
Ashville	7	183	$13\frac{1}{2}$	.95	21
Jacksonville	8	188	15	.95	22
C	8	193	$18\frac{1}{2}$	.92	23
Stanton	11	257	$40\frac{1}{2}$	.90	24
Augusta	6	165	7	.86	25
Greenville	7	162	6	.86	26
Greensboro	9	215	27	.82	27
Lexington	11	257	$40\frac{1}{2}$	.80	28
Columbus	8	183	$13\frac{1}{2}$	.80	29
Daytona Beach	9	233	32	.72	30
Gadsen	9	198	21	.70	31
Durham	10	221	31	.68	32
Jackson	10	237	34	.67	33
Baton Rouge	12	293	44	.66	34
Winston-Salem	10	235	33	.65	35
Charleston	10	244	$36\frac{1}{2}$	.63	$36\frac{1}{2}$
Roanoke	10	244	$36\frac{1}{2}$	.63	$36\frac{1}{2}$
Knoxville	8	193	$18\frac{1}{2}$	.62	38
Newport News	11	259	42	.62	39
Tampa-St. Petersburg	9	217	28	.59	40
Norfolk	12	302	45	.55	41
Or lando	9	243	35	.52	42
Richmond	10	218	$29\frac{1}{2}$	.39	43
Charleston	8	212	23	.36	44
Miami	10	269	43	.27	45

suggested by Shimbel and Katz.[13] The operational definition of the method is as follows: Let X be the n by n matrix corresponding to the subsystem.

$$T = sX + s^2 X^2 + s^3 X^3 + \cdots + s^r X^r + \cdots$$

s is a scalar, $o < s \leqslant 1$, measuring the effectiveness of a one-route connection; s^2 is the effectiveness of a path with two routes; s^r is the effectiveness of an r-length path. Using this measure, accessibility of the ith place, a_i, is

$$a_i = \sum_{j=1}^{n} t_{ij} \qquad i = 1, \ldots, n$$

The relation

$$T + I = (I - sX)^{-1}$$
$$= I + sX + s^2 X^2 + s^3 X^3 + \cdots$$

may be used to find T, provided s is selected in a proper manner.

The scalar used was .3 so each one-route path has the weight .3. Two-route paths have the weight $.3 \times .3 = .09$. Three-route paths have the weight $.3^3$. Results of this analysis are presented in Table 1.

COMPARATIVE ANALYSIS

One regional subsystem might be compared with the subsystem in another region; a regional subsystem might be compared with subsystems of other transportation systems in the same or other regions; and a regional subgraph might be compared with some theoretical construct. A theoretical comparison has been made with a concept of a hierarchical arrangement of urban centers. Hierarchical notions flow from the work of Christaller and Lösch. Briefly, it is argued that there is a system of cities ranging from hamlets through villages, towns, regional capitals, and national capitals, and perhaps even international capitals.[14] The relative accessibility or status of each place might reflect a hierarchical ordering. This notion was tested using the data from the Shimbel-Katz analysis and applying the nearest-neighbor statistic. The results are shown in Table 2. Although there is a slight tendency for grouping, it is not significant. Consequently, the hypothesis that no grouping or hierarchy occurs cannot be rejected. This is by no means

TABLE 2

Nearest-neighbor analysis of places on the interstate system[a]

	Nearest neighbors		
	First	Second	Third
Observed Reflexive Points	34	21	12
Expected Reflexive Points	30	20	13

[a]The difference between the observed and expected distributions is not significant. The nearest-neighbor analysis is based on P. J. Clark, "Grouping in Spatial Distributions," *Science*, **123** (1956), 373–374.

a test of whether or not a hierarchical system of cities exists in the Southeast. It is a test of whether or not the connectiveness of the highway system so far as individual places is concerned indicates a hierarchy.

There are a number of ways transportation systems may be compared. The operational question that is most difficult to answer is that of recognizing the systems to be compared. A crude comparison of the Interstate System with the railroad network of the study area has been made by comparing the number of rays or routes at each place.[15] Only a partial analysis was made, using the data in Table 3. These results are quite interesting. For one thing, there are almost twice as many rays on the railroad system than there are on the Interstate System. The expected number of rays on the Interstate System (based on the distribution of rays on the railroad system) is quite like the observed number. However, Atlanta would seem to be better served by the Interstate System than by the railroad network and New Orleans and Montgomery less well served. This leads to the tentative observation that in spite of the fact of the relatively sprawling character of the Interstate System, certain central places on the network are emphasized more than are central places on the railroad network. The reverse is also true. This is an interesting conclusion, but it is relatively specious at this state of the investigation.

ACCOMPLISHMENTS

In this paper we have done no more than introduce the problem of the analysis of transportation networks and suggested some descriptive approaches via modern graph theory. Whether the approaches have merit remains

TABLE 3

Comparison of selected cities

City	Railroad routes	Interstate routes	
		Expected[a]	Observed
Atlanta	9	4.8	6
Birmingham	9	4.8	5
Petersburg	5	2.7	3
Columbia	9	4.8	4
Spartanburg	6	3.2	4
Statesville	4	2.2	3
Lake City	5	2.7	4
Macon	6	3.2	3
Florence	5	2.7	3
Mobile	6	3.2	3
Meridian	6	3.2	3
Savannah	7	3.8	3
Chattanooga	6	3.2	4
Montgomery	8	4.3	3
New Orleans	8	4.3	3
Charlotte	7	3.8	3
Total	106	56.9	57

[a]Number expected if Interstate Routes were distributed in the same manner as railroad routes. The difference between the observed and expected distributions is not significant.

an open question. There are two things in their favor, however. One is the relative simplicity of graph theory; another is the ability to look at the System as a whole or to look at individual parts of it in terms of the whole. There are alternate approaches that have the latter merit, but their application to problems of the scope of the Interstate System would require tremendous effort.[16]

At least two major inadequacies of the approach should be mentioned. For one, graph concepts are in no way normative. Whether or not some arrangement is good or bad, whether or not links should be added to [a] system, and like decision-making questions require empirical statements outside of the usual content of

graph theory. Just what sort of relationships need to be specified and how they may be introduced is a subject for study. Also, the user of this method must make rather arbitrary decisions regarding the content of the graph. In the case of the Interstate System, the content of the graph is pretty much by definition. Even this is questionable, since there are routes constructed, under construction, or planned which are very similar in character to the Interstate System, but not integral parts of it. Evaluation of the railroad system in comparison to the Interstate System also required definition of a graph. Problems of definition, and perhaps a host of others, will become clearer as work continues.

FOOTNOTES

[1] See U. S. Congress, *Interregional Highways*, 78th Cong., 2nd Sess., House Document 379; *Highway Needs of the National Defense*, 81st Cong., 1st Sess., House Document 249; and "Federal Aid Highway Act of 1956," U. S. 70 *Statutes at Large*, **374** (1956).

[2] Exact saving from freeway use is difficult to estimate. Including the value of time saved, passenger car savings are approximately two cents per vehicle mile and truck savings about ten cents. See American Association of State Highway Officials, *Road User Benefit for Highway Improvement* (Washington: The Association, 1953); City of Los Angeles, Street and Parkway Design Division, *A Study of Freeway System Benefits* (1954); and H. Joseph, "Automobile Operating Costs," *CATS Research News*, **3** (1959), 9ff.

[3] See, for example, J. Labatut and W. Lane, eds.,

Highways in Our National Life, A Symposium (Princeton: Princeton University Press, 1950).

[4] See note 1.

[5] The study is discussed in *Third Progress Report of the Highway Cost Allocation Study*, 86th Cong., 1st Sess., House Document 91.

[6] This problem has been discussed widely in the literature, e.g., *Highway Investment and Financing*, Highway Research Board (NAS-NRC, Publication 682), Bulletin 222 (Washington: The Academy, 1959).

[7] These notions are elaborated in W. L. Garrison, B. J. L. Berry, D. F. Marble, R. Morrill, and J. Nystuen, *Studies of Highway Development and Geographic Change* (Seattle: University of Washington Press, 1959).

[8] For bibliographies and expository discussions of graph theory, see D. Cartwright, "The Potential Contribution of Graph Theory to Organization Theroy," in M. Haire, ed., *Modem Organization Theory* (New York: John Wiley & Sons, Inc., 1959); F. Harary, "Graph Theoretic Methods in the Management Sciences," *Management Science*, **5** (1959), 387–403; and F. Harary and R. Z. Norman, *Graph Theory as a Mathematical Model in Social Science*, University of Michigan, Institute for Social Research, 1953. Basic references are D. König, *Theorie der endlichen und unendlichen Graphen* (New York: Chelsea Publishing Company, 1950), and C. Berge, *Théorie des graphes et ses applications* (Paris, 1958). Berge's Chaps. 8, 13, 14, and 20 are of special interest.

[9] Z. Prihar, "Topological Properties of Telecommunication Networks," *Proceedings of the Institute of Radio Engineers*, **44** (1956), 929–933.

[10] A. Shimbel, "Structural Parameters of Communication Networks," *Bulletin of Mathematical Biophysics*, **15** (1953), 501–507.

[11] This method counts paths from j to j, e.g., in four steps one might follow the path P_1P_2, P_2P_3, P_3P_2, P_2P_1. In certain cases, this may not be desired.

[12] Maps of the urban configurations of the Interstate System are in U. S. Department of Commerce, Bureau of Public Roads, *General Location of National System of Interstate Highways* (Washington: U.S.G.P.O., 1955).

[13] Shimbel, *op. cit.;* and W. Katz, "A New Status Index Derived from Sociometric Analysis," *Psychometrika*, **18** (1953), 39–43.

[14] There is a notion of hierarchy in graph theory, but it is not used here.

[15] The count of railroad rays was made using E. L. Ullman, *U.S. Railroads, Classified According to Capacity and Relative Importance* (map) (New York: Simmons-Boardman Publishing Corporation, 1950).

[16] It might be useful, for example, to merge information on mathematical programming with information on highway networks as is done for electrical networks in J. B. Dennis, *Mathematical Programming and Electrical Networks* (New York: John Wiley & Sons, Inc., 1957).

10

ASPECTS OF
THE PRECIPITATION CLIMATOLOGY OF CANADA
INVESTIGATED BY THE METHOD
OF HARMONIC ANALYSIS

MICHAEL E. SABBAGH and REID A. BRYSON

In this paper harmonic analysis is employed to investigate regional variations of the annual march of precipitation over Canada. The specific objectives are to identify and characterize the precipitation regimes, placing particular emphasis on the transition zones which separate one regime from another. Wherever the distribution patterns provoke curiosity, either because of their anomalous characteristics or because of associations with other natural phenomena, such as water bodies or vegetation, explanations are offered to account for such patterns.

In order to examine the regional variations of the annual march of precipitation, the researcher is confronted with the problem of presenting variations of space as well as time. A method of objectively describing and mapping these space-time characteristics of precipitation is that of harmonic analysis.[1] In this method the annual precipitation curve is translated into a definite number of variance components which together comprise the curve. Each component is determined inde-

pendently of the others, so that the characteristics of any particular variance component can be mapped and examined separately. The variance components are mathematically specified by sine curves or harmonics, so that the annual variance component or first harmonic is a simple, smooth sine curve with one maximum and one minimum occurring six months apart, while the semiannual variance component, or second harmonic, is a sine curve with two maxima and two minima spaced three months apart. Each harmonic is "fitted" to the precipitation curve for each station by the method of least squares, and the nature of the "fit" is specified by two parameters. The first is the amplitude, which is a measure of half the difference between the maximum and minimum of the sine curve, while the second is the phase angle, which determines the time of the year at which the maximum (and consequently, minimum) occurs. Altogether six harmonics,

Reprinted from *Annals of the Association of American Geographers,* **52** (1962), 426–440, by permission of the author and editor.

properly chosen, can describe the annual precipitation curve of a station based on twelve monthly values. In this analysis of precipitation over Canada, however, the first two harmonics account for so large a proportion of the variance of the annual precipitation curve that the first and second harmonics alone suffice to show the main outlines of precipitation variance.

Precipitation curves for some 500 Canadian stations were subjected to harmonic analysis, and charts of the first two harmonics are presented (Figs. 5–8). For each harmonic a map of amplitude and one of phase angle depict the spatial characteristics of that particular variance component. Hence in the case of the first harmonic, the amplitude chart reveals the relative importance, from place to place, of the annual component of variation of the precipitation in absolute units, while the chart of the phase angle specifies the month of

maximum and minimum of this component. Similarly, the charts of the amplitude and phase angle of the second harmonic reveal the regional and seasonal characteristics of the semiannual variance components.[2]

MAPS OF VARIANCE

Before proceeding to examine the reaal distribution of the two major variance components, the annual and semiannual, it is useful to establish the distribution of the total variance and also the relationship of the two major components to the total variance and to one another. For this purpose, four maps are presented showing, respectively, the total variance (Fig. 1), the annual variance (first harmonic) as a percentage of the total variance (Fig. 2), the semiannual variance (second harmonic) as a percentage of the total variance (Fig. 3),

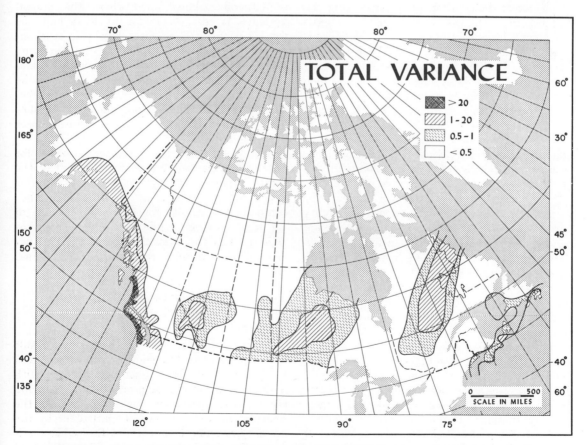

FIGURE 1.   Total variance of the annual march of precipitation over Canada, expressed in inches squared, and based on mean monthly values

and the semiannual as a percentage of the annual variance (Fig. 4).

TOTAL VARIANCE

Variance, which is a measure of the month-to-month fluctuation of precipitation, is equal to the square of the standard deviation and is expressed here as the sum of the variance accounted for by each of the six harmonics. The variance accounted for by each harmonic, except the last, is equal to half the amplitude squared (i.e., $V = A^2/2$). In the case of the last harmonic the variance is simply equal to the amplitude squared. Therefore the total variance equals

$$\left(1/2 \sum_{i=1}^{5} A_i^2\right) + A_6^2$$

where A = amplitude and i = order of the harmonic.[3]

The areal distribution of variance (Fig. 1), mapped in units of inches squared, reveals that over a large part of Canada the variance is relatively small, less than 0.5 inches squared. There are, however, five areas where the variance is relatively large, greater than one inch squared. The first is a strip along the west coast reaching inland up to about 150 miles, as far as the coast ranges. In this region, where precipitation is abundant, totaling fifty inches or more annually, by far the largest variance occurs. Along most of the immediate littoral of British Columbia, where the annual precipitation amount exceeds eighty inches, the variance is extremely high, exceeding twenty inches squared. It is in the east and west coastal regions that the largest concentrations of precipitation occur in Canada. The higher west coast variance is a reflection of the large amount of precipitation concentrated in one season (winter) in the West, as compared to the relatively even seasonal distribution of precipitation on the east coast, the second area.

A third area of relatively large variance is a small region just east of the Rockies, straddling the British Columbia-Alberta border. Annual precipitation here amounts to twenty-five to thirty-five inches, concentrated largely in early summer. The fourth area lies in the deep interior, extending from Lake Winnipeg almost to Hudson Bay, with an annual precipi-

tation of twenty to twenty-five inches. Here there is a strong midsummer maximum, partly as a result of the high frequency of midsummer thunderstorm activity in this deep continental region.[4] The fifth area of relatively large variance is the region east of Hudson Bay, which receives from twenty-five to forty inches of precipitation annually. Over part of this region the large variance is explained in a subsequent section of this paper in terms of the excessive late fall, early winter snowfalls.

THE RELATIONSHIP OF THE ANNUAL VARIANCE COMPONENT TO THE TOTAL VARIANCE

This relationship is presented by expressing the variance accounted for by the first harmonic (annual tendency with one maximum and one minimum) as a percentage of the total variance. It is immediately apparent from the map (Fig. 2) that the annual variance is of major importance over a vast part of Canada. Almost everywhere the annual variance is responsible for at least half the total variance. There are, however, two important exceptions. The first is the area lying largely between the coastal mountains and the Rockies, occupying therefore most of the intermontane region. A second area stretches from the Great Lakes along the St. Lawrence lowlands, including also most of the east coast of Newfoundland.

Everywhere else the variance accounted for by the first harmonic is more than half of the total variance. Throughout the vast interior and along the west coast the annual variance component accounts for over 75 per cent of the total variance, while in the high precipitation areas of the west coast more than 90 per cent of the variance results from the annual trend.

THE RELATIONSHIP OF THE SEMIANNUAL VARIANCE COMPONENT TO THE TOTAL VARIANCE

Most of the variance which does not result from an annual tendency can be accounted for by the semiannual tendency, a trend with a double maximum of precipitation occurring six months apart. On the map (Fig. 3) the areas where the variance accounted for by the second harmonic (sine curve with double maximum and minimum) exceeds 25 per cent of

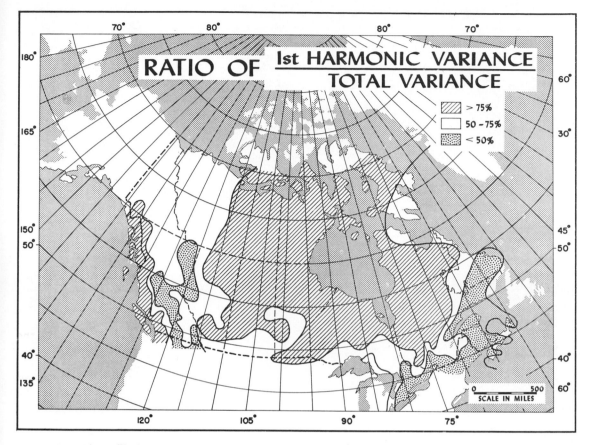

FIGURE 2. Variance accounted for by the first harmonic (annual variance) expressed as a percentage of the total variance

the total variance are shown by shading. Throughout the unshaded region the ratio is less than 25 per cent.

The semiannual trend is of relatively greatest significance in the intermontane region, while other, smaller areas of relative importance occur along the east coast of Newfoundland and along the Great Lakes-St. Lawrence lowland. It is significant that these areas coincide with the regions where the annual tendency is least important, so that over almost the whole of Canada the first two harmonic components account for at least 50 per cent and generally 75 per cent of the total variance. Only in very confined areas of the eastern part of Canada are the higher harmonics responsible for more than 25 per cent of the total variance, as a result not of distinctive peaks in the precipitation curve, but rather because

of the lack of a strong month-to-month fluctuation.

THE RELATIONSHIP OF THE SEMIANNUAL TO THE ANNUAL VARIANCE COMPONENT

The relative importance of the two major variance components is shown by expressing the variance accounted for by the second harmonic as a percentage of that of the first harmonic (Fig. 4). There are only two regions where the semiannual exceeds the annual component. The first is confined to the intermontane region of British Columbia, while the second is comprised of a narrow stretch along the Great Lakes-St. Lawrence lowlands, and a section of continental Newfoundland. Along the Pacific coast and in the continental interior the annual variation term is ten times as large as the semiannual term.

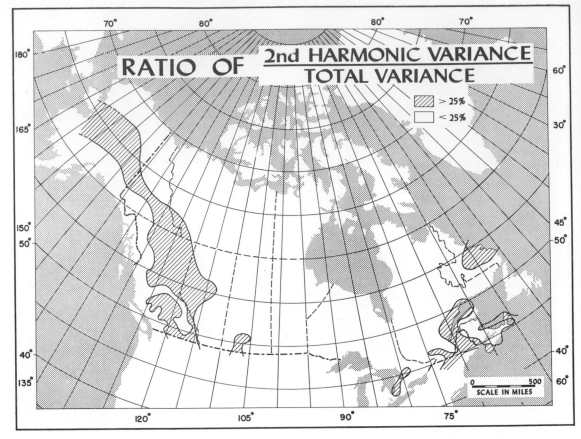

FIGURE 3. Variance accounted for by the second harmonic (semiannual variance) expressed as a percentage of the total variance

HARMONIC CHARTS

Each of the first two harmonics, representing the annual and semiannual variance components, is portrayed by charts of amplitude and phase angle (Figs. 5–8). The intervals between the isolines on these charts are consistent, so that where the gradient is steep, rapid changes or boundary zones occur, whereas gradual gradients reflect homogeneous areas. It is the depiction of the march of precipitation and the nature of boundaries that is one of the major merits of the method of harmonic analysis.

WESTERN REGIME

The most distinctive boundary portrayed by the harmonic maps is that separating the western maritime regime from the continental interior regime. Although this division coincides fairly closely with the western cordillera of the Rocky and Mackenzie Mountains, the precise nature of the boundary, as depicted by the phase angle of the first harmonic (Fig. 6), varies considerably. In southern British Columbia the boundary is well defined, being a northward continuation of the striking boundary marking the eastward limit of the area over which the Pacific coast type has influence, as recognized by Horn and Bryson[5] and subsequent investigators.[6] However, the sharp definition of this boundary is maintained only as far north as north-central British Columbia, where the Peace River penetrates the Rockies. North of this break in the mountains the boundary becomes diffuse and can no longer be identified, even by a steep gradient, where the Liard River valley cuts deeply through the cordillera. At this second break in the mountains, the zone of steep gradient

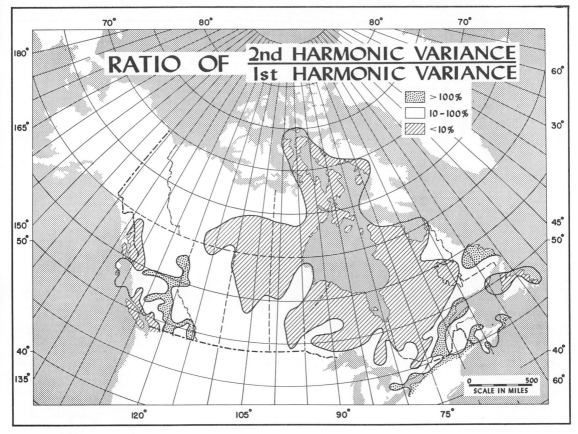

FIGURE 4. Ratio of the variance contained in the second harmonic (semiannual variance) to the variance contained in the first harmonic (annual variance), expressed as a percentage

is no longer aligned in a general north-south direction parallel to the mountains, but turns toward the coast of northern Alaska. North-central British Columbia, therefore, is a part of the interior regime (of summer maximum) rather than the regime of Pacific marine influence, where winter precipitation is dominant.[7]

Two possible explanations may account for the change from a sharp boundary in the south to a diffuse transition in the north. In the northern region, the interior mountains no longer furnish a barrier either to continental rain bringing influences during summer or to Pacific disturbances during winter. Moreover, while the summer precipitation from Pacific disturbances is stifled south of about 55°N by the frequent appearance of a northward-extending arm of the Pacific anticyclone,[8] the region north of here is subject to exposure to

eastward-moving cyclones which provide increased summer precipitation. Consequently, the strength of the winter regime west of the mountains is emphasized in the south, whereas it is minimized in the north.

At the point where the boundary between the western and interior regimes becomes diffuse, the vegetation divide also changes character. In northern British Columbia, the boreal forest, which in the south has been confined to the region east of the Rockies, penetrates westward to the coast of the Alaskan panhandle, so that northern British Columbia has vegetation similar to that of the subarctic interior region.

On the basis of the phase angle of the first harmonic, therefore, a distinctive boundary separates the western regime from the interior. This boundary extends along the British Columbia-Alberta southern border (where the

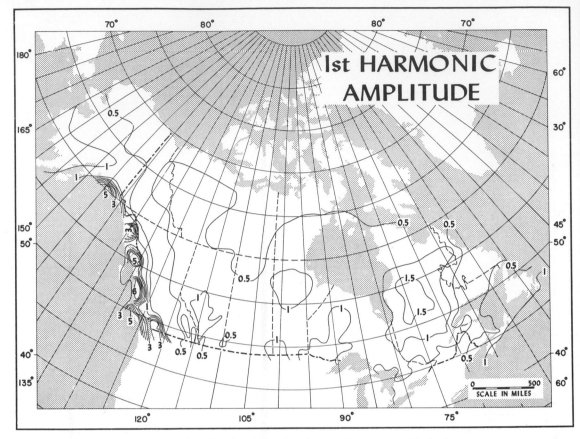

FIGURE 5. Amplitude of the first harmonic expressed in inches

Rockies have strongest definition and highest relief). North of the Rockies the boundary becomes diffuse and veers west at the point where the coastline trends west, so that the Mackenzie and Selwyn ranges are not part of the western regime. From 60°N the boundary no longer can be identified in the interior, though a steep gradient can be traced extending toward the coast, hugging the coastline from the Alaskan panhandle into northern Alaska. West of this boundary lies the region of Pacific maritime influence, generally characterized by winter precipitation.

Within this western region itself, complexities of precipitation regime can be identified. West of the Coastal Mountains, a strong winter regime with an extremely high amplitude of the first harmonic (Fig. 5) can be recognized. This coastal littoral is closely associated with the west coast region, where the total variance is greater than one inch squared (Fig. 1) and

where the first harmonic accounts for over 75 per cent of the total variance (Fig. 2). Topographically it comprises a coastal stretch, less than 150 miles wide, of fiords, islands, and valleys. The interior boundary of this region can be defined as corresponding to the steep gradient of the phase angle of the first harmonic. The core of this gradient is closely aligned to the October isochrone (Fig. 6), so that the Pacific coast region includes therefore only the zone of cool season precipitation maximum occurring in October, November, December, or January.

Although the general position of this boundary has been defined by other techniques,[9] the method employed here reveals certain significant fluctuations along the boundary. In southern British Columbia on the mainland, just east of Vancouver Island, the coastal regime pushes inland beyond the coastal mountains proper, to the Cascades. This

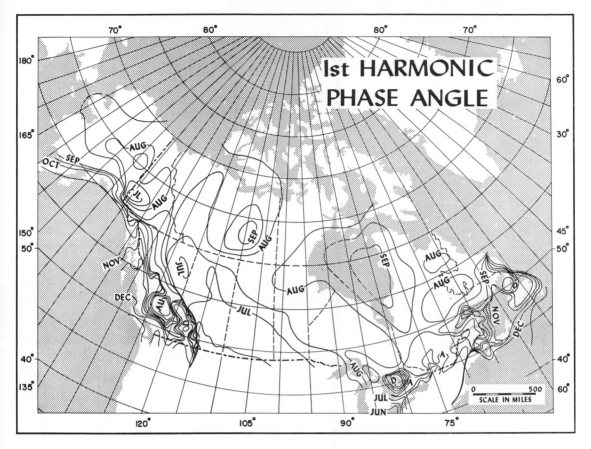

FIGURE 6. Phase angle of the first harmonic. The phase angles are converted to the corresponding dates on which the maximum occurs. The labelled isochrones indicate the middle of each month; for example, *August* represents a maximum occurring near August 15. The minimum consequently occurs six months later, near February 15. Isochrones are drawn at 15-day intervals, the unlabelled isolines representing, therefore, about the beginning of a particular month.

intrusion may be due partly to the fact that the coastal mountains are broken in this area so that they lose some of their effect as a barrier to western disturbances. A similar interior intrusion of the coastal regime occurs farther north, leeward of the Queen Charlotte Islands (latitude 54°N). Here again the coastal ranges are broken and do not provide a strong barrier to disturbances moving in from the Pacific or to the maritime air in which these disturbances operate to provide heavy coastal winter precipitation. Between Vancouver and Queen Charlotte islands, in the Fraser Plateau area, the coastal regime is confined to the immediate coast, so that the winter regime occurs only along the littoral, while the Fraser basin itself

has a summer maximum occurring in August (Fig. 6).

North of British Columbia the coast becomes one of islands, fiords, and deep valleys, with frequent breaks through the coastal mountains. This allows the coastal regime to extend inland so that no well-defined boundary limits this regime, but rather it gradually disappears with distance from the coast. The regime changes here from a fall maximum on the coast to a summer maximum in the Liard Plains (Lat. 55 to 60°N), and the gradual transition continues inland where there is no Rocky Mountain range to confine the western regime.

The Pacific coast regime is restricted,

therefore, for the most part to the coastal region, with a fairly well-defined boundary in the south. The region narrows, losing its identity, however, in the north, where the boundary becomes diffuse.

It is of some significance that within the Pacific coast regime the isolines of phase angle of the first harmonic are aligned generally in the same direction as the coastline. There is, however, a considerable latitudinal change in the month of maximum precipitation. From a late December maximum in the vicinity of Vancouver Island (Lat. 50°N), the precipitation peak occurs progressively earlier northward. At latitude 55°N, just south of the Alaskan panhandle, the peak is in late November, changing to October at about latitude 60°N. Certain aspects of this progression of the precipitation peak from late fall in the north to early winter in the south have been previously investigated.[10] A fairly logical explanation for this progression is that relating the peak of precipitation to the southward movement of the storm tracks.[11] The smooth gradient of the north-to-south shift of the peak of the annual variance component (Fig. 6) suggests that the climatic controls which are responsible for the cool season precipitation of the west coast, namely, the jet stream and its associated eastward-moving cyclonic disturbances, move steadily south from a position of about 60°N in fall to a location about 50°N in winter. The progression does not, however, continue at the same rate in the United States, and consequently, south of the Canadian border the change in time of maximum precipitation is only slight, the peak occurring less than a month earlier in southern California.[12]

Within the Pacific coast regime regional variations in the relative magnitude of the annual variance component are depicted by the amplitude charts. In Fig. 1 the total variance was revealed to be extremely high, more than twenty inches squared on the littoral of British Columbia, with a sharp decrease inland. Since over 75 per cent (Fig. 2) and in some places over 90 per cent of this variance is accounted for by the annual variance component, the regional character of the total variance is therefore largely represented by the amplitude chart of the first harmonic (Fig. 5). Although the general orientation of the isolines is similar to that of the coastline, so that the variance decreases from the coast inland, the detailed pattern reveals significant complexities. While everywhere within the Pacific coast region the annual variance component is high, above one inch squared, areas of particularly large amplitude can be recognized. The first is the western section of Vancouver Island, the side of the island exposed to westerly disturbances. Here the change in variance, from the exposed western side of the island to the side leeward of the Vancouver Island ranges, is directly related to the remarkable precipitation decrease from the western to the eastern part of the island. The sharp division between the marine climate of the west and the "Mediterranean" summer-dry climate of the east of the island is evidenced by the steep gradient of amplitude of the first harmonic. This unusual northward continuation, even beyond 50°N, of the dry-summer type of climate,[13] which occurs not only in the southeast of Vancouver Island and the Georgia Straits, but also in some of the intermontane valleys and in the lower Fraser delta, associated with grassland vegetation and prairie-type brown podzolic soils, has been explained in terms of the northward extention of a drought-inducing tongue of the subtropical anticyclone along the Pacific coast in summer.[14]

A second area of particularly high amplitude of the annual variance component is the coastal stretch in southern British Columbia between Vancouver and Queen Charlotte Islands. This area, like that of western Vancouver Island, receives 100 inches or more of precipitation annually. Here, without any protection from offshore islands, all the vigor of the cyclonic disturbances carried in the westerly stream is felt in winter, while in summer the coastal anticyclonic tongue subdues the precipitation; consequently, a strong annual variance component results. A third area of high amplitude is the northernmost remnant of the strong winter maximum in Canada at latitude 55°N, just north of the Queen Charlotte Islands. North of here, two further areas of relatively large amplitude occur in the extremely high precipitation region of the Alaskan coast.

Between the Pacific coast cool season regime and continental interior warm season regime lies the northward extension of the intermontane region of the United States.[15] As indicated earlier, distinctive boundaries delimiting this regime can only be traced as far north as about 57°N. It would seem that this intermontane region is in the nature of a transition zone between the Pacific coast and continental interior regimes, each of which is manifested to a lesser or greater degree in the intermontane area, depending on the orientation of topographic barriers, local relief, exposure, and latitude. Only in the south is there a fairly well-defined semiannual type of regime with distinctive summer and winter precipitation peaks, whereas north of 57°N the transition area between Pacific and continental influences is diffuse. Figure 3 shows the general extent within the western region, where the semiannual variance component is relatively strong, but Fig. 4 more properly defines the region of relative importance of the semiannual to the annual variance component. Within the western region, only in a relatively confined area indicated by a broken stretch in southern British Columbia is the semiannual term greater than the annual (Fig. 4), whereas north of 55°N the annual variation component accounts for more of the variance than the semiannual component. South of 55°N, in the region which includes the Fraser Plateau, the Kamloops Plateau, and the Fraser River basin, a fairly marked semiannual regime is present, although complex terrain characteristics exert strong influences on the regime. Whereas the winter precipitation, which is largely due to the interior penetration of the controls of the coastal regime, is to be found in excess on the west-facing highlands, many of the valley stations indicate a summer maximum of precipitation. In fact, the regime can best be comprehended as occurring in a three-dimension pattern, with maritime winter influences exerting themselves more in the west and on the exposed highlands, and continental summer influences prevailing in the valleys, which also receive much less precipitation.

It is noteworthy that the phase angle chart of the first harmonic reveals the interior intrusion of a marine precipitation regime in the region of the Columbia mountains, where west-facing slopes exceeding 8000 feet are to be found receiving a precipitation maximum during October, November, and December. These high mountains are exposed to westerly disturbances, particularly in the southernmost part, leeward of Vancouver Island, where a natural break in the coastal mountains occurs.

Phase angle charts of the first and second harmonics show that the winter peak of the semiannual regime of the intermontane region in southern British Columbia occurs at the same time as the winter maximum on the coast. On the coast in southern British Columbia the winter maximum is approximately specified by the December isochrone of the first harmonic, while in the interior in the Kamloops and Fraser Plateau area, the second harmonic isochrone of December approximately specifies the time of occurrence of the interior winter peak of the semiannual regime. This close correlation in time of the annual variance component on the coast and the semiannual variance component in the intermontane region, especially when it is noted that these components are determined independently, adds strong support to the generally accepted notion that Pacific air associated with eastward-moving disturbances provides midwinter precipitation to parts of the intermontane region as well as the coast.

In southern and south-central British Columbia, in the Kamloops and Fraser regions, a distinctive warm season regime is evidenced by the phase angle of the first harmonic (August isochrone). In the Kamloops Plateau region, for example, summer is the season of maximum precipitation, with over 33 per cent of the annual precipitation of ten inches occurring in summer, as compared to the stronger winter regime of the high Selkirks, directly east, where Gerard and Glacier both have over 40 per cent of the annual precipitation of thirty-four inches and fifty-four inches, respectively, occurring in winter. In the Fraser Plateau region, where the first harmonic phase angle indicates a summer regime, precipitation is low, less than fifteen inches, and the dominant vegetation is a grassland variety,[16] similar to the short grass prairie of southern Saskatchewan. Moreover, in the Okanagan Valley, precipitation is so low that irrigation is necessary for crop growth. In contrast, the winter regime region of the Columbia mountains in places receives snowfall on over 100 days of the year.

In order to understand the precipitation regime of the intermontane region, it is useful to examine the winter and summer regimes separately. In interior British Columbia the winter precipitation isohyets run parallel to both the mountains and coastline from north-northwest to south-southeast, so that the gradient is from the coast inland, while the orientation of the summer isohyets bear little relationship to that of the coastline or mountains.[17] Moreover, isolines showing the coefficient of variation of winter precipitation are also aligned parallel to the ranges, so that there is a distinct south-southeast to north-northwest trend of isolines in December, while in July, on the other hand, the trend is from west to east, bearing no correlation with the topographic barriers.[18]

Not only are there complexities of regime from west to east and from valley to highlands, but significant regime changes occur also from south to north. In the extreme south of the intermontane region of British Columbia the secondary warm season maximum occurs in June, with a primary minimum in July and August, so that at several stations June has twice as much precipitation as May and July, whereas in the north the dry season is in spring and early summer. The June maximum in southern British Columbia may be explained by the "high pressure jump" of the Pacific anticyclone.[19] According to this concept, in May and June the anticyclone maintains a position of about 34°N, about the latitude of Arizona, whereas in July the center shifts abruptly to the vicinity of the United States-Canadian border. The effects of the sudden high pressure shift in midsummer are, however, confined to the southernmost parts of British Columbia, since 5° north of the United States-Canadian border the July-August minimum disappears and June is no longer characterized by a substantial precipitation increase. Moreover, in northern interior British Columbia the semiannual character of the precipitation profile is quickly lost and the seasonal distribution is surprisingly even, despite the relatively easy access of maritime air. Precipitation amounts are, nevertheless, low, less than twenty inches, with both continental and maritime influences prevailing.

CONTINENTAL INTERIOR REGIME

Between the western and eastern regimes lies the vast continental interior regime of Canada, which has its counterpart in the central United States. The boundaries delimiting the Canadian interior region are fairly well defined in parts of the west, though somewhat diffuse in the east. The nature of the western boundary has already been examined, since it forms the eastern boundary of the western region. Unlike the west, however, the east is without strong physical barriers which could act to confine the east coast marine influences, so that east of Hudson Bay a broad transition zone occurs in which the precipitation regime changes gradually from continental to marine. Steep gradients occur only along broken stretches of the immediate east coastal area (Fig. 6), although a complex pattern prevails throughout the region east of a zone between the Great Lakes and northern Newfoundland. This eastern region will be examined in the following section.

The interior region is one of moderate variance (Fig. 1), most of which is accounted for by the annual variance component. Over much of the region the first harmonic accounts for over 75 per cent of the variance (Fig. 2), whereas less than 10 per cent is accounted for by the semiannual component (Fig. 4). In general, the amplitude chart of the first harmonic reveals an absence of steep gradients, most of the interior having an amplitude approaching one inch, while the phase angle chart of the first harmonic depicts a summer maximum throughout the continental interior.

As is to be expected, however, so vast an area is not without regional climatic variations. The three major vegetation zones which characterize the interior, boreal forest in the middle, tundra in the north, and prairie in the south, are evidence of climatic differences. Some writers consequently have resorted to vegetation, "a visible biotic expression of climatic influences,"[20] as a basis for climatic regionalization.

The harmonic charts support evidence from other precipitation maps that in the north precipitation alone plays a relatively minor role in determining the transition from the forest to the tundra region. The southern limit of trees, however, can be more specifically related to precipitation. It is interesting that the transition from forest to prairie in western Canada is evidenced by a steepening of gradient of the first harmonic, between the July 15 and August 1 isochrones. The grasslands of Manitoba, Saskatchewan, and Alberta are confined to the region where the precipitation maximum occurs in July, while the prairie proper has a maximum in early summer. It is recognized that the time of precipitation maximum alone can at best be considered only one of a number of climatic determinants. The relationship of the prairie wedge to environmental influences is a complex one, and factors such as precipitation amount in each season; snow cover; intensity, reliability, and variability of summer rainfall; temperature anomalies; and wind streams have all been considered partial determinants.[21] Kendrew and Currie[22] have delimited the prairie as a climatic region largely on the basis of hot, sunny, and long summers and the small affective precipitation. Nor is precipitation amount responsible for the vegetation change. Northward from the grasslands the precipitation decreases, despite the change to a forest complex. However, in the zone of transition from prairies to forest, the expectancy of serious drought changes from 25 per cent in the prairie proper to only 5 per cent expectancy in the forest region. It has, moreover, been demonstrated[23] that the grasslands have the greatest variability of precipitation and the forests least.

In examining the prairie-forest boundary, consideration must be given to a number of climatic parameters. It may be of some significance that not only do the first harmonic phase angle lines align parallel to the major vegetation boundary between prairie and forest, but within a region of relative homogeneity a definite steepening of gradient occurs along the prairie-forest transition zone.

While the vast interior is topographically relatively homogeneous, consisting mainly of fairly uniform plains with only minor depressions and uplands which do not exert any strong climatic manifestations, the occurrence of large water bodies does affect the precipitation pattern. The most outstanding examples are the influence of Hudson Bay and the Great Lakes. Since the eastern Great Lakes are considered a part of the eastern maritime rather than the interior continental regime, the discussion of the Lakes is postponed until the following section. Around Hudson Bay, phase angle charts of the first and second harmonics show a change in precipitation regime from a summer maximum on the west

side of the Bay to a fall maximum on the east side. From the west to the east shore of Hudson Bay the first harmonic changes from an August to a September maximum. Moreover, the second harmonic, which has a low amplitude in this region (Fig. 7) and therefore depicts a more subtle, or secondary, trend, reveals a related phase angle shift (Fig. 8) from a July maximum on the west shore to an October maximum on the east shore.

This fall maximum of precipitation on the eastern side of Hudson Bay results largely from snowfall due to the modification of cold polar continental air as it traverses the open water of the Bay in late fall.[24] Addition of heat and moisture in the lower layers develops instability, and heavy snowfalls, similar in nature to those in the Great Lakes snowbelt, result. Since the prevailing direction of air flow during fall and early winter is from the northwest, not only at the surface but even at 850 mbs,[25] the air has ample opportunity to pick up heat and moisture in the lower layers from the relatively warm water surface, thus becoming unstable by the time it reaches the southeast shore of the Bay, so that heavy snowfall occurs to the southeast of the Bay. Moreover, since the air is forced to ascend some 2000 feet leeward of the Bay, the conditions for heavy snow deposit are made more favorable. The first harmonic chart shows a surprisingly high amplitude in the region between the Bay and the Otish Mountains of north-central Quebec, delimited by the 1.5-inch isoline (Fig. 5). Evidence indicates that this high variance may result largely from snowfall induced by Hudson Bay, since both the direction of air flow and the high terrain would make this a favorable region for early winter snowfall. The region receives snowfall on over 100 days of the year, a higher snowfall frequency than any other part of Canada.[26] It would seem likely, therefore, that the precipitation character of this region results at least partly from the influence of Hudson Bay.

In the northwest territories, sparse data do not allow a detailed examination of the precipitation regime. On the chart of the phase angle of the first harmonic, however, a tendency toward an early fall maximum (September isochrone) occurs east of Great Slave Lake. This development may be induced by the open water of the lake in September.

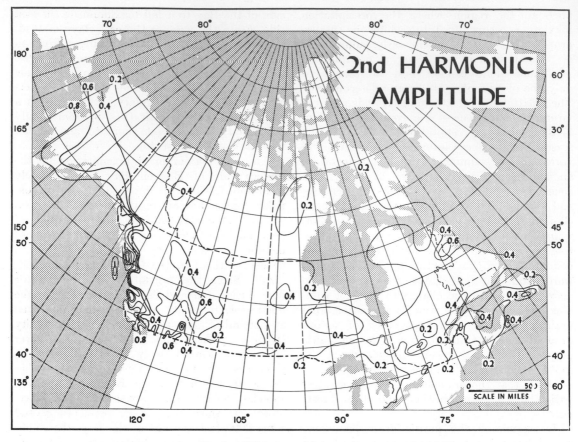

FIGURE 7. Amplitude of the second harmonic expressed in inches

THE EASTERN REGIME

The eastern region, which includes the east coastal lowlands as well as the St. Lawrence valley and the lowlands of the Great Lakes, cannot be delimited by a well-defined boundary. Generally the area lies eastward of a zone running from Lake Nipigon, paralleling the lake shores, then following along the Laurentide scarp to the coast of Labrador, then turning northward to include the southern Newfoundland coast.

Almost throughout the region the annual variance component is low, less than 50 per cent of the total variance being accounted for by the variance of the first harmonic (Fig. 2), while in most parts of the region the semi-annual tendency is relatively strong, accounting for over 25 per cent of the total variance (Fig. 3).

A relatively flat precipitation curve prevails throughout the eastern region, except for spe-

cific lake and marine locations, which have a winter maximum of precipitation.[27] Consequently, each of the harmonics contribute[s] a significant portion of the total variance. Cyclonic disturbances occurring throughout the year provide the eastern region with most of its precipitation. Storms not only from the Atlantic seaboard, but also from the interior and western United States and southern Canada, converge on this region.

Within the eastern regime, a secondary Atlantic coastal regime with a distinct winter maximum can be identified. The boundary of the coastal region, as determined by the phase angle of the first harmonic, varies from place to place in strength and definition. In southern New Brunswick the well-defined east coast regime boundary portrayed over New England[28] weakens rapidly. The trend of the boundary is complicated by offshore islands and oceanic inlets. It is interesting to note (Fig. 6) that most of the island of Newfound-

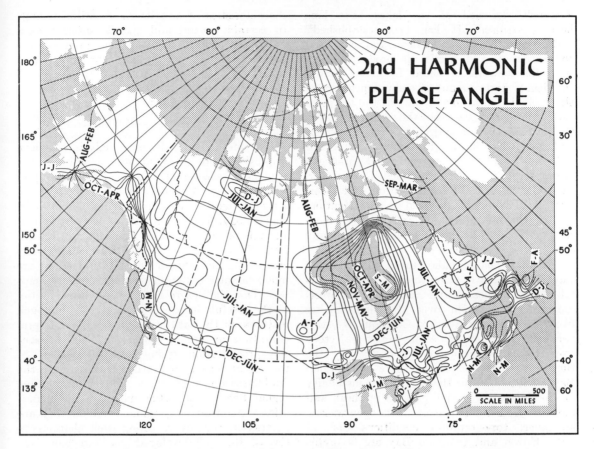

FIGURE 8. Phase angle of the second harmonic. The phase angles are converted to the corresponding dates on which the maxima occur. The labelled isochrones indicate the middle of each month; for example, *August-February* represents maxima occurring near August 15 and February 15. The minima consequently occur three months later, November 15 and May 15. Isochrones are drawn at 15-day intervals, the unlabelled isolines representing, therefore, about the beginning of the particular months.

land has a regime of summer maximum, while only the outer coastal stretches, exposed to the open ocean, can be properly delimited as being maritime. The littoral of Nova Scotia and the island of Newfoundland have a winter maximum of precipitation (November, December—Fig. 6) and consequently a relatively high variance (Fig. 1).

A winter regime is also to be found some distance from the coast, east of Lake Huron and Georgian Bay. Here the rapid change in phase angle of the first harmonic (Fig. 6) from a winter regime (December isochrone) in the immediate vicinity of the Lakes to a summer regime (August) less than a hundred miles away is remarkably well developed, and is almost as strong as the similar change indi-

cated east of Lakes Ontario and Erie in the United States.[29] In fact, the winter maximum of precipitation in the area immediately east of Lake Huron and Georgian Bay is stronger than that in the Erie-Ontario snowbelt area.[30] Moreover, within a hundred miles of Lake Huron, snowfall amount decreases to less than half that in the immediate leeward vicinity of the lake. This rapid change of precipitation regime is revealed by the marked gradient of phase angle of the first harmonic which coincides very closely with the limits of the lake snowbelt area.

As is the case with Hudson Bay, the change in precipitation regime leeward of the Great Lakes water body is probably the result of heavy snowfall, largely induced by the Lakes.

Snowbelts leeward of the lakes have long been recognized. It has been established[31] with regard to Lakes Ontario and Erie that the surge of cold arctic air produces heavy snowfalls leeward of these Lakes in winter, the degree and amount of snow depending on the cyclonic curvature of the air, the temperature differential between the air and water, the path of the air trajectory over the water, and the wind shear. Particular snowstorms induced by Lakes Superior and Michigan have recently been examined.[32] However, snowfalls leeward of Lake Huron and Georgian Bay have not received much attention, despite the fact that this area receives more snowfall (over 120 inches annually) than any of the other lake areas.

The area east of Lake Huron and Georgian Bay is particularly favorable for heavy snowfall. Great Lakes storms originating in western Canada loop in over the Great Lakes from the west-northwest.[33] Consequently, this very cold arctic air has a long water trajectory over Lakes Superior and Huron.[34] By the time it reaches the eastern shore of Georgian Bay it has had ample time to develop instability in the lower layers by picking up heat and moisture from the relatively warm open waters. Moreover, topographical conditions east of Lake Huron and Georgian Bay are favorable for snowfall, since the air is subject to an ascent of almost 1000 feet after it leaves the water.

It is apparent that no extensive distinctive eastern regime exists. The harmonic charts do not depict a continuous region having characteristics of an eastern maritime regime. In certain coastal and specific interior locations, a winter precipitation maximum occurs, while over most of the region the annual precipitation curve is flat with an even seasonal distribution of precipitation.

CONCLUSION

The method of harmonic analysis has been employed here to examine objectively the regional characteristics of the march of precipitation over Canada and has proved to be a useful auxiliary tool in studying precipitation climatology. The major merits of this kind of analysis, as employed in this paper, are twofold. First, each of the variance components comprising the annual precipitation curve are independently determined and separately mapped. This allows a realistic examination, particularly useful in genetic analysis, of such features as the latitudinal progression of precipitation maximum along the Pacific coast, the precipitation regime change leeward of the Great Lakes and Hudson Bay, and the double-season regime in the intermontane region. Second, the actual nature of the boundaries separating one regime from another are portrayed, thereby revealing such characteristics as the well-developed southern boundary of the western regime as opposed to a diffuse boundary to the north, the meandering characteristics of the boundary confining the Pacific coast regime, and the gradual transition in the east from the continental to the eastern maritime type of precipitation regime.

FOOTNOTES

[1] For a detailed description of the application of harmonic analysis to precipitation data, see L. H. Horn and R. A. Bryson, "Harmonic Analysis of the Annual March of Precipitation over the United States," *Annals of the Association of American Geographers*, **50** (1960), 157–171.

[2] The complete mathematical expression for six harmonics is:

$$R = A_0 + A_1 \sin (30°t + \phi_1) + A_2 \sin (60°t + \phi_2) + \ldots + A_6 \sin (180°t + \phi_6)$$

where t = time (in months), January $t = 0$, February $t = 1$, etc.

A_0 = arithmetic mean of the twelve monthly means

$A_1, A_2, \ldots, A_6$ are the amplitudes of the six harmonics

$\phi_1, \phi_2, \ldots, \phi_6$ are the phase angles of the six harmonics

R = precipitation in time t.

For a complete description of the technique of harmonic analysis, see C. E. P. Brooks and N. Carruthers, *Handbook of Statistical Methods in Meteorology* (London: Her Majesty's Stationery Office, 1953), p. 335.

[3] H. A. Panofsky and G. W. Brier, *Some Applications of Statistics to Meteorology*, Pennsylvania State University, Mineral Industries Extension Services, College of Mineral Industries (1958), p. 133.

[4] R. W. Longley, *Thunderstorm Data for Canada*, Meteorological Division, Dept. of Transport, Canada (Ottawa, 1952).

[5] Horn and Bryson, *op. cit.*, 165.

[6] G. T. Trewartha, *The Earth's Problem Climates*

(Madison: University of Wisconsin Press, 1961), p. 268.

[7] *Ibid.*, p. 278.

[8] D. P. Kerr, "The Summer-Dry Climate of Georgia Basin, British Columbia," *Transactions of the Royal Canadian Institute*, **29**, Part I (1951), 28.

[9] Trewartha, *op. cit.*, p. 268.

[10] P. W. Williams, Jr., "The Variation of the Time of Maximum Precipitation Along the West Coast of North America," *Bulletin of the American Meteorological Society*, **29** (1948), 143–145.

[11] Trewartha, *op. cit.*, p. 269.

[12] See Horn and Bryson, *op. cit.*, 162. Chart of first harmonic shows a January peak almost throughout California and a late December peak in Washington and Oregon.

[13] J. D. Chapman, "The Climate of British Columbia," *Transcripts of the British Columbia Natural Resources Conference*, **5** (1952), 8–37.

[14] Kerr, *op. cit.*, 24.

[15] R. De C. Ward, *The Climates of the United States* (Boston: Ginn & Co., 1925), pp. 183–213.

[16] E. W. Tisdale, "The Grasslands of the Southern Interior of British Columbia," *Ecology*, **32** (1947), 346–382.

[17] *Atlas of Canada*, Geographical Branch, Dept. of Mines and Technical Surveys (Ottawa, 1957), Plate 27.

[18] W. G. Kendrew and B. W. Currie, *The Climate of Central Canada* (Ottawa: Edmond Cloutier, Queen's Printer and Controller of Stationery, 1955), p. 50.

[19] R. A. Bryson and W. P. Lowry, "Synoptic Climatology of the Arizona Summer Precipitation Singularity," *Bulletin of the American Meteorological Society*, **36** (1955), 329–339.

[20] Kendrew and Currie, *op. cit.*, p. 4.

[21] J. Borchert, "The Climate of the Central North American Grasslands," *Annals of the Association of American Geographers*, **40** (1950), 1–39.

[22] Kendrew and Currie, *op. cit.*, p. 10.

[23] B. W. Currie, *Prairie Provinces and Northwest Territories Precipitation*, University of Saskatchewan (July 1953), p. 11.

[24] F. E. Burbidge, "The Modification of Continental Polar Air over Hudson Bay," *Quarterly Journal of the Royal Meteorological Society*, **77** (1951), 365–374.

[25] T. J. G. Henry, *Maps of Upper Winds over Canada*, Meteorological Branch, Dept. of Transport (Toronto, 1957), p. 22.

[26] M. K. Thomas, *Climatological Atlas of Canada*, Meteorological Division, Dept. of Transport (Ottawa, 1953), p. 125.

[27] Trewartha, *op. cit.*, p. 304.

[28] Horn and Bryson, *op. cit.*, 162.

[29] *Ibid.*, 162.

[30] *Climatology and Weather Services of the St. Lawrence Seaway and Great Lakes*, U.S. Dept. of Commerce, Weather Bureau, Technical Paper No. 35 (Washington: U.S.G.P.O., 1959), p. 35, fig. 22.

[31] B. L. Wiggin, "Great Snows of the Great Lakes," *Weatherwise*, **3** (1950), 123–126.

[32] S. Petterssen and P. A. Calabrese, "On Some Weather Influences Due to Warming of the Air by the Great Lakes in Winter," University of Chicago, Dept. of Meteorology, Scientific Report No. 7 (1959).

[33] *Climatology and Weather Services of the St. Lawrence Seaway*, *op. cit.*, p. 6 (Fig. 5).

[34] Henry, *op. cit.*

V

STUDY
OF SPATIAL ASSOCIATION

1

THE DISTRIBUTION OF LAND VALUES
IN TOPEKA, KANSAS

DUANE S. KNOS

HYPOTHESES, DEFINITIONS, AND PRELIMINARY TESTS OF HYPOTHESES

... Discussions ... indicate that the pattern of urban land values is related in some manner to the structure of urban land uses. If such is the case, certain aspects of the distribution of land uses may be used to describe and explain spatial variations in land values. But what aspects of the land-use structure are to be used in such a description? What is the connection between the selected aspects of the land-use pattern and the spatial pattern of land values? How are the aspects of the land-use distribution to be measured?

Answers to these questions take the form of hypotheses posed for testing, four of which have been selected for attention in this study. These are:

1. Urban land values vary inversely with distance from the center of the city
2. Urban land values vary inversely with distance from major business thoroughfares intersecting the center
3. Urban land values vary directly with the distribution of population potentials within the city
4. Urban land values vary with the direction of growth within the city.

Each of these hypotheses [is] related to certain aspects of the location of land uses within the city. As they stand, however, the hypotheses are extremely general and, as a consequence, cannot be subjected to empirical tests. It is necessary at this point to consider these hypotheses in greater detail; to provide a rationale for each of the hypotheses ... ; to define operationally the component parts of each hypothesis; and to provide preliminary tests of the hypotheses to make explicit the

Reprinted from *The Distribution of Land Values in Topeka, Kansas,* University of Kansas, Bureau of Business and Economic Research, pp. 15–33, by permission of the author and director.

existence, nature, and degree of relationships suggested by the hypotheses. These points are considered in the subsequent sections . . . .

HYPOTHESIS I: *Urban land values vary inversely with distance from the center of the city.*

RATIONALE

. . . The intensity of business activity is greatest at the center of the city and declines with distance toward the periphery. Likewise, residents, in their desire to locate with easy access to certain focal points within the city, place a premium on sites in close proximity to those focal points. Since the central business area is one of the most important focal points, both in terms of shopping and employment, residential uses tend to be more intense in the vicinity of the central business district. There is a decline in intensity with distance toward the periphery, where land is more abundant and

a greater number of essentially equal alternatives are available. If the value of land declines with a decrease in the intensity of use, land values would be expected to decline with distance from the center.

MEASUREMENT

The measure of distance used in testing this hypothesis is the shortest street distance measured in inch units on an all-street base map of Topeka (scale—1 : 24,000) between the center of the central business district and the center of each block in the sample. This measure has been taken rather than a straight, airline distance because movement in the city is channeled, and as a result, distance, in the sense of the hypothesis, must measure the actual distance that is to be overcome in the interaction of urban activities. No attempt has been made, however, to weight the various distances in terms of the time and convenience

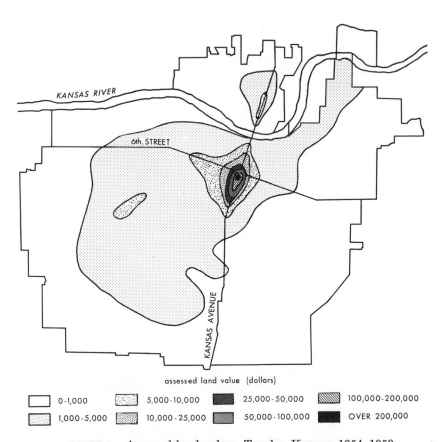

FIGURE 1. Assessed land values, Topeka, Kansas, 1954–1959

costs of moving from each point to the center. This would seem to be desirable since . . . these are pertinent cost factors in the definition of distance. On the other hand, it is quite unlikely that variations in these costs from route to route in Topeka are of significant importance in comparison with variations in simple street distances. Since these variations would produce such small differences in the measure of accessibility, expenditures for this kind of refinement may be considered as unwarranted.

The center of the central business district is taken as the intersection of Kansas Avenue and Seventh Street, for it is here the blocks adjoin that contain the highest intensity of business activity, the greatest pedestrain traffic, and the highest land values.

THE NATURE OF THE HYPOTHESIZED RELATIONSHIP

Thus far the hypothesis has been considered only in terms of a gradient decline in value with distance from the center. Nothing has been said about the nature of the hypothesized relationship between land values and the distance variable. What is the rate of decline in land values with distance from the center? Is the decrease of values of a linear nature, or is it best described by some curvilinear function?

In this connection it is clear from an inspection of the land value surface in Fig. 2 that the values of plots of land decline at a different rate with each unit increment of distance from the center. Indeed, values decline very sharply for a short distance from the center, with the gradient becoming more gentle with increasing distance beyond. . . . Characteristically, the center of the central business district is devoted to highly intensive commercial uses, while a short distance away from the center, commercial uses give way to residential uses. Within this short distance the average revenue per square foot of land declines to only a small fraction of that found at the center. If revenue is related to the rent-paying ability of utilities, and if the ability to pay rent is related to the value of the land occupied, a steep gradient would be expected in the central area. Since the remainder of the area is devoted largely to residential uses, and since there are relatively small variations in rent-paying ability among residential utilities, the gradient in the remainder of the area would be expected to be

relatively gentle. Thus the function that best describes the relationship between land value and distance from the center should have a negative slope which is quite concave from the top.

In view of the foregoing considerations, a regression model that incorporates the curvilinear characteristics outlined above was selected to approximate the distribution of land values in relation to the distance variable. This model is a type of reciprocal function and is expressed algebraically as:

$$Y = a + bX'$$

where: Y is taken as land value,
X' is taken as the reciprocal of the distance from the center, $1/X$, and
a and b are constants.

Fitting this model to the sample data and estimating the constants a and b, the equation is found to be

$$Y = 1691.1 + 19,975.78X'$$

When this curve is plotted, its form is that shown in Fig. 3. If the curve in Fig. 3 were to be rotated around the Y-axis, it would describe a cone-like shape approximating more or less the land-value surface shown in Fig. 2.

In a very real sense, the foregoing equation is a generalized description of the structure of land values in Topeka. Its value as a description, however, depends on how accurately it "fits" the distribution of land values. It is necessary, therefore, to obtain a measure of its fit, or it is necessary to obtain measures of the degree of association between land values and distance from the center. For this purpose, the index of curvilinear correlation (ρ), ρ^2, the standard error of estimates (σs), and a test of statistical significance (F) was computed. These statistics are shown in Table 1.

From Table 1 it may be noted that an association between the two variables does exist in the universe of blocks from which the sample used in this study was drawn. Moreover, the degree of association observed in the test is moderately high. Nearly 64 per cent of the variation in assessed land values is accounted for by the model.

Some caution should be exercised, however,

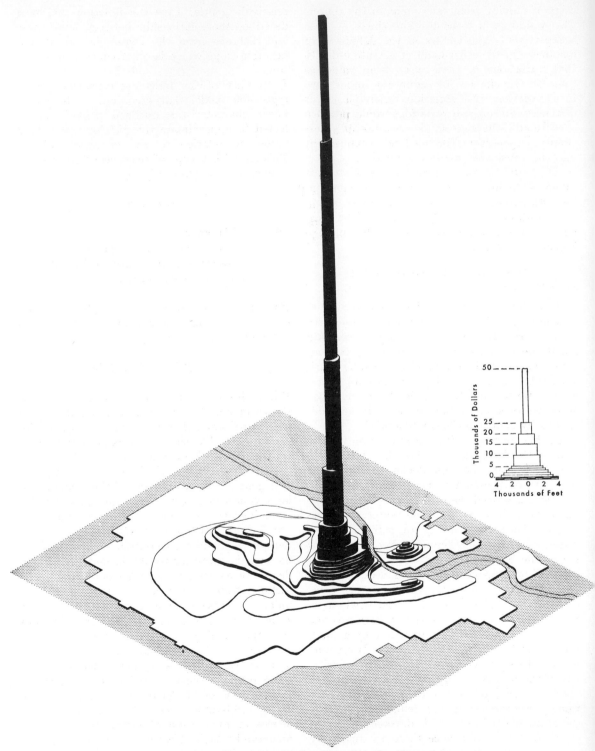

FIGURE 2.   Isometric land values, Topeka, Kansas

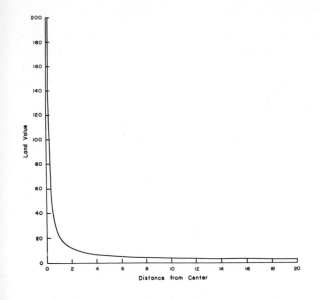

FIGURE 3. Regression of land value on distance from center, Topeka, Kansas

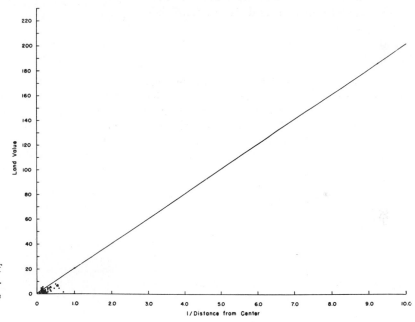

FIGURE 4. Regression of land values on the reciprocal of distance from the center, Topeka, Kansas

TABLE 1

Results of tests of the relationship between land values and distance from the center, Topeka, Kansas

$$\rho = .7995$$
$$\rho^2 = .6392$$
$$\sigma s = \$24,841$$
$$F = 129.33^a$$

[a] The least highly significant value of F ($P = .001$) with 1 and 74 degrees of freedom is 11.84.

in the interpretation of the results indicated in Table 1. It is apparent that the bivariate distribution is to some degree nonhomoscedastic (Fig. 4). As a result, ρ is probably somewhat overestimated. Nevertheless, the regression model is taken as descriptive of the relationship between land values and distance from the center. Thus the hypothesis may be refined and restated for further testing as: Land values vary inversely with the reciprocal of the distance from the center of the central business district.

HYPOTHESIS II : *Urban land values vary inversely with distance from major business thoroughfares intersecting the center.*

RATIONALE

. . . Business activities tend to take up locations along major thoroughfares leading into the central business district. This is the major business thoroughfare of which Proudfoot[1] speaks in discussing different types of business and service locations. In effect, such locations produce an intensity of land use that reaches out like fingers into areas of less intensive uses. In a sense, these major business thoroughfares form ridges of high land value extending finger-like into areas of relatively low value land. The value of land would be expected, then, to decrease with increasing distances from these thoroughfares.

DEFINITIONS

In Topeka, there is but one major business thoroughfare, namely, Kansas Avenue, that passes through the center of the central business district. The thoroughfare traverses the city in a generally north-south direction and is the street to which the central business district is oriented. Indeed, the central business district is elongated along the axis of the thoroughfare extending north and south for a distance of more than five blocks, while the east-west dimension is no more than three blocks. Moreover, commercial activities extend along the thoroughfare with considerable continuity for nearly a mile to the south and across the Kansas River to the north in excess of a mile from the center of the central business district. For these reasons, Kansas Avenue has been taken as the major business thoroughfare for tests of the hypothesis.

Distance from Kansas Avenue has been taken as the shortest measurement from the center of each block to Kansas Avenue, and, as in the case of the measure of distance from the center, distances have been expressed in inches measured on an all-street base map of Topeka (scale—1 : 24,000).

THE NATURE OF THE HYPOTHESIZED RELATIONSHIP

It is postulated here that land values are related to distance from Kansas Avenue in the same manner and for the same reasons as outlined in connection with the first hypothesis. The intensive use of land associated with non-residential activities tends to lie adjacent to the

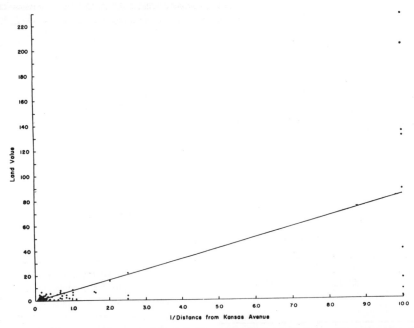

FIGURE 5. Regression of land values on the reciprocal of distance from Kansas Avenue, Topeka, Kansas

thoroughfare, with less intensive uses taking up land away from the major street. Consequently, the gradient decline in value with unit increments of distance from the thoroughfare would be expected to be precipitous close to the thoroughfare, becoming more gentle beyond. Therefore the reciprocal regression model was again applied to describe the nature of the relationship suggested in the hypothesis. Fitting the model to the data and estimating the constants a and b, the equation is found to be

$$Y = 8498.06X_2' - 1182.5$$

hewre: Y is taken as the value of land, and X_2' is taken as the reciprocal of the distance from Kansas Avenue.

This equation is presented graphically in Fig. 5.

Again, tests of the existence and degree of association were applied to measure the degree to which the model "fits" the actual land-value structure in Topeka. Results of these tests are listed in Table 2.

TABLE 2

Results of tests of the relationship between land values and distance from Kansas Avenue, Topeka, Kansas

$$\rho = .6811$$
$$\rho^2 = .4639$$
$$\sigma s = \$29,873$$
$$F = 63.169^a$$

[a] The least highly significant value of F ($P = .001$) with 1 and 74 degrees of freedom is 11.84.

Information in Table 2 indicates that, as in the previous tests, an association exists between land values and distance from Kansas Avenue in the universe from which the sample was drawn. The degree of association, however, is not so great as that found in the previous tests. The distance variable accounts for only 46 per cent of the variation of land values, while the improvement in describing the distribution of land values by using this model rather than the mean is only about 27 per cent. Nevertheless, these tests support the notion that an association of the type suggested by the regression model exists. Therefore the hypothesis may be restated for further testing as: Urban land values vary inversely with the reciprocal of distance from Kansas Avenue.

HYPOTHESIS III: *Urban land values vary directly with the distribution of population potentials within the city.*

RATIONALE

Population potential is a measure of the closeness of people taken in the aggregate. Defined precisely, it is:

$$V_i = \Sigma \frac{P_n}{D_n}$$

where: V_i is the population potential at point i, P_n is the population at n points, and D_n is the distance from i to n points.

Thus the population at any given point contributes to the population potential at any other given point by the amount of the reciprocal of the distance between the two points. The point within the city having the highest population potential is, then, the point that is closest to the entire population taken in the aggregate.[2]

... It would seem that the area of highest population potential would be the area most desirable for central business district activities, everything else being equal. In spite of the desirability of the high potential point for commercial activities, however, the existing central business district may not be located at the point of highest potential. Indeed, the existing business center may be quite eccentric to the point of highest potential, if the city has expanded more in certain directions than in others. Although the point of highest potential tends to move in the direction of greatest growth, the central business district tends to resist such movements. Capital improvements on the land within the central business district are of a more or less permanent nature. Therefore movements of this district, in response to changes in the total distribution of population, can be done only at the cost of the very large volume of sunk capital invested in the established central business district. Consequently, there is a tendency for the central business district to stay put or to move very slowly in response to changes in the distribution of population.

If, on the other hand, additional capital investments are made in new central business district activities, these activities would tend to locate on that side of the district facing the direction of city growth. In this manner, the central business district tends to migrate toward the point of highest population potential. This, in turn, tends to inflate the value of land with a high potential relative to lands devoted to similar utilities with low potentials. This inflation may be due in part to the prospects of a change in land use to a higher rent paying utility, which in turn produces propects of substantial profits in the form of unearned increments to the land and results in a higher market value. It may also be due partly to the fact that areas of highest population potentials are most likely to be found in areas of dense population, since a dense population close to a point will contribute more to the potential than a sparse population close to the point or a dense population far from the point. As a consequence, land is likely to be more intensely used with a greater return per square foot of space occupied resulting in higher land values.

DEFINITION AND MEASUREMENT

The distribution of population potentials in Topeka is shown in Fig. 6. This map was prepared on the basis of thirty-five control points distributed evenly over the city area. A grid with squares approximating .1 of a square mile was overlaid on a dot map of the distribution of population in Topeka for the year 1958, and the total number of people was computed for each square. Then concentric circles were drawn around each control point on a map (scale— 1 : 12,000), with the radius of the inner circle equal to two inches and the radius of each succeeding circle increasing by two inches. The population of the squares located within each of the zones defined by the concentric circles was then totaled and divided by the distance from the control point to the midpoint of each zone. These values were then summed to obtain an approximation of the population potentials at each of the thirty-five control points. The potentials were then plotted on a map, and isolines connecting points of equal population potential were constructed. From this map (Fig. 6), a potential value was assigned to each block in the sample.

It should be noted that the lines of equal potential in Fig. 6 are based upon the population residing within Topeka's city limits and do not take into account the population that might be considered in the Topeka trade area but residing outside the city. What effect these populations have on the distribution of potentials within the city is not known. It is quite likely, however, that they do not materially affect the distribution shown in Fig. 7, since

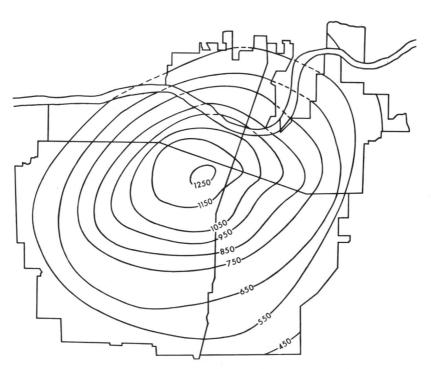

FIGURE 6.   Potentials of population, Topeka, Kansas, 1958

these outside populations are relatively small.

THE NATURE OF THE HYPOTHESIZED RELATIONSHIP

In the development of this hypothesis, it has been suggested that urban land values vary directly with population potentials, that is, the greater the population potential the higher the land value. There is nothing in the rationalization of the hypothesis, however, to suggest the nature of the function that best describes the relationship. Consequently, tests of the hypothesis have been applied assuming that the relationship is linear. The coefficient of simple correlation (r), r^2, standard error of estimate (σs), and a test of statistical significance (F) were computed to test the efficacy of the hypothesis as an explanation of the distribution of land values using the linear regression model. The results of these computations are shown in Table 3.

A highly significant association exists between population potentials and land values, but the degree of association is quite low (Table 3). Only 14 per cent of the variations in land values are accounted for by the linear relationship, while the decrease in the standard

TABLE 3

Results of tests of the relationship between land values and population potentials, Topeka, Kansas

$r = .3736$
$r^2 = .1396$
$\sigma s = \$37,846$
$F = 11.85$[a]

[a] The least highly significant value of F ($P = .001$) with 1 and 74 degrees of freedom is 11.84.

error of estimate ($\sigma s = \$37,846$) from the standard deviation of the land-value series ($s = \$40,800$) is only 7 per cent.

It is quite possible, of course, that the apparent low order of correlation between these two distributions may be due partly to errors in the assumption of linearity, for the nature of the relationship may be, in fact, curvilinear. To test for possible curvilinearity in the relationship, the correlation ratio (E) was computed and a test of the significance of the difference between E^2 and r^2 ($E^2 - r^2$) was applied. The squared correlation ratio was found to be .3000. Thus:

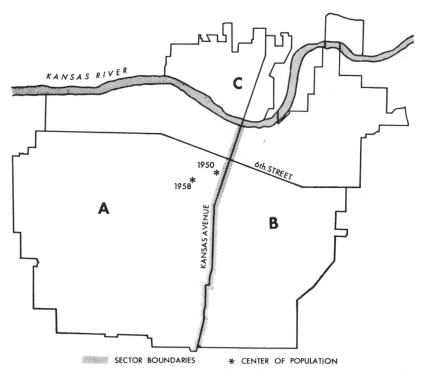

FIGURE 7. Sectors of differential growth, Topeka, Kansas

$$E^2 - r^2 = .3000 - .1396 = .1604$$

The statistic F was computed to test the null hypothesis that the difference of the parameters of E^2 (ϵ^2) and r^2 (ρ^2) are equal to zero ($\epsilon^2 - \rho^2 = 0$) and this statistic was found to be 2.20. Since the least significant value of F ($P = .05$) with 6 ($m - 2$) and 67 ($N - m$) degrees of freedom is 2.24, the computed value of F is not significant. Thus the null hypothesis may not be rejected, and the assumption of the essential linearity of the relationship may be retained.

On the basis of these preliminary tests, the hypothesis may be retained for further testing as it was originally stated: Urban land values vary directly with the distribution of population potentials within the city.

HYPOTHESIS IV: *Urban land values vary with the direction of growth within the city.*

RATIONALE

If Hoyt is correct in his assertion that city growth is channeled within sectors of the city, it would seem reasonable to expect that urban land values would also be greater in those sectors. According to the theory, growth occurs in certain sectors because the land, for various reasons, is more desirable for residential uses. Moreover, this growth encourages the movement of more intense land uses, business activities in particular, in these same directions. As has been pointed out, such activities continually search for locations that offer greater accessibility (proximity) to the changing distribution of customers. As a result of the greater desirability of the land in the sectors of largest growth, more potential land users enter the market for locations in these sectors. The market value of such land is thereby bid upward, and differentials in land values develop from sector to sector within the city.

DEFINITIONS

It is evident from population data that Topeka has experienced rather substantial differentials in growth among the various parts of the city in recent years. Greatest growth has occurred in the south, southwestern, and western parts of the city south of the Kansas River, while growth has been more limited to the east and in the area north of the Kansas River. One evidence of this differential growth may be seen in the migration of the center of gravity of population during the eight-year period from 1950 to 1958 toward the areas of greatest growth. The data in Fig. 7 indicate the relative position of the two centers of population for those two years, and it may be noted that the migration has been substantial in distance, and toward the southwest in direction.

On the basis of the differential growth within the city, three sectors have been delimited (Fig. 7). The sector of greatest growth (A in Fig. 7) has been defined as the area lying south of the Kansas River and west of Kansas Avenue. An area of lesser growth (B in Fig. 7) is defined as the area south of the Kansas River and east of Kansas Avenue, while the area of most limited growth (C in Fig. 7) is the area north of the Kansas River. The percentage increase in population within these three sectors is shown in Table 4.

TABLE 4

Population growth by sectors, Topeka, Kansas, 1950–1958 (percent)

Sector	Average population increase[a]
A	67
B	41
C	35

[a] Based upon a random area sample ($N = 200$) of standard areal units measuring 1,000,000 square feet.

THE NATURE OF THE HYPOTHESIZED RELATIONSHIP

A different set of methods has been employed in preliminary tests of Hypothesis IV than has been utilized in the previous manipulations. Since the sectors of differential growth are not scalable in the usual sense, models of the form applied to obtain descriptions of the nature of the other hypothesized relationships are not appropriate here. Rather, the problem is one of testing the significance of differences of mean land values among the three sectors. For this purpose, analysis of variance has been utilized. The statistic F has been computed to test the significance of differences of sector means, and the unbiased correlation ratio (ϵ) has been obtained to determine the degree of relationship

TABLE 5

*Results of analysis of variance between urban land values
and sectors of growth, Topeka, Kansas*

Source of variation	Sum of squares	Degrees of freedom	Mean square variance	F[a]
Total	124,851,668,348	74	1,687,184,707	
Between-sector	16,819,224,611	2	8,409,612,305	
				5.60
Within-sector	108,032,443,737	72	1,500,450,607	

$\epsilon = .333$

[a] The least highly significant value of F ($P = .01$) with 2 and 72 degrees of freedom is 4.94.

between land values and the three sectors. The results of these computations are shown in Table 5.

Although the degree of relationship is not great ($\epsilon = .333$, Table 5), an association between land values and the sectors of differential growth is indicated in the universe from which the sample was drawn. To this extent, then, the hypothesized relationship is substantiated.

It is necessary, however, to go a step further in the preliminary tests of the hypothesis, for in the rationalization of the hypothesis it was postulated that the areas of greatest population growth would also tend to contain the highest land values. Thus if the sectors are ranked according to the mean land value in each sector, the resulting order should follow essentially the rankings obtained on the basis of population growth. That such is the case may be seen in the second column of Table 6. These means, however, should be regarded with some caution, for they include sample blocks drawn from the area of the central business district. It was pointed out previously that the greatest variation in the range of land values within the city is found in the central business district and, as a consequence, very small sampling variations in this area may produce rather substantial differences in the computed means. Indeed, the addition of one block close to the center of the central business district to the sample of blocks within a sector may result in a difference in the mean of as much as $5000. Thus the relative magnitude of differences in the observed means among the sectors is dependent upon the number of these very high value blocks included in the sector. Moreover, it should be remembered that the hypothesis has to do essentially with population growth

TABLE 6

*Rank of sectors by mean land value,
Topeka, Kansas*

Sectors in order of population growth	Mean land value (including Central Business District)	Mean land value (excluding Central Business District)
A	$16,985	$3880
B	12,799	2701
C	957	957

or with pressures for land in areas of predominantly residential land uses. In view of these considerations, it would be interesting to compare the mean land values among sectors for the areas outside the central business district. The sample blocks drawn from the central business district have been eliminated and the sector means recomputed. This second set of means are listed in the third column of Table 6.

Although the comparison of rankings of the sectors in terms of population growth and mean land values is quite crude, and not definitive of the nature of the hypothesized relationship, the rankings are consistent with the hypothesis. Coupling this consistency with the observation that the sector means are significantly different gives at least preliminary evidence to substantiate the hypothesis. Thus the hypothesis stands for further testing.

SUMMARY

Hypotheses purporting to explain and describe the structure of land values in Topeka have been stated and rationalized [here] to make explicit the connection between the observed distribution of land values and certain aspects of the land-use structure of the city. The land-use variables have been operationally defined, and preliminary tests have been applied to determine the existence, nature, and degree of the hypothesized relationships. On the basis of these manipulations the hypotheses have been restated, where necessary, to provide a more precise statement of the postulated relationship. These hypotheses are as follows:

1. Urban land values vary inversely with the reciprocal of the distance from the center of the central business district
2. Urban land values vary inversely with the reciprocal of distance from Kansas Avenue
3. Urban land values vary directly with the distribution of population potentials within the city
4. Urban land values vary with sectors of growth within the city.

Further tests will be [now] applied . . . to test the efficacy of these hypotheses to explain and describe the structure of Topeka land values when considered simultaneously.

TESTS OF HYPOTHESES

. . . Preliminary tests [have been] applied to the sample data to ascertain the existence, nature, and degree of [the] four hypothesized relationships. . . . Some evidence was obtained to substantiate each of the hypotheses. These tests, however, are crude in the sense that each test is based on the assumption that variations in all other relevant factors in explaining the distribution of land values are everywhere constant (equal). Were each of the hypothesized independent variables in fact, the only relevant variables in such an explanation, then, indeed, the results of the preliminary tests could be taken as a solution for the problem posed for investigation in this study. Such is not the case, for it seems that the four hypothesized variables are, at least to some degree, relevant in the explanation of land value structures, and it is most likely that there are others as well. Consequently, the four hypotheses . . . are treated simultaneously in the following discussions to determine the relationship between

land values and the hypothesized independent variables taken together, and the relationship between each variable and the land value series when the other factors are, in effect, held constant.

THE REGRESSION MODEL

The methods of analysis selected for use in the consideration of the four hypotheses that follow are those of multiple correlation and regression analyses. These methods, of course, are usually applied in situations where each of the variables is numerically scaled. However, variations in one of the independent variables in this study—sectors of differential growth—are identified not in a numerical scale, but in terms of mutually exclusive areas. Consequently, it is necessary to define the sectors of differential growth in such a way that they may be inserted in the analysis on a par with the other three independent variables. To accomplish this, two "dummy" variables[3] have been defined to have the following properties:

R_1—a sample block takes the value of 1 if it occurs in sector A, all other blocks taking the value 0;
R_2—a sample block takes the value of 1 if it occurs in sector B, all other blocks taking the value 0.

Thus the regression model becomes in this study:

$$Y = a + b_1 X' + b_2 X_2' + b_3 X_3 + b_4 R_1 + b_5 R_2$$

where: Y is taken as the value of land,
X' is taken as the reciprocal of distance from the center of the central business district,
X_2' is taken as the reciprocal of distance from Kansas Avenue,
X_3 is taken as population potentials,
R_1 and R_2 are dummy variables associated with sectors of differential growth, and
a and $b_1 \ldots b_5$ are constants.

The model reflects shifts of the intercept of the regressions (a) among the three sectors. For example, in sector A, $R_2 = 0$. Hence the term $b_5 R_2$ has no effect in the computation of Y. Moreover, in the same sector $R_1 = 1$. Thus the intercept of the regression becomes $a + b_4$.

TABLE 7

Zero-order coefficients of correlation between Y, X', X'$_2$, X$_3$, R$_1$, R$_2$ and the interaction series, Topeka, Kansas

Variable	X'	X'$_2$	X$_3$	R$_1$	R$_2$	X$_1$R$_1$	X$_1$R$_2$	X$_2$R$_1$	X$_2$R$_2$	X$_3$R$_1$	X$_3$R$_2$	Y
X'	1.0000	.5564	−.3502	−.0923	.1454	.6596	.8070	.3441	.4402	−.0285	.2601	.7995
X'$_2$		1.0000	.3404	−.1765	.1515	.3219	.1458	.5732	.6621	−.1117	.2981	.6811
X$_3$			1.0000	.3212	−.1548	.2460	.2423	.2458	.3000	.5079	.0809	.3737
R$_1$				1.0000	.0000	.2140	.0000	.2991	.0000	.9490	.0000	−.0063
R$_2$					1.0000	.0000	.0037	.0000	.4762	.0000	.9360	.0626
X$_1$R$_1$						1.0000	.0000	.5868	.0000	.2871	.0000	.6640
X$_1$R$_2$							1.0000	.0000	.6673	.0000	.5103	.4367
X$_2$R$_1$								1.0000	.0000	.3551	.0000	.5843
X$_2$R$_2$									1.0000	.0000	.6510	.3914
X$_3$R$_1$										1.0000	.0000	.0860
X$_3$R$_2$											1.0000	.1613
Y												1.0000
Mean	.63157	1.82273	8.39	.59	.33	.29623	.32256	.79830	.84127	5.27	2.64	14,307
Standard Deviation	1.63308	3.27088	2.19	.493	.472	1.16145	1.23353	2.23943	2.49597	4.65	3.98	40,800

By the same token, the intercept of the regression in sector B becomes $a + b_5$. Since both R_1 and R_2 are equal to zero in sector C, neither b_4 nor b_5 affect [s] the computation of Y.

It is also clear from the foregoing that the model does not take into account differences in the slopes of the regressions among the three sectors. The possibility that the slopes do, as a matter of fact, vary significantly among the three sectors may be investigated by introducing into the model interaction variables involving the two dummy variables and the three independent variables. When the six interaction series are added, the regression model takes the form:

$$Y = a + (b_1 + d_1 R_1 + d_2 R_2) X'$$
$$+ (b_2 + d_3 R_1 + d_4 R_2) X'_2$$
$$+ (b_3 + d_5 R_1 + d_6 R_2) X_3$$
$$+ b_4 R_1 + b_5 R_2$$

Given the above regression model, the zero-order coefficients of correlation were computed between each variable and every other variable (Table 7). These coefficients were then inserted in a matrix for solution by the Doolittle method to obtain estimates of the necessary regression coefficients. Substitution of these coefficients in the regression model results in the following equation:

$$Y = 3524 + (11{,}200.09 + 5841.87 R_1$$
$$+ 876.51 R_2) X' + (1673.97$$
$$+ 4603.92 R_1 + 2926.00 R_2) X'_2$$
$$+ (-225.42 + 2485.73 R_1$$
$$- 1765.27 R_2) X_3 - 26{,}267.59 R_1$$
$$+ 4417.12 R_2$$

THE EXISTENCE AND DEGREE OF RELATIONSHIP

The foregoing equation is, of course, a generalized description of the manner in which the four hypothesized independent variables are related to the distribution of land values in Topeka when considered simultaneously. Since it is a generalization, it is necessary to test the equation to determine the degree to which it fits the actual structure of land values. Consequently, statistics were computed to measure the existence and degree of multiple correlation. These statistics are listed in Table 8.

TABLE 8

Results of multiple correlation analysis, land values with distance from the center (X'), distance from Kansas Avenue (X'$_2$), population potentials (X$_3$), two dummy variables (R$_1$, and R$_2$), and six interaction variables, Topeka, Kansas

$$R = .8870$$
$$R^2 = .7868$$
$$\sigma s = \$20{,}555$$
$$F = 21.14^{\text{a}}$$

[a] The least highly significant value of F ($P = .001$) with 63 and 11 degrees of freedom is approximately 3.35.

From Table 8 it is clear that an association between the structure of land values in Topeka and the four hypothesized independent variables exists in the universe from which the sample was drawn. Moreover, the degree of association is high. More than 78 per cent of the variations in land values are accounted for by the model. In addition, the standard error of estimate (in a sense, the average amount of error committed when the equation is used as a description of the land value structure) is $20,555 per acre. On the other hand, the standard deviation of the land-value series (in a sense, the average amount of error committed when the mean of the land-value series is used as a description of the land-value structure) is $40,800 per acre (Table 7). Thus the improvement (decrease in the average amount of error) in describing land values by using the equation rather than the mean is approximately 50 per cent.

TEST OF PARTIAL ASSOCIATION

Although the existence and degree of the multiple association between land value and the four independent variables have been established, there remains the possibility that one or more of the independent variables are not significantly related with Y when variations in the other series are, in effect, held constant. To investigate this possibility, the four independent variables were withdrawn from the analysis one by one, and the coefficients of multiple correlation were recomputed and adjusted for differences in degrees of freedom. An increase in the adjusted coefficients of multiple correlation with the elimination of a variable from the analysis indicates, of course, that the excluded factor is not statistically significant. The adjusted coefficients are listed in Table 9.

TABLE 9

Adjusted coefficients of correlation between land values and combinations of distance from the center, distance from Kansas Avenue, population potentials, and sectors of differential growth, Topeka, Kansas

Variable	Adjusted R
Y with:	
Distance from center, distance from Kansas Avenue and population potentials	.8462
Distance from center, distance from Kansas Avenue and sectors	.8672
Distance from center, population potentials, and sectors	.8014
Distance from Kansas Avenue, population potentials, and sectors	.7264
All variables	.8658

It may be noted from Table 9 that an increase in the adjusted coefficient of multiple correlation is obtained in only one case. The adjusted R increases from .8658 obtained when all four independent variables are included in the analysis to .8672 when the population potential factor is eliminated. Thus the null hypothesis that there is no partial association between land value and population potentials cannot be rejected when variations in the two distance factors and sectors of differential growth are taken into account in the universe of blocks from which the sample was drawn.

Not only is the population potential variable not statistically significant, but it adds little to the level of explanation obtained from the model. Indeed, comparison of the R^2's in Tables 8 and 10 indicates that the decrease in the per cent of variation in the distribution of land values, when the population potential factor is dropped from the analysis, is only .5 of a percentage point. Therefore the population poten-

tial factor was discarded and new regression coefficients were computed for substitution in the regression model. This operation results in the equation:

$$Y = 1129.6 + (10{,}163.27 + 7478.86R_1$$
$$+ 1528.10R_2)X' + (3188.28$$
$$+ 3273.94R_1 + 619.53R_2)X_2'$$
$$- 1886.90R_1 - 4615.93R_2$$

DIFFERENCES AMONG SECTOR REGRESSIONS

It was noted previously that the dummy variables, R_1 and R_2, reflect variations in the intercept of regressions within sectors, while the interaction variables produce variations in the slopes of the sector regressions. In this respect, a question may be asked about the nature of differences among the sector regressions. Do the sector regressions vary in regard to their Y intercepts, their slopes, or in both respects? Put more precisely, are there signifi-

TABLE 10

Results of multiple correlation analysis, land values with distance from the center (X'), distance from Kansas Avenue (X_2'), two dummy variables (R_1 and R_2), and four interaction variables, Topeka, Kansas

$R = .8842$
$R^2 = .7818$
$\sigma s = \$20{,}315$
$F = 29.56^a$

[a] The least highly significant value of F ($P = .001$) with 8 and 66 degrees of freedom is 3.28.

cant differences in the slopes and Y intercepts of regressions among the three sectors?

To answer this question, tests of the significance of the dummy and interaction variables were applied. The adjusted coefficients of multiple correlation were computed, dropping first the interaction variables and then the dummy variables from the analysis. The adjusted R obtained after excluding the interaction series is .8512; the adjusted R obtained after excluding both the interaction series and the dummy variables is .8439. Comparison of these statistics with the adjusted R obtained between the land-value series with the two distance variables and sectors of differential growth found in Table 9 reveals a decrease in the adjusted R in each case. From this, then, it is apparent that the within-sector regressions vary significantly both in the slope and the intercept of the regressions.

EXISTENCE AND DEGREE OF THE MULTIPLE ASSOCIATION

Statistics listed in Table 9 provide evidence to support Hypotheses, I, II, and IV as an explanation of the structure of land values in Topeka when taken together. That an association exists in the universe from which the sample of blocks was drawn is indicated by the statistic F, which is highly significant. It is also apparent that the degree of association is relatively high. Slightly more than 78 per cent of the variations of the land-value series is accounted for by the independent variables. Moreover, the standard error of estimate ($\sigma s = \$20,315$) is less than half the standard deviation of the Y series ($s = \$40,800$). The hypotheses taken simultaneously may be accepted, therefore, as a partial explanation of the distribution of land values in Topeka.

THE DISTRIBUTION OF RESIDUALS

The regression equation presented in the previous section is, in a very real sense, a generalized description of the structure of land values in Topeka. The appropriate values of X', X'_2, R_1, and R_2 for points within the city may be inserted in the equation, and a solution for Y may be obtained for each of the points. The resulting computed values of Y (Yc) form the generalized structure of land values described by the regression model, and, as in the case of the actual distribution of land values (Fig. 1–2), may be shown as a map or a three-dimensional diagram (Fig. 8).

Now the accuracy with which the regression model describes the actual distribution of land values in Topeka depends upon the degree to which the equation surface of Fig. 8 approximates the actual surface of Fig. 2. Measures of the "fit" of the two surfaces, of course, have already been presented in the previous section; that is, measures of fit in terms of the proportion of the total variation of the actual surface that is accounted for by the equation surface, and the standard error of estimate (the average

amount Yc differs from Y in the universe from which the sample was drawn). These measures, although they are most important in the analysis, do not, however, indicate spatial variations in the degree to which the equation fits the actual structure of land values. In some parts of the city, differences between the two surfaces (hereafter referred to as residuals) may be considerably greater than the average, while in others the error is relatively small. This raises questions concerning the distribution of the residuals within the city. Where are the large residuals found? Where are the areas in which the equation performs with reasonable accuracy? Is there any recognizable pattern in the distribution of residuals that might suggest additional hypotheses to be tested, or that might provide a guide to judgments concerning the definitions and testing procedures utilized in the present study?

Residuals are measured by subtracting the computed value of Y from the actual land value for each block ($Y - Yc$). The residuals have, therefore, either a negative sign (in cases where the equation overestimates the value of Y) or a positive sign (in cases where the equation underestimates the value of Y). By plotting the residuals on a map, areas of overestimation and underestimation may be delimited according to the magnitude of the residuals. Such a map shows graphically, then, spatial variations in the performance of the equation in describing the land value structure (Fig. 9).

Three types of areas have been delimited in Fig. 9. Two of these are areas of "large" residuals; one an area of overestimation (shown in black), and the other an area of underestimation (shown in white). The criterion for differentiating these two areas from the area of "small" residuals is quite arbitrary, since there are no a priori standards for determining objectively how a "large" residual should be defined. It is a matter of judgment and depends largely upon how the map and the equation are to be used. For example, if a high degree of accuracy in estimating values of Y is required of the equation, a rigorous definition of the "large" residuals would seem to be demanded. On the other hand, if only a very general description of the land-value structure is expected, a more moderate definition may be adequate. In this study, the concern is simply with a description of the spatial distribution of residuals; there are no predetermined requirements made for the performance of the regression model. Consequently, the definition of "large" residuals in this case is virtually a matter of indifference. In view of the lack of any compelling reasons for the selection of any particular lower limit for the "large" residual

category in Fig. 9, the mean of the residuals for the seventy-five sample blocks ($8450) has been selected. All blocks where the residuals are greater than $8450, then, are included in the areas of "large" residuals.

The third category of residuals shown in Fig.

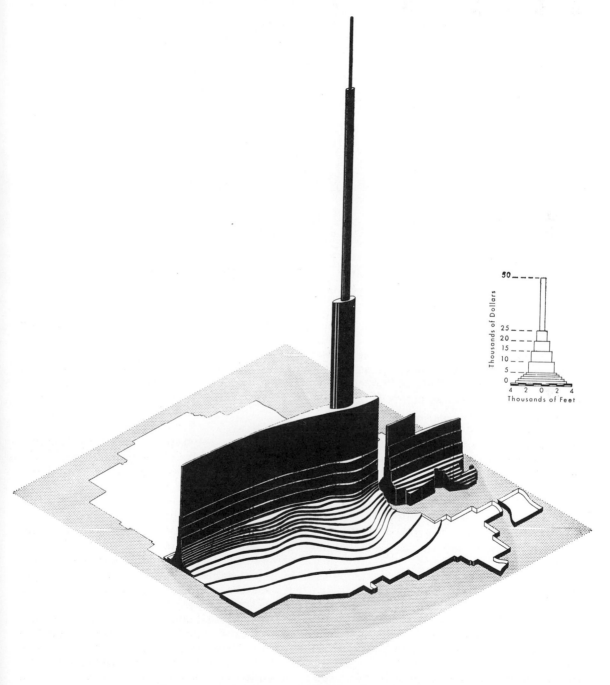

FIGURE 8.   Isometric accuracy of estimated land values, Topeka, Kansas

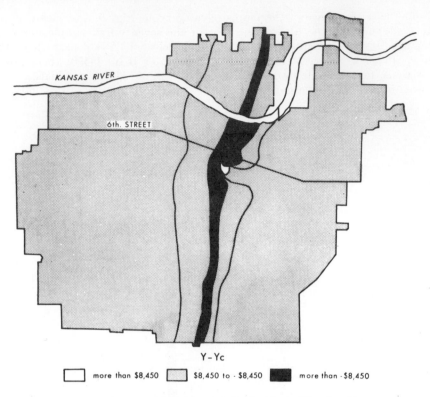

FIGURE 9.   Accuracy of estimated land values, Topeka, Kansas

9 are designated as "small" residuals. Because it is considered desirable to focus attention primarily upon the distribution of the "large" residuals, areas of overestimation and underestimation in the "small" residual category have not been differentiated in Fig. 9, although the map shows the line connecting points where the computed value of Y is equal to the actual land value $(Y - Yc = 0)$.

There are two areas of "large" residuals, both of which appear to be oriented toward Kansas Avenue. One is the small area of extreme underestimation located just to the south of the center of the city. The other area is a band of extreme overestimations extending north and south from the central business district along Kansas Avenue.

THE AREA OF EXTREME UNDERESTIMATION

This area seems to be related to irregularities in the rate of decline of land values with direction from the center of the city toward the periphery. To illustrate, two cross sections of the actual and equation surfaces have been constructed. One cross section (Fig. 10) includes the blocks adjacent to Kansas Avenue to the west, while the other (Fig. 11) lies perpendicular to the first and includes blocks adjacent to Seventh Street. These figures, then, show the profiles of the actual and equation surfaces from the center toward the periphery in four directions.

It may be noted from these illustrations that the higher land values extend farther to the south of the center than in the other directions. The point taken as the center of the city is, therefore, quite eccentric to the center of the area of high land values.

The equation, on the other hand, produces a profile that is symmetrical. That is, the same computed values of Y are obtained for points at equidistances from the center and from Kansas Avenue within the same sector. It is obvious, then, that when the asymmetrical profile of the actual land value surface is superimposed on the symmetrical profile of the equation surface, disparities in the "fit" of the two profiles must occur. This is illustrated in Fig. 10, in which the equation surface is submerged to

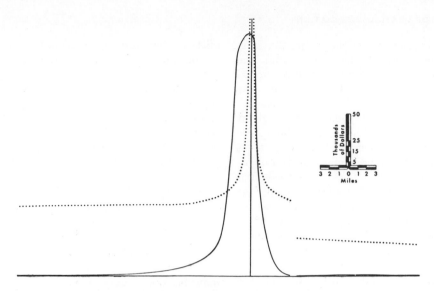

FIGURE 10. North-south cross section of the actual and equation assessed land value surfaces, Topeka, Kansas

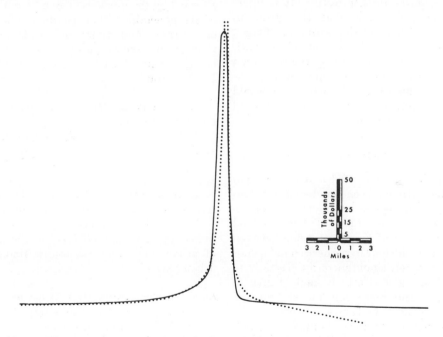

FIGURE 11. East-west cross section of the actual and equation assessed land value surfaces, Topeka, Kansas

an extreme degree by the actual surface in the segment of the figure just to the left of the center. This segment corresponds to the area of extreme underestimation shown in Fig. 9.

THE AREA OF EXTREME OVERESTIMATION

Although the distance from the Kansas Avenue variable is significant in the description

of the structure of land values in the total universe, the function which has been used to describe the relationship produces an area of large overestimation along the thoroughfare to the north and south of the central business district (Fig. 10). This reflects, perhaps, an error in the definition of the variable. It may be remembered that the reciprocal function was chosen to describe the relationship between land values and distance from the major business street on the basis of the notion that the intensity of land use varies with the reciprocal of distance away from such thoroughfares. The intensity of land use adjacent to Kansas Avenue, however, is not constant throughout its entire length. Beyond a certain point to the north and south of the central business district, business uses of the land facing the thoroughfare ceases and the street takes on a residential character. Since this is the case, it should be expected that the reciprocal function is not descriptive of the relationship beyond a certain point from the center along the avenue, hence the observed extreme overestimation of land values.

What measures should be taken to minimize the residuals found in the two areas of extreme overestimation and underestimation is problematical and requires further testing. It is interesting to note, however, that the errors in estimation included in the areas of "large" residuals account for 97 per cent of the variations of Y not accounted for by the regression model. Thus any measures designed to improve estimations in these rather limited areas would most likely be important in the explanation of urban land-value structures.

SUMMARY

The hypotheses formulated and tested separately ... have [now] been combined for consideration .... A regression model was formulated to describe the structure of urban land values on the basis of the relationship between land values and the four hypothesized independent variables taken simultaneously. Tests were applied indicating a relatively high degree of "fit" between the regression model and the pattern of Topeka land values. Analysis of the partial association between land values and population potentials revealed, however, a lack of association when variations in the two distance variables and sectors of differential growth were held constant. This variable, therefore, was eliminated from the analysis, and the regression model was reformulated. Again tests of the existence and degree of an association between the land-value series and the three remaining independent variables indicate the existence of a relatively high degree of multiple association. The average amount of error committed when the model rather than the mean of the land-value series is used to describe the pattern of land values in Topeka is slightly more than halved. Moreover, the spatial distribution of residuals obtained by use of the model shows the great bulk (97 per cent) of the errors are restricted to a relatively small proportion of the Topeka area.

Thus the equation:

$$Y = -1129.6 + (10{,}163.27 + 7478.86R_1$$
$$+ 1528.10R_2)X' + (3188.28$$
$$+ 3273.94R_1 + 619.53R_2)X_2'$$
$$- 1886.90R_1 - 4615.93R_2$$

may be taken as a reasonably accurate description of the structure of land values in Topeka. In a sense, of course, the description afforded by the model is "naïve," for no evidence of its generality, that is, its applicability to other areas and times, is available. In this connection, several questions must be answered before the model may be considered as "general." For example:

1. What is the degree of applicability of the model in other cities?
2. Does the model vary importantly when applied to cities of different sizes?
3. Does the model vary importantly when applied to cities with different economic bases?
4. What other factors are relevant in describing the structure of urban land values?
5. Are there important differences in the relevancy of factors effective in the description of urban land-value structures among various urban places?

Since answers to questions such as these have not been provided in this study, the equation reported above must be considered as applicable to only a unique place and time.

If, on the other hand, the model shown above is considered as an instance of a more general description, it may be considered as a partial step in the empirical testing of a general model. In this sense, the results obtained in this study are submitted as evidence of the efficacy of the model to explain and describe the structure of urban land values in general. Additional verification of the model awaits further investigations.

FOOTNOTES

[1] M. J. Proudfoot, "City Retail Structure," *Economic Geography.* **13** (1937), 425–428.

[2] For a discussion of population potentials, see J. Q. Stewart, "Empirical Mathematical Rules Concerning the Distribution and Equilibrium of Population," *Geographical Review*, **37** (1947), 461–485.

[3] For a discussion of the use of "dummy" variables in regression analysis, see D. B. Suits, "Use of Dummy Variables in Regression Equations," *Journal of the American Statistical Association*, **52** (1957), 548–551.

2

A CORRELATION
AND REGRESSION ANALYSIS
APPLIED TO RURAL FARM POPULATION
DENSITIES IN THE GREAT PLAINS

ARTHUR H. ROBINSON, JAMES B. LINDBERG, LEONARD W. BRINKMAN

The geographer's interest in modern descriptive and analytical statistical methods is growing, especially with respect to their potential usefulness in regional analysis. Correlation techniques, including multiple correlation and regression, are particularly suited to aiding the geographer in his traditional study of the areal variations of related phenomena, since the variables always exist in complex interconnection.[1] One may properly employ these statistical-cartographic techniques after he has established tentative descriptive hypotheses regarding the mutuality that may exist among the distributions of an area, inferred through the study of individual maps and other sorts of data. Coefficients of correlation and related indices provide general quantitative statements of the degree to which each hypothesis is valid. These may be sharpened through the use of partial correlation techniques which statistically hold constant designated variables while investigating any two. Regression mapping portrays the areal distribution of the degree of correspondence, shows the locations of departures

from the average relationship, and provides a basis for formulating additional hypotheses.

In this paper attention is focused on the areal variations in the density of the 1950 rural farm population in the Great Plains. Several distinct phenomena are believed to vary in a reciprocal fashion with rural farm population density; these interrelationships are examined, and statements are made about the closeness of correspondences among them. Average annual precipitation, distance to urban centers, and per cent of crop land are several of the factors that are considered to be important "determinants" in the variations from place to place of farm population density. But in the Great Plains just how significant are they individually and relative to one another? If there is a general pattern of covariation, where are the areas that depart from it? Such questions, in an areal setting, form the core of much of modern geographical study, and the techniques that are

Reprinted from *Annals the Association of American Geographers*, **51** (1961), 211–221, by permission of the authors and editor.

presented here as partial answers are believed to have wide applicability.

This paper is also concerned with several questions of statistical-cartographic methodology which are as yet only partially solved. Among these are: (1) the question of what sampling method to use when a map of uniform validity is desired, as opposed to a single summary measure; (2) the problems that arise when one wishes to employ both point data and unit-area data in a statistical computation; (3) the problem occasioned by the unequal sizes of units areas; and (4) the question of how best to map departures from certain mean relationships (regression residuals).[2]

If modern statistical tools that are appropriate to geographical analysis are to find their way into the research repertoire of geographers, they must be subjected to the rigors of repeated testing in a variety of geographical contexts. It is only through such testing that the usefulness, and the limitations, of these tools can be understood.

The Area and the Hypotheses

The focus of interest is on the area in the United States generally designated as the Great Plains and its marginal areas extending from the Canadian border to central Texas. It was arbitrarily defined by centering a rectangle on the intersection of the 40th parallel and the 100th meridian (Fig. 1). This includes more than 600 counties. A majority of the population is dependent directly or indirectly on agriculture, and the census group "closest to the land" is the rural farm population. The basic question, given the regional variations of rural farm population density in this region, is simply: how do other factors that hypothetically may be significant vary in interrelationship with the rural farm population density?[3]

The pattern of farm population density in any area is naturally the composite result of numerous physical, cultural, historical, and economic "influences." To understand their areal interrelationship completely is out of the question, but one can sort out what seem likely to be the dominant factors in a logical relationship, and then examine their relative significance. This is what the authors attempt to do.

The first hypothesis subjected to analysis is

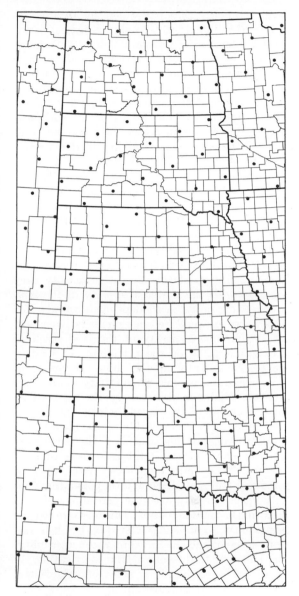

FIGURE 1. The area dealt with in the study. The pattern of dots shows the arrangement of control points used for computation and mapping purposes.

that the variations from place to place in the density of rural farm population are directly related to the variations in average annual precipitation. Such a hypothesis would probably bring forth few dissenting voices,[4] but unanimity as to the relative importance of annual precipitation as compared to other variables or the closeness of the relationship over the entire area is less certain. In order to study this hypothesis, in the statistical-cartographic sense, the population density is designated the dependent variable and average annual precipitation, the independent variable.[5]

The second hypothesis, scrutinized with the aid of correlation methods, is that rural farm population density varies inversely with distance from an urban center. Brunner and Kolb have demonstrated the validity of this general statement for the United States as a whole with respect to cities having over 20,000 inhabitants.[6] The independent variable used herein is the straight-line mileage from each population density control point to the nearest urban center that had 10,000 people or more within its municipal boundaries in 1950.[7]

The third hypothesis examined is that differences in rural farm population density vary directly with the potential quality of the land for growing crops. An independent variable for this purpose would be some quantitative aspect of the potential quality of the land, such as the soil fertility or the percentage of land in gentle slope. Unfortunately, however, quantitative measures of soil productivity or fertility are unavailable, and moreover, the topographic map coverage of the Great Plains is incomplete and much of it is unreliable. Consequently, the independent variable selected is the percentage of crop land in the total land area of each county.[8] The third hypothesis must then be modified and stated: rural farm population density varies directly with the percentage of crop land in the total land area. This measure reflects some of the wanted characteristics, but it is also influenced by such factors as market accessibility, or the susceptibility of the land to irrigation. As is shown later, however, some of these interconnections can be isolated.

PROBLEMS OF DATA PREPARATION

The data used to characterize the four variables described in the foregoing section required special types of processing for two reasons: (1) because the results of the analyses were desired in a form suitable for geographical description and analysis, and (2) the more than 600 counties which make up the study area are arranged in a generally rectangular pattern, as well as having a variety of sizes and shapes. These aims and facts conspire to create several

problems that will, no doubt, often arise when one uses statistical techniques in a geographical study in which a major objective is to map variations from place to place.

Correlation and regression analysis of an area can be undertaken in a variety of ways, depending upon the manner in which the data occur and the aims of the researcher. Some of the data used herein apply to points and some to unit areas. To attempt to treat the data as a population of unit areas would require conversion of the point data to unit-area data and would have two major disadvantages: the variation in unit-area sizes would necessitate weighting,[9] and the rectangular pattern would create interpolation problems in mapping.[10] Random sampling would not necessarily provide equal representation for all parts of the study area, and the results of the statistical analyses could not, therefore, properly be used to map variations within the area, although they would yield useful summary values for the area as a whole.

In order to bypass these several difficulties and to obtain cartographic advantages, the county population data were transformed to values for uniform hexagonal unit areas, the centers of which serve as data control points. The point data were derived (by measurement and interpolation) for these hexagonally arranged control points. Thus the rural farm population and the per cent of cropland data are used in their entirety, so to speak, but the unit areas are merely rearranged in compilation to provide more adequate mapping control. On the other hand, the precipitation data and the distance-to-urban-center data are sampled by obtaining values that refer to the centers of the hexagons.

A hexagon is the most economical geometric figure with which to subdivide an area without overlap. The average distance from the central point of a hexagon to its perimeter is less than in a rhombic, square, or rectangular figure of an equal area. Hence an hexagonal control-point value is less influenced by extreme portions of the area it represents, and therefore, theoretically, should be more representative. Furthermore, the center points of adjacent hexagons form the apexes of triangles; consequently, whatever the values at adjacent control points, there is only one place between them that an isarithm of intermediate value can be located, thus eliminating the problem of alternative choice.[11] These advantages were obtained by (1) randomly orienting an hexagonal overlay from a randomly chosen point of origin, (2) obtaining both point values for the centers and deriving average unit-area values for the sections covered by each hexagon, and (3) assuming the center of the hexagon as a control point for all mapping purposes. The selection of the size, i.e., the number, of hexagons to employ is important, since this establishes the number of sets of data available for correlation analysis and the number of control points for constructing the isarithmic maps. The overlay illustrated in Fig. 2 yields 161 hexagons. This number provides adequate control for both purposes.[12]

The method of obtaining the control-point values varied according to whether the data were functions of area or points. For those that were functions of area (population density and per cent of crop land), resultants were obtained as follows: the county averages were assumed to exist uniformly throughout the county; the value for each county that was included within a hexagon was multiplied by the fraction of the hexagon that the county occupied; and the products were then summed to provide the resultant (see Fig. 3). A different procedure was used to obtain precipitation and distance data. Rainfall data exist only at the locations of the recording stations; consequently, values at the centers of hexagons were interpolated from these stations. Straight-line distance between

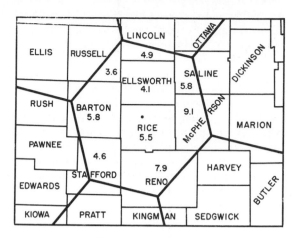

FIGURE 3. A portion of the hexagonal grid in central Kansas showing how county rural farm population density data were converted to unit area values for the hexagons. The numbers are the densities and the data for each hexagon were processed as follows:

County	Density	$\times$	Estimated portion of hexagon	$=$	Product
Rice	5.5		.17		.93
Ellsworth	4.1		.17		.70
Reno	7.9		.16		1.26
Barton	5.8		.13		.75
Stafford	4.6		.12		.55
McPherson	9.1		.12		1.09
Saline	5.8		.06		.35
Lincoln	4.9		.04		.20
Russell	3.6		.03		.11
			1.00		5.94

The resultant density used for the hexagon centered on Rice County is 5.94 persons per square mile.

the center of a hexagon and the nearest city of over 10,000 people is also a function of points, and it was measured directly from base maps.

THE CORRELATION ANALYSIS

Three kinds of correlation coefficients for the entire study area were obtained from the four sets of data: (1) coefficients of simple correlation (r), which describe the degree to which two of the variables are associated; (2) coefficients of partial correlation, which also describe the association between two of the variables, but do so by eliminating the effect

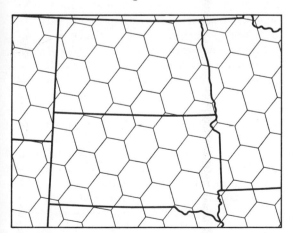

FIGURE 2. A portion of the hexagonal grid used for data compilation and processing

of one or more other variables which may be interrelated; (3) coefficients of multiple correlation (R), which describe the degree to which three or more of the variables are associated. These are tabulated in Table 1. These kinds of measures of association are summary values, that is, they apply to the entire area under study, and they cannot be used for mapping internal variation of the degree of association. Their role is merely to describe the degree of spatial correspondence among the areal variations of the variables as measures of the validity of hypotheses constructed for the area as a whole. Coefficients of $+1.00$ and -1.00 indicate, respectively, perfect direct and inverse correspondence of variations from place to place.

The coefficient of correlation between rural farm population density and average annual precipitation, $r_{12} = +.78$, confirms the general hypothesis that variations in rural farm population density in the Great Plains are directly and closely associated linearly with variations in average annual precipitation.[13] In a similar manner, the simple coefficients between rural farm population density and the other two variables (distance from a city of 10,000 and percentage of crop land in the total land area of the county) provide descriptions of the degree to which variations of these correspond to the variations of population density. The negative coefficient obtained for population density and distance from a city $(r_{13} = -.43)$ confirms the hypothesis that these two factors are inversely related. The direct relationship between population density and percentage of crop land is also confirmed by the correlation coefficient $(r_{14} = +.58)$. With a series of these coefficients, the second use of this analytical tool, namely, as a comparative device, is apparent. The areal association between population and distance is clearly not as close as that between population and precipitation, as indicated by the smaller value of the r describing the former. On the other hand, when more than two variables are being considered, judgments of this kind as to relative importance must be made with some caution, since the calculations also show that there is a negative relationship between the distance from a city and rainfall $(r_{23} = -.42)$.

In order to eliminate the effect of concomitant relationships among other variables while examining the relationship of any pair, one may employ coefficients of partial correlation.[14] These remove the effects of simultaneous correlations with other factors, and the relative sizes of the coefficients of partial correlation provide a truer description of the relative correspondence of the independent variables with the dependent variable. In the present study, two sets of coefficients were computed (see Table 1). In the first set, two factors, average annual precipitation and distance from a city of over 10,000 people, were included, in addition to the dependent variable, rural farm population density. The size of $r_{12.3}$ $(+.73)$ as compared to $r_{13.2}$ $(+.12)$ in dicates the much greater importance of rainfall as compared to distance from a city.[15] For the second set, a third independent variable, percentage of crop land in the total land area, was included, and a new set of coefficients of partial correlation was computed (Table 1). The hypotheses remained confirmed, and again the relative sizes of the coefficients express the relative importance of the factors.

The final step was the calculation of the coefficients of multiple correlation (R). The meaning of R is similar to that of r, in that it is a numerical description of the linear association between the dependent variable and all the independent variables included in its

TABLE 1

Results of correlation analysis

A. *Coefficients of simple correlation*

$$r_{12} = +.78$$
$$r_{13} = -.43$$
$$r_{14} = \pm.58$$
$$r_{23} = -.42$$
$$r_{24} = +.26$$
$$r_{34} = -.16$$

B. *Coefficients of partial correlation*

Three variables:

$$r_{12.3} = +.73$$
$$r_{13.2} = +.12$$

Four variables:

$$r_{12.34} = +.63$$
$$r_{13.24} = -.10$$
$$r_{14.23} = +.39$$

C. *Coefficients of multiple correlation*

$$(r_{12} = +.78)$$
$$R_{123} = +.79$$
$$R_{1234} = +.90$$

---

computation. The results (Table 1) show that as additional independent variables are taken into account it is possible to "explain" more and more of the variation in the distribution of rural farm population density. The addition of distance from an urban center of more than 10,000 people increased the correlation coefficient from $+.78$ to $+.79$ (r_{12} and R_{123}, respectively). This small increase was to be expected from the small size of the $r_{13.2}$ value ($+.12$). The inclusion of the percentage of crop land, on the other hand, increased the correlation coefficient from $+.79$ to $+.90$ (R_{123} and R_{1234}, respectively).

PERFORMANCE MAPPING

The preceding analysis provides only summary statements for the entire area of the relationships between rural farm population density and three other variables. The geographer, however, is ordinarily not satisfied with the areal anonymity of such summary figures. Being interested in the character of specific areas, he wishes to know where these relationships hold close to the regional generalizations and where they do not.

Mapping residuals from regression equations provides a means by which the relationships among phenomena can be seen in their areal setting, generally expressed in the form of isarithmic maps. Linear regression equations ($Y_c = a \times b_1 X_1 \ldots b_n X_n$) express the average relationship that exists between the dependent variable and the elements selected as independent variables. For example, when the values of rural farm population density, as computed from these formulae (Y_c), are plotted at the centers of the hexagons, they define the density surface that would exist if the distribution of variations in population density corresponded perfectly in a linear fashion with variations of the independent variables considered. The actual rural farm population density surface (Y) naturally does not coincide with the computed surface (Y_c), since in none of the instances is the linear correlation perfect. Therefore, when one maps $Y - Y_c$ he obtains a map showing the performance of the regression equation, that is, a map that shows the magnitudes (and their locations) of the density variations that make the linear correspondence of the variables less than perfect.

One may properly ask: why employ a linear function (from which to map the residuals) rather than a more complex, curvilinear function? The answer is that in studying these data the linear function was found to be usable, as is indicated on the maps by the relatively small sizes of the residuals over large areas as well as by the values of the coefficients of multiple correlation. Furthermore, it is easier to comprehend the spatial variations of a linear function than those of a more complex function; and if the purpose of a study is primarily to map geographical relationships in such a fashion as to lead to the formulation of additional tentative hypotheses,[16] then the descriptive statistical base that is least complex yet generally applicable provides the most easily interpreted results.

Three sets of performance maps have been prepared. These show, in effect, the locations of the deviations from the average regional relationship that result in the values $r_{12} = +.78$, $R_{123} = +.79$, and $R_{1234} = +.90$ being less than unity, which would indicate perfect linear correspondence. If the correlations were perfect, the regression equations would also describe the relationships perfectly, and there would be no point in making the maps. The departures from the relationship (regression) equations have been calculated and mapped in two ways in each instance. One employs the absolute difference in densities expressed as a number of persons per square mile ($Y - Y_c$), while the other employs the difference as a percentage departure from the actual density ($Y - Y_c$)/Y $\times 100$. The three sets of maps show progressively the effect of utilizing one, two, and three independent variables in the analysis.

Figures 4a–b are the comparison of actual rural farm density with the density that would exist if rural farm population held exactly to its general linear relationship with precipitation ($Y_c = 3.9517 + .3746X_2$). The most extensive areas of positive departure on both maps are in the area generally east of the Missouri River, and especially in southwest Minnesota and northwest Iowa. Other areas of positive departure are in north-central Colorado and in west Texas. There are several possible reasons for these positive departures from "normal." For example, the "Corn Belt" type of agriculture prevailing in Iowa, southern Minnesota, and parts of the Dakotas requires a more intensive labor input per land unit. The same reasoning may also apply to the irrigated regions in Colorado and west Texas. Other areas of positive departure in eastern Texas and Oklahoma apparently coincide with the presence of urban centers that seem to attract rural farm population.

Major areas of negative departure are also apparent, particularly on the western portions of the percentage map, where a smaller denom-

inator results in large percentage deviations. On both maps of Fig. 4 the areas in southeastern Oklahoma and south-central Kansas coincide with rougher terrain—the Ouachita Mountains and Flint Hills, respectively. The negative departures that occur in much of the southern and western portions of the area may reflect more extensive types of agriculture or may merely suggest that some more sophisticated expression of water availability should be

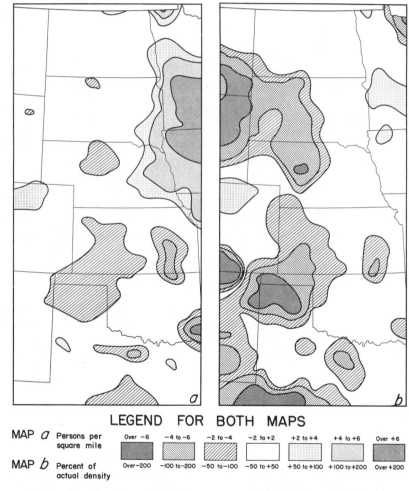

LEGEND FOR BOTH MAPS

MAP *a* Persons per square mile | Over −6 | −4 to −6 | −2 to −4 | −2 to +2 | +2 to +4 | +4 to +6 | Over +6

MAP *b* Percent of actual density | Over−200 | −100 to −200 | −50 to −100 | −50 to +50 | +50 to+100 | +100 to+200 | Over+200

FIGURE 4. Maps showing the differences between (1) the actual rural farm population densities and (2) the densities that would exist if the variations of rural farm population density corresponded perfectly with the variations of average annual precipitation. The left-hand map (*a*) expresses the differences in density terms $(Y - Y_e)$ and the right-hand map (*b*) expresses the same thing in terms of percentage departure from the actual value $\left(\dfrac{Y - V_e}{Y} \times 100\right)$.

utilized in place of gross average annual precipitation.

Even this brief look at the pattern of deviations from the mean regional relationship of rural farm population density and average annual precipitation has suggested several factors, such as proximity to urban centers, irrigation, roughness of terrain, and labor input per unit area, which merit further consideration.

When the factor of distance from an urban center of over 10,000 people is added to the analysis (Figs. 5a–b), few major changes occur, indicating little improvement in the "performance" of the regression equation (Y_c

$= -2.6166 + .3498X_2 - .0142X_3$). (Compare Figs. 4 and 5.) Boundaries have changed somewhat, but on the whole the core areas of departures are almost the same as in Fig. 4, even near the larger cities in the area, indicating that the factor of distance as measured here is relatively not very important. Somewhat greater changes appear on the percentage map, as, for example, the positive area in northeast Montana, far from an urban center. When the overall differences between Fig. 4 and 5 are compared with the small changes in the corresponding correlation coefficients and the small sizes of the values of the coefficients of partial

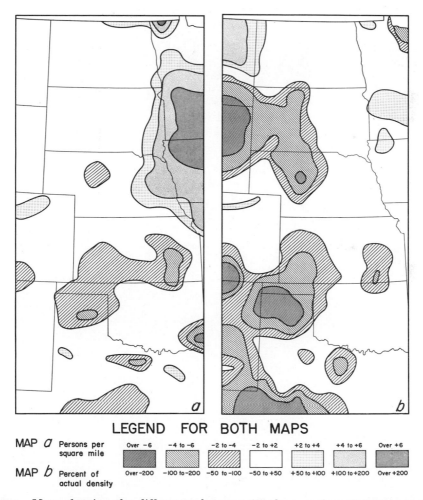

LEGEND FOR BOTH MAPS

MAP a	Persons per square mile	Over −6	−4 to −6	−2 to −4	−2 to +2	+2 to +4	+4 to +6	Over +6
MAP b	Percent of actual density	Over −200	−100 to −200	−50 to −100	−50 to +50	+50 to +100	+100 to +200	Over +200

FIGURE 5. Maps showing the differences between (1) the actual rural farm population density and (2) the densities that would exist if there were perfect multiple correlation among the variations of density and average annual precipitation and distance from an urban center of 10,000 or more. Map a expresses the differences in density terms and b in percentages of actual densities.

correlation, it is apparent that this result could have been anticipated. Consequently, the change in R and the magnitude of the coefficient of partial correlation can be used to estimate whether or not the additional steps of performance calculation and mapping will be worthwhile for a particular variable.

Figures 6a–b show the effect of including percentage of crop land in the total land area as the third independent variable. The pattern of departures of actual rural farm population density from the computed density based on all three independent variables undergoes considerable change on both maps

$(Y_c = -4.8540 + .3043X_2 - .0118X_3 + .0798X_4)$. This is consistent with the increase in the coefficient of multiple correlation ($R_{123} = +.79$ compared with $R_{1234} = +.90$), and with the size of the coefficient of partial correlation ($r_{14.23} = +.39$). Areas of rough terrain are no longer so apparent at they were on Fig. 4–5.

Negative deviations occur generally in a band running north and south through the center of the area, being particularly strong in western Kansas. Positive departures occur throughout most of the western portions of the area under study, although Fig. 6a shows that the deviations from "normal" are small in

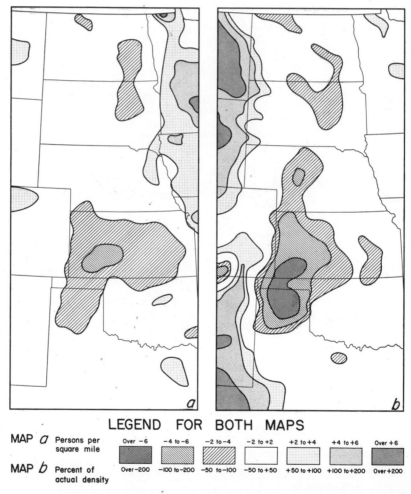

FIGURE 6. Maps showing the differences between (1) the actual rural farm population density and (2) the densities that would exist if there were perfect multiple correlation among the variations of density and annual precipitation, distance from an urban center of 10,000 or more, and the percentage of total land in crops. Map a expresses the differences in density terms and b in percentages of actual densities.

absolute terms. The same areas in Iowa and Minnesota that have been positive throughout are still present, although considerably reduced in size. This may indicate that differences in the labor intensity of the various types of farming prevailing in the Great Plains have not been sufficiently accounted for by any factor included in the study. The inclusion of some measure of farm labor per unit of crop land thus might be the next step in a more thorough study.

The authors conclude that the methods of correlation analysis have considerable merit when applied to the study of regional variations. These techniques cannot be applied without difficulties, but these seem no greater than their worth justifies. Certainly the relative precision of these descriptive and analytical tools, together with their cartographic applicability, make them useful in geographical study.

FOOTNOTES

[1] As demonstrated, for example, in H. H. McCarty, J. C. Hook, and D. S. Knos, *The Measurement of Association in Industrial Geography* (State University of Iowa, Department of Geography, 1956), G. W. Hartman and J. C. Hook, "Substandard Urban Housing in the United States: A Quantitative Analysis," *Economic Geography*, **32** (1956), 95–114; E. J. Taaffe, "Trends in Airline Passenger Traffic: A Geographic Case Study," *Annals of the Association of American Geographers*, **49** (1959), 393–408.

[2] Since the research reported in this paper was completed, a good technical summary of the use of residuals from linear regression has appeared: E. N. Thomas, *Maps of Residuals from Regression: Their Characteristics and Uses in Geographic Research*, pp. 326–352. Although carried forward without what would have been the considerable aid of Thomas' [s] monograph, this paper may be considered as an illustration of some of the methods he treated. The technically interested reader should refer to the monograph for a fuller description of the methods.

[3] The pattern of rural farm population density is defined as that which results from dividing the rural farm population of each county (as given in the 1950 census) by the total area of the county. The authors recognize the severe limitations of any simple "population category" as given by a census definition when a general definition is applied to a particular area, especially one characterized by high mobility and economic complexity. To attempt to correct the census category would be quite another, and larger, study.

[4] Robinson and Bryson obtained a correlation coefficient of +.83 for Nebraska in "A Method for Describing Quantitatively the Correspondence of Geographical Distributions," *Annals of the Association of American Geographers*, **47** (1957), 379–391.

[5] Average annual precipitation for the period 1940–49 was computed for 134 stations in the area with which this paper is concerned. The ten-year period was selected because it was felt that although farm population may change in response to periodic fluctuations in precipitation, under present-day social and economic conditions in the United States a period of several years would be necessary for these changes to be felt.

[6] E. deS. Brunner and J. H. Kolb, *Rural Social Trends* (New York: McGraw-Hill Book Company, 1933), pp. 111–143.

[7] Several other ways of expressing this same idea in commensurable terms could have been used. For example, a different limiting city size could have been selected, or measures of distance, such as travel-time or paved-road distance, could have been employed.

[8] Total crop land is the summation of the following census items for each county: crop land harvested, crop land now used for pasture, land from which hay was harvested, summer fallow, land in soil improvement, land on which crops failed. A detailed definition and the figures used are contained in U. S. *Census of Agriculture* (Washington: U.S.G.P.O., 1950), Vol. I, Part I.

[9] A. H. Robinson, "The Necessity of Weighting Values in Correlation Analysis of Areal Data," *Annals of the Association of American Geographers*, **46** (1956), 233–236, presents an illustration of this problem and one method of solving it.

[10] J. R. Mackay, "The Alternative Choice in Isopleth Interpolation," *Professional Geographer*, **5** (July 1953), 2–4.

[11] The reader will note that the hexagons illustrated in Fig. 2–3, although uniform, are not equilateral. A slight departure from regularity was made in drawing the hexagonal grid, but since the most important attribute of the grid is that the centers of the figures form a pattern of triangles, the irregularity was not corrected.

[12] Although tests of significance are common, their application in an essentially descriptive study is not usually explicitly treated. Putting it simply: if two distributions are quite unrelated, it is nevertheless likely that purely random fluctuations in the two may produce a correlation coefficient other than zero. In this study the probability of such a circumstance producing a value of r that departs far from zero is very low, since n (the number of data points) is relatively large (161). For example, when $n = 150$, an r over .20 is likely to occur accidentally only about once in 100 times.

[13] Throughout this paper the subscripts refer as follows:

    1—Rural farm population density (1950).

2—Average annual precipitation for the ten-year period 1940–49.

3—Straight-line distance from the nearest urban center of 10,000 or more people (1950).

4—Percentage of crop land in the total land area (1950).

[14] Formulae for calculating coefficients of partial correlation can be found in any good statistics text.

Most make use of the solution of simultaneous equations, the "Doolittle method" often being used for ease of computation if machine methods are not employed.

[15] The subscripts in this case identify the factors being tested, as follows: $r_{12.3}$ means the correlation of variables 1 and 2 is obtained, with the effect of 3 being eliminated.

[16] Thomas, *op. cit.*, pp. 8–10.

3

MAPPING THE CORRESPONDENCE
OF ISARITHMIC MAPS

ARTHUR H. ROBINSON

Consider two isarithmic maps of continuous actual or abstract phenomena in the same area. Each map portrays the undulations of a statistical surface at some level of detail by delineating irregularities of various magnitudes consisting of elevations, depressions, and gradients, uniquely organized and variously positioned and oriented.[1] Whether or not the phenomena are in any way causally interconnected, the two surfaces necessarily bear some relationship to one another; the recognition, description, and analysis of this are central aims in geographical research.

Research into the character of the relationship may be pursued in various way, depending upon the interests of the investigator and the level of generalization he hopes to obtain. For example, the degree to which the two surfaces are positively or negatively related may be determined by simple correlation analysis.[2] The single coefficient of correlation is little more than a broad generalization, however, and it is not very revealing. Comprehension may be increased by mapping

residuals from regression. This process involves determining the mean relationship between the undulations of the two surfaces and then mapping the degree to which one of the surfaces departs from it.[3] A third approach is to establish the planes in space which best fit each surface (by least squares) and then determine the relation between the orientation and tilt of the planes in the manner that the structural geologist compares strike and dip.[4] All the methods, in one way or another, depend upon summary measures derived from the entire mapped area. Their effectiveness is therefore limited, in a sense, to the analysis of the correspondence between the first-order elements of the undulations of the two cartographic surfaces. It may be assumed, however, that there will also exist a relationship among the second order elements, i.e., the undulations of lesser magnitude. This underlying pattern of

Reprinted from *Annals of the Association of American Geographers*, **52** (1962), 414–425, by permission of the author and editor.

correspondence may be different and more or less significant than the correspondence between the first order elements.

OBJECTIVES OF THE STUDY

This paper treats some of the cartographic problems inherent in such an investigation and presents the results of an inquiry into the relation between two statistical surfaces in the Great Plains area. An illustration is in order. Maps *a* and *b* in Fig. 1 are isarithmic maps of rural farm population density in 1950 and the average annual precipitation for the period 1930–49. If a correlation analysis were undertaken employing data derived from these two maps, the resulting index of simple correlation would reveal that the two distributions are *in general* highly correlated positively, which is not a suprising fact.[5] If one were to use the same data to obtain the regression of population on precipitation, and were then to map the population residuals from the regression, a map similar to *c* (Fig. 1) would result.[6] This map shows effectively the locations of the areas that do and do not conform to the *average* relationship that exists throughout the area. Both operations may be useful: in the one case the

existence of an expected relationship is confirmed, and in the other additional understanding is provided. But more information is available from a further analysis of maps *a* and *b*.

If one studies these two maps, visualizes the statistical surfaces they portray, and compares the directions of the gradients at the same places on the two maps, one may then construct a mental map of internal correspondence similar to map *d* (Fig. 1). Where the directions of the gradients (e.g., downslope) on maps *a* and *b* are similar, the positive correspondence is high; where the directions approach being opposite, the negative correspondence is high; and where the directions of the gradients approach perpendicularity, or where there are no clear gradients discernible, the correspondence is low.[7] Such a visual analysis of internal correspondence adds considerably to one's understanding of the relation the two mapped surfaces bear to one another. It is unwise, however, to rely heavily upon the mental integration of the complex surfaces of isarithmic maps.[8]

One may proceed with more confidence by deriving precise values of the various degrees of correspondence in sections of the area. By so doing he may obtain data on which a more

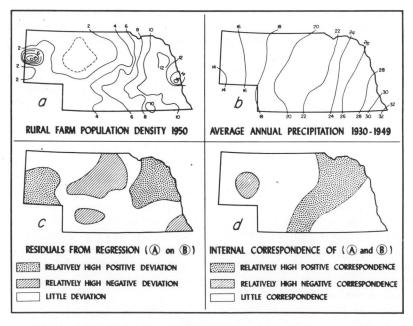

RURAL FARM POPULATION DENSITY 1950

AVERAGE ANNUAL PRECIPITATION 1930-1949

RESIDUALS FROM REGRESSION (Ⓐ on Ⓑ)

INTERNAL CORRESPONDENCE OF (Ⓐ and Ⓑ)

RELATIVELY HIGH POSITIVE DEVIATION
RELATIVELY HIGH NEGATIVE DEVIATION
LITTLE DEVIATION

RELATIVELY HIGH POSITIVE CORRESPONDENCE
RELATIVELY HIGH NEGATIVE CORRESPONDENCE
LITTLE CORRESPONDENCE

FIGURE 1

rigorous isarithmic map of the internal correspondence may be based. Although the level
of geographical generalization must necessarily
be raised in order to obtain significant results,
such a map showing the distribution of correlation between two mapped surfaces has great
potentialities. The pattern of the derivative
surface shows clearly where, how, and to what
degree geographical variations in one phenomenon correspond with variations in the other.
Furthermore, by preparing a series of such
maps for different periods, the changes of the
pattern through time may be observed.

In connection with a number of other
investigations, the author frequently compared
by eye isarithmic maps of average annual
precipitation and rural farm population density
for various parts of the Great Plains. The
isarithmic patterns suggested that there might
exist a meridional zone of high positive correlation through the central section of the
area, flanked by north-south zones of lesser,
or even negative correlation (map *d*, Fig. 1).
Such a pattern of internal correspondence
could be caused by numerous factors, namely:
(1) chance, (2) cartographic error, (3) a primary
interconnection between the two phenomena,
(4) complexly interwoven cultural and physical
factors. A full-scale study was undertaken in
order, first, to investigate the problems involved
in preparing a set of such derivative maps for
different periods as free of chance and cartographic error as possible; second, to determine
whether such a zone of higher correspondence
did actually exist throughout the entire area;
and third, if it did, to determine if it had
changed position through time.

THE AREA AND THE DATA

The area was chosen carefully so as to
embrace the full range of precipitation and
population in the transitional area of the Great
Plains. It seemed especially important to
include the clearly humid areas on the east
and the clearly dry areas on the west in case
there were any basic interconnection between
the factors. Accordingly, a sufficiently wide
rectangle was plotted on a standard Albers
projection. It was centered at the intersection
of the 40th parallel and the 100th meridian
and made close to 500 miles wide (E-W) and
1200 miles long (N-S)

The preparation of derivative correspondence
maps requires considerable care in the prior
isarithmic mapping of the phenomena. To
reduce cartographic error as much as possible,
each map should have a comparable distribution of horizontal control upon which the
isarithms are based. Without this, variations
in detail from one part of the map to another
could easily affect the degree of correspondence
of one isarithmic surface with the other. It is
not necessary that the *amount* of control be
the same on each map; instead it is necessary
that, whatever the distribution of variations
in detail on the one map, the other should
match it in this respect.[9]

Figure 2*a* shows the control points (the
approximate centers of the counties) used for
constructing the isarithms of population density. The spacing is relatively even, with only
a modest increase toward the west, since the
differences among sizes of counties within the
area are neither great nor are they systematically organized. Consequently, one can assume,
with respect to the variance of the population
density values, that relatively little of it can be
ascribed to differences in control point density,
i.e., the frequency with which county boundaries occur.

Since the control used for mapping population density is rather evenly spaced, considering the area as a whole, a relatively uniform
distribution of control for mapping precipitation
is also necessary. Accordingly, the area was
divided into 120 equal rectangles with dimensions of 50×100 miles. Each of these contains
one meteorological station from which an
adequate number of years of record is available.
In addition, thirty-eight stations adjacent to
the area are included so as to provide control
along the margins. Figure 2*b* shows the spacing
of these control points. Although they are
farther apart than the control points for the
population density maps, the difference in
spacing is not of great consequence for the
reasons outlined above. The important factor
is rather the extent to which both maps
(Figs. 2*a–b*) approach the same degree of
evenness.[10]

It was decided to prepare correspondence
maps for three periods. If a definite arrangement of correspondence between population
density and annual precipitation did result,
it would be interesting to see whether it
persisted. Furthermore, if a similar pattern

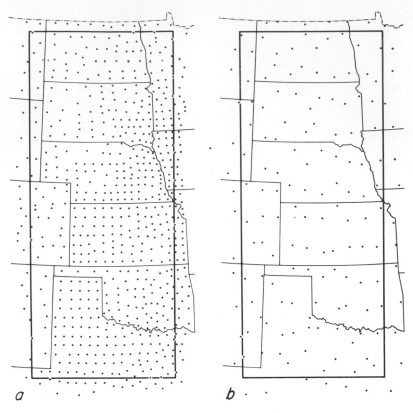

FIGURE 2

occurred at three different periods, a reasonable conclusion would be that its explanation would probably lie outside the categories of chance and cartographic error. Three pairs of maps made from relatively independent data are not likely to produce a consistent pattern of internal correspondence. The periods chosen were dictated by the availability of data. The U.S. Census first enumerated the category of rural farm population density in 1930. Consequently, isarithmic maps of rural farm population density were prepared for 1930, 1940, and 1950, with a standard interval of two persons per square mile (Figs. 3a, 4a, and 5a).[11]

Each population density surface should, of course, be correlated with a precipitation map based upon records of a previous period of given length. Because of rather rigid limitations placed upon the selection of the stations to be used, and because climatic data have not been gathered for a long period at many stations, it was necessary to limit rather strictly the period for which the averages of annual precipitation would be obtained. After careful consideration it was decided that a twenty-year period was the maximum attainable. Accordingly, isarithmie maps of average annual precipitation with an interval of two inches were prepared for the periods 1910–29, 1920–39, and 1930–49 (Fig. 3b, 4b, and 5b). Each is shown alongside the population density map with which it was compared.

DETERMINING THE CORRESPONDENCE

As was implied earlier, the distribution of the internal correspondence for each pair of maps may be obtained by deriving the coefficients of correlation for subsections of the mapped area. These then serve as control-point values permitting the construction of an isarithmic map showing the degree to which the variations on one map correspond to the variations on the other. This procedure requires a number of important interrelated decisions, namely: (1) the manner by which the requisite paired data are to be obtained from the maps; (2) the determination of the sizes of the unit areas for which to obtain the paired data; (3) the selection of the number of pairs to be used in calculating the coefficients of correlation; and (4) the spatial organization of the areas to be represented by the *n* pairs selected. There has been little or no study of the first three problems as they relate to statistical–cartographic procedures, particularly as to how

a variation in the procedures will affect the results.

The data from which the maps were made consist of two kinds, unit-area (population) and point (precipitation). In order to obviate any sampling difficulties, the entire statistical population was utilized by obtaining average values for each class of data for a series of artificially created, geometrically arranged unit areas on each map. Ideally, the average value for a unit area would be obtained in the

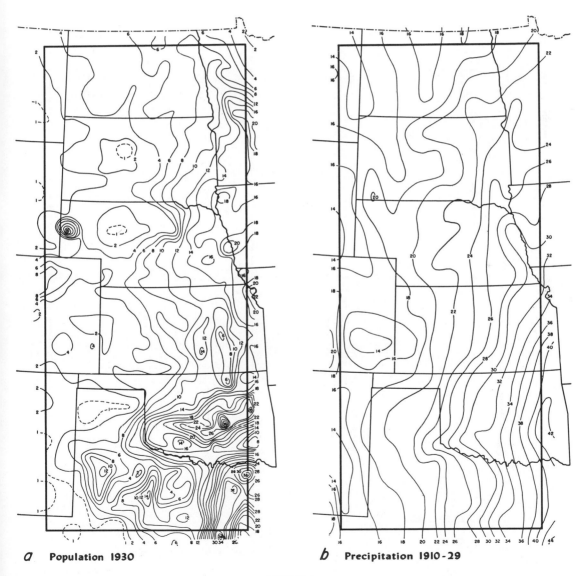

a   Population 1930   *b*   Precipitation 1910-29

FIGURE 3

standard manner one obtains mean elevation from a contour map, but in this case it was done by estimation.[12]

Because each class of data had been transformed to the form of a continuous variable, namely, an isarithmic map, one might deduce that the size of the uniform unit areas is immaterial. Within limits this may be valid, but only for a phenomenon which is in fact a continuous variable, such as precipitation; it probably cannot be applied to one which is not. Consequently, the use of density of

population as one of the variables apparently imposes the restriction that one should not attempt to obtain data from the map at a level of detail much greater than that which was used in preparing it. It was therefore decided to employ unit areas of a size equal to the average of all the counties contained in, or partially inside, the chosen region. The 612 counties have a total area close to 651,000 square miles, thus prescribing an average of 1064 square miles.

Although the size of the unit areas to be

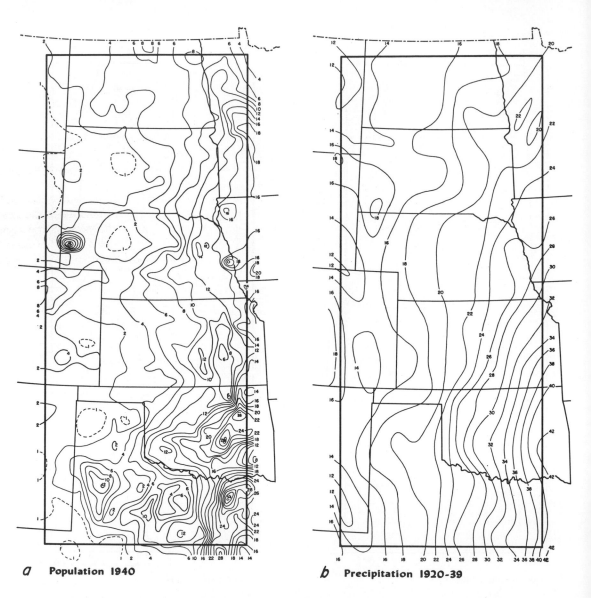

a **Population 1940**

b **Precipitation 1920-39**

FIGURE 4

used to obtain the paired data was thus easily determined, the selection of the number (n) to be used to calculate each correlation coefficient (r) and the arrangement of the control points for mapping r-values were not. With the size of unit area specified, it is apparent that as n increases, the number of r-values decreases. A too-small n will produce r-values of little significance, while a too-small number of r-values over the area will result in a correspondence map of little significance. Furthermore, the n-unit areas must be spatially arranged so that the r-values derived therefrom will be reasonably representative of the zones to which they refer. The entire plan had to be a sort of nesting arrangement consisting of the one large rectangular Great Plains area, containing a series of smaller areas (to which each r-value referred), and each of these containing a series (n) of smaller unit areas, each of the last to have an area of 1064 square miles.

After some experimentation, the mapped area was divided into forty subrectangles, each con-

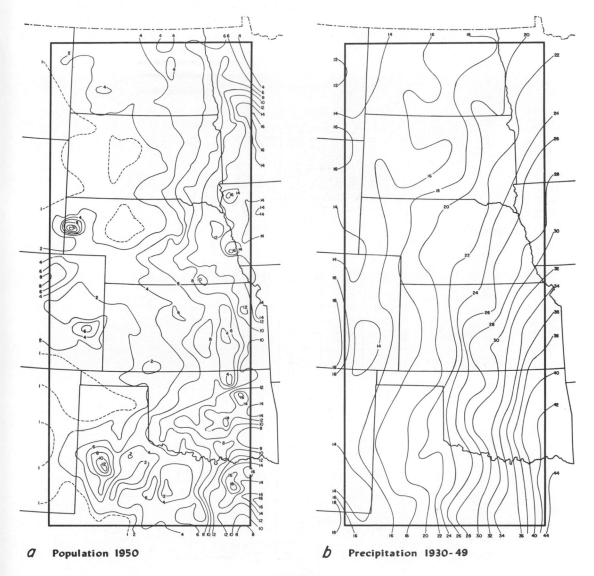

a   **Population 1950**   *b*   **Precipitation 1930-49**

FIGURE 5

taining sixteen unit areas of the prescribed size (Fig. 6). The larger rectangles are offset in adjacent columns so that the forty centers (the control point positions for the *r*-values) are triangularly arranged, thus eliminating the problem of alternative choice when locating isarithms of correspondence. Although the plan required overlapping the edge of the mapped area, this created no problem, since the data had been purposely mapped in the peripheral zone.[13]

The grid system of 640 small unit area rectangles (Fig. 6) was registered with each of the isarithmic maps in turn, and the average value of a variable within each unit area determined. The paired values were punched on cards, and the standard correlation routine of the IBM 650 was used to obtain values of *r*.[14] After these had been plotted at the centers of the forty rectangles, the "correlation surface" so defined was delineated by isarithms located by linear interpolation drawn with an interval of 0.2 within the possible range of *r*, $+1.0$ to -1.0.[15]

THE RESULTS

The mapped correlation data (Figs. 7*a*, *b* and 8*a*) show the degree to which the character of the undulations on the population density maps corresponds to those on the maps of

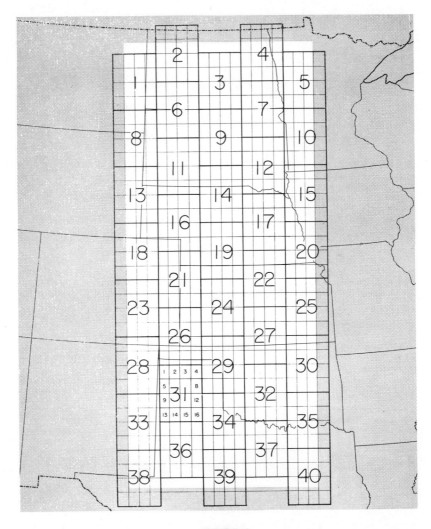

FIGURE 6

annual precipitation. Even a glance at these maps reveals a striking similarity in their patterns of internal correspondence. In fact, if one were in turn to subject these isarithmic maps to the same process that produced them, a remarkably uniform surface of high positive correlation would result, indicating a strong persistence of the pattern of correspondence that had developed by 1930. There are a few areas of low persistence, notably in the marginal sections, but these are clearly excepetions to the general character of the maps.

The similarity of the maps suggests that neither chance nor cartographic error is likely to have played a great part in producing the patterns. On the other hand, neither of these factors can be ruled out unless there are sound geographical reasons to account for the pattern. Although the author is not a student of this area, and therefore must defer to others, nevertheless the general pattern does not appear to be the geographical absurdity it would probably be if it were caused primarily by chance or error. To examine this briefly,

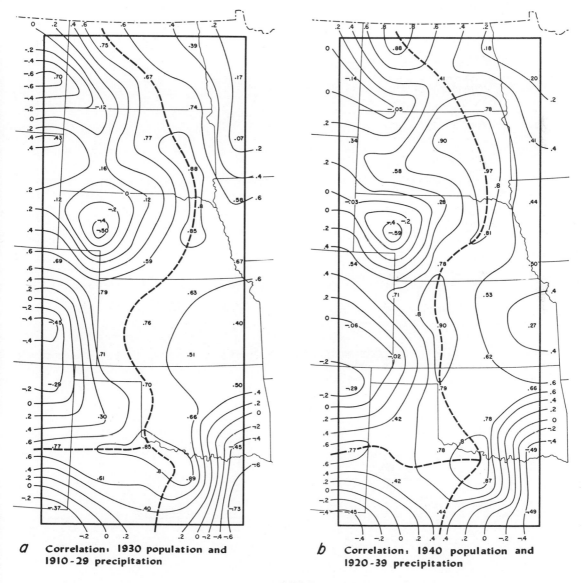

a Correlation: 1930 population and 1910-29 precipitation

b Correlation: 1940 population and 1920-39 precipitation

FIGURE 7

consider the character of the correspondence surfaces (Figs. 7a, b and 8a).

The isarithms of correspondence portray an arrangement of "rises" and "hollows" of positive and negative correlation values with considerable intermediate areas of low correspondence. These are not haphazardly located, however, for through the central and northern portions of all three maps there exists an unbroken, sinuous ridge of high positive correlation. In the southern section it becomes

less pronounced and connects with a prominent east-west ridge that extends across northwest Texas and adjacent New Mexico. On individual maps a number of other spurs can also be recognized; but these are lower in elevation, of lesser extent, and they do not persist clearly from one period to the next. The central ridge is unquestionably the dominant feature in the map area. Only in the southern section does this north-south backbone descend to an elevation as low as +.40; for the remainder

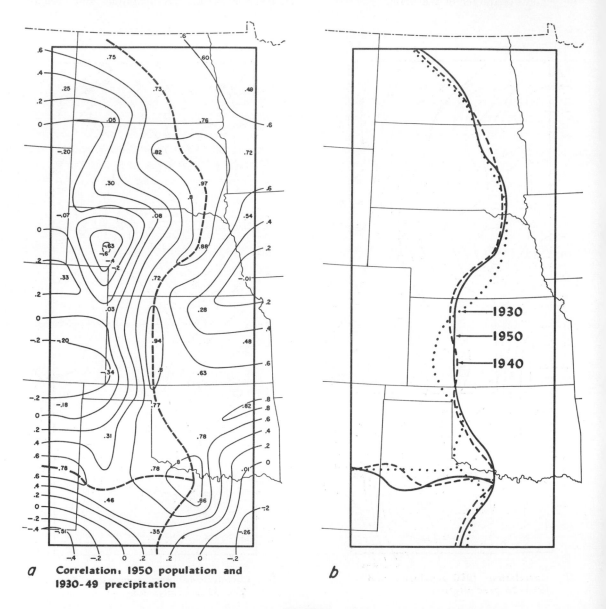

a   Correlation: 1950 population and 1930-49 precipitation

b

FIGURE 8

of its length on each map it maintains an average altitude of well over $+.70$, and commonly rises much above $+.80$. (The probability of such correlation coefficients occurring by chance is remote.) The central ridge of high correspondence forms a definite divide separating the consistently lower and less organized correspondence values on the eastern and western margins. On each map the position of the crest of this north-south ridge was located and is shown as a dashed line (Figs. 7a, b and 8a).[16]

Two characteristics of the north–south ridge are notable: first, the remarkable coincidence of its positions at the three census periods; and second, its general relation to the dry–humid transition zone in the Great Plains, especially its westward bend in the north.

When the three positions of the crests are plotted together, they fall almost on top of one another (Fig. 8b). It takes an unusual amount of skepticism to suggest that such a contiguity, derived from the kinds of data employed, does not have some rational explanation. To be sure, its diagnosis may be as complex a problem as one wishes to make it. It could easily involve all the physical and cultural influences that might in any way affect the distribution of the special census category of rural farm population. Nevertheless, the continuity of the correspondence ridge, the contiguity of its position at the three periods, and its clearly defined sweep to the northwest in the Dakotas suggest the possibility that, in addition to the local effects of many unique factors, there may exist some general relationship that operates throughout this entire area, especially to the north of Texas.

Clearly the band of higher correspondence embraces a major portion of the transition zone between humid and dry that occurs in the Great Plains, including the westward curve in the north. It seems quite reasonable to this author that in this region the total farm population might in general tend to show a close correspondence with differences in precipitation wherever precipitation amounts approach the threshold of effectiveness. Certainly on the western side of the map area the average annual precipitation is sufficiently meager and ineffective as a locational factor to the extent that irrigation and other elements could well play a more important role. On the eastern side the converse, in terms of precipitation amounts, might well result in a similar effect, namely, a lack of correspondence between precipitation and population variations. The net effect would be a higher degree of correspondence between. Of course no suggestion is made that such a set of conditions would obtain in all dry–humid transition areas. Nevertheless, where a clear and consistent pattern of correspondence between maps of these two phenomena is observed, such a simple unifying concept comes to mind immediately.[17]

CONCLUSION

The author concludes that the technique of mapping the correspondence of isarithmic maps is likely to be a useful tool in geographical research. By combining standard statistical and cartographic methods it can be accomplished with relative case. To insure that the result will be as free of cartographic error and chance effects as is possible, considerable care must be taken in preparing the maps to be compared, especially in terms of control distribution. The difficulty of obtaining reliable cartographic data for the statistical computations suggests that the correspondence analysis cannot at present by extended to more than two original maps at a time.

FOOTNOTES

[1] A. H. Robinson, "The Cartographic Representation of the Statistical Surface," *International Yearbook of Cartography*, **1** (1961), 53–63; E. Imhof, "Isolineankarten," *ibid.*, 64–98.

[2] A. H. Robinson and R. A. Bryson, "A Method for Describing Quantitatively the Correspondence of Geographical Distributions," *Annals of the Association of American Geographers*, **47** (1957), 379–391.

[3] E. N. Thomas, *Maps of Residuals from Regression: Their Characteristics and Uses in Geographic Research*, pp. 326–352; A. H. Robinson, J. B. Lindberg, and L. W. Brinkman, "A Correlation and Regression Analysis Applied to Rural Farm Population Densities in the Great Plains," pp. 290–300.

[4] A. H. Robinson and L. Caroe, "Some Techniques of Generalization and Graphic Analysis of the Character and Relation of Geographical Distribution" (Evanston: Dept. of Geography, Northwestern Univ., 1967).

[5] Several such analyses with comparable data have been completed at various times and have each produced values of r in the vicinity of $+0.8$ or more. See Robinson and Bryson, *op. cit.*

[6] *Ibid.*

[7] In this sense, one must think of cartographic correspondence as a relationship that has the same sort of variation as has the correlation coefficient. Therefore, assuming that there are gradients between horizontal and vertical in the same area on each map, then neither differences in the numbers of isarithms employed per units map distance nor differences in the absolute magnitudes of the gradients have any bearing. So far as it has been analyzed to the present, cartographic correspondence in this sense is primarily a function of the directions of the gradients.

[8] H. H. McCarty and N. E. Salisbury, *Visual Comparison of Isopleth Maps as a Means of Determining Correlations Between Spatially Distributed Phenomena*, State University of Iowa, Department of Geography, Monograph No. 3 (1961).

[9] As suggested earlier, the correspondence of two three-dimensional surfaces depends basically upon (*a*), the relation between the directions of the two gradients. The measurement of correlation, however, is also influenced by (*b*), the amount of variance of each surface. If (*a*) is held constant, an increase in (*b*) will decrease the measured correlation. Variation of (*b*) in an isarithmic map can occur not only because of such real variations in the phenomenon, but because of regional differences in the density of control points. Consequently, if one is measuring correspondence between maps, the latter would act as a bias, and its influence must be reduced as far as practicable.

[10] The stations were selected by careful analysis of the coverage included in U.S. Weather Bureau, *Bulletin W: Climatic Summary of the United States*. In a few instances where there was a choice of stations within a rectangle, it was made on several bases, with the general aim being quality, continuity of record, and uniformity of control spacing. Since a record covering forty years was desired, choices were not often available. In some instances, breaks in the record or extensions back to 1910 had to be filled in from nearby stations.

[11] Each density value was carried to one decimal place. The total land area of the county, as determined for the 1940 census corrected for boundary differences at the times of the 1930 and 1950 censuses, was employed. The areas of incorporated places, etc., were not subtracted from the total land area figure, since it was felt such a refinement would have had little effect on the correspondence maps, which were the ultimate objective.

[12] Naturally estimation will produce error. The coefficient of correlation is herein derived from mapped data, and therefore cannot be very precise for obvious reasons. Consequently, the coefficients have somewhat more relative than absolute validity, and for this reason a small amount of error is not of great concern. Subsequently, a number of small trials have revealed that results obtained by estimation by various individuals (who know how to read isarithmic maps) are closely consistent.

Another observation is in order. The coefficient of correlation here being used is based upon two variables, but there is no theoretical reason why one could not obtain the correspondence among three or more maps by means of multiple correlation methods. There is, however, a good practical reason. Isarithmic maps as yet contain an unknown amount of error, and to compare only two without great care is risky; to attempt three or more would require uncommon faith.

[13] The process of settling upon the arrangement, shapes, and nesting of the rectangles was greatly facilitated by a simple nomograph, which showed the various combinations of multipliers which would produce a product of 1064, the number of square miles to be contained in each small unit area. The entire hierarchy was determined with a minimum of adjustment by constructing the nomograph on a sheet of graph paper and combining the numerical scales with an assumed scale of miles.

[14] The machine computation was done in the Numerical Analysis Laboratory of the University of Wisconsin.

[15] J. K. Rose has suggested the use of the term "*isocorrelates*" as appropriate for the specific name of such isarithms ("Corn Yields and Climate in the Corn Belt," *Geographical Review*, **26** [1936], 88–102). In general, I take the view that no useful purpose is served by differentiating the statistical surfaces that may be delineated by isarithms and thus endlessly proliferating our technical vocabulary. See J. L. M. Gulley and K. A. Sinnhuber, "Isokartographie," *Kartographische Nachrichten*, **11** (1961), 89–99; also W. Horn, "Die Geschichte der Isarithmenkarten," *Petermann's Geographische Mitteilungen*, **103** (1959), 225–232.

The statistical qualities of data from which one may infer isarithmic maps may vary in many ways, but isarithms are isarithms.

[16] Where the position of the crest is doubtful, a location was determined as carefully as possible by drawing smooth, curved, gradient lines normal to the isarithms in the fashion one would construct hachures from a contour map.

[17] The discrepancy in Kansas and Oklahoma of the 1930 crest (Fig. 8*b*) from the other two suggests that in 1930 the distribution of rural farm population may have been "out of line," so to speak, with the precipitation. Presumably, if this were so, the effects of the drought of the thirties would have been especially severe to the population of these areas.

4

REGIONAL AND LOCAL COMPONENTS IN THE DISTRIBUTION OF FORESTED AREAS IN SOUTHEAST BRAZIL: A MULTIVARIATE APPROACH

PETER HAGGETT

There are few sins in which geographers indulge with more relish than generalizing our field findings at a local level over the whole of an adjacent region. The writer was made keenly aware of this commission in returning in 1962 to travel more widely over the southeastern part of Brazil. Speculations on the persistence of forested zones based on localized field work in the Taubaté area were only partly sustained when the survey was extended, via sampling methods, over an adjacent area some hundreds of times larger.[1]

In this paper the results of a localized study based on a small, 100 square kilometer area are reported alongside those of a wider regional study. It is shown that not only is the distribution different at the two levels, but that the appropriate pattern of study changes in sympathy. Data available at one level are unobtainable at another, levels of measurement possible at one level are too fine at another, and statistical tests appropriate at one level are inapplicable at another.

FORESTED AREAS IN SOUTHEASTERN BRAZIL

The pattern which is studied in both parts of this paper is that of forest distribution. It is ironic that in a country which has the largest remaining stands of tropical timbers in the world, the Southeast of Brazil, should be a zone of timber shortage. The present forest pattern is largely residual, in the sense that the stands represent the fraction still remaining after four centuries of persistent attack. James has shown for eastern Brazil how the westward advance of Portuguese settlement from the Atlantic coast was marked by a trail of forest clearing

Reprinted from *Geographical Journal*, **130** (1964), 365–377, by permission of the author and editor.

and burning.[2] Two recent studies of the original vegetation of the Southeast have shown from botanical evidence, from place names, and from eighteenth- and nineteenth-century travel records both the limits of the main vegetation zones and something of the timing of the onslaught on the forest.[3] It is clear that in the first centuries of Portuguese occupation the effect on the forest area in the Southeast was slight. Although the first settlement, São Vicente, was established as early as 1532, population growth was slow. The great centers of Brazilian wealth lay north and northwest, in Bahia and Minas Gerais, and by 1800 population densities in the two southeastern states of Rio de Janeiro and São Paulo probably did not exceed five inhabitants per square mile.[4]

The nineteenth century brought dramatic changes in the forest area of the Southeast. The sweep of the coffee-growing areas through the Paraíba valley has been examined elsewhere.[5] Certainly its effect on the area of forest was immediate and drastic. Stein has recounted an 1878 description of the felling process by Lacerdo Werncek: ". . . the trees on a slope are weakened; . . . the cutters choose one which they calculate will bring down those below it; . . . and with a roar heard for miles one tree after another topples, a huge wave of trees crashing to the ground."[6] The Mineiro graziers who followed in the wake of the coffee plantations insured that land so cleared would generally remain unforested. Outside the coffee zones the spread of bush-fallowing peasant agriculture (the roça system) made steady, but less striking inroads on the forest area. By 1900 the gross population density of the Southeast had risen to around 120 inhabitants per square mile.

While the population of the Southeast has risen sharply in the last sixty years to give a gross density of around 500 inhabitants per square mile over the area shown in Fig. 1, the reduction in forest area over the same period has been less dramatic.[7] Most of the population increase has gone to the large cities, of which two, Rio de Janeiro and São Paulo, now are past the 3,000,000 mark, and a further seven past the 100,000 mark. Three out of four of the area's 12,000,000 population live in towns of 10,000 or greater, so that a more realistic view of rural population density based on farm returns is below 100 inhabitants per square mile.[8]

Incursions into the forested areas for roças and charcoal burning continue to rise, but against this the need of watershed protection and water supply control is being more widely recognized.[9]

LOCAL ANALYSIS: THE FORTALEZA BASIN

The Fortaleza basin is a term used by the writer to describe a 10×10 kilometer square block of country lying in Taubaté country, in eastern São Paulo (Fig. 1). This 25,000-acre tract had been used by the writer in 1959 in a study of the effects of forest clearing on sedimentation.[10] It lies at the junction of two of Hueck's forest facies, the Subtropischer Wald and the Halbtrockenwald,[11] but most of the forest cover was removed during the height of the plantation period, 1840–80. The remaining forest remnants are heavily thinned and degraded remnants of the original forests, which are periodically used for charocal burning and local timber needs. They make up about one-seventh of the total land area in the Fortaleza basin and lie in a series of discrete stands. Analysis of the stands from the air photographs showed that there were about thirty-six stands of ten acres or more in extent, with the largest some 600 acres in area. Stand boundaries were plotted from the 1:25,000 photographs[12] and transferred to base maps at similar scales made available by the Serviço do Vale do Paraíba, at Taubaté.

FACTORS ASSOCIATED WITH LOCAL FOREST PERSISTENCE

Clearly the forest cover of the Fortaleza basin was much modified by nineteenth-century agriculture. In drawing up a short list of factors modifying the pattern, we should then certainly expect them to be linked in an inverse way with the agricultural possibilities of the area; we might expect land with "good soils" to be cleared, those with "poor soils" to be left undisturbed, and so on. Arguing in this way, four major factors were recognizable. They are designated here by A, B, C, and D.

The first factor, terrain (A), was readily identified. There is a very marked land form contrast in the basin between the flat, alluvium-filled bottomlands (the varzeas) and the steeply sloping hills (the morros) between them. The hills of crystalline rocks, with micaschists and

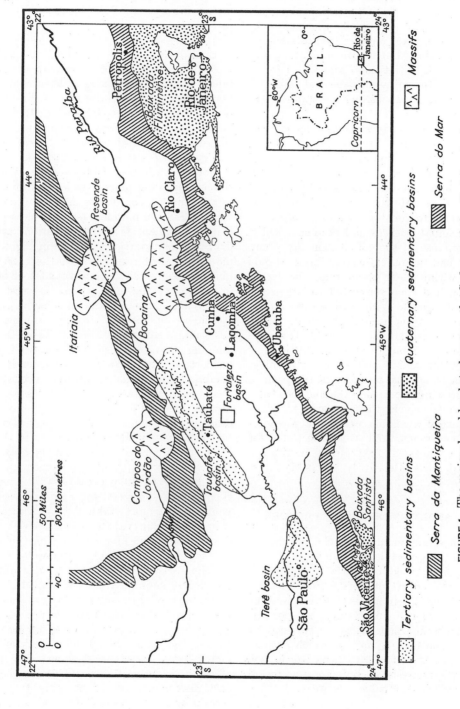

FIGURE 1. The regional and local study areas: the *Sudeste* and the *Fortaleza* basin

Legend:

- Tertiary sedimentary basins
- Serra da Mantiqueira
- Quaternary sedimentary basins
- Serra do Mar
- Massifs
- Serra do Mar (hatched) — the *Fortaleza* basin

granite gneisses predominating, rise to 400–500 feet above the flood plains, with steep slopes up to 80 per cent. Terrain is closely linked to the second factor, soils (*B*), which arise with both catena position and with basement rock. Detailed soil maps exist only for the sedimentary parts of the basin,[13] but field examination suggested some differentiation in amount of forest cover between the micaschist-derived soils and those on the other rocks, where stands were less extensive.

The second two factors, farm size (*C*) and farm access (*D*), are directly linked to the settlement history of the area in the *época de café*. Inspection on the ground of the farm property boundaries, often marked by bamboo "hedges," suggested that the medium-sized holdings were frequently "rumps" left over when the original *fazendas* had been subdivided after the collapse of the coffee economy. They commonly had more extensive forest stands remaining within their areas than the larger farms which had been converted to large-scale livestock enterprises. With farm access it was arguable that farms nearer the main trails through the area, notably the old Taubaté–Ubatuba mule trail, might retain slightly heavier forest cover for felling and charcoal burning. For an area which lay squarely in the path of the coffee-growing wave along the southern bank of the Paraíba river, the pressure to plant coffee on every available part of a *fazenda*'s land was enormous, and we must look for equally strong motives to explain the persistence of uncleared areas. Relatively accessible forest reserves provide such a motive.[14]

VARIANCE ANALYSIS OF LOCAL FACTORS

The method used in analyzing the four factors identified in the Fortaleza basin is that of a factorial design based on variance analysis.[15] To explore the effects of each factor, all combinations of the different factor levels must be examined in order to understand the possible ways in which each factor may be modified by variation in the others, e.g., in which accessibility may be modified by variation in soil types. In this analysis, each factor was tested at two levels. The actual levels were:

A (1, *a*): terrain; slopes below and above 5°
B (1, *b*): soils; other soils and micaschist soils

C (1, *c*): farm size; large and medium-sized holdings
D(1, *d*): farm accessibility; beyond and within two kilometers of the compacted dirt roads through the area.

Boundaries for each of the four levels were plotted on a 1 : 10,000 base map of the Fortaleza basin. The crossing and recrossing of the boundaries gave over 100 sectors (Fig. 2). Each of these sectors was classified in terms of the factor combination into sixteen types: Type I, through *a*, *b*, *c*, *d*, *ab*, *ac*, *ad*, *bc*, *bd*, *cd*, *abc*, *abd*, *bcd*, *acd*, *abcd*, as shown in Table 1.

For each of these factor-combination types, sixteen sampling plots were located on the map using random coordinate methods to give a total of 256 sample plots (sixteen plots for each of the sixteen factor-combination types of land).[16] Their location is shown in Fig. 2. These plots were then transferred to the 1 : 25,000 air photographs as circles equivalent to 2.50 acres in area and the proportion of forest within the circle calculated under an enlarged graticule.

The results of this analysis are set out in a standard summary form in Table 2. In examining the table, it should be noticed that the proportion of forested area in each factor-combination type is not given in a conventional form, as percentage of the total area, but in angular units. Percentage data are notoriously difficult to accommodate in statistical analysis, and particularly difficult when, as in this case, the percentage values are largely drawn from the lower extremes of the percentage range, i.e., from 0 to 30 per cent. It was necessary therefore to convert the original percentage values into a more stable form by transforming it into angular values of between 0 and 90 degrees via a standard conversion table.[17] The case for this conversion has been well established for the earth sciences, and the relevant issues are clearly summarized by Krumbein.[18]

Analysis of the results of Table 2 was carried out using a standard Yates 2^n procedure, and the findings are shown in Table 3.[19] In the first part of the table, the effects of each individual factor [are] assessed and shown as a positive effect in degrees. It is worth noting that while each factor has an effect, only two factors, terrain and farm accessibility, are shown to be significant in a statistical sense at the 95 per cent confidence level. One interesting point

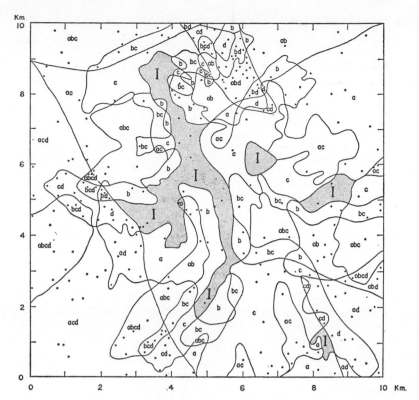

FIGURE 2. *Fortaleza* basin: location of sampling points and of factor-combination regions

TABLE 1

Fortaleza Basin; derivation of factor-combination regions

Factor A Terrain	Factor B Soils	Factor C Farm size	Factor D Farm accessibility
Fortaleza Basin {			
a Slopes above 5° {	ab Micaschist — {	abc Medium —— {	abcd Within 2 km. abc Beyond 2 km.
		ab Large ——— {	abd ditto ab
	a Others ——— {	ac ——— {	acd ditto ac
		ditto	
		a ——— {	ad ditto a
I Slopes below 5° {	b ——— {	bc ——— {	bcd ditto bc
		ditto	
		b ——— {	bd ditto b
	ditto		
	I ——— {	c ——— {	cd ditto c
		ditto	
		I ——— {	d ditto I

TABLE 2

Fortaleza Basin: Summary table of forest cover under four-factor analysis*

		FARM ACCESS (D):			
		Poor (I)		Good (d)	
		Farm size (C):		Farm size (C):	
Terrain (A):	Soils (B):	Large (I)	Medium (c)	Large (I)	Medium (c)
Lower slopes (I)	Others (I)	12.9 (I)	23.6 (c)	19.4 (d)	10.0 (cd)
	Micaschist (b)	8.1 (b)	22.1 (bc)	30.1 (bd)	22.0 (bcd)
Upper slopes (a)	Others (I)	24.4 (a)	30.0 (ac)	31.3 (ad)	17.5 (acd)
	Micaschist (b)	8.2 (ab)	23.6 (abc)	37.5 (abd)	54.9 (abcd)

* Proportion of forest cover given in degrees.

TABLE 3

Fortaleza Basin: Results of multiple-variance analysis of factor effects on forest cover

Nature of the effect	Source	Amount of the effect angular units	F-ratio	Conventional significance level
MAIN FACTORS:				
	Terrain (A)	+9.8	9.3	Probably significant*
	Soils (B)	+4.7	1.6	Not significant
	Farm size (C)	+4.0	1.2	Not significant
	Farm access (D)	+8.7	8.2	Probably significant*
INTERACTIONS:				
	BD (soils × farm size)		10.7	Probably significant*
	Other interactions between pairs		1.8	Not significant
	Higher order interactions (ABC, ABD, . . . ABCD)	—	—	—

* 95 per cent confidence level.

from the second part of the table is the strong interaction between soils and farm accessibility (*BD*). It suggests that the accessible farms tend to be located in areas of micaschist-derived soils, and there may thus be a "hidden" soil factor coming into the high apparent effect of accessibility on forest cover.

REGIONAL ANALYSIS: THE SUDESTE

For the second part of the study, the scale of inquiry was raised to include a major part of southeast Brazil. The area selected, here termed the *Sudeste*, forms a rectangular shaped area demarcated by the meridians of 43° and 47° W and by the parallels of 22° and 24° S (Fig. 1). It covers a land area of about 24,000 square miles, similar to the American state of West Virginia, and some 600 times as large as the local study area: the Fortaleza basin.

PROBLEMS OF REGIONAL DATA

Reconstruction of the present residual pattern of forest in the Sudeste is possible, at least theoretically, in a number of ways. An original attempt was made to use air photographs for this purpose, arranging them in a two-stage stratified sampling method.[20] This proved useful in part, but failed to give a thoroughly reliable picture. Air photographs of the area derived from a number of organizations (ranging from national survey companies like Cruzeiro do Sul S.A. through to foreign organizations, like the United States Air Force) and ranged in scale, accuracy, and age (1944–62) over too wide a range to form the basis of a comprehensive regional survey. Use was therefore made of available statistical returns collected in the Census of Agriculture of July I, 1950.[21]

Like all government surveys, the data in the 1950 census is not entirely satisfactory for geographical analysis. Two problems of particular importance were those of coverage and of definition. Coverage was restricted to those agricultural holdings returning the *questionário geral*, and as Romariz has pointed out for another Brazilian area, Paraná, these holdings may account for varying proportions of the total land surface.[22] In the Sudeste, the highly urbanized areas of São Paulo county and the then Federal District of Rio de Janeiro (now the state of Guanabara) were omitted from the survey. Of the remaining part of the Sudeste, the total area for which returns were made under the 1950 Agriculture Census was 76 per cent of the land area. If allowance is made for urban areas, roadways, etc., it is clear that the bulk of the area is represented.

The second problem, definition, revolves around the term "forest." In the section of the July 1st questionaire concerned with land use, Question 19 asks for the respondent to state the "area of woods and natural forests" (*área das matas e florestas naturais*). Reforested areas are specifically excluded and recorded in the following question. So also are second-growth forests (*capoeiras*), which are returned under the general category of "unproductive and uncultivated lands." While it seems clear that much will depend on the occupier's ability to distinguish forests from old secondary forest, an ability on which Sternberg has thrown some doubt,[23] there is a valid attempt in the census to define clearly and record separately the natural forest areas.

A further general problem in handling the 1950 census material lies in the areal collecting units for which information is made available. State volumes are published which break down the material to the level of the "county" (*município*). Since there are some 126 counties (excluding the Rio de Janeiro and São Paulo urban areas), this would have provided a fine enough grid for statistical analysis at the regional level were it not for the variability in the size of county. These range from counties like Cunha, with an area of 500 square miles (about the size of a small English county), down to units scarcely larger than a London borough. This intense variability between areal units has been the subject of extensive analyses by McCarty, Hook, and Knos and by Duncan, Cuzzort, and Duncan.[24] Both studies agree that variations in the size of collecting area cause fluctuations in the reliability of the results of statistical analysis sufficiently grave to cast doubts on the validity of statistical analysis. It is easier to diagnose this problem than to suggest solutions. Robinson, Lindberg, and Brinkman have used a method of extending regular hexagons over the irregular network of counties, and Krumbein has shown that more sophisticated trend-surface methods may be of help.[25] The solution used here is the relatively simple one suggested by Coppock, that of combining many small, irregularly sized units into fewer, larger units of more uniform size.[26] The success of the method clearly depends on whether the gains in reliability are sufficiently great to offset the losses in detail as the smaller units are merged into larger aggregates. By measuring the variability between the area of the counties a statistical index, the coefficient of variation, it is possible to plot this variability against the number of units used.[27] By working in this way, the original 126 counties were merged into twenty-four "supercounties." As Table 4 shows, these super counties are about five times as large as the original counties, but are much less variable in size. In this case, the loss of detail of some 81 per cent was more than offset by an 89 per cent reduction in the variability of the areas.

TABLE 4

Sudeste: Comparison of original and aggregated county areas

Collecting unit	Number of units	Mean area (square miles)	Coefficient of variation
County (*Município*)	126	133.2	74.20
'Super County'	24	699.1	7.91

REGIONAL DISTRIBUTION OF FORESTED AREAS

The distribution of forested areas based on the 1950 census is shown in Fig. 3. This map uses a technique developed by Robinson and

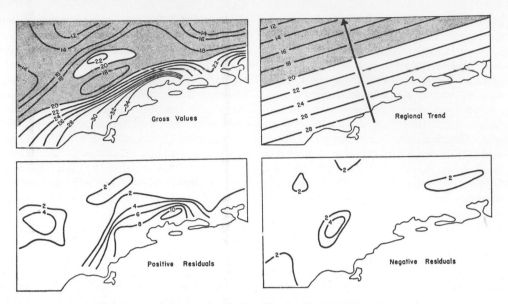

FIGURE 3.   *Sudeste*: forest distribution in the regional area

Caroe to break down the original contour map of forest cover into (1) the regional trend and (2) anomaly areas, which either project above this, the positive residuals, or fall below it, the negative residuals.[28] The contours on the first map are drawn at 5° intervals where the original percentage data for each of the super-counties have been converted into angular units. The arguments for making this conversion have already been discussed for the local study above and apply with equal force in the regional case.

The general trend shown by the forest-distribution map is that the forest cover falls off inland, dipping, according to the regional trend, roughly orthogonally to the coastline. Areas which rise above this plane are notably parts of the coastal escarpment of the Serra do Mar and the second escarpment of the Serra da Mantiqueira. "Lows" in the pattern occur in the Taubaté basin and gain in the northwest part of the Paulista sections of the Sudeste.

FACTORS ASSOCIATED WITH REGIONAL FOREST PERSISTENCE

Examination of the factors used in the Fortaleza basin suggested that similar arguments might be applied at the regional level. However, lack of comparable data for farm size and accessibility, and the restriction of soil surveys to the state of Rio de Janeiro[29] and São Paulo made this impracticable.[30] The five

factors chosen are therefore only roughly comparable with those used at the local level.

The first factor, terrain, was readily identified. The Sudeste is an area in which the alteration of relatively flat surfaces and steep escarpments is strongly marked (Fig. I). Whether these escarps should be associated with erosional levels as suggested by King, or with tectonic movements, as argued by Ruellan, is peripheral to our argument;[31] to the early colonist or railroad constructor the Serra do Mar and the Serra da Mantiqueira were 3000-feet barriers that needed crossing in the least costly manner. To reduce complex land forms to simple comparative indices is no easy task, and here we have to compromise between the known complexity of the land surface and a simple average measure. The *terrain index* (X_1) used here was based on the mean elevation of the supercounty multiplied by standard deviation, where height values were read from available 1 : 100,000 or 1 : 400,000 maps on a five-mile coordinate grid. It is a rough measure of both the height and the ruggedness of the country, and as such we should expect a direct relationship, i.e., the higher the index, the greater the proportion of forest.

The second factor, settlement spacing, is linked to the settlement history of the area. Most of the county towns (*sedes municipais*) were founded between 1550 and 1850; those near the coast and along the colonist trails earlier, those inland and away from these routes later. Certain parts of the Sudeste, notably in the Baixada Fluminense, the Paraíba valley, and around São Paulo are particularly rich in such settlements; in other areas they are thinly scattered. On the grounds that the forested areas tend to lie, like the forested waste of medieval England, on the margins between settlements, we might expect the lightly settled areas to be more thickly wooded. The *settlement spacing index* (X_2) was calculated from the mean distance in kilometers between the county towns in each supercounty.

The third factor, population density, is clearly related to the second as a reflection of the settlement possibilities of an area. The *rural population density index* (X_3) was calculated from the 1950 Census of Agriculture and is composed of the total area for which agricultural returns were made for the supercounty divided by the total occupied persons (*pessoal occupado*) for the same area. As such it is a measure of the density of farm population rather than total population. As rural population density increases, we might expect the forest area to decrease, and hence the relationship postulated is an inverse one.

The fourth factor, forest density, is included in an attempt to introduce some notion of the known variety of forest cover in the Sudeste into the analysis.[32] Direct classification on the lines of Hueck's divisions did not provide a level of measurement high enough to allow its use as multivariate statistical analysis. Fortunately Langbein and Schumm have shown that a direct relationship exists between annual precipitation in inches and a gross measure of forest density, vegetation weight in pounds per acre.[33] By using a more refined index of precipitation effectiveness for southeastern Brazil,

that of Setzer's P-E index, it was possible to derive a substitute *forest density index* (X_4) and measure its mean value for each supercounty.[34] A direct relationship is postulated between this index and the persistence of forest cover on the grounds that very heavily forested areas were more difficult to clear and to penetrate than the more lightly forested areas on the back slopes of the plateaus.

The final factor, land value, was directly calculated from estimates of land values given in the 1950 Agricultural Census to give a *land value index* (X_5). It is suggested that areas with high land values are likely to be largely cleared for intensive types of agriculture, while those with lower values are less likely to be worth the expenditure of conversion to more valuable uses, i.e., the relationship is a direct one.

REGRESSION RELATIONSHIPS: THE "EXPLAINED" ELEMENT

The average relationship between the five factors and the forest cover may be expressed as five simple regression equations or combined into a single multiple equation including the five factors.[35] This technique of deriving general relationships between patterns ("dependent variables") and possible controlling factors ("independent variables") was used over a quarter of a century ago . . .[36] and is now very widely used in the handling of geographical problems.[37] The procedures for its use are very fully described by Ezekiel and Fox and will not be repeated here.[38]

The success of the general equations in predicting the forest cover is shown in Table 5. Here the relative success of each factor in 'explaining' the distribution of forest cover in the Sudeste is shown in the column headed

TABLE 5

Sudeste: Results of regression analysis of factor effects on forest cover

Factors	Transformation	Relationship	Variance reduction (per cent)
Terrain Index (X_1)	Logarithmic	Direct	38.4
Settlement Spacing Index (X_2)	//	//	7.2
Rural Population Density Index (X_3)	//	Inverse	19.4
Forest Density Index (X_4)	//	Direct	47.5
Land Values Index (X_5)	//	Inverse	13.2

"variance reduction." If the total variation from place to place in the forest cover is reduced to an index of 100 per cent, then we can similarly express the reduction in that variation achieved by introducing our factors in percentage terms. It is clear that the forest density index and the terrain index, with values of 47 and 38 per cent, respectively, appear to be particularly important factors in determining the forest pattern.

One major difficulty of the five simple equations is that they each suggest a simple relationship, whereas we know intuitively that each factor is working as part of a complex of factors. The multiple equation allows the factors to be combined, either in pairs, or threes, or fours, or as five together. This combination (shown diagrammatically in Fig. 4) shows the improvement in predictive performance as more factors are built into the equation. With all five factors operating together, about two-thirds of forest pattern of the Sudeste is predictable.

RESIDUAL MAPS; THE "UNEXPLAINED" ELEMENT

An extremely interesting, and perhaps more easily appreciated example way of showing the results of regression analysis, residual mapping, has been proposed by Thomas and is illustrated in Fig. 5.[39] Shaded areas show those areas which are above the value they would have were they to conform exactly to the regression hypothesis. Similarly, dotted areas show negative anomalies. Indices which provide a better "fit" with the forest areas are shown with rather small highs and lows, while, conversely, rather poor fits are indicated by long zones of anomalies.

Examination of the maps of residuals (Fig. 5) shows location of areas which are either 10 per cent or more above the expected values or 10 per cent or more below the expected values, where the "expected" values are those predicted by the regression equations. Examination of the positive residuals shows that for all five single equations and for the combined five-factor equation the positive residuals are located in a strip within thirty miles of the coast. Within this coastal strip, certain hard-core areas appear and reappear on successive residual maps. The eastern part of the Serra do Mar in the state of São Paulo is one such area; the lowlands around Guanabara Bay another. It is interesting that when all five factors are combined, the area of positive residuals shrinks

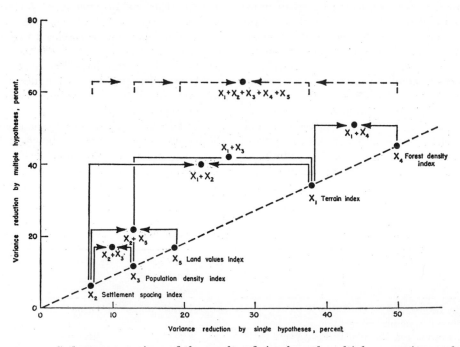

FIGURE 4. *Sudeste*: comparison of the results of simple and multiple regression analysis on forest distribution

to two small elliptical "highs," each about twenty miles by ten miles along their major and minor axes, respectively, and centered on Lagoinha and Rio Claro, respectively.

Examination of the negative residuals shows a similar pattern of concentration, with in this case the location being shifted to the interior margins of the area. Two important areas of recurring concentration stand out. First, the northwestern corner of the São Paulo State part of the Sudeste; second, the lower part of the Paraíba Valley and the adjacent parts of Minas Gerais State. The areas are broken by the high ground of the second escarpment, the Serra da Mantiqueira, and are less stable in area than the positive residuals. The five-factor analysis left only one residual "low" in the second of the two areas centered as a forty-mile

deep wedge thrusting southwest toward Itatiaia.

Both the positive and negative residual areas are probably zones where other factors not included in this analysis are operating. They are clearly just those areas which would repay the close-up "case history" type of analysis.

This paper has set out through a study of the persistence of forested areas in the Brazilian Southeast to test McCarty's thesis that "... every change in scale will bring about the statement of a new problem."[40] At the *regional* level, multiple regression analysis was used to test five alternative hypotheses, and two factors, forest density and terrain ruggedness, were shown to explain over half the distribution. At the *local* level differences in data limited both the hypotheses and the method of testing

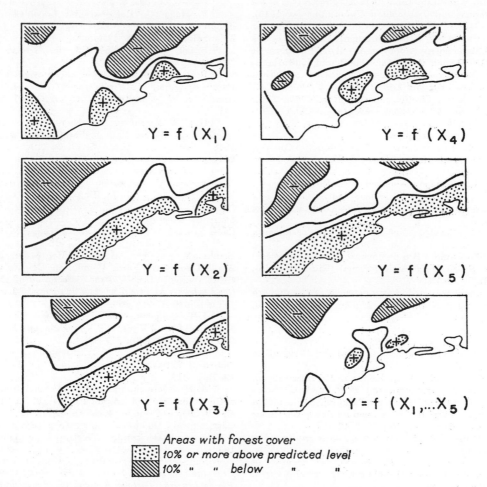

$$Y = f(X_1)$$

$$Y = f(X_4)$$

$$Y = f(X_2)$$

$$Y = f(X_5)$$

$$Y = f(X_3)$$

$$Y = f(X_1, ... X_5)$$

Areas with forest cover
10% or more above predicted level
10% "   " below   "   "

FIGURE 5. *Sudeste*: residual maps showing 'unexplained' areas after simple and multiple regression analysis

them. Multiple variance analysis suggested that terrain was again important, as also was accessibility. Differences between the results at the two levels, in particular the inversion of accessibility as a factor, tends to support McCarty's view. Perhaps the wider application that can be drawn from this survey is the need to tie all our findings in land-use studies to the size of area on which they are based.

FOOTNOTES

[1] P. Haggett, "Land Use and Sediment Yield in an Old Plantation Tract of the Serra do Mar, Brazil," *Geography*, **127** (1961), 50–62.

[2] See S. Kuznets, W. E. Moore, and J. J. Spengler, *Economic Growth: Brazil, India, Japan* (Durham: Duke University Press, 1955), p. 86; W. B. Langbein and S. A. Schumm, "Yield of Sediment in Relation to Mean Annual Precipitation," *Transactions of the American Geophysical Union*, **39** (1958), 1076–1084.

[3] D. de A. Romariz, R. Tauile, and O. Valverde, "Mapa da vegetação original das regões central, Sul e Mata do Estado de Minas Gerais," *Proceedings of the 16th International Geographical Union Congress* (1949), pp. 831–847; K. Hueck, "Wandlungen im Antlitz der Landschaft um São Paulo (Brasilien): Ein Beispiel aus den feuchten subtropen für den Anteil der Pflanzenwelt an den Problemen von Urlandschaft und Kulturlandschaft," *Forschungsund Sitzungsberichte der Akademie für Raumforschung und Landesplanung*, **5** (1958), 1–41.

[4] C. R. Boxer, *The Golden Age in Brazil, 1695–1750: Growing Pains of a Colonial Society* (Berkeley: University of California Press, 1962).

[5] Haggett, *op. cit.*, p. 50.

[6] S. J. Stein, *Vassouras: A Brazilian Coffee Country, 1850–1900* (Cambridge: Harvard University Press, 1957), p. 32.

[7] Brasil, Serviço Nacional de Recenseamento, "Sinopse preliminar do censo demografico," *VII Recenseamento Geral do Brasil: 1960* (Rio de Janeiro, 1962).

[8] Brasil, Serviço Nacional de Recenseamento, "Censo agricola 1 Julho 1950: Estados de Minas Gerais, São Paulo e Rio de Janeiro, *VI Recenseamento Geral do Brasil: 1950*, serie regional (Rio de Janeiro, 1955–56).

[9] "Guanabara pedirá providêncis Federal para garantir a águas," *Correio da Manha* (Rio de Janeiro, June 24, 1962).

[10] Haggett, *op. cit.*

[11] Hueck, *op. cit.*, pp. 10–26.

[12] [Photographs taken and owned by] Cruzeiro do Sul S. A. (1953).

[13] F. C. Verdade, L. S. Hungria, R. Russo, A. C. Nascimento, F. Grohman, and H. P. Medina, "Solos da bacia de Taubaté (Vale do Paraíba), Series monotípicas, suas propriedades genético-morfológicas, físicas e químicas," *Bragentia*, **20** (1961), 43–222.

[14] S. Milliet, *Roteiro do café e outros ensáios* (São Paulo, 1946).

[15] O. L. Davies, ed., *The Design and Analysis of Industrial Experiments* (Edinburgh: Oliver and Boyd, Ltd., 1956), p. 247.

[16] B. J. L. Berry, *Sampling, Coding and Storing Flood Plain Data*, U.S. Department of Agriculture, Handbook No. 237 (1962).

[17] R. A. Fisher and F. Yates, *Statistical Tables for Biological, Agricultural and Medical Research* (Edinburgh: Oliver and Boyd, Ltd., 1957), p. 70.

[18] W. C. Krumbein, "Trend-Surface Analysis of Contour-type Maps with Irregular Control-Point Spacing," *Geophysical Research*, **64** (1959), 823–834; Krumbein, "Comparison of Percentage and Ratio Data in Facies Mapping," *Journal of Sedimentary Petrology*, **27** (1957), 293–297.

[19] Davies, *op. cit.*, p. 283.

[20] P. Haggett, "Regional and Local Components in Land-Use Sampling: A Case Study from the Brazilian Triangulo," *Erdkunde*, **17** (1963), 108–114.

[21] Brasil, Serviço Nacional de Recenseamento, "Censo agricola."

[22] D. de A. Romariz, "A Vegetação original de bacia Paraná-Uruguai," *Condicões geográficas e aspectos geoeconómicos de bacia Paraná-Uruguai* (1955), pp. 111–131.

[23] H. O'R. Sternberg, "Enchentes e movimentos coletivos do solo no Vale do Paraíba en dezembro de 1948," *Revista Brasiliensa Geografia* (1949), pp. 233–261.

[24] H. H. McCarty, J. C. Hook, and D. S. Knos, *The Measurement of Association in Industrial Geography*, State University of Iowa, Department of Geography (1956); O. Duncan, R. P. Cuzzort, and B. Duncan, *Statistical Geography: Problems in Analyzing Areal Data* (New York: Free Press of Glencoe, Inc., 1961).

[25] A. H. Robinson, J. B. Lindberg, and L. W. Brinkman, "A Correlation and Regression Analysis Applied to Rural Farm Population Densities in the Great Plains," *Annals of the Association of American Geographers*, **51** (1961), 211–221; and Krumbein, "Trend-Surface Analysis."

[26] J. T. Coppock, "The Parish as a Geographical Statistical Unit," *Tijdschrift Voor Economisch en Sociale Geographie*, **51** (1960), 317–326.

[27] M. G. Kendall and W. R. Buckland, *Dictionary of Statistical Terms* (Edinburgh: Oliver and Boyd, Ltd., 1957), p. 313.

[28] A. H. Robinson and L. Caroe, "Some Techniques of Generalization and Graphic Analysis of the Character and Relation of Geographical Distributions," in W. L. Garrison, ed., *Quantitative Geography* (Evanston: Department of Geography, Northwestern University, 1966).

[29] Ministério da Agricultura, Commissão de Solos, *Levantamento de reconhecimento dos solos do Estado do Rio do Janeiro e Distrito Federal: Contribuicao da carta de solos do Brasil* (Rio de Janeiro, 1958).

[30] Verdade, *et. al.*, "Solos da bacia de Taubaté"; J. Setzer, *Os Solos do Estado de São Paulo* (Rio do Janeiro, 1949).

[31] L. C. King, "A Geomorfologia do Brasil oriental," *Revista Brasiliensa Geografia*, **18** (1957), 147–265; F. Ruellan, "Excursão geográfica à região do vale do Rio Paraíba e à Serra da Mantiqueira," *Panamerican Conseil Geografia*, **2** (1952), 206–251.

[32] R. M. Klein, "Aspectos fitofisionômicos de mata pluvial da costa atlântical do sul do Brasil," *Bulletin of the Argentine Botanical Society*, **9** (1961), 191–240; H.P. Veloso and R.M. Klein, "As comunidades e associações vegetais da mata pluvial do sul do Brasil," *Sellowia*, **9** (1957), 81–235; **10** (1959), 9–124.

[33] W. B. Langbein and S. A. Schumm, "Yield of Sediment in Relation to Mean Annual Precipitation," *Transactions of the American Geophysical Union*, **39** (1958), 1082.

[34] J. Setzer, "A New Formula for Precipitation Effectiveness," *Geographical Review*, **36** (1946), 246–263.

[35] These five equations are, respectively:

$$Y = \log. 3.39 + 0.31 \log X_1$$
$$Y = \log. 24.6 - 0.44 \log X_2$$
$$Y = \log. 57.3 - 0.25 \log X_3$$
$$Y = \log. 0.02 + 1.38 \log X_4$$
$$Y = \log. 34.7 - 0.21 \log X_5$$

where Y is the forest cover, X_1 the terrain index, X_2 the settlement spacing index, X_3 the rural population density, X_4 the forest density index and X_5 the land values index. The joint five-factor equation is

$$Y = \log. 0.16 + 0.16 \log X_1 - 0.07 \log X_2 - 0.08 \log X_3 + 1.10 \log X_4 + 0.05 \log X_5$$

[36] C. D. Forde, "Land and Labour in a Cross River Village, Southern Nigeria," *Geography*, **90** (1937), 35.

[37] Robinson, Lindberg, and Brinkman, *op. cit.*, p. 214.

[38] M. Ezekiel and K. A. Fox, *Methods of Correlation and Regression Analysis: Linear and Curvilinear* (New York: John Wiley & Sons, Inc., 1959).

[39] E. N. Thomas, *Maps of Residuals from Regression: Their Characteristics and Uses in Geographic Research*, State University of Iowa, Department of Geography (1960).

[40] McCarty, *et al.*, *op. cit.*, p. 16.

5

MAPS OF RESIDUALS FROM REGRESSION

EDWIN N. THOMAS

Investigations have been in progress for several years at the State University of Iowa concerning the usefulness of maps in geographic analysis. These investigations have disclosed that one of the most promising types of maps for the presentation and analysis of statistical data is the so-called *map of residuals* from regression. Some of the properties, uses, and limitations of such maps are described in the present monograph.

The purpose of this monograph is therefore to present the results of investigations into the ways in which maps may be employed most judiciously as an aid to contemporary quantitative geographic research. Situations in which the map may be readily employed are exemplified on theoretical and operational levels. The notions and suggestions embodied in this paper are presented as partial solutions to essentially traditional geographic problems. These solutions derive logically from prior development within the discipline.

The map is unquestionably the research device to which geographers have turned most frequently. It is the one tool, above all others, which is unequivocally accepted as "geographic." As Robinson states:

. . . Cartography and geography have been intimately associated. The relationship is appropriate and necessary, for neither can the geographer deal with differences from place to place on the earth without maps, nor can the cartographer map the face of the earth without an understanding of what is significant.[1]

The central position of the map in geographic research also was recognized and stressed by Hartshorne:

So important, indeed, is the use of maps in geographic work, that, without wishing to propose any new law, it seems fair to suggest to the geographer a ready rule of thumb to test the geographic quality of any study he is making: if his

Reprinted in its entirety by permission of the author and the editor of the Department of Geography publications, State University of Iowa.

problem cannot be studied fundamentally by maps—usually by a comparison of several maps—then it is questionable whether or not it is within the field of geography.[2]

The clear and long-standing devotion by geographers to map analysis is stated most succinctly in *American Geography: Inventory and Prospect:* "The map is the fundamental instrument of geographic research."[3]

Broader understandings of the characteristics of maps, improved techniques for portraying different kinds of data on maps, and more incisive abilities to interpret and analyze the distributional patterns that are portrayed on maps have significantly affected the scope and content of the discipline of geography. For example, the development and eventual refinement of the fractional code system,[4] which permitted precise recording of field observations on a larger scale than had previously been feasible, stimulated geographers to perform increased amounts of intensive field investigation and aroused an interest in land-use analysis and areal associations which continues to this day.

Research techniques available to the geographer also were considerably broadened with the development of "statistical-distribution cartography." By use of the statistical map, the spatial pattern of magnitudes for a given phenomenon may be portrayed. Within the framework of a particular problem, the spatial pattern on one statistical map may be analyzed by comparison and contrast with the spatial patterns of phenomena portrayed on other, similar maps. Geographers have found many of their problems amenable to such analyses and have incorporated statistical maps in many of their investigations. The general acceptance by geographers of the statistical map and the close relationships between geography and cartography are pointed out by Robinson: "[Statistical-distribution cartography] has steadily progressed, and the application of the techniques today are wide indeed."[5] Throughout the remainder of this monograph attention is focused upon the use of the statistical map in quantitative geographic research.

The statistical map, as it is most often employed by geographers, is a graphic device, and from this characteristic derives its basic weakness as an analytical tool.[6] Visual examination of a statistical map does not provide the critical values that are required for describing a single-variable spatial distribution with rigor and precision. Inadequate for the description of a single spatial distribution, the statistical map is even more poorly suited to the analytical phase of a multivariable problem in which it is necessary to establish and measure areal associations between one variable and a set of hypothetical factors.

Recognizing the limitations of the statistical map as a research tool, geographers have been engaged in a quest for statistical techniques that might be employed in traditional geographic problems. For example, McCarty has recently endeavored to appraise the relative usefulness of five different statistical techniques, including Pearsonian coefficients of correlation and rank correlation methods;[7] Zobler investigated the use of the analysis of variance and chi-square procedures in establishing regional groupings;[8] and a group of geographers at the University of Washington, largely under the direction of Garrison, has experimented with a variety of techniques, including linear programming and nearest-neighbor methods, to determine their applicability in a wide variety of geographic problems.[9] The value of these and other statistical techniques has been realized; studies employing them are an accepted segment of geographic literature, and geographic training increasingly stresses their use.

The need to test specific hypotheses is common to geographic studies employing statistical techniques. For example, when attempting to establish meaningful areal associations between a dependent variable and a set of hypothetical independent variables by means of multiple regression analyses, the magnitude of certain precise critical values, which are provided by the technique, are tested by means of statistical significance tests. Those critical values, standard partial regression coefficients or beta coefficients, which exceed predetermined magnitudes are accepted as representing hypotheses which are valid. The variables derived from those accepted hypotheses then are taken to have a significant areal association with the dependent variable in question. Contrariwise, beta coefficients which are not of significant magnitude are assumed to represent invalid hypotheses, which are rejected, and the variables which are supported by these unaccepted hypotheses are assumed to have no significant areal association with the dependent variable.

Prior to the computation of critical values, a phase of the research must be devoted to the formulation of the hypotheses which are to be tested. After the testing of hypotheses is accomplished, there is usually a phase in which some or all of the rejected hypotheses are reformulated and new hypotheses are developed.[10] These phases, particularly the latter, require special devices. The remainder of this monograph is devoted to discussing a specific kind of statistical map which may be employed as a unique device to provide possible solutions for three traditional geographic problems: (1) the formulation and modification of hypotheses concerning the existence of an areal association between a dependent variable and a set of independent variables; (2) the establishment or modification of regional boundaries; and (3) the judicious selection of areas for intensive field investigation.

THE ROLE OF THE STATISTICAL MAP IN QUANTITATIVE GEOGRAPHIC RESEARCH

It is necessary to establish the characteristics of the broad research goals which the geographer entertains in order to give meaning to any suggestions regarding the use of the statistical map as a research tool. Obviously, any tools available have use only when they can be used to solve geographic problems. However, only the broadest and most general definition of goals is needed here; hence the present discussion does not represent an attempt to define in detail the scope, content, or methodology of geography, but rather to provide a minimal background for the consideration of the materials which follow.

For the purposes of this monograph, the geographer is accepted as a scientist operating within the framework provided by modern science. As scientists, geographers ". . . are . . . seeking . . . descriptions, explanations, and predictions which are as adequate and accurate as possible in the given context of research."[11] Geographers may be distinguished from most other scientists by their preoccupation with the spatial characteristics of phenomena distributed over the earth's surface, i.e., the geographer's special interests are describing, explaining, and pre-

dicting spatial patterns of phenomena on the earth's surface. In other words: ". . . the problems of geography arise out of those every-day real life situations that involve areal differences in the occurrence or intensity of specific phenomena."[12] The solutions to these problems lie in generalizations based on the facts of spatial distributions, or, as Hartshorne states:

. . . Scientific advance in geography depends on the development of generic concepts and the establishment and application of principles of generic relationships . . . . It is in the search for universals, generic concepts as well as general principles which may be constructed from them, that we are pursuing fundamental research.[13]

The question arises, "How may the geographer establish universals, scientific generalizations, that are unique; that is, generalizations which would not normally be forthcoming from other disciplines?" If geography contemplated a body of unique subject matter, geographers certainly could establish scientific generalizations that would also be unique. But there is agreement among geographers that, in contrast to many other disciplines, there exists no phenomenon which can be considered as exclusively geographical in character.[14] Unique geographical generalizations, if they are forthcoming, apparently must arise from sources other than a unique subject matter.

Under what other circumstances might distinctly geographical generalizations arise? It is reasonable to think that unique generalizations might arise from some unique action performed during either the hypothesis-testing or the hypothesis-formulation phases of the investigation. Distinctive generalizations certainly might arise if geographers possessed techniques for testing hypotheses that were more incisive than those used by other disciplines. For example, such techniques could be used to measure more accurately the relationship between sets of data, and hence to establish generalizations which might be overlooked if the analysis of the data were undertaken by the use of less penetrating tools. It appears, however, that present-day geographers do not possess analytical techniques that are more incisive than those used in other disciplines,[15] and, furthermore, it is only recently that geographers have adopted some of the mathematical and statistical techniques already well established in those disciplines.[16] It appears that, within the foreseeable future, research in geography may be pursued on as precise a level and with the same technical acuteness as research in other disciplines, but not at more precise levels. Distinctive geographic generalizations may not be expected to arise from the techniques geographers use for testing hypotheses.

Generalizations which may be characterized as distinctly geographical also might be established if a unique tool for hypothesis formulation were available. Such a device must have at least one characteristic which would facilitate the formulation of hypotheses which might not be forthcoming from other techniques. These essentially unique hypotheses then would have to be validated by some rigorous and precise method, and then could be accepted as unique generalizations. The geographer has available a device which can be used to suggest these kinds of hypotheses. This device is the statistical map.

We have already indicated that the statistical map has characteristics that make it unsuitable for hypothesis testing. This deficiency, however, does not detract from its usefulness in hypothesis formulation. As stated [earlier], precision and rigor are necessary in testing; but these features are far less important in hypothesis formulations, and their absence does not detract seriously from the value of the statistical map in the latter use.

One way in which different hypotheses might be set up is through the portrayal of the set of data by different graphic means, each of which stresses a particular characteristic of the phenomenon under investigation. The statistical map is the only graphic device by which such data (for a set of observations) can be portrayed without destroying their spatial pattern. Inasmuch as the spatial character of a phenomenon by definition is different from its other characteristics, the statistical map is a unique device by means of which geographers, with their interests in spatial patterns and areal associations, may formulate distinctly geographical hypotheses.

A research system involving the formulation, testing, and reformulation of hypotheses, in which the statistical map is nicely integrated with statistical techniques, has been suggested by McCarty. The elements of this system are as follows:

1. examination of problem data to determine mean, variance, skewness, etc.
2. plotting data on an isopleth or choropleth map generalized according to parameters discovered in Step 1
3. examination of geographic literature and selection of hypotheses accounting for variations noted in Step 2
4. visual comparison of problem map with maps of independent variables noted in Step 3
5. analysis of association between problem data and variables discovered in Step 4, by means of scatter diagrams, regression lines, standard errors of estimate, and coefficients of correlation
6. use of regression equations to compute deviations of actual values (Y) from estimated values (Y_c). These deviations ($Y - Y_c$ or Y_c/Y) are plotted on new maps which show distributions of the unexplained variance of Y.
7. repetition of Steps 3 and 4 for the new map; selection of other independent variables
8. incorporation of new variables into the analysis; computation of a new (multiple) regression equation; repetition of Step 6
9. continuation of routine until desired degree of association is achieved.[17]

Thus the statistical map is used at relatively sophisticated levels of research in conjunction with precise and rigorous statistical tools. Portraying the spatial distribution of deviations from regression (henceforth referred to as *residuals from regression*, or merely as *residuals*) provides the geographer with a research system in which the spatial character of the data is systematically recreated and employed in the formulation of geographic hypotheses which can be tested with rigor and precision.

RESIDUALS FROM REGRESSION: DEFINITIONS, CHARACTERISTICS, AND LIMITATIONS

The multiple regression equation expresses a functional relationship between a dependent variable, Y, and a set of independent variables, $X_1, X_2, X_3, \ldots, X_m$. The basic linear regression equation is of the form:

$$Y_c = a_{y.123\ldots m} + b_{y1.23\ldots m}X_1 + b_{y2.13\ldots m}X_2 + \cdots + b_{ym.12\ldots m-1}X_m$$

In this equation, Y_c is an estimated, or computed, value of Y determined by the m independent variables. The b values in the formula are partial regression coefficients. In the subscripts attached to each coefficient, the symbol to the left of the decimal point stands for the dependent variable and the independent variable to which it is being related; the symbols to the right refer to the independent variables held constant statistically. Each b value indicates the amount of change in Y for each unit change in the given independent variable when the influence of the others is allowed for. The value of $a_{y.123...m}$ determines the height of the regression plane and is referred to as the "Y intercept." The subscript $_{y.123...m}$ identifies the regression plane as the one based upon the relationship between Y and independent variables, $X_1, X_2, \ldots, X_m$.

The partial regression coefficients and the Y intercept are weighted to provide composite Y_c values, which minimize the sum of the squared differences between Y and Y_c for each unit area. This is an important notion because the computed value, Y_c, employing the least-squares criterion, provides the best overall estimate of Y, for a group of unit areas, that is obtainable from a given set of independent variables.[18]

According to one regression model, variation in the dependent variable may be divided into two parts, one part of which is associated with, or explained by, the hypothesized variables and another part attributed to other factors, including chance occurrences.[19] From the geographic standpoint, part of the magnitude which a phenomenon reaches within a unit area may be attributed to the areal association with factors included in the investigation; the other part is allocated to an association with factors not included in the study. Included in the latter are locations or magnitudes which have occurred by chance.

A residual from regression for a particular observation is the difference in magnitude between an observed value, whose numerical value is determined by factors included and omitted from investigation, and an estimated value, determined only by variables included in the study. Stated differently, within a geographic context, a residual from regression is defined as that part of the magnitude which a phenomenon reaches within a given unit area which is independent of the areal association between the given phenomenon and the other factors included in the investigation.

It is possible to express these residuals in a great variety of ways. Among these expressions, however, four have been shown to be especially useful. Their characteristics are worthy of further description.

THE BASIC RESIDUAL

The basic residual from regression is $Y_{cn} - Y_n$, in which Y_n represents the observed value of Y for the nth unit area and Y_{cn} represents the computed value of Y for the nth unit area. Thus the term $Y_{cn} - Y_n$ expresses the difference between the observed value for the nth unit area and the value for that area as it is estimated from the regression equation.

The residual $Y_{cn} - Y_n$ is the basic and simplest residual value. Assuming both Y_{cn} and Y_n values are available, the arithmetic procedure for obtaining $Y_{cn} - Y_n$ is merely subtraction. This residual is thus very easily computed on a desk calculator or the computations may be easily programmed for a computer.

The value $Y_{cn} - Y_n$ is an absolute residual and is expressed in the same terms as the dependent variable. For example, if the dependent variable is total population per county, the magnitude of the residual $Y_{cn} - Y_n$ will be given in numbers of people.

Residuals of the type $Y_{cn} - Y_n$ take both positive and negative values, and for a large number of observations they usually occur in approximately equal numbers. The $Y_{cn} - Y_n$ values are negative for unit areas in which the estimated magnitude of the dependent variable is smaller than the observed magnitude, i.e., when $Y_{cn} < Y_n$; whereas the $Y_{cn} - Y_n$ values are positive for areas in which the observed magnitude of the dependent variable is smaller than the estimated, i.e., when $Y_n < Y_{cn}$.

Maps of the residual $Y_{cn} - Y_n$ may be particularly useful for the formulation of hypotheses under certain circumstances. The spatial pattern of this residual appears in positive and negative absolute values. Hence the spatial pattern of this residual may be compared directly with the spatial pattern of other phenomena which occur as absolute values, e.g., maps of numbers of people or inches of rainfall.

Circumstances arise in which $Y_{cn} - Y_n$ values are difficult to map or interpret. These residuals are particularly difficult to deal with when the data for the dependent variable have a very small range compared to their average magnitude. For example, this situation occurs when data have been subjected to a logarithmic transformation. Table 1 shows residuals computed for a group of outlying cities located in the Chicago urbanized area.[20] The dependent variable has been transformed by substituting logarithms of the numbers for the observed values. The value of all the residuals is small; differences in magnitude of such values are difficult to interpret, and division of these data into meaningful class intervals, preparatory to mapping them, presents a problem. Hence the use of $Y_{cn} - Y_n$ residuals is limited.

TABLE 1

Absolute and relative residuals from regression when a logarithmic transformation of the Y variable is employed

Observation	$Y_{cn} - Y_n$	$(Y_{cn} - Y_n)/Y_n$
1	−.10457	−.02762
2	.04086	.01134
3	−.08669	−.02206
4	−.00731	−.01661
5	.12696	.03628
6	−.02780	−.00727
7	.08798	.02360
8	.22570	.06462
9	−.00180	−.00052
10	−.02471	−.00703
11	.08937	.02486
12	−.07059	−.01912
13	−.11252	−.03014
14	−.11038	−.03027
15	−.03516	−.00948
16	−.06078	−.01648
17	−.10581	−.02728
18	−.22670	−.05628
19	.16915	.04705
20	.29503	.08608

One obvious solution to the problems of mapping data of the type mentioned above is to divide the data into class intervals based upon their position in an array, e.g., quintiles. When this is done, the small magnitude of all the residuals is not a serious hindrance. However, in some mapping situations it may not be desirable to eliminate the magnitudes of the observation and depend merely upon its position. When this is the case, it may be necessary to map some kind of residual other than $Y_{cn} - Y_n$.

THE RELATIVE RESIDUAL

Another residual from regression is defined by the expression $(Y_{cn} - Y_n)/Y_n$. Using previous definitions for each term in the expression, the residual gives the magnitude of the difference between estimated and observed values for the nth unit area, $Y_{cn} - Y_n$, relative to the magnitude of the observed value, Y_n. Hence the ratio $(Y_{cn} - Y_n)/Y_n$, which is a relative value, may be contrasted with $Y_{cn} - Y_n$, which is an absolute one.

The value $(Y_{cn} - Y_n)/Y_n$ is relative and is considered a nondimensional expression. This residual indicates the relative goodness of the estimate independent of the units in which the dependent variable is initially described. Because of this characteristic, several maps of the residual $(Y_{cn} - Y_n)/Y_n$ for different dependent variables may be compared directly.

COMPARISON OF BASIC AND RELATIVE RESIDUALS

As in the case of $Y_{cn} - Y_n$, these residuals may assume either positive or negative values, which occur in approximately equal numbers. However, for a given unit area, the sign of $(Y_{cn} - Y_n)/Y_n$ is not necessarily the same as $Y_{cn} - Y_n$. In fact, in terms of the possible algebraic combinations, $Y_{cn} - Y_n$ and $(Y_{cn} - Y_n)/Y_n$ will have like signs in only half of the cases.[21]

The spatial pattern of these relative residual values may be markedly different from the pattern of $Y_{cn} - Y_n$ values. This fact was pointed out by McCarty.[22] Differences between the spatial pattern shown by $(Y_{cn} - Y_n)/Y_n$ and $Y_{cn} - Y_n$ values may be attributed to two factors. First, as mentioned [above], certain differences in pattern are to be expected because of the algebraic nature of the two residual values. A residual value of the type $(Y_{cn} - Y_n)/Y_n$ for a given unit area may take a sign opposite to that from $Y_{cn} - Y_n$ under certain circumstances. These differences, obviously, may result in different spatial patterns.

The nature of the least-squares regression line also is a factor which frequently explains differences in the patterns presented by $(Y_{cn} - Y_n)/Y_n$ and $Y_{cn} - Y_n$ values. For many sets of data, fitting the least-squares regression line results in large absolute $Y_{cn} - Y_n$ values occurring within the range of the Y observations without regard to their magnitude.[23] However, two residuals of the type $(Y_{cn} - Y_n)/Y_n$ that hvae identical $Y_{cn} - Y_n$ values will differ if their Y_n values are different: a given $Y_{cn} - Y_n$ residual value, when divided by a large observed value, will form a comparatively small ratio; contrariwise, an absolute residual of the same magnitude will form a comparatively large ratio.[24] Thus even if the sign of $Y_{cn} - Y_n$ and $(Y_{cn} - Y_n)/Y_n$ is the same, an appreciable difference in spatial pattern may appear. If $Y_{cn} - Y_n$ and $(Y_{cn} - Y_n)/Y_n$ have different signs, the patterns formed by the two residuals may differ even more markedly.

$(Y_{cn} - Y_n)/Y_n$ residuals are subject to the same limitations as $Y_{cn} - Y_n$ when they are mapped and interpreted. When the data have a small range compared to their average magnitude, i.e., large mean and small standard deviation, the ratio $(Y_{cn} - Y_n)/Y_n$ may result in residuals which are consistently quite close to unity (Table 1). In this case, the residuals may be difficult to divide into meaningful class intervals and hence difficult to map and interpret. As mentioned before, one solution to the problem of mapping data of this type is to assign the observations to class intervals according to position within the group rather than by their magnitudes.

Because the spatial pattern of $(Y_{cn} - Y_n)/Y_n$ residuals may differ from the pattern of $Y_{cn} - Y_n$ residuals, the spatial distribution of $(Y_{cn} - Y_n)/Y_n$ may suggest variables that are different [from] those brought to mind by $Y_{cn} - Y_n$ values. $(Y_{cn} - Y_n)/Y_n$ expresses relatively the success of the set of independent variables in estimating the area. As a pattern of relative values, this spatial distribution may suggest additional variables which also are ratios. This result may appear even when a map of absolute residuals does not suggest those same variables. For example, a map of relative residuals may suggest a relationship between a dependent variable and relative decennial population change (e.g., percentage changes per county from 1940–50), while the absolute residuals would not suggest the absolute amount of decennial population change as a new independent variable.

RATIO OF ESTIMATE TO OBSERVATION

This expression defines a value closely related to the relative residual $(Y_{cn} - Y_n)/Y_n$. Y_{cn}/Y_n gives the magnitude of the estimated value for

the nth unit area as a proportion of the observed value for that area. Y_{cn}/Y_n thus is not a residual according to the strictest of definitions. True residuals, by definition, give the magnitude of the difference between estimated and observed values for particular unit areas in either absolute or relative terms, whereas, for given areas, Y_{cn}/Y_n measures the ratio of estimated values to observed values.

There is a close relationship between Y_{cn}/Y_n and $(Y_{cn} - Y_n)/Y_n$.[25] Y_{cn}/Y_n values greater than unity correspond to positive $(Y_{cn} - Y_n)/Y_n$ values, whereas Y_{cn}/Y_n values less than unity correspond to $(Y_{cn} - Y_n)/Y_n$ values which are negative. When Y_{cn}/Y_n equals unity $(Y_{cn} - Y_n)/Y_n$ equals zero; in this instance the estimated and observed values coincide.

Maps of Y_{cn}/Y_n may be of value in hypothesis formulation even though Y_{cn}/Y_n is not, in the strictest sense, a residual. Because this ratio is closely related to $(Y_{cn} - Y_n)/Y_n$, the spatial pattern formed by both values computed for the same set of observations will be identical if the same class intervals are mapped, e.g., deciles or quintiles for both sets of data. Since Y_{cn}/Y_n values are more easily computed than $(Y_{cn} - Y_n)/Y_n$ quantities, this ratio may often provide the easiest way to establish the spatial pattern of the $(Y_{cn} - Y_n)/Y_n$ residuals.

Values of the form Y_{cn}/Y_n are subject to essentially the same limitations when they are mapped as $(Y_{cn} - Y_n)/Y_n$ residuals. . . .

STANDARDIZED RESIDUALS

A third general residual value is defined by the expression $(Y_{cn} - Y_n)/K$, where Y_{cn} and Y_n are defined as before and K is any selected constant. Of the infinite number of residuals which are of this general form, an exceedingly useful residual is defined by $(Y_{cn} - Y_n)/S_{Y_c}$ where S_{Y_c} is the standard error of estimate. This expression gives the magnitude of the difference between the estimated and observed value for the nth unit area in terms of the standard error of estimate for the set of observations.

Residuals from regression of the form $(Y_{cn} - Y_n)/S_{Y_c}$ take both positive and negative numbers and occur, for large numbers of observations, in approximately equal numbers. The overall spatial pattern of these residuals will be similar to the pattern of $Y_{cn} - Y_n$ values if the class intervals on both maps are based on the position of observations within the group rather than on their magnitude.[26] However, "standardized" residuals have other characteristics which make them more amenable to mapping and interpretation than residuals of the form $Y_{cn} - Y_n$ in certain circumstances.

One desirable characteristic is that most $(Y_{cn} - Y_n)/S_{Y_c}$ values assume magnitudes ranging from -3.00 to $+3.00$. This is true regardless of what average magnitude and range characterize the data.[27] Such values are easily divided into class intervals which are appropriate for establishing the spatial pattern of the residuals, while at the same time providing a map which is comparable and compatible with maps of hypothetical factors. For example, a map of standardized residuals may be drawn employing eight class intervals: greater than $+1.5S_{Y_c}$, $+1.0S_{Y_c}$ to $1.5S_{Y_c}$, $+.5S_{Y_c}$ to $1.0S_{Y_c}$, Y_c to $+.5S_{Y_c}$, Y_c to $-.5S_{Y_c}$, $-5S_{Y_c}$ to $-1.0S_{Y_c}$, $-1.0S_{Y_c}$ to -1.5_{Y_c} and smaller than $-1.5S_{Y_c}$.[28] This map would be highly compatible with a map of a hypothetical variable if that factor also were expressed in standard terms, i.e., if the magnitude of each observation were given as a deviation from the arithmetic mean relative to the standard deviation of the set of observations.[29]

Another characteristic of residuals of the type $(Y_{cn} - Y_n)S_{Y_c}$ which makes them useful is that the long-term frequency of standardized differences between estimated and observed values is known. For this reason, the principles of statistical decision making may be applied for determining the relative rarity of individual $(Y_{cn} - Y_n)/S_{Y_c}$ values. For example, a $(Y_{cn} - Y_n)/S_{Y_c}$ value equal to or greater than 1.0 might occur approximately 32 per cent of the time; however, a magnitude equal to or greater than 2.6 will occur less than 1 per cent of the time. Knowledge of where statistically rare events occur might facilitate the selection of areas for field investigation.

Residuals of the type $(Y_{cn} - Y_n)/S_{Y_c}$ are not without limitation. One limitation arises out of the nature of the standard error of estimate. In almost all analyses, a few residual values may be expected to lie at a distance of two or three or even more standard errors from the regression plane. This situation obtains whether 10 per cent or 95 per cent of the total variation in the dependent variable is explained. Thus at the termination of a relatively complete analysis, the geographer may be analyzing extreme values which are merely chance occurrences in terms of the percentage of the total variation in the dependent variable which is already explained. This problem can be overcome, however, if the geographer employs other statistical values in addition to the standard error of estimate. For example, at any time during the study, the geographer may refer to either the coefficient of determination, r^2, or the coefficient of multiple determination, R^2, to decide whether or not he is satisfied with the relative variation in the dependent variable which his set of factors explain.

*   *   *   *   *

SOME THEORETICAL USES OF MAPS OF RESIDUALS FROM REGRESSION

The use of differences between observation and theory, or, more particularly, between specific events and generalizations, has long been used to gain greater insight into the behavior of a particular phenomenon. An early formulation of this technique for gaining understandings is attributed to John Stuart Mill. In *A System of Logic*, Mill presents the "method of residues" as the Fourth Canon; "Subduct from any phenomenon such part as is known by previous inductions to be the effect of certain antecedents, and the residue of the phenomenon is the effect of remaining antecedents." Mill thought highly of the method of residues as a research technique:

Of all the methods of investigating laws of nature, this is the most fertile and unexpected result: often informing us of sequences in which neither the cause nor the effect were sufficiently conspicuous to attract of themselves the attention of the observers. The agent C may be an obscure circumstance, not likely to have been perceived unless sought for, nor likely to have been sought for until attention had been awakened by the insufficiency of the obvious causes to account for the whole of the effect.[30]

The mapping and use of residuals from regression is merely the method of residues reformulated within a probabilistic framework. Explained variation and the Y_{cn} values may be identified as the parts known by "previous inductions"; unexplained variation and the

$Y_{cn} - Y_n$ residual values are "the residue of the phenomenon [which] is the effect of remaining antecedents." For the notion of causes, we substitute statistically significant relationships between variables.

DEVIANT CASE ANALYSIS

Mill's Fourth Canon has been successfully modified and has provided the basis for research techniques for many disciplines, e.g., in psychology, where relationships and interrelationships between variables are exceedingly complex and where only a small portion of the overall behavior of a given dependent variable can be ascribed to any one independent variable. The method of residues has been developed as "deviant-case analysis." As Horst points out: "One of the most interesting and useful parts of a prediction study should be the investigation of the cases which have been incorrectly predicted in the new sample."[31]

Sociologists, for reasons similar to those of the psychologists, also have adopted deviant-case analysis. Gordon has suggested that deviant cases provide an indication of the degree of control which a set of independent variables may [exert] on a dependent variable. He also suggests that deviant cases may provide additional knowledge germane to the behavior of the dependent variable.[32]

The use of "residues" generally involves identifying, according to some criteria, observations for which understandings are poor. These observations are used either collectively or individually to formulate new hypotheses, whose validity then is tested. Obviously, the actual details of the techniques or the content of the study is determined by the subject matter and specific nature of the discipline in which it is being conducted.

THE GEOGRAPHIC USES OF RESIDUALS FROM REGRESSION

Generally, maps of residuals from regression can be used to fulfill the same research needs in geography as deviant cases, or other "residues," provide for other disciplines. Specifically, maps of residuals from regression are useful to the geographer in three research situations:

1. to formulate new hypotheses and to identify new variables for inclusion in an investigation.

2. to establish or modify regional boundaries

3. to focus attention on, and aid in the selection of, specific unit areas in which to conduct a field investigation.

It is apparent that maps of residuals are suggested as aids to the solution of problems which are distinctly geographical in nature and whose solutions have long been sought after by geographers.

MAPS OF RESIDUALS USED TO IDENTIFY NEW INDEPENDENT VARIABLES

After a set of hypotheses is formulated and tested, certain independent variables are accepted as having a statistically significant areal association with the dependent variable, whereas others are rejected. It then is necessary to formulate new hypotheses and to reformulate some of the existing ones. In terms of the mechanics of the research, it is necessary to select new independent variables for inclusion in the investigation. A map of residuals from regression may be a valuable tool when used to select such variables, since in addition to factors selected on the basis of associations known a priori, variables also may be included because factual evidence indicates that an apparent areal relationship exists between them and the dependent variable, even if the logical basis for such relationships is obscure.

The map of residuals from regression shows the spatial distribution of that part of the total magnitude of the dependent variable which is associated with phenomena other than those included in the analysis. Hence the selection of new variables by use of this tool involves identifying phenomena which show the same spatial patterns as the residual values.

The identification of additional independent variables may be accomplished by means of the traditional techniques for comparing two or more spatial patterns; i.e., the "highs," "lows," and gradients that appear on the residual map are compared for correspondence with the "highs," lows," and gradients on maps of other phenomena (Fig. 1).[33] The spatial pattern presented by phenomenon W more closely approximates the distribution of $Y_{cn} - Y_n$ than does the spatial pattern of Z. Hence W is hypothesized as being related to

THREE SPATIAL DISTRIBUTIONS IN HYPOTHETICAL STUDY AREA A

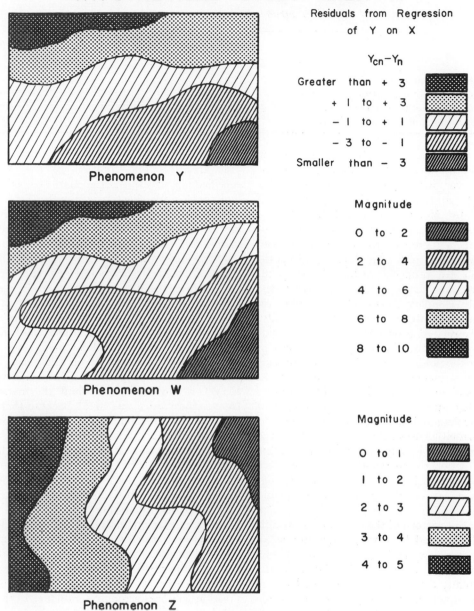

Residuals from Regression
of Y on X

$Y_{cn} - Y_n$

Greater than + 3	
+ 1 to + 3	
− 1 to + 1	
− 3 to − 1	
Smaller than − 3	

Magnitude

0 to 2	
2 to 4	
4 to 6	
6 to 8	
8 to 10	

Magnitude

0 to 1	
1 to 2	
2 to 3	
3 to 4	
4 to 5	

Phenomenon Y

Phenomenon W

Phenomenon Z

FIGURE 1

Y and is included, along with phenomenon X, as an independent variable in the regression analysis.

The regression of Y on X gives a simple correlation coefficient, r, of .76, and thus explains about 52 per cent of the total variation in Y (Table 2).

Standard partial regression coefficients for X and W indicate that both independent vari-ables are significantly related to Y (Table 2). The coefficient of multiple correlation, R, is .93. Thus the variation in Y explained by X and W amounts to approximately 87 per cent of the total. This is an increase of thirty-five percentage points.

The map of residuals is not a research pan-acea; there are definite limitations to its use. A whole series of visual problems arise because

TABLE 2

The correlation of dependent variable Y on independent variables X and W

	Y *on* X	*Relationship* Y *on* W	X *on* W	Y *on* X *and* W
Coefficient of correlation	.76	.52	−.20	
Coefficient of determination	.57	.28	.04	
Coefficient of multiple correlation				.93
Coefficient of multiple determination				.87

of the graphic nature of the map. These problems, however, are beyond the scope of this monograph and are . . . discussed in detail elsewhere by McCarty and Salisbury.[34] The limitations encountered when using maps of residuals from regression to identify new independent variables and formulate new hypotheses which are properly within the scope of this study are those which arise from the exceedingly complex nature of geographic relationships and interrelationships. Essentially, two closely related problems may be specified: in one situation, the overall spatial pattern of residuals does not appear to be similar to that of any phenomenon which might be hypothesized as related to the dependent variable; in the other situation, the spatial pattern of residuals looks much like that of the dependent variable. In either case, the effective use of the map of residuals is jeopardized; however, the course of action to be taken differs according to which situation is encountered, and for that reason each case is discussed separately and in greater detail.

The spatial pattern of the dependent variable may be determined by a very large number of factors; hence, even though numerous independent variables already are included in the analysis, many factors not yet included in the regression equation determine the magnitude of the residual values. In this case, no hypothetical variable can be expected to duplicate the spatial pattern of residuals because no single phenomenon has a very close areal association with the dependent variable. Thus the selection of independent variables may become difficult, because similarities of pattern between the residuals and any particular hypothetical variable are only vague.

Mapping the distributions of only the larger residual values, as opposed to values for all

unit areas, is one solution to the problem specified above. When the map of residuals is limited to only the larger values, the map of the hypothetical variable must likewise be limited to the spatial distribution of extreme values, i.e., the largest and smallest.[35] Mapping only extreme values provides simplified patterns which are more easily compared than the patterns which result when data for all observations are plotted.

Very frequently the statistical correlations between the dependent variable and a new independent variable will be smaller than had been expected, in view of the close correspondence between patterns of extreme values. However, the decision to limit the maps only to extreme values was made because there was not a close correspondence between the pattern of residuals, for their entire range of values, and the patterns of other variables. If extremes appear to coincide spatially, but the overall distributions do not, then the intermediate values for both distributions are not closely related. Thus when these are included in the multiple regression analysis, the overall relationship between the dependent variable and the new independent variable is not nearly so close as was indicated by the maps of extremes.

In some cases, a map of residuals from regression will bear strong resemblance to the map of observed data for the dependent variable. This situation arises frequently when an analysis is in its early phases and knowledge is meager concerning what factors are areally associated with the dependent variable, i.e., R^2 is quite small. When R^2 is small, $\Sigma(Y_{cn} - Y_n)^2$ differs little from $\Sigma(\bar{Y} - Y_n)^2$, and the regression plane offers little improvement over the mean of the dependent variable as regards prediction of values in specific unit areas.[36] When this is the case, each $(Y_{cn} - Y_n)$ differs little, on the average, from $(\bar{Y} - Y_n)$, and the overall spatial pattern of residuals appears similar to the initial pattern of the dependent variable.[37]

When the pattern of residuals closely follows the distribution of the observed data for the dependent variable, the best procedure to follow is merely to continue to select new independent variables whose patterns resemble those of the residuals. It must be borne in mind, however, that in this situation, the contribution of each new independent variable will be small, regardless of seeming similarities between residual patterns and those of the new variables. This result appears because high intercorrelations between independent variables decreases the contribution of each of them to the explained proportion of the total variation in the dependent variable.[38]

MAPS OF RESIDUALS USED TO ESTABLISH OR MODIFY REGIONAL BOUNDARIES

The desire to identify areas of the earth surface which are homogeneous according to some criterion or criteria has long been an integral feature of geographic analyses.[39] In terms of quantitative research, the desire to establish geographic regions may be identified essentially as a part of a more general problem faced by researchers in many disciplines, i.e., the need to recognize, identify, and group together, according to some characteristic which provides an element of homogeneity, observations which are otherwise heterogeneous.[40] For the geographer, this characteristic has been areal, and his observations, unit areas, have been identified as belonging to geographic regions which are defined as being homogeneous in terms of the criteria by which they are established. The effectiveness of such classifications can be assessed quantitatively by using analysis of variance or analysis of covariance, depending upon the sophistication of the model which is employed.

Maps of residuals from regression may be employed in two ways when attempting to establish homogeneous geographic regions: first, they may be used to determine the *location* of comparatively isolated large residual values; and second, they are useful in determining whether or not there is a *concentration* of large residual values of the same kind, e.g.,

all positive residuals may be concentrated in one part of the map.[41] In either instance the indication is that the observations do not form a homogeneous geographic region.

The existence of isolated large residual values located along the margins of the study area suggests that regional boundaries should be shifted to exclude those extreme values (Fig. 2). The magnitude which the dependent variable reaches in these unit areas either is not much affected by the independent variables included in the investigation or is affected in a very different way. Hence these observations do not fit the "accordant relationships" upon which the region is predicated.

Reclassifying extreme values by shifting regional boundaries so that the areas they occupy do not lie within the study area may produce a much different indication of the relationship between the variables in the study area and the overall closeness of their relationships. For example, shifting the locations of the eastern and western regional boundaries of the study area shown in Fig. 2 so as to exclude extreme observations changes the value of the regression coefficient from 4.43 to 4.15 (Table 3). The coefficient of determination (r^2) is increased from .72 to .90. The increase in the value of r^2 indicates that more desirable estimates of the absolute and relative relationships between variables has been achieved by modifying the boundaries of the study area.

For the purpose of this illustration, residual values lying at distances greater than 2.0 S_{Y_c} are eliminated from the study area. Such occurrences are apt to happen less than 5 per cent of the time. The selection of 2.0 S_{Y_c} as the criterion for eliminating an observation is completely arbitrary; other values indicating different levels of rarity might be used, depending upon the specific character of the phenomenon being investigated and the study area. In actual research situations, observations probably would not be omitted until they were found to lie at distances greater than 3.0 or even 4.0 standard errors from the regression estimate. Even in these circumstances, the observations would not be excluded without a strong logical justification based on the character of the particular unit areas.[42]

Appearance of spatial concentrations of either positive or negative values suggests that the study area lacks homogeneity as regards

ISOLATED LARGE RESIDUAL VALUES, $(Y_{cn}-Y_n)/S_{yc}$, ON THE MARGINS OF HYPOTHETICAL STUDY AREA B

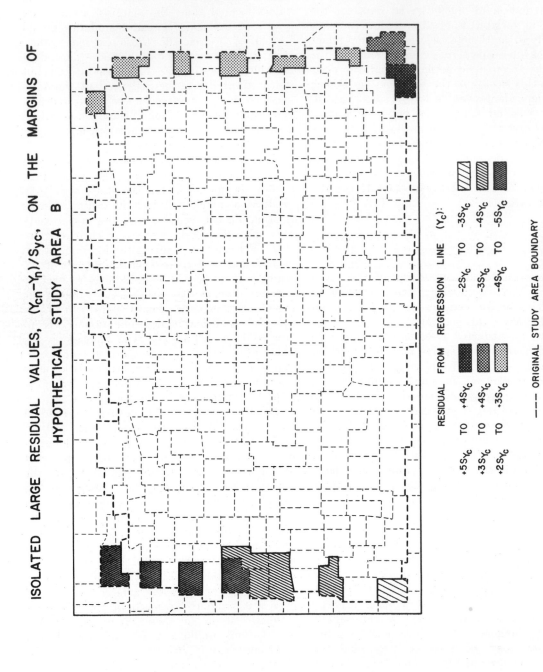

RESIDUAL FROM REGRESSION LINE (Y_c):

$+5S_{yc}$ TO $+4S_{yc}$

$+3S_{yc}$ TO $+4S_{yc}$

$+2S_{yc}$ TO $+3S_{yc}$

$-2S_{yc}$ TO $-3S_{yc}$

$-3S_{yc}$ TO $-4S_{yc}$

$-4S_{yc}$ TO $-5S_{yc}$

---- ORIGINAL STUDY AREA BOUNDARY

—— MODIFIED STUDY AREA BOUNDARY

FIGURE 2

TABLE 3

The effect on a correlation-regression analysis of excluding large residual values

	Coefficient of correlation (r)	Coefficient of determination (r²)	Regression coefficient
Before excluding extreme values	.85	.72	4.43
After excluding extreme values	.95	.90	4.15

the dependent variable. If a large proportion of all positive residual values is concentrated in one area, while most negative residuals are found in another, the study area often may be divided into two regions with consistent overestimation and underestimation providing the elements of homogeneity. One of the most apparent characteristics of the pattern of residuals shown in Fig. 3 is the location of positive residuals in the northern part of the study area, while negative residual values are concentrated in the south. This pattern suggests that the study area [should] be divided into one region in which consistent underestimation by the regression equation occurs and another in which consistent overestimation provides the element of homogeneity. The boundary separating the regions should follow the isoline indicating perfect estimation, i.e., $Y_{cn} - Y_n = 0$, as closely as the boundaries of individual unit areas will permit.

When residuals of the same kind are spatially concentrated and the study area is subdivided accordingly, the regression model then becomes a covariance analysis. By means of covariance, the significance of the regional classification can be tested while at the same time considering the effect of the relationships between variables within the subregions.[43] Should the regional classification be effective, the covariance analysis will result in an increase in explained variation in the dependent variable; as indicated in Table 4, the use of a regional classification has increased the proportion of total variation which is explained from 40.4 per cent to 95.9 per cent.

After effectively modifying regional boundaries, i.e., dividing the study area into several geographic regions, it remains for the geographer to provide a framework which logically explains the regional segmentation. This rationale ultimately may lead to the abandonment of regional classification and the substitution of one or several variable phenomena in its place.

TABLE 4

The effect of dividing a study area into two geographic regions

	Amount	Per cent of total
Total variation (measured from the arithmetic mean)	598.0	
Variation explained by regression	241.8	40.4
Variation explained by regional classification and regression	574.0	95.9

MAPS OF RESIDUALS USED IN THE SELECTION OF UNIT AREAS FOR FIELD INVESTIGATION

As stated [above], when large residual values are located on the periphery of a study area, they suggest that regional boundaries should be modified so as to eliminate from the study area the unit areas in which the extreme values are located. However, the location of extremely large residual values is not necessarily restricted to the margins of the study area; on the contrary, large residuals may occur anywhere. If the character of the unit areas in which very large residuals occur is not known, so that new variables cannot be identified or so that a reclassification of all unit areas cannot be made, the areas in which the large residuals occur may be selected for additional intensive field investigation.

Intensive field investigation in specific unit areas is another application of the research approach used in many disciplines; it is a direct application of the case study to geographic problems. Hence using the map of residuals from regression to specify unit areas in which to conduct the field investigation produces a

REGIONAL CONCENTRATION OF RESIDUALS FROM REGRESSION IN HYPOTHETICAL STUDY AREA C

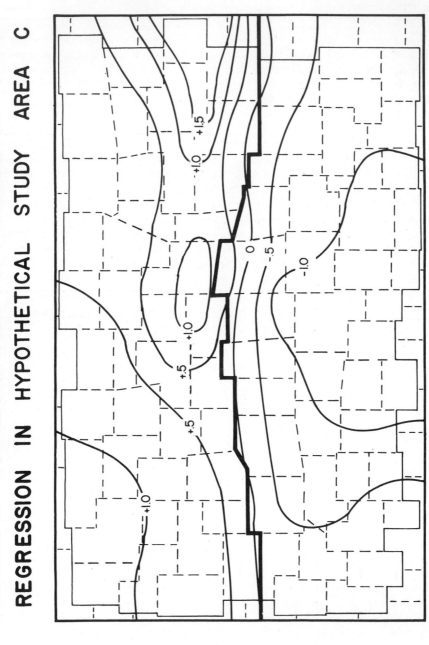

----- UNIT AREA BOUNDARY
—— STUDY AREA BOUNDARY

—— SUGGESTED SUBREGIONAL BOUNDARY
ᑎ ISOLINE INDICATING MAGNITUDE OF THE
RESIDUAL FROM REGRESSION, $(Y_{cn} - Y_n)/S_{Y_c}$

FIGURE 3

340

nice balance between statistical techniques and the case study approach. As Horst points out:

... The statistical and case study methods may be used profitably to supplement one another. The use of either method alone will probably yield less satisfactory results than when they are thus used in conjunction with one another. When the statistical analysis reaches a ceiling of prediction accuracy, it must await the aid of the case study. The investigator, by studying intensively those cases which he failed to predict correctly, may learn which factors previously used were irrelevant, which relevant factors were overlooked, and what particular relationships of factors should have been taken into account. By incorporating what has been learned into a new statistical analysis, mistakes previously made may be rectified, and new ideas may be tested for their contribution to prediction efficiency.[44]

Thus by employing residuals to specify areas for field investigation, the geographer is provided with a means of allocating his efforts so that they will be most fruitful of new hypotheses and the discovery of additional independent variables.

The spatial distribution of large residuals may take two patterns: they may be widely scattered, or they may be spatially concentrated. When either pattern appears, the unit areas in which extremes are located may be specified as ones in which field work will be conducted to develop hypotheses to be tested in all unit areas located in the study region. The field work may not lead to the identification of new independent variables. It may, however, indicate that the unit areas should be reclassified because they are heterogeneous in terms of the dependent variable; e.g., in a study of population distribution, it may be desirable to classify unit areas as urban and rural before proceeding with the analysis. If the extreme residuals are widely scattered and their number is small, there may be too few observations in any hypothesized subgroup to permit a realistic analysis. In this case, the heterogeneous observations are excluded from the study. If the extreme residual values are spatially concentrated and occur in relatively large numbers, it may be desirable to set them apart as a separate region and conduct a covariance analysis .... However, even if the extreme residual values are grouped to establish a separate

region, they still may be subjected to an intensive field investigation.

* * * * *

SOME OPERATIONAL USES OF MAPS OF RESIDUALS FROM REGRESSION

[We may now] exemplify, on an operational level, [the] three geographic research situations in which maps of residuals from regression may be useful as aids in the identification of new independent variables and in the reformulation of hypotheses. Some studies in which maps of residuals have been incorporated in the research design already have appeared in geographic literature. McCarty has used maps of residuals of the form $(Y_{cn} - Y_n)$ and $(Y_{cn} - Y_n)/Y_n$ to assess the predictive performance of a multiple regression equation.[45] Robinson and Bryson have incorporated a map of the form $(Y_{cn} - Y_n)$ to establish the spatial pattern of residual values and have speculated "as to what other factors are associated with the more significant divergences."[46] Thomas has used maps of residuals of the form $(Y_{cn} - Y_n)/S_{Y_c}$ to suggest new variables, modify regional boundaries, and specify unit areas for additional intensive field investigation.[47] However, the maps of residuals were largely incidental to the other parts of these investigations, and specific uses were not discussed in detail.

MAPS OF RESIDUALS USED TO IDENTIFY NEW INDEPENDENT VARIABLES

The use of maps of residuals from regression to suggest additional independent variables is nicely exemplified by a study in political geography.[48] The general goal of this investigation was to understand the spatial pattern of a particular voting behavior, i.e., the spatial distribution of the relative number of people per county who voted for Sen. Joseph H. McCarthy in the 1952 general election. The dependent variable in this investigation was the percentage of the total vote per county which was cast for McCarthy.

From the inspection of a series of statistical maps and from the logical consideration of the dependent variable, one independent variable was selected and hypothesized as being areally associated with the McCarthy vote. This independent variable was the percentage of the total population per county which was rural, henceforth referred to as relative rural population.

The relationship between the per cent of the total vote per county which was cast for McCarthy and the relative rural population gives a coefficient of correlation, r, of .58 (Table 5).[49] The relationship with relative rural population explains 34 per cent of the total variation in the dependent variable.

Explained variation of only one-third was not considered an adequate proportion. Hence it was necessary to formulate new hypotheses concerning independent variables which might more successfully explain the spatial variations in the per cent of the total vote per county which was cast for McCarthy. A map of residuals from regression was prepared to aid in the solution of additional independent variables to be included in the regression equation. Residuals of the form $(Y_{cn} - Y_n)/S_{Y_c}$ were mapped (Fig. 4). Six class intervals, .5 S_{Y_c} in width, were used along with two intervals which were open-end, i.e., greater than $+1.5S_{Y_c}$ and smaller than $-1.5S_{Y_c}$.

One of the most significant characteristics of the patterns of residuals from regression of the per cent of total vote per county which was cast for McCarthy on the relative rural population is the apparent gradient in all directions away from Appleton, which was his home

town. In the area nearest Appleton there is a marked tendency to consistently underestimate the per cent of the total vote which was cast for the Senator. In all directions from Appleton, the tendency to underestimate the per cent cast for McCarthy generally decreases until, at some distance from the city, estimated values of the dependent variable exceed observed ones. As distance from Appleton continues to increase the tendency to overestimate the per cent for McCarthy also increases and the absolute magnitude of the overestimates becomes larger.

The spatial pattern of residuals from the simple regression analysis leads to hypothesizing an areal association between relative McCarthy vote and distance from his hometown. Specifically, it is hypothesized that, when relative rural population per county is allowed for, McCarthy's popularity decreases with the distance of each county from Appleton, Wis. Operationally, the distance from Appleton of a given county is defined as the number of miles of straight-line distance between Appleton and the areal center of that particular county.

The hypothesis that distance from Appleton affects significantly the relative total vote per county which was cast for McCarthy was tested within the framework provided by multiple regression analysis. As before, the dependent variable is the per cent of the total vote per county cast for him. However, now two independent variables are employed in the analysis:

TABLE 5

Correlation-Regression of the Percentages of the Total Vote per County Cast for McCarthy (Y) on the Percentage of the Total Population per County Which Was Rural (X₁) and the Distance of the County from Appleton, Wisconsin (X₂)*

Relationship	Coefficient of correlation (r)	Coefficient of determination (r²)	Standard partial regression coefficient (β)	Coefficient of multiple correlation (R)	Coefficient of multiple determination (R²)
Y on X_1	.58	.34			
Y on X_2	−.18	.03			
Y on X_1 with X_2 held constant			.67		
Y on X_2 with X_1 held constant			−.35		
Y on X_1 and X_2				.67	.45

*Source: H. H. McCarty, *McCarty on McCarthy* (see note 48).

RESIDUALS FROM REGRESSION

$(Y_{cn} - Y_n)/S_{yc}$

The Regression of Percent of Total Vote

Cast for McCarthy on Percent of

Total Population That is Rural

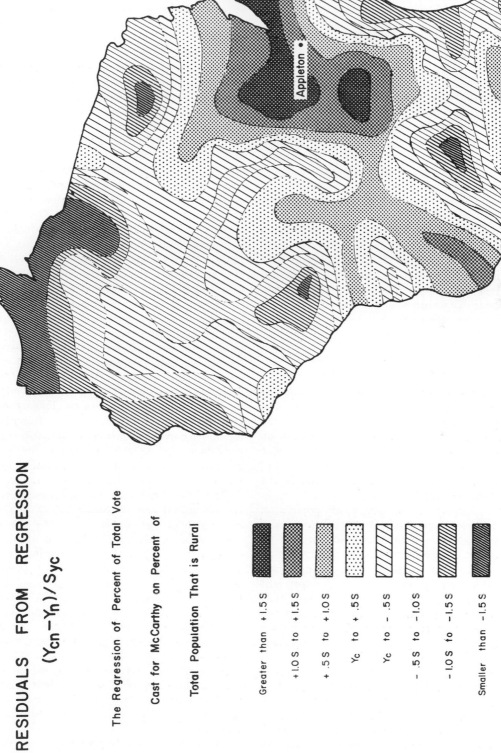

Greater than +1.5 S

+1.0 S to +1.5 S

+.5 S to +1.0 S

Y_c to +.5 S

Y_c to -.5 S

-.5 S to -1.0 S

-1.0 S to -1.5 S

Smaller than -1.5 S

FIGURE 4

343

(1) relative rural vote, the first independent variable employed in the investigation, and (2) the distance of a county from Appleton.

Standard partial regression coefficients for relative rural population and distance from Appleton indicate that both independent variables exert a significant influence on the spatial pattern of the relative McCarthy vote (Table 5). As indicated by the coefficient of multiple determination, R^2, explained variation has increased from 34 per cent, the value of r^2 for the simple regression analysis, to 45 per cent (R^2) for multiple regression. This is an increase of 32 per cent in the amount of variation in the dependent variable that is explained.

As specified [earlier], the map of residuals was employed to suggest a new independent variable to be included in the regression analysis. It might now be desirable to map residuals as determined by the regression equation, using two independent variables. These residuals then could be used to formulate additional hypotheses and select more independent variables to be included in the investigation.

MAPS OF RESIDUALS USED TO ESTABLISH OR MODIFY REGIONAL BOUNDARIES

An example of the way maps of residuals from regression may be employed to establish regional boundaries is provided in a study in urban geography. Specifically, the population growth which occurred (in the decade from 1940 to 1950) in a group of outlying cities located in the Chicago urbanized area is the dependent variable.[50]

After inspection of maps of population growth, field investigation in the area, and logical consideration of population growth as a spatially distributed phenomenon, a set of nine independent variables was hypothesized as being associated areally with the dependent variable. It was further hypothesized that regional differences in the distribution of population growth occurred, and that recognition of those differences would aid in understanding the overall spatial pattern.

A simple regression analysis was undertaken to establish the relationship between population growth and each independent variable; a multiple regression analysis which included all nine independent variables also was conducted. The simple and multiple regression analyses

were undertaken for the urbanized area as a whole and for each subsector within it, and maps of residuals were prepared for all variables in all regional groupings which demonstrated a statistically significant relationship with population growth.

The map of residuals from regression which exemplifies their use to suggest the location of regional boundaries is the one based upon the relationship, in outlying cities of the northern sector, between population growth and the birth-death differential. The independent variable, the birth-death differential for a given outlying city, is defined as the difference between the number of births and the number of deaths occurring [in] the resident population of that city.

The spatial distribution of residuals from regression in the northern sector shows a clear pattern of correlation based upon overestimation and underestimation (Fig. 5). The population growth in cities adjacent to Lake Michigan, excepting Evanston, is consistently overestimated; population growth in the other cities of the northern sector is underestimated.

The pattern of residuals ... suggests the hypothesis that two population growth regions occur in the northern sector of the Chicago urbanized area. Specifically, the cities adjacent to Lake Michigan, excepting Evanston, are grouped together to form one hypothetical region with overestimation of population growth providing the element of homogeneity. The remaining cities, in which population growth was underestimated, for the other region.

The hypothesis that the northern sector of the urbanized area is composed of two population-growth regions is tested by means of analysis of covariance.[51] The first step in the covariance analysis involved testing whether or not significant differences exist between the slopes of the subregional regression lines.[52] Evidence concerning this test is not conclusive (Table 6). The mean-square variation allocated to differences in slope of subgroup regression lines is equal to .02377; mean-square variation from the subgroup lines is .00494. The ratio between these variances is 4.91, which barely exceeds the value of F which might occur due to chance at the 5 per cent level, but is much smaller than the value permissible at the 1 per cent level.[53]

With only inconclusive evidence available

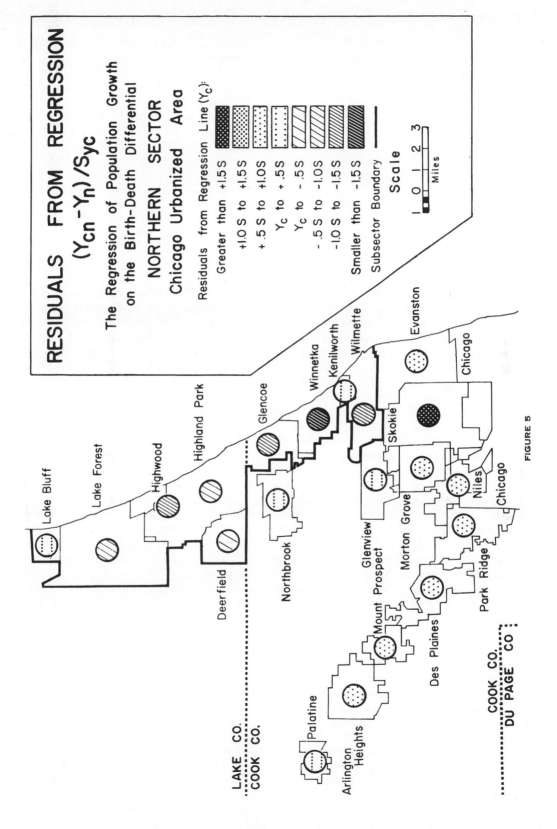

RESIDUALS FROM REGRESSION
$(Y_{cn} - Y_n)/S_{yc}$

The Regression of Population Growth
on the Birth-Death Differential

NORTHERN SECTOR
Chicago Urbanized Area

Residuals from Regression Line (Y_c):

Greater than +1.5 S
+1.0 S to +1.5 S
+.5 S to +1.0 S
Y_c to +.5 S
Y_c to −.5 S
−.5 S to −1.0 S
−1.0 S to −1.5 S
Smaller than −1.5 S
Subsector Boundary

Scale

0   1   2   3
Miles

FIGURE 5

Lake Bluff
Lake Forest
Highwood
Highland Park
Glencoe
Winnetka
Kenilworth
Wilmette
Evanston
Skokie
Chicago
Deerfield
Northbrook
Glenview
Morton Grove
Niles
Chicago
Park Ridge
Mount Prospect
Des Plaines
Palatine
Arlington Heights

LAKE CO.
COOK CO.

COOK CO.
DU PAGE CO.

TABLE 6

*The effect of dividing the northern sector
of the Chicago urbanized area into two
geographic regions*

	Amount	Per cent of total
Total variation (measured from the arithmetic mean)	.624	
Variation explained by regression	.244	39.0
Variation explained by regional classification and regression	.547	87.6

concerning the significance of differences in the *slopes* of the subregional regression lines, it then was necessary to determine whether or not their different *elevations* explained a significant amount of variation in the dependent variable. This was accomplished by testing to determine whether or not a statistically significant amount of the variation in population growth was explained by using a regression line with a common slope but lying at different elevations. This test established the importance of the regional subdivision, apart from regression.

Whether or not the regional classification, apart from regression, explains a significant amount of the total variation in the spatial distribution of population growth is established indirectly. Because the F-ratio was not significant at the 1 per cent level, the statistical hypothesis that subgroup regression lines differed as regards slope was rejected. Hence one regression line with a common slope fits all subregions. If there is significant difference between the magnitude of the variance from the common regression line and the magnitude of the variance from the regression line fitted to all unit areas in the northern sector, it is due to the elevation of the common regression line, which passes through each subgroup mean. Hence the significance of the regional classification, apart from regression, is determined by computing the F-ratio between the mean-square variation from the common regression line and the mean-square variation attributable to the subregional means. If the latter exceeds the former by a great enough magnitude, the subregional classification is accepted as statistically significant.

For the data used in this example, the F-ratio between mean-square variation from the common regression line and mean-square variation attributable to subregional means is 46.9. This value greatly exceeds the magnitude of the largest F-ratio which would have occurred by chance at either the 1 per cent or the 5 per cent level.[54] Hence the hypothesis that the northern sector can be divided into two subsectors having significantly greater homogeneity than the northern sector as a whole may be accepted. On a relative basis, the relationship between population growth and the birth-death differential, when established for the northern sector as a whole, explained about 39.0 per cent of the total variation in the spatial pattern of population growth. When the subregional classification and regression are emphasized, as indicated by the use of the common regression line, the proportion of total variation which is explained is increased to 83.8 per cent. Thus by recognizing heterogeneity with the study area, and relocating boundaries accordingly, the geographer was able to add considerably greater precision to his investigation.

MAPS OF RESIDUALS USED IN THE SELECTION OF UNIT AREAS FOR FIELD INVESTIGATION

The use of residuals from regression to specify unit areas as the ones in which to undertake additional field investigation is illustrated by a study in urban geography conducted within the confines of the central place theory. Specifically, the investigation attempted to eliminate one aspect of the spatial distribution of urban places.[55]

Based upon the initial formulation presented by Christaller, it was hypothesized that a systematic relationship obtains between the distance between a given city to its nearest neighbor of the same population size and the population size of that city.[56] This hypothesis was tested using a random sample of urban places in Iowa. Distance from a given city to its nearest neighbor of the same population size is the dependent variable. The notion of "same population size" was operationalized by means of probability functions. Hence the population of the nearest neighbor with the "same population size" as a given city was not identical to the population of the given city, but differed from it no more than would be expected by the operation of chance. Definition in terms of the probability function permits the notion of distance to the nearest neighbor of the same population size to be operationalized as a "logically discrete" variable, which was treated as a continuous one.[57] Hence a regression analysis between the distance from a given city to its nearest neighbor of the same population size and the population size of the given city may be undertaken.

The regression of "distance" on "population size" provides a coefficient of correlation of .59. Thus 34.8 per cent of this variation in the spatial pattern of distance between paired urban places is explained by the population size of the sample city. This proportion indicates that independent variables not included in the investigation affect the spatial distribution of "distances."

In order to secure greater depth of understanding about those factors which might affect the spacing of cities in Iowa, field work was undertaken. A map of extreme residuals from regression was prepared, and cities identified on this map were investigated as opposed to visiting all sample cities (Fig. 6). Only data falling into four class intervals are portrayed on this map; the intervals employed are (1) greater than $+1.5 S_{Y_c}$, (2) $+1.0 S_{Y_c}$ to $+1.5 S_{Y_c}$, (3) $-1.0 S_{Y_c}$ to $-1.5 S_{Y_c}$, and (4) smaller than $-1.5 S_{Y_c}$.

One hypothesis to be subjected to objective, quantitative evaluation was formulated because of the characteristics of cities for which distance to the nearest neighbor of the same population size is overpredicted, i.e., $Y_{cn} > Y_n$. Field investigation in cities which are located closer, on the average, to their nearest neighbors than would be expected, considering their populations, indicates that functions other than central ones are part of the economic base of these cities and provide support for a population which is larger than that which could be supported merely from providing central goods and services for the surrounding farm population.

The cities located near Lake Okoboji, in northwest Iowa, provide a good example of urban places with economic bases expanded by the presence of noncentral functions. The Okoboji area is noted for recreational facilities, and the urban places located there appear to have a disproportionate number of motels, cabins, restaurants, etc., when compared with most Iowa cities. Hence a comparatively large population is supported in these cities, which in turn are located closer than expected to their nearest neighbors of the same population size. This observation points to the need for assessing the importance to the spatial distribution of urban places of such noncentral activities as tourism and mining.[58] It was therefore hypothesized that urban places which have important noncentral components as parts of their economic bases are closer to their nearest neighbors of the same population size than cities which are more narrowly classified as central places.

Field examination of the cities for which distance to the nearest neighbor of the same population size was underpredicted, $Y_{cn} < Y_n$, also provided insight into the nature of factors affecting the spatial pattern of cities in Iowa. Those cities which were much farther than average from their nearest neighbors appear to have higher proportions of abandoned stores and other buildings in their business districts. For example, the business district of Hillsboro, an urban place which is located in southern Iowa, appears to have a higher proportion of empty stores than the average for the sample group. Furthermore, the presence of abandoned residences suggests a decrease in the number of persons residing in Hillsboro. Evaluated within the framework provided by the central place theory, this evidence suggests a decline in commercial importance from some more eminent position which the place enjoyed in the past. This interpretation focuses attention on the fact that the economic base and commercial importance of all cities may change over a period of time. Hence it seems reasonable to raise the question whether the central place theory might not be a closer approximation to reality during an earlier time period than at present. From this general question comes the specific hypothesis that in 1900 the population size of given urban places explains more completely the distances between those places and their nearest neighbors of the same size than does this same relationship in 1950.

The hypotheses presented in this section are not the only ones formulated during the field investigation. They are merely two out of several which suffice as examples of the kinds of substantive hypotheses which may be formulated when maps of extreme residuals from

SELECTED RESIDUALS FROM REGRESSION

$(Y_{cn} - Y_n) / S_{yc}$

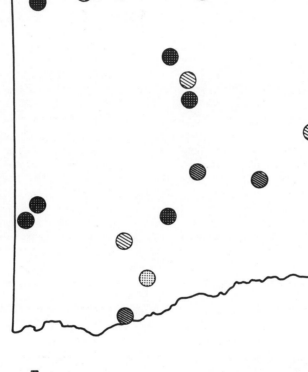

The Regression of Distance From Sampled

City to Nearest Neighbor of Same

Population-Size of Sampled City

Population-Size on

Greater than +1.5 S

+1.0 S to +1.5 S

-1.0 S to -1.5 S

Smaller than -1.5 S

FIGURE 6

regression are employed to specify areas for field work. It appears that as many pregnant hypotheses were forthcoming from the field investigation restricted to cities for which residual values were comparatively large as would have been developed had field work been conducted in all sample cities. However, the set of hypotheses developed by investigating only urban places for which extreme residuals occur were formulated with less expenditure of time and other travel cost than would have been the case had all sample cities been investigated.

SUMMARY

[This study] demonstrate[s] how the statistical-distribution map may be combined with statistical techniques to provide the geographer with an integrated system that is useful for the formulation and testing of hypotheses. Specific emphasis has been placed on identifying the uses and limitations characteristic of maps of residuals from regression.

Four values which are determined by the observed value for a given unit area, Y_n, and the value computed from the regression equation, Y_{cn}, are defined, and their mathematical characteristics which affect the spatial patterns that they present are discussed. The four values are (1) $Y_{cn} - Y_n$, (2) $(Y_{cn} - Y_n)/Y_n$, (3) Y_{cn}/Y_n, and (4) $(Y_{cn} - Y_n)/S_{Y_c}$, where S_{Y_c} is the standard error of estimate.

Three . . . research problems to which residuals may provide valuable insight are as follows:

1. identifying additional independent variables to be included in an investigation
2. establishing or modifying regional boundaries
3. selecting unit areas in which to conduct field work.

* * * * *

FOOTNOTES

[1] A. H. Robinson in P. E. James and C. F. Jones, eds., *American Geography: Inventory and Prospect* (Syracuse: Syracuse University Press, 1954), p. 555.

[2] R. Hartshorne, *The Nature of Geography* (Lancaster, Pa.: Association of American Geographers, 1939), p. 249.

[3] James and Jones, *op. cit.*, p. 9.

[4] *Ibid.*, pp. 512–516.

[5] *Ibid.*, p. 557.

[6] An obvious exception is the statistical map that is employed in a centrographic analysis of a spatial distribution. Centrographic methods are reviewed in J. F. Hart, "Central Tendency in Areal Distributions," *Economic Geography*, **30** (1954), 48–59.

[7] H. H. McCarty, *et al.*, *The Measurement of Association in Industrial Geography*, State University of Iowa, Department of Geography (1956).

[8] L. Zobler, Decision Making in Regional Construction," *Annals of the Association of American Geographers*, **48** (1958), 140–148.

[9] The reader is referred to the mimeographed discussion paper series available from the University of Washington, Department of Geography.

[10] This phase would not be undertaken if all of the variables relevant to the spatial distribution of some phenomenon were, for practical purposes, already included in the study.

[11] H. Feigl, "The Scientific Outlook: Naturalism and Humanism," in *Readings in the Philosophy of Science* (New York: Appleton-Century-Crofts, 1953), pp. 8–18.

[12] McCarty, *et al.*, *op. cit.*, p. 1.

[13] R. Hartshorne, *Perspective on the Nature of Geography* (Chicago: Rand McNally & Co., 1959), pp. 160–161.

[14] Hartshorne, *The Nature of Geography, op. cit.*, p. 372.

[15] Exceptions are the cartographic methods which geographers have used more frequently than researchers in other disciplines. However, at present these methods are crude and amenable to use on a descriptive level rather than an inferential one.

[16] W. L. Garrison has surveyed the statistical and mathematical techniques common in other disciplines which the geographer has adopted or may find useful in "Geographical Record," *Geographical Review*, **46** (1956), 427–428.

[17] H. H. McCarty, "Use of Certain Statistical Procedures in Geographic Analysis," *Annals of the Association of American Geographers*, **46** (1956), 263.

[18] The reader is referred to G. U. Yule and M. G. Kendall, *An Introduction to the Theory of Statistics* (New York: Hafner Publishing Co., Inc., 1950), or any other intermediate statistics textbook, for a more complete discussion of regression and the principle of least squares.

[19] G. W. Snedecor, *Statistical Methods* (Ames: Iowa State College Press, 1956), pp. 126–135.

[20] E. N. Thomas, "An Analysis of the Areal Association Between Population Growth and Selected Factors Within Outlying Cities in the Chicago Urbanized Area," unpublished Ph. D. thesis, Northwestern University (1958).

[21] For a given unit area, it is possible for Y_n to be

positive or negative, e.g., in a study of population change, some unit areas may show growth, others may show loss; likewise, Y_{cn} may be positive or negative. Furthermore, the absolute value of Y_{cn} may exceed the absolute value of Y_n, or the absolute value of Y_n may exceed the absolute value of Y_{cn}. Thus, symbolically, the following situations may occur: $+Y_n$, $-Y_n$, $+Y_{cn}$, $-Y_{cn}$, $|Y_n| < |Y_{cn}|$, $|Y_n| > |Y_{cn}|$, which give rise to eight different combinations, in half of which $Y_{cn} - Y_n$ and $(Y_{cn} - Y_n)/Y_n$ do not have like signs.

Case I
When $+Y_n$, $+Y_{cn}$, and $|Y_n| < |Y_{cn}|$ then

$$Y_{cn} - Y_n > 0$$

and
$$\frac{Y_{cn} - Y_n}{Y_n} > 0$$

The signs are the same.

Case II
When $+Y_n$, $+Y_{cn}$, and $|Y_n| > |Y_{cn}|$ then

$$Y_{cn} - Y_n < 0$$

and
$$\frac{Y_{cn} - Y_n}{Y_n} < 0$$

The signs are the same.

Case III
When $-Y_n$, $+Y_{cn}$, and $|Y_n| < |Y_{cn}|$ then

$$Y_{cn} - (-Y_n) = Y_{cn} + Y_n > 0$$

and
$$\frac{Y_{cn} - (-Y_n)}{-Y_n} = \frac{Y_{cn} + Y_n}{-Y_n} < 0$$

The signs are different.

Case IV
When $-Y_n$, $+Y_{cn}$, and $|Y_n| > |Y_{cn}|$ then

$$Y_{cn} - (-Y_n) = Y_{cn} + Y_n > 0$$

and
$$\frac{Y_{cn} - (-Y_n)}{-Y_n} = \frac{Y_{cn} + Y_n}{-Y_n} < 0$$

The signs are different.

Case V
When $+Y_n$, $-Y_{cn}$, and $|Y_n| < |Y_{cn}|$ then

$$-Y_{cn} - Y_n < 0$$

and
$$\frac{-Y_{cn} - Y_n}{Y_n} < 0$$

The signs are the same.

Case VI
When $+Y_n$, $-Y_{cn}$, and $|Y_n| > |Y_{cn}|$ then

$$-Y_{cn} - Y_n < 0$$

and
$$\frac{-Y_{cn} - Y_n}{Y_n} < 0$$

The signs are the same.

Case VII
When $-Y_n$, $-Y_{cn}$, and $|Y_n| > |Y_{cn}|$ then

$$-Y_{cn} - (-Y_n) = -Y_{cn} + Y_n > 0$$

and
$$\frac{-Y_{cn} - (-Y_n)}{-Y_n} = \frac{-Y_{cn} + Y_n}{-Y_n} < 0$$

The signs are different.

Case VIII
When $-Y_n$, $-Y_{cn}$, and $|Y_n| < |Y_{cn}|$ then

$$-Y_{cn} - (-Y_n) = -Y_{cn} + Y_n < 0$$

and
$$\frac{-Y_{cn} - (-Y_n)}{-Y_n} = \frac{-Y_{cn} + Y_n}{-Y_n} > 0$$

The signs are different.

[22] McCarty, *et al.*, *The Measurement of Association, op. cit.*, pp. 88–92.

[23] See, for example, Fig. 9.4 in Yule and Kendall, *op. cit.*, p. 211. Some implications of the case when the size of $Y_{cn} - Y_n$ values appears positively correlated with Y values [are] discussed [on pp. 336–337].

[24] Let Y_{c1} take the value 8.00, Y_1 the value 4.00, Y_{c2} the value 20.00, and Y_2 the value 16.00. Then

$$Y_{c1} - Y_1 = 8.00 - 4.00 = 4.00$$

and

$$Y_{c2} - Y_2 = 20.00 - 16.00 = 4.00$$

Thus:

$$Y_{c1} - Y_1 = Y_{c2} - Y_2$$

However:

$$\frac{Y_{c1} - Y_1}{Y_1} = \frac{8.00 - 4.00}{4.00} = 1.00$$

whereas:

$$\frac{Y_{c2} - Y_2}{Y_2} = \frac{20.00 - 16.00}{16.00} = .25$$

[25] The close correspondence between the expressions may be seen from the following:

$$\frac{Y_{cn} - Y_n}{Y_n} = \frac{Y_{cn}}{Y_n} - \frac{Y_n}{Y_n} = \frac{Y_{cn}}{Y_n} - 1$$

Thus a Y_{cn}/Y_n value for the nth unit area exceeds $(Y_{cn} - Y_n)/Y_n$ for the same area only by unity.

[26] This conclusion is obvious because S_{Y_c} is always positive. Dividing all observations by this positive constant will not change their rank order.

[27] This statement is strictly true only with data that initially form a normal frequency distribution, or have been transformed so that they do. However, considerable skewness must be present before skewness alone results in observations lying at distances greater than $\pm 3.0 S_{Y_c}$ from the regression line.

[28] It is not necessary to compute $(Y_{cn} - Y_n)/S_{Y_c}$ for each unit area if $Y_{cn} - Y_n$ already is available. It is merely necessary to compute the values needed to establish the ends of the class intervals being employed and then assign individual $Y_{cn} - Y_n$ values to the appropriate interval. The limits of the class interval can be had by solving the equation:

$$\frac{Y_{cn} - Y_n}{S_{Y_c}} = X_K$$

where X_K is any limiting value desired. The subscript K indicates the standardized quotient which results from solving the equation.

As an example, let S_{Y_c} take the value of 18.70 and assume that it is necessary to determine what values mark the ends of the interval $+.5 S_{Y_c}$ to $+1.0 S_{Y_c}$. Two equations are set up:

(1)
$$\frac{Y_{cn} - Y_n}{S_{Y_c}} = X_{.5}$$

and

(2)
$$\frac{Y_{cn} - Y_n}{S_{Y_c}} = X_{1.0}$$

Substituting in 1 and 2 gives:

(3)
$$\frac{Y_{cn} - Y_n}{18.70} = .5$$

and

(4)
$$\frac{Y_{cn} - Y_n}{18.70} = 1.0$$

Solving equations 3 and 4 gives 9.35 and 18.70, respectively. Thus $(Y_{cn} - Y_n)/S_{Y_c}$ residuals lying in the class interval $+.5 S_{Y_c}$ to $+1.0 S_{Y_c}$ will have values equal to or greater than 9.35, but less than 18.70.

[29] A standardized observation is defined by

$$\frac{Y_n - \bar{Y}}{S_y}$$

when Y_n is the magnitude of the observation for the nth unit area, $\bar{Y}$ the mean of Y, and S_y the standard deviation for the set of Y observations.

As in the situation encountered when standardizing residuals, it is not necessary to compute $(Y_n - \bar{Y})/S_y$ for all observations, but merely to compute the values which limit class intervals. For example, let 36.20 and 5.90 be the values of $\bar{Y}$ and S_y, respectively. (The mean frequently will be known because it is a valuable descriptive statistic and also because it is needed for computing S_y according to many formulae.) Assume

that it is desired to establish the limiting values for the interval $-.5 S_y$ to $-1.0 S_y$.

Set up two equations similar to 1 and 2.

(5)
$$\frac{Y_n - \bar{Y}}{S_y} = X_{-.5}$$

and

(6)
$$\frac{Y_n - \bar{Y}}{S_y} = X_{-1.0}$$

Substituting in 5 and 6 gives

(7)
$$\frac{Y_n - 36.20}{5.90} = -.5$$

and

(8)
$$\frac{Y_n - 36.20}{5.90} = -1.0$$

Solving equations 7 and 8 gives 33.25 and 30.30, respectively. Thus values of Y with magnitudes equal to or less than 33.25 but greater than 30.30 will lie in the interval $-.5 S_y$ to $-1.0 S_y$.

[30] J. S. Mill, *A System of Logic* (New York: Harper & Row, Publishers, 1874), pp. 284–285.

[31] Paul Horst, *et al.*, *Prediction of Personal Adjustment*, Social Science Research Council, Bulletin No. 48 (1941), p. 117.

[32] M. M. Gordon, "Sociological Law and the Deviant Case," *Sociometry*, **10** (1947), 250–258.

[33] Inasmuch as two or more maps are compared, the necessary for maintaining comparable class intervals is apparent. For an excellent discussion of the effect which the selection of class intervals has on the appearance of a spatial distribution see J. R. Mackay, "An Analysis of Isopleth and Choropleth Class Intervals," *Economic Geography*, **31** (1955), 71–81.

[34] H. H. McCarty and N. E. Salisbury, *Visual Comparison of Isopleth Maps as a Means of Determining Correlations Between Spatially Distributed Phenomena*, State University of Iowa, Department of Geography, Study No. 3 (1957).

[35] When only extremes of residual and original distributions are mapped, the selection of class intervals to develop comparable maps is important. As mentioned [above], eminently comparable maps may be constructed by mapping the data after they are standardized.

[36] If R^2 is zero, then

$$\Sigma(Y_{cn} - Y_n)^2 = \Sigma(\bar{Y} - Y_n)^2$$

[37] In conversation, Dr. W. L. Garrison has suggested that a similarity in the patterns of Y_n and $(Y_{cn} - Y_n)$ may result because spatially distributed events tend to be mutually interdependent. When observations are significantly interdependent, residuals from least-squares estimating equations also may be interdependent, i.e., correlated. When this is the case, the appropriate analytical tools may be selected from the body of techniques known as "autocorrelation" and "autoregression." However, an evaluation of the appropriateness of these methods for geographic re-

search is beyond the scope of this monograph. Further-more, it appears that the techniques suggested here for developing geographic hypotheses may be applied, with only slight modification necessary, to the formulation of hypotheses from residuals from autoregression.

A review of autoregression and autocorrelation techniques, as they apply to economic problems, may be found in G. Tintner, *Econometrics* (New York: John Wiley & Sons, Inc., 1952), pp. 239–300.

[38] Yule and Kendall, *op. cit.*, pp. 281–309, esp. p. 298.

[39] James and Jones, *op. cit.*, p. 21.

[40] A general solution to the problem of classifying observations in geographic research is suggested by B. J. L. Berry in "A Note Concerning Methods of Classification," *Annals of the Association of American Geographers*, **48** (1958), 300–303.

[41] Obviously, both uses are closely related. This division is quite arbitrary and is designed primarily for illustrative purposes.

[42] It is not always desirable or proper to exclude from consideration unit areas in which large residual values occur. A situation where isolated large residual values are not excluded from an investigation is discussed [below].

[43] Snedecor, *op. cit.*, pp. 394–446.

[44] Horst, *et al.*, *op. cit.*, p. 118.

[45] McCarty, *et al.*, *The Measurement of Association*, *op. cit.*, pp. 88–92.

[46] A. H. Robinson and R. A. Bryson, "A Method or Describing Quantitatively the Correspondence of Geographical Distributions," *Annals of the Association of American Geographers*, **47** (1957), 379–391.

[47] E. N. Thomas, "Areal Associations Between Population Growth and Selected Factors in the Chicago Urbanized Area," *Economic Geography*, **36** (1960), 158–170.

[48] H. H. McCarty, *McCarty on McCarthy: The Spatial Distribution of the McCarthy Vote*, 1952, un-published manuscript, State University of Iowa, Department of Geography.

[49] The least significant value for r at the 1 per cent level with 69 degrees of freedom is .30.

[50] Thomas, "Areal Associations, *op. cit.*

[51] Analysis of covariance procedures are explained by Snedecor in *Statistical Methods*, Chaps. 13–14 using areal data (states).

[52] The initial assumption of the covariance analysis, that standard deviations for subregions are homogeneous, is fulfilled. The evidence that this is the case is provided by an F-test. Mean-square variation, variance, in Subregion I is .19081; in Region II it is .06897, which gives an F-ratio of 2.87. With 8 and 10 degrees of freedom, this value is not statistically significant at the 1 per cent level.

[53] The critical value of the F ratio for the 5 per cent level is 4.49; for the 1 per cent level it is 8.53. [See] H. Arkin and R. R. Colton, *Tables for Statisticians* (New York: Barnes & Noble, Inc., 1950), p. 118.

[54] With 1 and 17 degrees of freedom, the largest chance value of F is 4.45 at the 5 per cent level and 8.40 at the 1 per cent level.

[55] This study, undertaken by the writer, is in progress.

[56] W. Christaller, *Die zentralen Orte in Süddeutschland*, C. W. Baskin, trans., *The Central Places of Southern Germany* (Englewood Cliffs, N. J.: Prentice-Hall, Inc., 1966).

[57] E. E. Lewis, *Methods of Statistical Analysis in Economics and Business* (Boston: Houghton Mifflin Company, 1953), p. 69.

[58] Where precise quantitative data concerning economic activities are lacking, factors such as tourism or mining can be added qualitatively to the regression equation merely by classifying cities on as objective a basis as possible from inspection and then evaluating the importance of this classification by means of covariance analysis.

6

A MULTIVARIATE STATISTICAL MODEL
FOR PREDICTING MEAN ANNUAL FLOOD
IN NEW ENGLAND

SHUE TUCK WONG

Quantitative geomorphology has made rapid strides in recent years. During the last decade considerable literature has been added to the field. Old concepts of hydrologic analysis have been revised,[1] new concepts have evolved in landform studies,[2] and new techniques have been developed to aid in the quantitative evaluation of empirical work.[3] In addition to these, new insights to fluvial morphology have been gained by the application of the physical laws of thermodynamics and fluid mechanics.[4]

The advent of electronic digital computers has greatly facilitated data processing and analysis, and has made possible the solution of many kinds of multivariate problems. With these high-speed machines available, multivariate methods should be more widely encouraged in geomorphic and hydrologic research, since many of the topographic and fluvial properties of watersheds are of a multivariate nature. Except for multiple regression analysis, few multivariate statistical methods have yet been applied in geomorphology or hydrology, however. There are, therefore, great possibilities whereby these methods may be gradually introduced.[5]

The purpose of this paper is to show how principal components analysis—a multivariate statistical technique—can be readily adapted to quantitative geomorphology and hydrology in reconstructing a multiple regression model for estimating the magnitude of mean annual flood in New England.

BACKGROUND OF THE STUDY

The study came about as a consequence of an initial investigation of the relation between mean annual flood at ninety gauged basins in New England and a number of selected topographic characteristics. The hypothesis that variations in log mean annual flood (log $Q_{2.33}$) were a function of: (1) log average land slope (X_1), (2) log mean altitude (X_2), (3) log tributary channel slope (X_3), (4) log stream density (X_4), and (5) log shape of the drainage basin (X_5),

Reprinted from *Annals of the Association of American Geographers*, **53** (1963), 298–311, by permission of the author and editor.

was tested by multiple regression analysis, and the regression equation obtained was:

$$(1) \quad \log Q_{2.33} = -0.227 + 0.544 \log X_1$$
$$(0.278)$$

$$- \; 0.076 \log X_2 + 0.282 \log X_3$$
$$(0.169) \qquad (0.171)$$

$$+ \; 0.359 \log X_4 + 0.547 \log X_5$$
$$(0.327) \qquad (0.046)$$

(See the Appendix for an the elaboration of the operational measurement of each of these variables.)

A t-test showed that the regression coefficients of $\log X_1$ and $\log X_5$ were significant. This means that mean annual flood in New England increases as does average land slope and deviations in shape of the basin from a circular form.

The cumulative multiple correlation coefficient as the five independent variables were added to the equation was as follows: log average land slope, 0.517; log mean altitude, 0.517; log tributary channel slope, 0.699; log stream density, 0.705; and log shape of basin, 0.899.

An F-test indicated that log average land slope, log tributary channel slope, and log shape of basin contributed significant additions to the explanation of variations in the dependent variable at the 1 per cent level. Log mean altitude and log stream density contributed little to the final multiple correlation coefficient, however.

Although a significant multiple correlation coefficient was obtained from the five variables, the study was not very satisfactory from a technical standpoint. Some reasons can be given for deficiencies in the analysis. First, the independent variables were not well selected, for the first four were multicollinear, that is, a linear relation existed among them; second, they were not properly arranged in order of importance of contributions of the variables to the estimated multiple regression equation.

There are a number of ways in which these problems might be tackled. R. Frisch,[6] who first coined the term, has developed a geometric technique to detect the presence of multicollinearity in a regression equation. One way to handle the ordering problem is by stepwise multiple regression analysis.[7] A second possi-

bility for handling multicollinearity is by means of an orthogonalization process through Taylor series expansion.[8] A third possibility of tackling it is by variable feedback system analysis.[9] Principal components analysis affords a fourth possibility to solve for multicollinearities.

The last suggestion is perhaps the most suitable. Since floods are a function of geomorphic and hydrologic factors, and since these factors are highly interrelated, it might be interesting to find out the underlying dimensions of interrelatedness. Principal components analysis is ideal to handle such a problem, for it eliminates all redundant factors within a set of variables and produces an underlying set of orthogonal variables. This the approach that will be taken in the ensuing pages.[10]

The paper is embedded in hydrologic theory. To begin with, the laws of river systems are reviewed, and the relations between floods and fluvial characteristics discussed. Principal components analysis is then applied to isolate the geomorphic and hydrologic dimensions of New England, because our initial multiple regression analysis failed to produce satisfactory results. The factors extracted by principal components analysis are then used as [a] basis for reformulating the previous multiple regression equation, to provide a means of predicting the magnitude of mean annual flood in New England.

THE THEORY OF RIVER SYSTEMS

The first thorough quantitative evaluation of the study of river systems was the work of Horton.[11] His contributions to fluvial morphology are best summarized in his three laws, namely:

1. the law of stream numbers
2. the law of stream lengths
3. the law of stream slopes.

These three laws of river systems may perhaps be conveniently reviewed in the form of a series of mathematical equations.

THE LAW OF STREAM NUMBERS

According to the first law, "the number of streams of different orders in a given drainage basin tends closely to approximate an inverse geometric series in which the first term is unity and the ratio is the bifurcation ratio."[12]

Symbolically, this law may be represented as follows:

$$(2a) \qquad N_0 = r_b^{(s-o)}$$

where N_0 is the number of streams of order o in a given drainage basin, s is the order of the main stream, o is the order of a given class of tributaries, and the r_b is the bifurcation ratio. The latter may be defined as the ratio of branching in stream orders of a drainage network, that is, the ratio of the number of stream segments of a given order N_o to the number of channel segments of next higher order, N_{o+1}, i.e., $r_b = N_o/N_{o+1}$. Moreover,

$$(2b) \qquad N = \frac{r_b^s + 1}{r_b - 1}$$

where N represents streams of all orders. This law was empirically verified and substantiated by Strahler, Schumm, Maxwell, Coates, Ore and White, Morisawa, and Brush.[13]

THE LAW OF STREAM LENGTHS

The second law of Horton[14] postulates that "the average lengths of streams of each of the different orders in a drainage basin tend closely to approximate a direct geometric series in which the first term is the average lengths of the first order." Thus,

$$(3a) \qquad l_o = l_1 r_e^{o-1}$$

where l_o is the average length of streams of order o, l_1 is the average length of the first-order streams, r_e is the stream length ratio, or the ratio of the average length of streams of a given order l_0 to the average length of streams of the next lower order l_{o-1}, i.e., $r_e = l_o/l_{o-1}$. The total stream length of a given order is the product of the average length and number of streams (Eq. 2a and 3a combined):

$$(3b) \qquad L_o = l_1 r_b^{s-o} r_e^{o-1}$$

where L_o represents the total length of streams of order o. From Eq. 3b, the sum of the total

lengths of streams of different orders may be derived:

$$(3c) \quad \Sigma L = l_1[r_b^{s-1} + r_b^{s-2}r_e + r_b^{s-3}r_l^2 + \cdots + r_b^o r_l^{s-1}]$$

This is the total length of all streams in a drainage basin with the main stream of a given order s.[15] Schumm[16] tested this law and found the relationship was consistent with his study for the mean stream lengths of Perth Amboy, Chilileno Canyon, and Hughesville.

THE LAW OF STREAM SLOPES

The third law of Horton,[17] which concerns average channel slope, states that "there is a fairly definite relationship between slope of the streams and stream order, which can be expressed by an inverse of geometric series law." In symbolic terms,

$$(4) \qquad S_0 = \frac{S_1}{r_s^{o-1}}$$

where S_o is the average slope of stream order o, S_1 is the average slope of the first-order streams, r_s is the slope ratio, or the ratio of the average slope of streams of given order S_0 to the average slope of streams of the next higher order S_{o+1}, $r_s = S_o/S_{o+1}$. The consistency of this law is again verified by the Perth Amboy stream slopes in New Jersey.[18]

Horton's three laws may be summed up in a single equation, which he called the formula of drainage composition:[19]

$$(5) \qquad D_d = \frac{l_1 r_b^{s-1}}{A_s} \cdot \frac{p^s - 1}{p - 1}$$

where D_d is the drainage density, defined as the ratio of all streams in a draiange basin to the drainage area, measured in miles per square mile; l_1 is the average length of streams of first order; r_b is the bifurcation ratio, i.e., the ratio between the number of streams of one order to the number of streams of the next higher order; A is the total drainage basin area, having a main stream order of s; and p is the ratio r_l/r_b, or ratio of length ratio to bifurcation ratio.

Schumm[20] suggested a fourth law in the manner of Horton's equation of drainage composition. He called it the *law of stream areas*, which states that "the mean drainage basin areas of streams of each order tend closely to approximate a direct geometric series in which the first term is the mean area of the first order basins."

Symbolically this is expressed as follows:

$$(6) \qquad \bar{A}_0 = \bar{A}_1 R_a^{o-1}$$

where $\bar{A}_o$ is the mean drainage basin streams of order o, $\bar{A}_1$ is the mean drainage basin of first-order streams, R_a is the area ratio, i.e., the ratio of the average basin area of the stream of given order A_o to the average area of basins of the next lower order A_{o-1},

$$(7) \qquad R_a = \frac{A_o}{A_{o-1}}$$

Hack[21] tested Horton's law of drainage composition for basins in Maryland and Pennsylvania, and verified it by deriving equations for length and drainage area of the principal stream of any order s. Thus given

$$p = \frac{r_l}{r_b} \text{ and } D_d = \frac{l_1}{a_1}$$

$$A_s = \frac{l_1 r_b^{s-1}}{\dfrac{l_1}{a_1}} \cdot \frac{p^s - 1}{p - 1}$$

Since $\qquad A_s = a_1 r_b^{s-1} \cdot \dfrac{p^s - 1}{p - 1}$

and $\qquad L_s = l_1 r_l^{s-1}$,

$$(8) \text{ therefore } \quad A_s = a_1 r_b^{s-1} \cdot \frac{p^s - 1}{p - 1}$$

where L_s and A_s are length and drainage area of the principal stream of any order s.

Morisawa[22] in her empirical analysis of the geometry of fifteen watersheds in the Appalachian Plateau found that the geomorphic characteristics conform to Horton's equation of drainage composition, but only in horizontal properties, and not in vertical properties, owing to variations in geologic and lithologic structure.

An interesting property, related to drainage networks, is that of texture. Smith[23] in his comparative study of erosional topographies for fifty-four basins, found that "texture ratio" could be expressed:

$$(9) \qquad T = \frac{N}{P}$$

where T is the texture ratio, N is the number of crenulations on a selected contour, and P is the length of the basin perimeter, and that this was a logarithmic function of Horton's drainage density formula, i.e., the ratio of the sum of all stream lengths to the drainage area (see Eq. 5).

RELATIONS BETWEEN RIVER DISCHARGE AND BASIN CHARACTERISTICS

More recent studies have shown that the interrelationship between stream discharge and the geometric properties of watersheds can be expressed by simple power or exponential functions.[24] These interrelationships between the geometric properties of stream and discharge may best be summarized by a series of equations:

$$(10) \qquad W = aQ^b$$

$$(11) \qquad D = cQ^f$$

$$(12) \qquad V = kQ^m$$

$$(13) \qquad L_d = pQ^j$$

$$(14) \qquad S = tQ^z$$

$$(15) \qquad n' = rQ^y$$

where W is the width of channel in feet; D is the depth in feet; V is the velocity in feet per second; L_d is the suspended sediment load in tons per day; S is the stream slope in feet per foot; n' is the roughness or friction factor, defined as the ratio of grain size to the depth of flow; and Q is the discharge in cubic feet per second; a, c, k, p, t, and r are numerical constants, and b, f, m, j, z, and y are numerical exponents.

Leopold and Miller[25] found that stream order, O, was related to the number of streams, N; stream length, L; stream slope, S; drainage area, A_d; and discharge, Q; all of which seem to be consistent with Horton's scheme of classification. These relations may be expressed in the following forms:

(16) $$O \; \alpha \; \text{Log} \; N$$

(17) $$O \; \alpha \; \text{Log} \; L$$

(18) $$O \; \alpha \; \text{Log} \; S$$

(19) $$O \; \alpha \; \text{Log} \; A_d$$

(20) $$O \; \alpha \; \text{Log} \; Q$$

Several interrelations among the above equations may be noted. One relation is that between stream length and drainage area:

Since $$L \; \alpha \; Q^j$$

and $$Q^j \; \alpha \; A_d^k$$

(21)   therefore $$L \; \alpha \; A_d^{jk}$$

Another example of a similar interrelation is that between stream slope and discharge:

Since $$S \; \alpha \; A_d^k$$

and $$A_d^k \; \alpha \; Q^j$$

(22)   therefore $$S \; \alpha \; Q^{jk}$$

It is evident that stream length, drainage area, discharge, and stream slope are all interrelated and can be expressed in exponential forms. When plotted on log–log paper these relationships of drainage network factors form straight lines, indicating that there is not only interrelatedness, but also collinearity.

The logarithmic relationships of stream length to stream order, and stream lengths to drainage area, were recently tested by Leopold and Langbein[26] in a random-walk model of stream networks. It was found that the logarithmic increase of stream length and the number of streams with order checked by the average position of random walks corresponded well to uniform increases in entropy.

RELATED HYDROLOGIC STUDIES OF REGIONAL FLOODS

A number of statewide magnitude and flood-frequency studies undertaken by the U.S. Geological Survey in cooperation with some State Highway Departments have just been completed,[27] and a succinct summary of the evolution of methods and empirical formulae for evaluating the occurrence of floods can be found in the U.S. Geological Survey Water-Supply Paper No. 1580-A (1962).[28]

Most of the flood-frequency studies for evaluating peak discharge are generally expressed by multiple regression of the following form:

(23) $$Q_T = a B^b C^c D^d E^e \cdots$$

where Q_T is the T-year peak discharge; B, C, D, and E are independent variables characterizing the topographic and hydrologic conditions; and a, b, c, d, and e are the numerical constants of the regression equation.

The T-year peak discharge is based on the theory of extreme values,[29] and is determined at the probabilities which correspond to the recurrence intervals of 1.2, 2.33, 5, 10, 25, 50, 100, ..., 1000 years. A peak discharge with a recurrence interval of ten years means that there is a probability of 1 in 10 that a flood would return in any year. Q with the subscript 2.33 is generally known as the mean annual peak discharge or mean annual flood, which can easily be read off from Gumbel extreme value probability paper—a special kind of graph paper specially designed for recording flood recurrences. This is frequently used as the index flood in flood-magnitude studies.

Previous flood reports have revealed that the factors which are most significantly related to mean annual flood are: drainage area, channel slope, annual runoff, mean distance to outlet, mean altitude, basin lag, surface storage, climate, vegetation, and soil.

Kinnison and Colby[30] found that mean annual flood was related to drainage area, mean distance to outlet, mean altitude above gauge, and storage area. Potter[31] in a multiple regression on peak flows, related length and slope of principal waterway as the geomorphic factors. Bigwood and Thomas[32] used drainage area, main channel slope, degree of urbanization, and channel storage in their development of a flood-flow formula for Connecticut. Morisawa,[33] in her study of Little Mill Creek Watershed, Ohio, found average stream discharge was significantly correlated with basin area, relief ratio, elongation ratio, circularity, and total stream length. Cross and Webber,[34] in their report on floods in Ohio, correlated mean annual flood with drainage area, main channel slope, and type of soil. Benson[35] showed significant correlations existed for peak discharges at nine recurrence intervals in New England, using drainage area, channel slope, surface storage, precipitation intensity, temperature, and an orographic factor.

From the summary of the literature and the list of the independent variables cited, it is evident that many of these factors are highly interrelated with one another, either directly or inversely. None of the studies reviewed, however, has ever attempted to solve this problem of collinearity and interdependency among the independent variables in their multiple regression analyses.[36] We have noted earlier how the initial investigation of the present paper encountered this difficulty of multicollinearity. It is in an attempt to eliminate some of these redundancies of interrelated variables that we now turn to a principal components analysis of certain data for New England.

THE NEW ENGLAND ANALYSIS

Ninety gauged basins in New England, ranging in size from ten square miles to 2000 square miles, were selected for study. These observations were the same as those used in the original multiple regression analysis. The ninety basins were the only ones which were gauged and for which adequate information characterizing the physiographic and hydrologic environments was available.

The reasons for selecting New England for this study are: first, the good stream-flow records available for the area; second, the fact that the region has been well studied and fully mapped, and many indices for evaluating the physiography of the area have already been computed by Walter Langbein and the U.S. Geological Survey.[37]

Since this study is an extension of the initial investigation, more variables taken from Water-Supply Paper No. 968-C have been added. The geomorphic and hydrologic variables considered include the following: (1) drainage area, (2) basin shape, (3) main channel slope, (4) tributary channel slope, (5) percentage of area in ponds and lakes, (6) average land slope, (7) mean altitude, (8) length of longest watercourse, (9) length of the main stream, (10) stream density, (11) precipitation-frequency intensity, (12) mean annual flood.[38]

These variables were used because they are all related to stream flow and topography in one way or another, as the previous theories indicate.

A preliminary graphic analysis indicated that all the data were distributed log-normally. Therefore, all observations were transformed into common logarithms and a 90×12 data matrix was prepared. This data matrix was in turn reduced to a symmetric, 12×12 correlation matrix (Table 1).

PRINCIPAL COMPONENTS ANALYSIS

The correlation matrix was subjected to principal axis analysis.[39] After varimax orthogonalization,[40] four eigenvectors and their corresponding eigenvalues were obtained (Table 2). Table 3 summarizes the percentage of total variance extracted by the four components.

Notice the conspicuous importance of components I–II. Together they account for more than four-fifths of the total variance and covariance of the original twelve variables. This means that the variance between the twelve variables can be attributed to two major factors, while the third and fourth factors may be regarded as minor terms, since they account for such a small percentage of the total variance. A summary of the percentage of the variance of each of the twelve variables accounted for by each of the principal components is presented in Table 4. Essentially, then, principal components analysis shows that the interrelatedness of the twelve variables is due to two underlying common dimensions, which account for approximately 86 per cent of the total explained variance.

INTERPRETATION OF THE COMPONENTS

Let us now examine the basic dimensions in greater detail and see how each variable is related to each of the components. The degree of association between a variable and a component is indicated by the "factor loadings" outlined in Table 2. These loadings have much the same meaning as the correlation coefficients in the correlation matrix.

As an arbitrary decision rule to determine the significance of the variables related to each component, we shall regard as far as possible only those variables between the limits of

TABLE 1

Correlation matrix

		D.A. X_1	Shape X_2	Ch.Sl. X_3	Tr.Sl. X_4	%P&L X_5	Av.Sl. X_6	M.Alt. X_7	St.D. X_8	L.W.C. X_9	L.M.Str. X_{10}	Pr.Int. X_{11}	M.A.F. X_{12}
D.A.	X_1	1											
Shape	X_2	0.9384	1										
Ch. Sl.	X_3	−0.4647	−0.5395	1									
Tr. Sl.	X_4	−0.2210	−0.2963	0.6879	1								
% P & L	X_5	0.0309	0.0959	−0.5063	−0.5960	1							
Av. Sl.	X_6	0.1385	0.0700	0.5114	0.8663	−0.6282	1						
M. Alt.	X_7	0.1062	0.0357	0.5369	0.8092	−0.4575	0.8691	1					
St. D.	X_8	−0.3097	−0.3814	0.5388	0.5093	−0.2167	0.3735	0.4168	1				
L. W. C.	X_9	0.9134	0.9614	−0.5750	−0.3102	0.1412	0.0347	0.0136	−0.3478	1			
L. M. Str.	X_{10}	0.9267	0.9585	−0.5395	−0.3007	0.1595	0.0464	0.0370	−0.3616	0.9591	1		
Pr. Int.	X_{11}	−0.2144	−0.1469	−0.0945	−0.4909	0.2948	−0.6048	−0.5215	−0.0734	−0.1456	−0.1846	1	
M. A. F.	X_{12}	0.7998	0.7709	0.0369	0.2179	−0.2940	0.5172	0.4458	−0.0477	0.7197	0.7436	−0.3452	1

TABLE 2

Table of varimax normalized column eigenvectors

Variables X		Varimax Normalized Column Eigenvectors			
		b_1	b_2	b_3	b_4
X_1	D. A.	0.895	0.356	0.093	−0.023
X_2	Shape	0.942	0.277	0.089	−0.034
X_3	Main Ch. Sl.	−0.732	0.443	0.237	−0.164
X_4	Trib. Ch. Sl.	−0.537	0.784	−0.059	0.048
X_5	% A in P & L	0.303	−0.631	0.063	0.622
X_6	Av. Land Sl.	−0.200	0.939	0.069	0.010
X_7	Mean Alt.	−0.219	0.877	0.038	0.174
X_8	Stream density	−0.542	0.343	0.542	0.400
X_9	Longest W. C.	0.940	0.243	0.094	0.037
X_{10}	Length of M. S.	0.939	0.263	0.072	0.057
X_{11}	Pr.-Frq. Int.	−0.036	−0.652	0.619	−0.323
X_{12}	Mean An. Fld.	0.600	0.708	0.185	−0.124

TABLE 3

Percentage of total explained variance

	Eigen-values (λ)	Percentage of total explained variance
	5.12	46.97
	4.24	38.90
	0.81	7.43
	0.73	6.70
Grand total sum	10.90	100.00

TABLE 4

Percentage of variance of the twelve variables accounted for by each of the components

	Variable	Component				
		I	II	III	IV	*H^2 in %
1	Drainage area	80.10	12.67	0.86	0.05	93.68
2	Basin shape	88.74	7.67	0.79	0.12	97.32
3	Main channel slope	53.87	19.62	5.62	2.69	81.80
4	Trib. channel slope	28.87	61.46	0.35	0.23	90.91
5	Percentage A in P & L	9.10	39.82	0.39	38.69	88.00
6	Average land slope	4.00	88.17	0.47	0.01	92.65
7	Mean altitude	4.79	76.91	0.14	3.03	84.87
8	Stream density	29.38	11.76	29.38	16.00	86.52
9	Length of longest W. C.	88.36	5.90	0.88	0.14	95.28
10	Length of main stream	88.17	6.92	0.52	0.32	95.93
11	Precip.-Frq. intensity	0.13	42.51	38.32	10.43	91.39
12	Mean annual flood	36.00	50.13	3.42	1.54	91.09

* H^2 refers to the communality in percentages of each variable. The communality of a variable is the sum of its independent common variances. The percentages in the above table are obtained by squaring the factor loadings and multiplying by 100.

0.500 and −0.500 as "important," although the simple correlation coefficients for a couple of variables may be less than 0.50 or −0.50.

Component I, which accounts for 46.97 per cent of the total variance, obviously is the most significant factor. The variables which are significantly correlated with this component are: drainage area, shape of basin, main channel slope, tributary channel slope, stream density, length of longest watercourse, length of main stream, and mean annual flood (see Table 2). These relationships agree with the high associations found in the correlation matrix (Table 1). Among the fluvial characteristics, it can be observed that length of longest watercourse and length of the main stream are directly related to drainage area, basin shape, and mean annual flood. That is not surprising, for the length of a river determines its area and shape, and hence the magnitude of the discharge. The simple correlation coefficients between length of longest watercourse and the three variables—drainage area, basin shape, and mean annual flood—respectively, are 0.91, 0.96, and 0.72, while that between the length of the main stream and the same variables are 0.93, 0.96, and 0.74. It is obvious that length of the longest watercourse and length of the main stream are collinear. They suggest that component I represents a size dimension in conformity with Horton's law of stream lengths.

Power functions were obtained for some of the simple relations for the ninety gauged basins, and the resulting regression equations were:

(24)   log length of the main stream vs.
        log drainage area: $0.30 A_d^{0.54}$

(25)   log length of the main stream vs.
        log basin shape: $0.31 S_H^{0.35}$

(26)   log length of the main stream vs.
        $\log Q_{2.33}$: $0.23 Q_{2.33}^{0.34}$

A t-test indicated that the exponential functions of Eqs. 24–26 were highly significant at the 1 per cent and 5 per cent level. This means that drainage area, basin shape, and mean annual flood increase proportionately with the length of the main stream, indicating that their high dependency of increase in size is due to the proportionate increase in the length of the main stream. These regression equations compare favorably with similar observations made by Hack[41] for streams in the Appalachian Mountain area and by Brush[42] for rivers in central Pennsylvania.

While both length of the longest watercourse and length of the main stream are directly correlated, they vary inversely with the main channel slope, tributary channel slope, and stream density. Table 5 summarizes the correlation coefficients of these variables. All the correlation coefficients are significant at the 5 per cent level. However, an F-test for the regression coefficients of these variables indicated that the power function were not significant. Nevertheless, their inverse relationships manifested a geometric regularity consistent with Horton's law of stream slopes.

TABLE 5

Simple correlation coefficients of log length of the longest watercourse and log length of the main stream

	Log length of the longest watercourse	Log length of the main stream
Log main channel slope	−0.58	−0.54
Log tributary channel slope	−0.31	−0.30
Log stream density	−0.34	−0.36

The slope dimension is clearly revealed in component II, which accounts for 38.90 per cent of the total variance. The variables that are highly associated with this component are: average land slope, mean altitude, main channel slope, tributary channel slope, mean annual flood, percentage area in ponds and lakes, and precipitation-frequency intensity (see Table 2). While the topographic variables, average land slope and mean altitude, are positively related to the fluvial characteristics, main channel slope, tributary channel slope, and mean annual flood, they vary inversely with the hydrologic factors, percentage area in ponds and lakes and precipitation intensity. The simple correlation coefficients for these variables are presented in Table 6.

The high degree of association between these morphometric and hydrologic variables indicates their interdependence with one another. The orderly hydraulic relations that exist in the

New England topography accord well with the empirical findings of Gray in his analysis of watershed interrelationships.[43]

The significant inverse relationship between average land slope and the percentage area in ponds and lakes and precipitation intensity suggest the dependence of surface storage and climate on relief. This means that the more rugged the topography, the less is the percentage area in ponds and lakes, and the less intense is the precipitation frequency, or vice versa. The strong influence of topography on mean annual flood is evident from the correlation coefficients given in Table 6.

TABLE 6

Simple correlation coefficients of log average land slope and log mean altitude

	Log average land slope	Log mean altitude
Log main channel slope	0.51	0.54
Log tributary channel slope	0.87	0.81
Log mean annual flood	0.52	0.45
Log % area in ponds and lakes	−0.62	−0.46
Log precipitation intensity	−0.60	−0.52

Component III, which accounts for 7.43 per cent of the total variance, is a weak doublet dimension of wetness related to climate. Only two factors have high loadings: stream density and precipitation intensity. The high positive correlation between these two variables suggests the effect of climate on the evolution of stream networks. This means that the greater the precipitation, the higher is the stream density.

Component IV has hardly any significant factor loadings. This component accounts for the smallest portion of the variance of the twelve variables—6.70 per cent. Perhaps this might best be designated as a term comprising random covariations.

GRAPHIC REPRESENTATION OF TWO PRINCIPAL COMPONENTS

The hydrologic associations in New England, therefore, have been reduced from twelve vari-

ables to four underlying dimensions. Actually only the first two of these dimensions are of real substantive significance because they account for more than 85 per cent of the total variance.

For the purpose of visual presentation, the two basic dimensions may be represented graphically on two coordinate axes with their component vectors located (see Fig. 1). Component I is measured along the horizontal axis, and component II along the vertical axis. All the major size variables are located in the positive quadrant, while the slope variables are in the negative quadrant. Note the orthogonality of variables 1, 2, 9, and 10 and 6 and 7; and notice the angles between variables 1, 2, 9, and 10 in component I; and 3, 8, and 6, 7 in component II. The closer the component vectors are to one another, the more common are the elements underlying these physical variables. When two or more vectors overlie one another in the same direction, they are said to be collinear. If the angle between vectors approaches 90 degrees, the correlation of the two approaches zero, i.e., they are independent and orthogonal.

REFORMULATED MULTIPLE-REGRESSION ANALYSIS OF MEAN ANNUAL FLOOD IN NEW ENGLAND

The graphic analysis of the factor loadings indicates that two variables that are orthogonal and at the same time related to mean annual flood are: length of the main stream and average land slope (see Fig. 1). The former is a member of dimension 1 (size and length), and the latter of dimension 2 (slope and topography). These two variables are now used as surrogates for the two basic dimensions to reconstruct the initial multiple regression equation. The resulting reformulated regression equation has the form:

$$(27) \qquad Q_{2.33} = aL^b S^c$$

where $Q_{2.33}$ is the mean annual flood, L is the length of the main stream, S is the average land slope, and a, b, and c are numerical constants of the regression equation. In this equation, floods are said to be a function of two orthogonal dimensions: (1) size—a combination of Horton's first two laws, which are

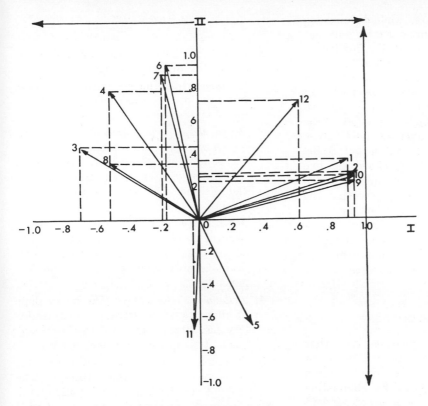

FIGURE 1. Location of the first and second component vectors for twelve variables in two dimensions

not independent, and (2) relief—Horton's third law.

The resulting least-square fit has the form:

$$(28) \qquad \log Q_{2.33} = -1.02 + 1.29 \log X_1$$
$$(0.08)$$
$$+ \; 0.97 \log X_2$$
$$(0.09)$$

A t-test shows that both the regression coefficients for log length of the main stream (X_1) and log average land slope (X_2) are highly significant.

The multiple correlation coefficient, R, was 0.895, while the coefficient of determination, R^2, was 0.80, which means that 80 per cent of the variation in the mean annual flood of New England can be accounted for by the combination of two variables alone, namely, log length of the main stream and log average land slope, or, more generally, by the two basic dimensions —size of basin and relief.

The increments of the R for X_1 and X_2 are 0.74 and 0.89, while their respective F-values are 108.85 and 160.20. It is obvious that the F-ratios of the multiple regression coefficients

are highly significant, and doubtless this verifies the power of the model. A summary of the analysis of variance for the multiple regression is given in Table 7.

TABLE 7

Analysis of variance for the multiple regression

Source of variation	D.F.	Sum of squares	Mean square	F-ratio
Due to regression	2	12.160866	6.080433	160.19759
Deviation about regression	87	3.902157	0.037955	
Total	89	15.463024		

Partial correlation coefficients, which measure the separate effect of the individual independent variables on the dependent variable holding the other variables constant, [were] also computed. The coefficient of partial correlation of log mean annual flood with log length of the main stream, while holding log average land slope constant, was 0.84, and that with log average land slope, holding log length of the main stream constant, was 0.72.

The magnitude of the mean annual flood in New England thus can be determined with an appreciable degree of accuracy using just two explanatory variables, namely, log length of the main stream and log average land slope. Although the R^2 of the reconstructed model is the same as the original R^2, which used five independent variables, the reformulated multiple regression equation is more precise than the previous one, for the problem of multicollinearity has now been eliminated, and much simpler, for fewer variables are used. The highly significant values of the regression coefficients in the new regression equation clearly reflect the power of the model.

CONCLUSION

Principal components analysis has thus facilitated the selection of a more effective set of parameters for the evaluation of mean annual flood in New England. By eliminating the redundancies of a battery of interdependent variables among the physiographic and hydrologic factors into two independent components of size and slope, it has provided a sound rationale for the reformulation of the initial multiple regression equation. Furthermore, in the elimination process, interesting commentaries have been produced related to current geomorphic theory.

The interesting feature revealed by the study is that in spite of the meager data used, systematic regularities of drainage composition were manifested. For example, a geometric orderliness of the relations of log length of the main stream to log size of the drainage area, log basin shape, and log mean annual flood was revealed and that these simple relations could be expressed in terms of power functions. Also, we noted that there exists an inverse relation between log length of the main stream and log main channel slope and log tributary channel slope. These direct and inverse relations of the morphometric properties of New England accord well with Horton's laws of stream lengths and stream slopes, and serve to indicate the power of current descriptive morphometric models.

APPENDIX

Definitions of morphometric and hydrologic properties of the drainage basins:

1. *Drainage area:* The entire basin in square miles drained by the whole river system and its tributaries.

2. *Basin shape, or the area–distance distribution measured in cubic miles:* This is the summation of small subdivisions of the drainage area, each multiplied by the distance of travel to the gauging station.

3. *Main channel slope:* The main slope of all parts of the channel which drains between 85 per cent and 10 per cent of the total drainage area. This is measured in feet per mile.

4. *Tributary channel slope:* The mean slope of all parts of the stream, which drains less than 10 per cent of the total drainage basin. It is measured in feet per mile.

5. *Percentage area in ponds and lakes:* This is a measure of surface storage. The amount of land in ponds and lakes shown on topographic maps is divided by the drainage area times 100.

6. *Average land slope:* This is the mean slope of the gradient of the drainage area in feet per mile. It is computed from Horton's formula of mean slope, $S_g = 1.571\, D\dot{N}/\Sigma l$, where D is the contour interval of difference in elevation in feet; N is the number of contours crossed; Σl is the total length of the subdividing lines (see Horton, "Drainage Basin Characteristics," *Transactions of the American Geophysical Union* [1932], 350–361).

7. *Mean altitude:* This is the mean elevation of the basin determined by planimetering the areas between contours. It is the area–altitude distribution of the basin computed by means of hypsometric curves, measured in feet above sea level.

8. *Length of longest watercourse:* The length measured in 0.1-mile chords to the source of the most headward stream.

9. *Length of main stream:* The length of the stream measured in miles from the gauge to the farthest point as stream on the map.

10. *Stream density:* The number of stream segments per unit of drainage area. It is derived by dividing the total number of stream segments with total area of the basin in square miles. Thus $F_s = N/A$, where F_s is the stream frequency, N is the total number of streams in a drainage basin, A is the drainage area in square miles.

11. *Precipitation-frequency intensity:* The volume of rain falling on a basin of unit area per unit time expressed in inches per hour. Here it is twenty-four-hour duration over a period of ten years.

12. *Mean annual flood:* This is the average of the values of the annual floods for a given area over a period of years. It is obtained by reading from a graph, visually fitted to a plot of annual floods whose magnitude corresponds to a recurrence interval of 2.33 years.

FOOTNOTES

[1] See A. N. Strahler, "Revisions of Horton's Quantitative Factors in Erosional Terrain" (Abstract), American Geophysical Union, Hydrology Section (Washington, 1953); J. C. Maxwell, "The Bifurcation Ratio in Horton's Law of Stream Numbers" (Abstract), *Transactions of the American Geophysical Union*, **36** (1955), 520; M. A. Melton, "A Derivation of Strahler's Channel-Ordering System," *Journal of Geology*, **67** (1959), 345–346.

[2] See A. N. Strahler, "Hypsometric (Area-Altitude) Analysis of Erosional Topography," *Bulletin of the Geological Society of America*, **63** (1952), 1117–1142; Strahler, "Accelerated Land Erosion as a Drainage-Density Transformation" (Abstract), *Program: Annual Meeting of the Geological Society of America* (1955), 99A; Strahler, "The Nature of Induced Erosion and Aggradation," in W. L. Thomas, Jr., ed., *Man's Role in Changing the Face of the Earth* (Chicago: University of Chicago Press, 1956), pp. 621–638.

[3] A. N. Strahler, "Dimensional Analysis Applied to Fluvially Eroded Landforms," *Bulletin of the Geological Society of America*, **69** (1958), 279–300; A. N. Strahler and D. Koons, *Objective and Quantitative Field Methods of Terrain Analysis*, Columbia University, Department of Geology, Final Technical Report, Office of Naval Research, Project No. NR 387–021 (1960); M. A. Melton, "Correlation Structure of Morphometric Properties of Drainage Systems and Their Controlling Agents," *Journal of Geology*, **66** (1958), 442–460; D. M. Gray, *Derivation of Hydrographs for Small Watersheds from Measurable Physical Characteristics*, unpublished Ph. D. thesis, Iowa State University (1960); R. L. Miller and J. S. Kahn, *Statistical Analysis in Geological Sciences* (New York: John Wiley & Sons, Inc., 1962), Chaps. 12–14, pp. 245–345. See also W. F. Wood and J. B. Snell, "Predictive Methods in Topographic Analysis, I: Relief, Slope, and Dissection on 1"-to-the-Mile in the United States," U. S. Army Quartermaster Research Center, Technical Report No. EP–112 (1959); A. B. Taylor and H. E. Schwartz, "Unit Hydrograph Lag and Peak Flow Related to Basic Characteristics," *Transactions of the American Geophysical Union*, **33** (1952), 235–246; M. W. Busby and M. A. Benson, "Grid Method of Determining Mean Flow-Distance in a Drainage Basin," *Bulletin of the International Association of Scientific Hydrology*, **20** (1960), 32–36; and N. C. Matalas, *Statistics of a Runoff Precipitation Relation*, U. S. Geological Survey, Professional Paper No. 434–D (1963).

[4] For an excellent account of the recent developments in thinking about river systems, see L. B. Leopold and W. B. Langbein, *The Concept of Entropy in Landscape Evolution*, U. S. Geological Survey, Professional Paper No. 500-A (1962); L. B. Leopold, "Rivers," *American Scientist* (Sigma Xi Publication), **50** (Dec. 1962), 511–537; and R. J. Chorley, *Geomorphology and General Systems Theory*, U. S. Geological Survey, Professional Paper No. 500-B (1962).

[5] See W. M. Snyder, "Some Possibilities for Multivariate Analysis in Hydrologic Studies," *Journal of Geophysical Research*, **67** (1962), 721–729. The best reference work on multivariate analysis from the numerical approach is M. G. Kendall, *A Course in Multivariate Analysis* (London: Griffin's Statistical Monographs, 1957); C. R. Rao, *Advanced Statistical Methods in Biometric Research* (New York: John Wiley & Sons, Inc., 1952) also contains a good treatment of some multivariate techniques; for a more mathematical approach to the subject, T. W. Anderson, *Introduction to Multivariate Statistical Analysis* (New York: John Wiley & Sons, Inc., 1958) is recommended; for an advanced text using the nonparametric approach, see S. N. Roy, *Some Aspects of Multivariate Analysis* (New York: John Wiley & Sons, Inc., 1958).

[6] For a discussion on the detection of multicollinearity, see R. Frisch, *Statistical Confluence Analysis by Means of Complete Regression Systems*, Oslo University, Institute of Economics, Publication No. 5 (1934).

[7] On the use of stepwise multiple regression for digital computers, see A. Ralston, *Mathematical Methods for Digital Computers* (New York: John Wiley & Sons, Inc., 1960).

[8] A treatment of this orthogonalization process is discussed in B. Harris, A. L. Sharp, A. E. Gibbs, and W. J. Owen, "An Improved Statistical Model for Evaluating Parameters Affecting Water Yields of River Basins," paper read at the Annual Meeting of the American Geophysical Union, Apr. 18–19, 1961.

[9] For an illustration of the application of variable feedback-system analysis, see M. A. Melton, "Correlation Structure," *op. cit.*

[10] There are numerous examples of the application of principal components analysis. Some of the fine

studies using this technique include the following: J. R. N. Stone, "The Interdependence of Blocks of Transactions," *Journal of Royal Statistical Society, Supplement* **9**, No. 1, (1947); B. J. L. Berry, "Basic Patterns of Economic Development," in N. S. Ginsburg, *Atlas of Economic Development*, University of Chicago, Department of Geography, Research Paper No. 68 (1961), pp. 110–119; C. A. Moser and W. Scott, *British Towns: A Statistical Study of Their Social and Economic Differences* (London: Oliver & Boyd, Ltd., 1960); and R. A. Reyment, "Quadrivariate Principal Components Analysis of *Globigerina Yeguaensis*," *Stockholm Contributions in Geology*, **8** (1961), 17–26.

[11] See R. E. Horton, "Erosional Development of Streams and Their Drainage Basins," *Bulletin of the Geological Society of America*, **59** (1945), 275–370.

[12] *Ibid.*, p. 286.

[13] See A. N. Strahler, "Hypsometric (Area-Altitude) Analysis," *op. cit.*, 1137; S. A. Schumm, *Evolution of Drainage Systems and Slopes in Badlands at Perth Amboy, New Jersey*, Columbia University, Department of Geology, Technical Report No. 8, Office of Naval Research, Project No. NR 389–042 (1954); J. C. Maxwell, *Quantitative Geomorphology of the San Dimas Experimental Forest, California*, Columbia University, Department of Geology, Technical Report No. 19, Office of Naval Research, Project No. NR 389–042 (1955); D. R. Coates, *Quantitative Geomorphology of Small Drainage Basins of Southern Indiana*, Columbia University, Department of Geology, Technical Report No. 10, Office of Naval Research, Project No. NR 389–042 (1958); H. T. Ore and E. D. White, "An Experiment in Quantitative Analysis of Drainage Basin Characteristics," *The Compass of Sigma Gamma Epsilon*, **36** (1958), 23–38; M. E. Morisawa, *Relation of Quantitative Geomorphology to Stream Flow in Representative Watersheds of the Appalachian Plateau Province*, Columbia University, Department of Geology, Technical Report No. 20, Office of Naval Research, Project No. NR 389–042 (1959); and L. M. Brush, Jr., *Drainage Basins, Channels, and Flow Characteristics of Selected Streams in Central Pennsylvania*, U. S. Geological Survey, Professional Paper No. 282-F (1961).

[14] Horton, *op. cit.*, 291.

[15] *Ibid.*, 292–293.

[16] Schumm, *op. cit.*, p. 13.

[17] Horton, *op. cit.*, 295.

[18] Schumm, *op. cit.*, p. 13.

[19] Horton, *op. cit.*, 296–298.

[20] Schumm, *op. cit.*, p. 14.

[21] See J. T. Hack, *Studies of Longitudinal Stream Profiles in Virginia and Maryland*, U. S. Geological Survey, Professional Paper No. 294-B (1954), p. 65.

[22] M. E. Morisawa, *op. cit.*

[23] K. G. Smith, "Standards for Grading Texture of Erosional Topography," *American Journal of Science*, **248** (1950), 655–668.

[24] For further discussion on simple power relations, see L. B. Leopold and T. Maddock, Jr., *The Hydraulic Geometry of Stream Channels and Some Physiographic Implications*, U. S. Geological Survey, Professional Paper No. 252 (1953); Leopold and J. P. Miller, *Ephemeral Streams—Hydraulic Factors and Their Relations to the Drainage Net*, U. S. Geological Survey, Professional Paper No. 282-A (1956); and Leopold and M. G. Wolman, *River Channel Patterns: Braided, Meandering and Straight*, U. S. Geological Survey, Professional Paper No. 282-C (1957).

[25] See Leopold and Miller, *op. cit.*, pp. 16–21.

[26] For a detailed discussion of the application of the second law of thermodynamics to the study of fluvial morphology, see Leopold and Langbein, *op cit.*

[27] The following statewide magnitude and flood-frequency studies have been completed: V. K. Berwick, *Floods in Eastern Montana, Magnitude nad Frequency*, U. S. Geological Survey, Open-File Report (1958); B. L. Bigwood and M. P. Thomas, *A Flood-Flow Formula for Connecticut*, U. S. Geological Survey, Circular No. 365 (1955); G. L. Bodhaine and D. M. Thomas, *Floods in Washington, Magnitude and Frequency*, U. S. Geological Survey, Open-File Report (1960); R. W. Carter, *Floods in Georgia, Frequency and Magnitude*, U. S. Geological Survey, Circular No. 100, (1951); J. S. Crawgwall, Jr., *Floods in Louisiana, Magnitude and Frequency* (Baton Rouge: Louisiana State Highway Dept., 1952); W. P. Cross and E. E. Webber, *Floods in Ohio, Magnitude and Frequency*, Ohio Department of Natural Resources, Division of Water, Bulletin No. 32 (1959); J. M. Darling, *Floods in Maryland, Magnitude and Frequency*, U. S. Geological Survey, Open-File Report (1959); D. W. Ericson, *Floods in Wisconsin, Magnitude and Frequency*, U. S. Geological Survey, Open-File Report (1961); L. W. Furness, *Floods in Nebraska, Magnitude and Frequency* (Lincoln: Nebraska Department of Roads and Irrigation, 1955); F. W. Kennon, *Magnitude and Frequency of Summer Floods in Western New Mexico and Eastern Arizona*, U. S. Geological Survey, Open-File Report (1954); J. A. McCabe, *Floods in Kentucky, Magnitude and Frequency*, U. S. Geological Survey, Open-File Report (1958); J. A. McCabe and D. A. Crosby, *Floods in North and South Dakota, Frequency and Magnitude*, U. S. Geological Survey, Open-File Report (1959); W. D. Mitchell, *Floods in Illinois, Magnitude and Frequency* (Springfield: Illinois Department of Public Works and Buildings, Division of Waterways, 1954); L. B. Pierce, *Floods in Alabama, Magnitude and Frequency*, U. S. Geological Survey, Circular No. 342 (1954); R. W. Pride, *Floods in Florida, Magnitude and Frequency*, U. S. Geological Survey, Open-File Report (1958); C. H. Prior, *Magnitude and Frequency of Floods in Minnesota*, Minnesota Department of Conservation, Division of Waters, Bulletin No. 1 (1949); H. C. Riggs, *Floods in North Carolina, Magnitude and Frequency*, U. S. Geological Survey, Open-File Report (1955); H. H. Schwob, *Iowa Floods, Magnitude and Frequency*, (Iowa Highway Research Board, Bulletin No. 1, 1953); J. K. Searcy, *Floods in Missouri, Magnitude and Frequency*, U. S. Geological Survey, Circular No. 370 (1955); W. D. Simons, *Relations of Flood Frequencies to Basin Characteristics, Upper Columbia River Basin*, U. S. Geological Survey, Water Resources Bulletin (May, 1948); R. H. Tice, *Delaware River Basin Flood Frequency*, U. S. Geological Survey, Open-File Report (1958); *Floods in Youghiogheny and Kiskiminetas River Basins, Pennsylvania and Maryland, Frequency and Magnitude*, U. S. Geological Survey, Circular No. 204

(1952); L. A. Wiard, *Floods in New Mexico, Magnitude and Frequency*, U. S. Geological Survey, Circular No. 464 (1962); V. K. Wilson and I. L. Trotter, *Floods in Mississippi, Magnitude and Frequency* (Jackson: Mississippi State Highway Dept., 1961).

[28] See M. A. Benson, *Evolution of Methods for Evaluating the Occurrence of Floods*, U. S. Geological Survey, Water-Supply Paper No. 1580-A (1962); a sequel by the same author is *Factors Influencing the Occurrence of Floods in a Humid Region of Diverse Terrain*, U. S. Geological Survey, Water-Supply Paper No. 1580-B (1963).

[29] See E. J. Gumbel, *Statistics of Extremes* (New York: Columbia University Press, 1958).

[30] See H. B. Kinnison and B. R. Colby, "Flood Formulas Based on Drainage-Basin Characteristics," *Transactions of the American Society of Civil Engineers*, **110** (1945), 849–904.

[31] See W. D. Potter, "Rainfall and Topographic Factors that Affect Runoff," *Transactions of the American Geophysical Union*, **34** (1953), 67–73.

[32] See Bigwood and Thomas, *op. cit.*

[33] M. E. Morisawa, *Relation of Morphometric Properties to Runoff in the Little Mill Creek, Ohio, Drainage Basin*, Columbia University, Department of Geology, Technical Report No. 17, Office of Naval Research, Project No. 389–042 (1959).

[34] See Cross and Webber, *op. cit.*

[35] See M. A. Benson, "Areal Flood-Frequency Analysis in a Humid Region," *Bulletin of the International Association of Scientific Hydrology*, **19** (1960), 5–15.

[36] For a related discussion on this point, see B. J. L. Berry, "Width of Flood Plain in Relation to Drainage Area and other Factors," appendix to *Classification and Mapping of Critical Combinations of Flood Characteristics*, University of Chicago, Department of Geography, a report under Contract No. 12-14-100-4507 [43] with the Agricultural Research Service, U. S. Department of Agriculture (July, 1962).

[37] See W. B. Langbein, *et al.*, *Topographic Characteristics of Drainage Basins*, U. S. Geological Survey, Water-Supply Paper No. 968-C (1947), pp. 125–157.

[38] See the Appendix for definitions of list of independent variables.

[39] For a clear exposition of the principal axis method, see B. Fruchter, *Introduction to Factor Analysis* (Princeton: D. Van Nostrand Co., Inc., 1954), Chap. 6.

[40] See H. F. Kaiser, "The Varimax Criterion for Analytic Rotation in Factor Analysis," *Psychometrica*, **23** (1958), 187–200; Kaiser, "Computer Program for Varimax in Factor Analysis," *Educational and Psychological Measurement*, **19** (1959), 413–420.

[41] See Hack, *op. cit.* Hack's equation for the length of stream to size of drainage area was: $L = 1.43 A_d^{0.60}$.

[42] See Brush, *op. cit.* Brush's equation for the same variables was: $L = 1.43 A_d^{0.59}$.

[43] See D. M. Gray, "Interrelationships of Watershed Characteristics," *Journal of Geophysical Research*, **66** (1961), 1215–1223.

7

A MONTE CARLO APPROACH
TO DIFFUSION

TORSTEN HÄGERSTRAND

The nebula-like cluster is a common trait in the spatial picture of man's attributes. Take any atlas showing economic or cultural elements and you will find an endless sequence of spatial distributions which have a concentrated core surrounded by a border zone of outward-decreasing density.

There is nothing such as one single and simple explanation of the "nebula-distribution." But nevertheless, one particular process which creates this type of distribution—temporarily or as an end result—seems to be highly significant: diffusion of techniques and ideas through the network of social contacts.

THE NEIGHBORHOOD EFFECT

On the empirical level, the author has tried to get hold of the spatial aspects of diffusion by seeking out different kinds of innovations which for some reason have been recorded over a period of time from the very moment when the new item was first introduced.

The ideal case for analysis is one in which every adopter as well as nonadopter of the spreading trait can be individually discerned. This is possible in the literal sense only in microscale. As an example, a very small area (depicted in Fig. 1a–b) is chosen, and the introduction of two different farm techniques is followed over five years.

In the first case, the item is a subsidy which the government from 1928 and onward granted the farmers of small units (less than twenty acres of tilled land, forest not taken into account) for fencing in and improving new pasture acreage at the edge of their woodland. The purpose was to persuade the farmers to give up their time-honored habit [of] graz[ing] . . . cattle in the open forest during the summer season, a practice which caused severe damage to the young trees. A more efficient grazing could also help to increase milk production, which was much needed on such small units. The aid given consisted of a sum of money presented without other provisos than that the

Reprinted from *European Journal of Sociology*, **6** (1965), 43–67, by permission of the author and editor.

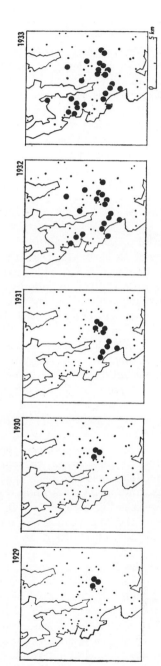

FIGURE 1A. *Spread of subsidy for improved pasture on small farms.* Small points: potential adopters. Black dots: adopters.

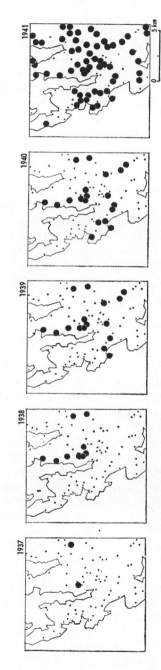

FIGURE 1B. *Spread of systematic control of bovine tuberculosis.* Small points: potential adopters. Black dots: adopters.

measures had to be taken within a certain ... time. Incidentally, this innovation has up to now caused marked changes in the visual rural landscape in parts of Sweden.

In Fig. 1a, small points indicate farms entitled to get a subsidy if asked for. A black circle represents a farm which has received the subsidy after request.

In 1929, three farms forming a cluster had adopted the new government-aided practice. No followers appeared during the next year, but in 1931 a new cluster was added immediately to the west of the first one. In 1932, further adopters came forth immediately to the north of the existing group. Next year, again we find additional ones in radial directions.

The second series of maps (Fig. 1b) show for the same area how another new farm technique was introduced a few years later. The item is the systematic control of cattle for detecting bovine tuberculosis. Also, this innovation was subsidized inasmuch as the government paid for the first examination of the stock on the request of the owner, irrespective of the size of the farm. In this case, the small points are somewhat more in number, since all farms have to be considered as potential adopters of the innovation.

1937 saw two adopters in the area. These two gained, in 1938, followers in the immediate vicinity. In 1939, new clusters were added south and southwest for the core. In 1940, again only a few adopters appear, but this happens in close connection to the existing group. So in 1941 the entire area is explosively covered. If, however, we divide the year in[to] shorter periods, we will find that there is a spatial order also in this speedy development.

The two processes are similar as to the spatial course of events. Of particular interest are the reactions among the farmers on the longish, rather isolated peninsula in the western part of the area. There, in both cases, the innovations literally move step by step from south to north.

Ample material can be brought forward which shows that the demonstrated process is a typical one. A start is made by a rather concentrated cluster of adopters. This cluster expands step by step in such a way that the probability of new adoptions always seems to be higher among those who live near the earlier ones than among those who live further away.

The potential adopters become "blackened" with a spatial continuity [reminiscent] of the development of a photographic plate seen under the microscope. A convenient term for the phenomenon could be borrowed from this physical process: "neighborhood effect."[1]

The neighborhood effect brings itself out not only on the grass-root level, as in the case of innovations among farmers, but in a hierarchy of scales. Examples can be given covering areas from regional up to continental size in which the same general trends repeat themselves time and again. Of course in each case "nearness" has to be interpreted in relation to the extent of the whole area under observation.

THE NETWORK OF SOCIAL COMMUNICATION

The spatial order in the adoption of innovations is very often so striking that it is tempting to try to produce theoretical models which simulate the process and eventually make certain predictions achievable. In the following, some experiments in this field will be demonstrated.[2]

It is self-evident that nobody can adopt an innovation without first having gained knowledge about its existence. (We do not consider the inventor's case.) This does not mean that information about a novelty immediately—or ever—causes the adoption of it. But nevertheless, information is so important that an understanding of the geographical structure of social communication is a prerequisite for diffusion models including the space aspect. Such understanding involves many things: the spatial range, the "fields of influence," of newspapers, radio and television broadcasts, books, ordinary talk, and observation. It is no wonder that George Kimble in his essay on the "Inadequacy of the Regional Concept" maintained that although ideas "can be a most potent force in shaping the geographical ensemble" they "cannot be measured or card-indexed or dissected." It is doubtful if the situation is as bad as that. In any case, does the neighborhood effect indicate that the importance of mass media should not be exaggerated. The situation is therefore simplified, insofar as we are left with mainly one means of communication to concentrate upon, namely, the direct—or, if you prefer, primitive—face-to-face communication between individuals.

The talking and listening individual is part of a huge, world-embracing network of links. A good many observations suggest that this network has a definite spatial structure which probably is rather stable, that is, the links connect different places with probabilities which presumably change only slowly and thus to some extent are predictible.

From daily experience we know that the links in the network of private communications must differ in spatial range between different socioeconomic groups. As a demonstration, and entirely arbitrar[il]y, we may consider three main groups operating in international, regional, and local range.

Some individuals are wholly bound to the local range, others operate in the regional and local range, and still others more or less in all three ranges. Those belonging to a wider range and at the same time having links in common with lower ones form the channels through which information disseminates between the levels.

In the following, attention is concentrated on the local level. To begin with, we are interested in face-to-face communication as a function of distance and as a function of geographical anisotropy. The sample region is a rural area in southern Sweden, . . . of which Fig. 1 covers only a small part.

In the sample region, two sets of data have been used as [an] indirect means of investigating face-to-face communication: (a) telephone traffic, (b) local migration.

TELEPHONE TRAFFIC

Our assumption is that telephone calls which are not commercial well reflect the structure of private communication links in general. The telephone is very common in the area. Data about telephone[s] were collected all through Sweden several times in recent decades. For six-days periods, the destination of every call from all local exchanges (having thirty to 100 subscribers) was recorded up to a thirty-mile distance. Also, long-range calls were recorded, but in less detail. The main weakness of this material for our purpose is that the number of calls between subscribers within exchange areas

was not included in the census. This means that we can get no idea about conditions close to the origin (a one- or two-mile radius) for comparisons with calls directed out from the exchange area.

A typical six-day distribution of calls of a small farmers' village (Svenningeby, forty-one subscribers) is given below.

Distance km	Outgoing calls		Incoming calls	
	Abs.	Rel.	Abs.	Rel.
5–10	239	219,3	66	60,6
10–15	105	34,9	33	11,0
15–20	76	30,6	19	7,5
20–30	50	3,6	20	1,3
30–40	5	0,3	3	0,2
	475		141	

We notice that outgoing calls are far more frequent than incoming ones. From the spatial distribution, one can conclude that the former ones contain as an important part the farmers' ordering of services from central places in the area, whereas the latter ones better reflect scattered "fraternal" contacts.

The number of calls decreases rapidly—and in the outgoing case somewhat unevenly—with increasing distance. This effect is particularly strong when measured in relation to the increasing number of potential destinations as we proceed outward in the distance zones (relative figures in the table).

For the sample region taken as a whole, the relative frequency of calls decreases on the average very nearly with the square of the distance.

LOCAL MIGRATION[3]

Local migration was included after the following considerations. Movements between farms in a rural area occur in mainly three situations: marriage, exchange of farm laborers between farms, exchange of farms between farmers.

In all three cases, opportunities are evenly scattered in proportion to the distribution of farms and occur in an almost constant number from year to year, at least over short periods. All such movements have to be preceded by personal negotiating, which is believed to take place within the framework of already existing connections. Further, the one who moves tends to keep contacts back in the environment which he left. All in all, there is reason to believe that the distribution of local migrations as to distance well reflects characteristics of social contacts on the whole. Further evidence in this direction are certain striking similarities between deviations from the inverse distance rule in the migration data and in telephone-traffic destinations.

Local population movements from 1935 through 1939 *within* and *out from* a part of the sample area having about 1500 inhabitants distributed themselves in this way:

Distance km	Moving units[4]	Units per sq km
0,0–0,5	9	11,39
0,5–1,5	45	7,17
1,5–2,5	45	3,58
2,5–3,5	26	1,38
3,5–4,5	28	1,11
4,5–5,5	25	0,80
5,5–6,5	20	0,53
6,5–7,5	23	0,52
7,5–8,5	18	0,36
8,5–9,5	10	0,18
9,5–10,5	17	0,27
10,5–11,5	7	0,10
11,5–12,5	11	0,15
12,5–13,5	6	0,07
13,5–14,5	2	0,02
14,5–15,5	5	0,05

The gradient of local migration in relation distance is less steep than was the case of telephone traffic. One conceivable explanation may be that telephone traffic is influenced by the fact that the cost of calls increases by steps at fixed boundaries with increasing distance.

From observations of local telephone traffic and local migration, it seems permissible to conclude that the communication links of the average individual on the local level very rapidly decrease in number with increasing distance or, in the sample region, roughly with the square of the distance. This information will be used as input in our simulations of diffusion. Thus the communication matrix is not estimated from our observations of diffusion, but inferred from independent sources, a procedure which is looked upon as particularly important when it comes to comparisons between observations and simulations.

THE DIFFUSION MODEL I

We are going to simulate diffusion of an innovation within a population by the aid of the Monte Carlo technique. In this connection the Monte Carlo approach may be said to imply that a society of "robots" is created in which "life" goes on according to certain probability rules given from the start. The technique can best be described as a game of dice in which the gaming table represents a part of the earth's surface, the pieces represent individuals living in the area, and the rules of the game constitute the particular factors which we want to study in operation. The dice produces step by step new situations within the range of variation which is implicit in the rules. The dice is the motive power of life in the model.

In practice, the random element does not stem from a dice, but from tables of random numbers or from random numbers produced in an electronic computer.

We start on a gaming table or "model plane" which is supposed (*a*) to have an entirely even population distribution and (*b*) to be an ideal transportation surface.

This isotropic model plane is divided into square cells which are supposed to be inhabited by the same number of individuals, N, in each. Every individual is a potential adopter of the hypothetical innovation.

The new element is spreading from one single individual living at the center of the model plane. In this process, only face-to-face communication between pairs of individuals is considered. Newspapers, radio, television, books, public lectures, and demonstrations are nonexistent in the model situation.

The following rules are adopted as governing life in the model:

1. Only one person carries the item at the start
2. The item is adopted at once when heard of
3. Information is spread only by telling at pairwise meetings
4. The telling takes place only at certain times, with constant intervals (generation

intervals) when *every* adopter tells one other person, adopter or nonadopter

5. The probability of being paired with an adopter depends on the geographical distance between teller and receiver in a way determined by empirical estimate.

The second postulate is at . . . first glance rather unrealistic. It is, indeed, very improbable that people react without delay in that way. But still, it was considered important to start with this simple assumption in order to see how far it can be shown useful.

Also, the fourth postulate, assuming a constant interval of time between tellings, is unrealistic. It [would have] been closer to known facts to assume some kind of probability distribution over time. This makes it, however, considerably more difficult to work out the program, and very little is gained by such a complication at this stage.

According to postulate 4, the tellings of the first carrier, and later on the further tellings of the future adopters, have to be directed to definite receivers in the surroundings. Addresses to the receivers are provided by the aid of random numbers and a "target" with symmetrically arranged probabilities of hits, "the mean information field":

P_1	P_2	P_3	P_4	P_5
P_6	P_7	P_8	P_9	P_{10}
P_{11}	P_{12}	P_{13}		
	and	so	on	

where $P_{13} > P_8 > P_7 > P_3 > P_2 > P_1$ and $\Sigma P_1 = 1$.

The grid is floated over the model plane, so that the teller is every time located [in] cell number 13.

Individuals living in the same cell run the same risk of being hit.

To find an address is thus a two-step procedure. In the first step, a random number η from a rectangular distribution locates the cell i according to the rule

$$\sum_{r=1}^{i-1} P_r < \eta < \sum_{r=1}^{i} P_r$$

In the second step, a new random number from a rectangular distribution with the range 1 to N gives the receiver in the cell.[5] If he happens to be identical with the teller, a new address is sought instead.

Input Data I

It is now assumed that the cells on the model plane are 5×5 km and have $N = 30$ inhabitants.

The target is constructed from data of local migration, with P-values as below:

.0096	.0140	.0168
	.0301	.0547
		.4431
and	so	on

$$\Sigma\ 1.0000$$

With a start in M 14, a typical run of the simulation comes out as in Fig. 2, where the distribution and number of adopters are given in successive generations (g_0 excluded).

In the first stages, the number of adopters forms a geometrical progression, each generation having twice the preceding number of adopters ($g_n = 2^n$). From g_5 and onward it more and more often happens that tellings become directed to individuals who are already adopters or that two or more tellings in the same generation converge on the same individual. This effect is of course implicit in assumptions 1–4, but comes earlier in the process and has definite spatial consequences because of the distance bias introduced in assumption 5. After some time, individuals in the central cells contribute less and less to further growth.

After a few generations, the distribution of adopters becomes rather irregular. The starting point does not coincide with the center of gravity. However, the neighborhood effect makes the distribution in g_n always strongly dependent on the situation in g_{n-1}. A secondary center, as that in Q 13–14 or in O 15, has its roots back at single jumps earlier. The distribution of the carriers in the very first generations creates the skeleton of the later morphology of the permeated region.

This simulation is of course possible to com-

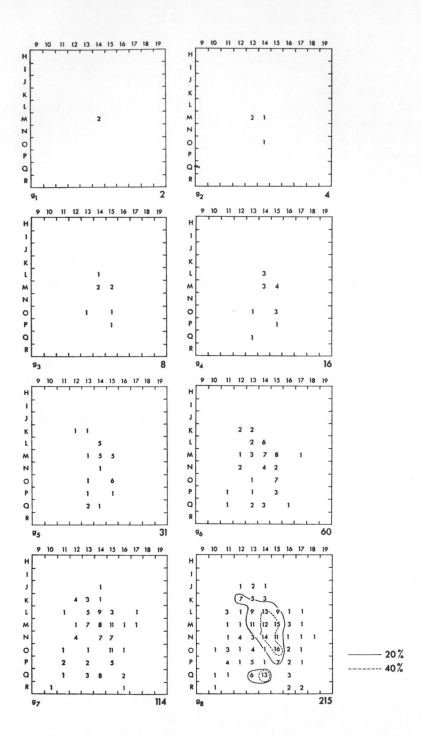

FIGURE 2. *Run of simulation under isotropic conditions.* (Even distribution of potential adopters and no barriers to communication.) For g_5 isolines indicate relation between adopters and potential adopters.

pare with empirical data only in very general terms. It is too idealized. But more runs of this kind nevertheless have their importance, because they make it possible to study the variation of outcomes on an isotropic plane without distorting factors outside the fundamental set of postulates.

Let us now go back to empirical observations, namely, the introduction of the subsidized pasture land of which Fig. 1a showed only a minor part. Figure 3 exhibits what happened in the entire sample region. The square cells indicated at the edges of every map are 5 × 5 km. The figures give the absolute number of farms where the innovation had been adopted from 1929 through 1932. In the last graph is also indicated the percentage of adopters in relation to all farms entitled to receive the subsidy.

Earlier [it] was said that as a rule it is unrealistic to assume that people are willing to adopt an innovation immediately after having received information about its existence, as was assumed in our battery of postulates. But if we ever can come close to the realization of such a postulate, it is likely to be in connection with government subsidies given to farmers. It is difficult to conceive of a situation provoking a lower resistance to a new idea.

If fact, there are some rather striking similarities between the simulation and the empirical data. In spite of the fact that farmers entitled to the subsidy are very evenly scattered over the area, the development of the new item was not at all even. We find a distinct difference between the western and the eastern parts of the region. And it seems not to be too much to say that the morphology of the distribution in 1932 can in outline be discerned already [in] 1929, a relationship through time of a kind which was evident in our simulation. Superficially seen at least, the actual growth process is similar to what was demonstrated in the run of our model. We find an outward spread from a few centers rather than an even and simultaneous condensation over the whole area. One or a few adoptions in an earlier, empty area may later on give rise to a secondary core.

So it seems to be worthwhile to take a further step and try to work on a model plane which is not isotropic, but has some of the irregularities of the actual sample region, in particular

(a) unevenly distributed population and (b) barriers to communication.

INPUT DATA II

We are now going over to a more complicated application, which is supposed to approach actual conditions closer. The model plane was this time given the same shape as in Fig. 3. N was distributed according to the actual number of farmers entitled to subsidies in our sample region. In order to handle the boundary conditions properly, the model plane was further enlarged with two rows of cells all around, every cell having its full number of farms. This made it possible for the item to spread outside the sample region and then jump back again, something which certainly might happen in an actual case.

The target is supposed to be the same as in I. But this time N varies irregularly from cell to cell. Before deciding a new address, we therefore have to observe how the population is distributed in the surrounding[s], and then adjust our probabilities so that cells with many inhabitants get a better chance to become chosen as addresses than cells with few inhabitants. This was carried through in the following way:

The probability Q_i of a hit in cell i with population N_i is obtained from

$$Q_i = \frac{P_i N_i}{\sum\limits_{i=1}^{25} P_i N_i}$$

If η is the random number from a rectangular distribution, the hit is located [in] cell i according to the rule.

$$\sum_{r=1}^{i-1} Q_r < \eta < \sum_{r=1}^{i} Q_r$$

A second random number from a rectangular distribution in the range 1 to N_i locates the receiver in the cell. If he happens to be identical with the teller, a new address is sampled instead.

The uneven population distribution is not the only deviation from isotropic conditions. In the actual geographical region, the road net is rather unevenly developed as well. Long lakes, fens, and deep forests separate the settle-

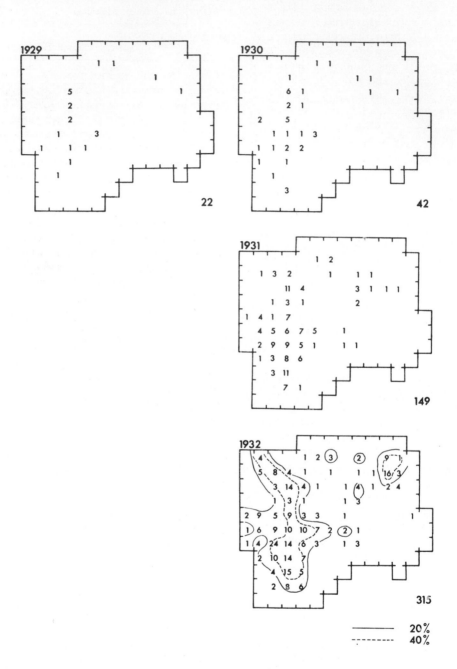

FIGURE 3. *Observed spread of subsidy for improved pasture on small farms.* Cells are 5 × 5 km in size. Figs. give the absolute number of adopters from the start up to the end of given years. Potential adopters have an approximately uniform distribution over the area. For 1932 isolines indicate relation between adopters and potential adopters.

ment groups. Some of these obstacles are likely to strongly affect communication habits. In order to disclose such irregularities, an analysis of telephone traffic between neighboring settlements as represented by exchange stations was carried through. It was found that the number of calls now exceeded and now fell below what could be expected, taking only geometrical distance into account. Of course considerable random fluctuations occur in a one-week sample, but the largest deviations must be highly significant, as they were consistent with the pattern of roads and physical obstacles.

Of particular interest now are the various zones and boundaries which form barriers to communication. Some of the long lakes seem to form absolutely deadening barriers. In other cases, contacts are only reduced in number. These irregularities have been incorporated with the model plane in a very simplified fashion as two types of barriers: zero contact and half contact (full and dotted lines, respectively in Fig. 4, upper left graph). It was necessary to locate these barriers between cells, even if sometimes a division of cells had been closer to observations.

Whenever an address was directed over a zero barrier, the telling was cancelled. When the address line passed a weaker barrier, it was on the average cancelled every second time by the aid of a new random number. Two weak barriers in combination were considered equal to one zero barrier. Also, a few other similar conditions had to be incorporated.

This device of course makes people near the barriers in the model less influential, gives them fewer contacts in the long run, than is the case in the center of an area open to communication in all directions. In the lack of empirical evidence, this assumption seems at least reasonable. An alternative—and less probable—course [would have] been to give them compensation in the direction away from the barrier.

Point 1 in the postulates of the initial model is not valid this time. Not one, single individual is chosen as the input situation, but twenty-two having the same distribution as the actual adopters in 1929.[6]

A stochastic process of this sort never repeats itself. A good many runs would be necessary to get a full idea of the distribution of different outcomes. Only three have been performed so far, as every run proved to be rather time-consuming.

In the three runs, the following development took place:

	Ser. 1	Ser. 2	Ser. 3	Observations
Input g_0	22	22	22	22 (1929)
g_1	38	36	42	42 (1930)
g_2	69	63	74	
g_3	115	108	128	149 (1931)
g_4	199	179	209	
g_5	318	294	322	315 (1932)

The three simulations follow each other quite well, and it is possible to find corresponding numbers in the actual growth process. The trouble is of course that there is no independent means available to compare the time scales. There is no reason to demand that the generations as defined here should coincide with even years.

Now the vital point is how . . . stages with corresponding sum total of adopters in the simulations and in the observed case show a similar areal distribution.

By mere inspection of Figs. 3–6, we can find that this is the case to a reasonable extent (cf. isolines in the end stages). There are obvious differences between each run and the given data, but there are also similar differences between the separate runs, something which is implicit in the stochastic nature of the model. But still, the similarities are such that it seems not to be entirely out of place to look upon the actual diffusion as just another of the possible realizations of our game.

COMPARISONS BETWEEN SIMULATION AND EMPIRICAL DATA

Because of the variable number of potential adopters in the cells, a direct comparison between absolute figures is not very useful. If the figures are converted to percentages, we get a more smooth picture, as illustrated by the isolines. Percentages also have disadvantages, owing to the small base in most cells.

The statistical distribution of the full set of percentages is given in Fig. 7, which is intended to provide a synoptical idea of the growth

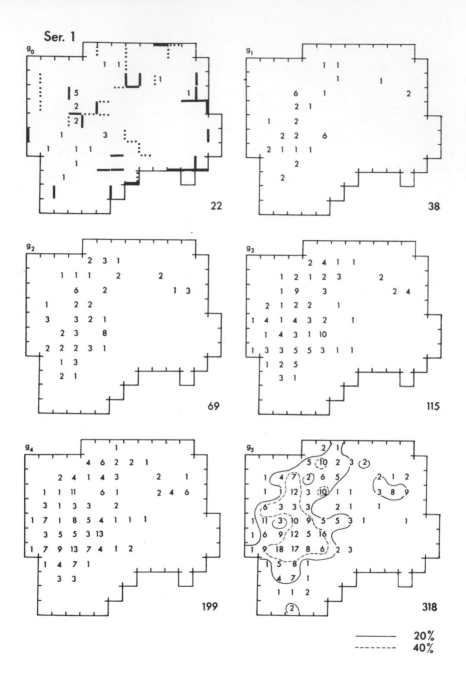

FIGURE 4. *First run of simulation under anisotropic conditions.* (Potential adopters and barriers to communication as in actual area.) Full line: no telling is allowed to pass. Dotted line: tellings reduced by factor two on the average. g_0 equals 1929 in the observed case (cf. Fig. 3).

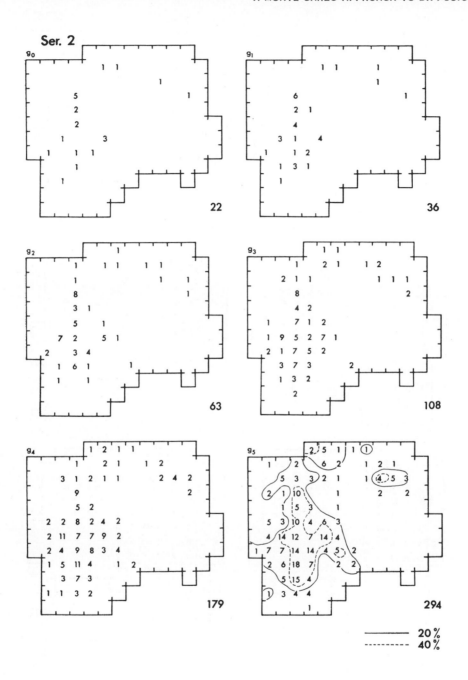

FIGURE 5. *Second run of simulation*

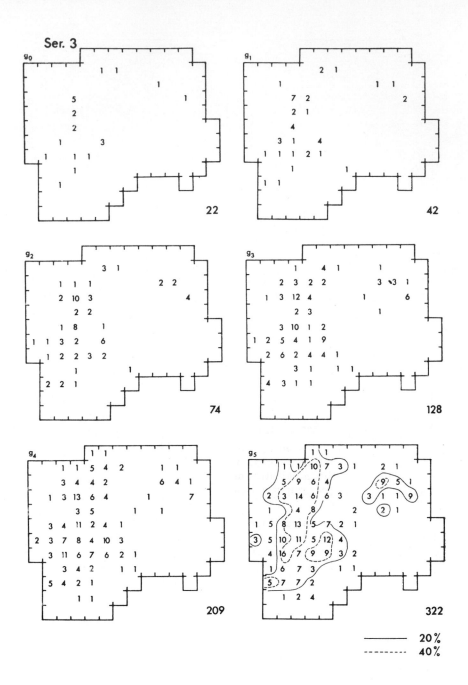

FIGURE 6. *Third run of simulation*

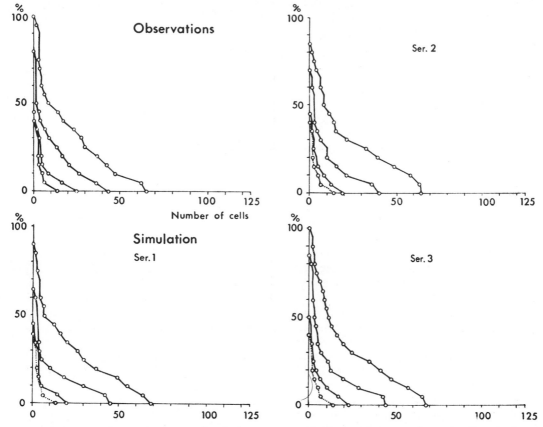

FIGURE 7. *Observations and simulations compared.* Curves show number of cells which have reached above a certain percentage of adoptions at comparable stages of observations and simulations. The initial situation—short left curve in each graph—is everywhere the same as it represents input values.

process in reality and in corresponding stages of the simulations. The horizontal axis represents percentages of adopters in relation to potential ones. The curves show year by year—or, in the case of simulations, generation by generation—in a cumulative way how many cells which have reached above a certain percentage of adoptions. Thus, for example, in 1932 (upper left graph, outer curve), sixty-five cells were above zero per cent, thirty-seven cells above 20 per cent, seventeen cells above 40 per cent, and one cell had reached 100 per cent.

The short and steep curve in the left corner is in all cases the same, and depicts the input situation as given by the data from 1929.

The course of the growth is in all four cases of a similar kind. The number of empty cells diminishes with an equal pace, and the curves have successively about the same slopes. Seen

in this perspective, the simulation repeats quite well the history of the given case.

There is, however, also another point of view, namely, that of spatial patterns. The number of runs performed so far is by no means sufficient to give a full idea of the geographical distribution of different outcomes following a certain input situation. This being the case, it is for the moment hardly of most importance to compare individual figures in detail cell by cell, but rather to consider the overall pattern of spatial arrangements, in the data and simulations. The problem is essentially one of growth and form. In this realm, appropriate measurement techniques are sadly neglected.

An attempt will be made here to compare only the given situation of 1932 and the corresponding end stages of simulations. The statistical surfaces provided by the percentages are cut into pieces level for level, and the location of these levels is compared graphically.

Figure 8 shows the result. Four levels have been separated: empty cells (o), cells in the intervals 1–20 per cent, 21–40 per cent, and 41 per cent.

The top level is, with a few scattered exceptions, well concentrated to a narrow, north-south band in the western part of the sample region. Also, the zero-level stands out in a uniform manner as a concentration to the southwest corner, from which a ring extends along the edges of the region. The intermediate levels form two diffuse rings around the top level. In addition, there is a beginning of a secondary core in [the] northeast, mainly belonging to these two levels.

In the table below, the number of cells on every level is compared, and, further, the pairwise coincidences of corresponding levels [have been] counted cellwise.

The number of cells on every level varies to about the same extent between data and simulations as between the different simulations reciprocally. The coincidence of levels measured in cell units is above the zero level, somewhat less between data and simulations than between the pairwise compared simulations. This fact is also visually suggested by Fig. 8. The intermediate levels in the simulations show a clearer ring structure than corresponding observed levels.

The conclusion is that the simulations probably exhibit a more smooth picture than the given data. This is of course not unexpected. The actual case must include also other factors than pure face-to-face communications. And even these must be rather crudely depicted in the simulations, since the mean information field only in a very generalized way can approach the actual network of social contacts in the area.

But apart from minor details, it has been made reasonable to look upon the considerable difference in interest displayed for the innovation between eastern and western parts of the sample region as a function of diffusion through the network of private communication. Normally, geographers would be inclined to look for physical or economic background factors. It seems as if we have to include the possibility of spatial arrangements which owe their location and form to a rather randomly located

Level	Number of cells		Coincidences
	Actual	Sim. ser. 1	
0%	60	57	46
1–20	28	31	11
21–40	20	21	6
41–	17	16	5
			68
	Actual	Sim. ser. 2	
0%	60	60	43
1–20	28	26	8
21–40	20	25	6
41–	17	14	8
			65
	Actual	Sim. ser. 3	
0%	60	57	43
1–20	28	27	7
21–40	20	25	4
41–	17	16	5
			59
	Sim. ser. 1	Ser. 2	
0%	57	60	44
1–20	31	26	10
21–40	21	25	7
41–	16	14	7
			68
	Sim. ser. 1	Ser. 3	
0%	57	57	46
1–20	31	27	15
21–40	21	25	10
41–	16	16	9
			80
	Sim. ser. 2	Ser. 3	
0%	60	57	45
1–20	26	27	12
21–40	25	25	10
41–	14	16	6
			73

initial stage which could as well have been found elsewhere.

CONCLUDING REMARKS

The model used so far is structurally a very simple one and has to be looked upon as a mere beginning. The present author has worked out a more complicated, and probably more lifelike, version which contains an element of resistance to change which seems to have

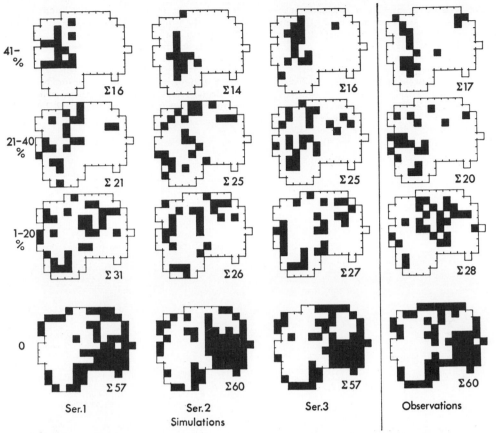

FIGURE 8. *Percentages of adoptions at the end-stages of simulations and observations split into levels as indicated at left*

important spatial consequences. So far this version has been tried only on an isotropic plane corresponding to Fig. 2. To bring this simulation over to an isotropic plane would call for a memory capacity of the computer which has not as yet been available.

The resistance implies that several tellings are required before adoption takes place. The resistance factor can in various ways be varied between individuals and between regions. Generally speaking, the resistance factor leads to a slower development over time, but also

to a spatial concentration. The more spread out, erratic tellings have little chance to cause adoptions.

A further version under work in which the Monte Carlo approach may be the only practicable one is the very important case when competing tellings operate in the same area outgoing from different centers.

None of the cases mentioned have been carried through to a stage which allows comparisons with empirical observations along the lines discussed in this paper.

FOOTNOTES

[1] The phenomenon as such has of course been noticed many times. In American writings, reference should be made to J. Pemberton, "The Spatial Order of Culture Diffusion," *Sociology and Social Research*, **22** (1936), and E. C. McVoy, "Patterns of Diffusion in the United States," *American Sociological Review*, **5** (1940), 219–227.

[2] A full treatment is found in T. Hägerstrand, *Innovationsförloppet ur korologisk synpunkt* (Lund, 1953). Cf. also T. Hägerstrand, "Quantitative Tech-

niques for Analysis of the Spread of Information and Technology," in C. A. Anderson and M. J. Bowman, eds., *Education and Economic Development* (Chicago: Aldine Publishing Company, 1965).

[3] In Sweden, migration is recorded in full detail. It is possible from the population registers to follow each individual from dwelling to dwelling all his life. The data go back about 200 years.

[4] Single individuals or family groups.

[5] Several other routines for finding a receiver are conceivable. In the first instance, a system of con-centric circles seems to be nearest at hand. In practice, however, the square cells are easier to handle, and this is particularly so when we are going to apply the model on unevenly distributed populations, as demonstrated later.

[6] The runs were performed on the electronic computer SMIL of Lund, and I am indebted to Prof. C.-E. Fröberg for taking care of the machine program. The random numbers were produced by a built-in routine.

VI

REGIONALIZATION

1

THE GEOGRAPHICAL DISTRIBUTION
OF CROP PRODUCTIVITY IN ENGLAND

M. G. KENDALL

It is well known that an area producing high yields of wheat will, as a rule, produce yields of other cereals which are better than the average—in other words, the yield of wheat is positively correlated with the yields of other cereals. The starting point of this inquiry was the discovery that a similar relationship exists between county yields of the principal crops which are grown commercially in England at the present time.

Estimates of crop yields for each county in England and Wales are obtained every year by the Ministry of Agriculture and are published in *Agricultural Statistics*, Part I. Partly to save arithmetic and partly because of the greater homogeneity of farming type in Wales, the inquiry was confined to England, which, for the purposes of the Ministry's estimates, is divided into forty-eight crop counties. Apart from sugar beet (which was excluded for reasons given below) the following ten crops are regularly recorded: wheat, barley, oats, beans, peas, potatoes, turnips and swedes, mangolds, hay (temporary grass), hay (permanent grass).

For every possible pair from the above list, the product-moment coefficient of correlation was computed between the forty-eight yields of one crop and the forty-eight yields of the other. In some counties, certain crops occupy a very small proportion of the crop acreage, but it was decided not to adopt any criterion of rejection on that account. The calculations were carried out for each of four years, 1925, 1930, 1935, and 1936, the last being the latest year for which figures were available when the investigation was begun. The correlation coefficients obtained are shown in Tables 1–4.

These tables have several points of interest, but the outstanding feature is the fact that 168 of the 180 different correlation coefficients are positive. That is to say, a county which is good at producing one crop will, in general, be better than the average at producing any other. The strength of the correlation varies between dif-

Reprinted from *Journal of the Royal Statistical Society*, **102** (1939), 21–48, by permission of the author and editor.

TABLE 1

Coefficients of correlation between the crops shown for 1925

	Wheat	Barley	Oats	Beans	Peas	Pota-toes	Tur-nips	Man-golds	Hay (tem-porary grass)	Hay (per-manent grass)
Wheat	—	.866	.822	.418	.324	.524	.490	.270	.298	.487
Barley	.866	—	.764	.360	.247	.468	.467	.256	.365	.488
Oats	.822	.764	—	.627	.483	.503	.381	.405	.256	.436
Beans	.418	.360	.627	—	.683	.348	.120	.281	.124	.236
Peas	.324	.247	.483	.683	—	.098	−.041	.431	.011	.336
Potatoes	.524	.468	.503	.348	.098	—	.587	.200	.352	.334
Turnips	.490	.467	.381	.120	−.041	.587	—	.611	.512	.670
Mangolds	.270	.256	.405	.281	.431	.200	.611	—	.119	.431
Hay(Tem-porary grass)	.298	.365	.256	.124	.011	.352	.512	.119	—	.673
Hay (Per-manent grass)	.487	.488	.436	.236	.336	.334	.670	.431	.673	—

TABLE 2

Coefficients of correlation between the crops shown for 1930

	Wheat	Barley	Oats	Beans	Peas	Pota-toes	Tur-nips	Man-golds	Hay (tem-porary grass)	Hay (per-manent grass)
Wheat	—	.761	.443	−.113	.262	.255	.145	.003	.335	−.052
Barley	.761	—	.490	.035	.304	.104	.242	.036	.307	.019
Oats	.443	.490	—	.258	.124	.431	.385	.376	.388	.229
Beans	−.113	.035	.258	—	.942	.018	.103	.447	.144	.461
Peas	.262	.304	.124	.942	—	.146	−.565	.794	.157	.708
Potatoes	.255	.104	.431	.018	.146	—	.153	.191	.247	.195
Turnips	.145	.242	.385	.103	−.565	.153	—	.382	.534	.418
Mangolds	.003	.036	.376	.447	.794	.191	.382	—	.398	.687
Hay(Tem-porary grass)	.335	.307	.388	.144	.157	.247	.534	.398	—	.629
Hay (Per-manent grass)	−.052	.019	.229	.461	.708	.195	.418	.687	.629	—

ferent crops, as one would expect. That between wheat and barley is high, and so is that between turnips and clover hay; whereas the correlation between potatoes and peas is small. But the general effect is clear. Of the twelve negative coefficients, only one is significant, the correlation between turnips and peas in 1930; and having regard to the fact that in two other years the correlation between these two crops is positive, I think we can dismiss this anomalous value as unimportant.

Four different years were taken because it was felt that the uneven incidence of weather on crop yields might make a single year's figures unreliable. It is not easy to pick four years which, taken together, can be regarded as average for all the meteorological circumstances affecting crop yields. 1925 was a moderate

TABLE 3

Coefficients of correlation between the crops shown for 1935

	Wheat	Barley	Oats	Beans	Peas	Pota-toes	Tur-nips	Man-golds	Hay (tem-porary grass)	Hay (per-manent grass)
Wheat	—	.790	.872	.558	.354	.522	.224	.195	.355	−.009
Barley	.790	—	.802	.509	.457	.382	.257	.336	.442	.101
Oats	.872	.802	—	.467	.301	.614	.163	.301	.317	−.007
Beans	.558	.509	.467	—	.289	.116	.349	.141	.011	−.178
Peas	.354	.457	.301	.289	—	.080	.012	.181	−.003	.051
Potatoes	.522	.382	.614	.116	.080	—	.090	−.015	.118	−.043
Turnips	.224	.257	.163	.349	.012	.090	—	.368	.626	.519
Mangolds	.195	.336	.301	.141	.181	−.015	.368	—	.574	.605
Hay(Temporary grass)	.355	.442	.317	.011	−.003	.118	.626	.574	—	.687
Hay (Permanent grass)	−.009	.101	−.007	−.178	.051	−.043	.519	.605	.687	—

TABLE 4

Coefficients of correlation between the crops shown for 1936

	Wheat	Barley	Oats	Beans	Peas	Pota-toes	Tur-nips and Swedes	Man-golds	Hay (tem-porary grass)	Hay (per-manent grass)
Wheat	—	.766	.837	.467	.344	.215	.289	.305	.496	.244
Barley	.766	—	.821	.278	.393	.224	.221	.432	.386	.134
Oats	.837	.821	—	.398	.325	.219	.205	.437	.439	.208
Beans	.467	.278	.398	—	.284	.003	.105	.502	.440	.663
Peas	.344	.393	.325	.284	—	.144	.131	−.019	.328	.332
Potatoes	.215	.224	.219	.003	.144	—	−.011	.116	.030	.023
Turnips and Swedes	.289	.221	.205	.105	.131	−.011	—	.250	.413	.400
Mangolds	.305	.432	.437	.502	−.019	.116	.250	—	.372	.381
Hay(Temporary grass)	.496	.386	.439	.440	.328	.030	.413	.372	—	.625
Hay (Permanent grass)	.244	.134	.208	.663	.332	.023	.400	.381	.625	—

year for cereals and potatoes, rather below average for legumes, and good for grass and roots. 1930 was moderate for most crops, good growing conditions being offset by rain at harvest. Legumes did fairly well, and roots were slightly below average. 1935 was good for cereals. Potatoes and root crops were good, but rather light owing to early drought. 1936 was a poor year, particularly for cereals and hay, but the quantity of the latter was fair.

The four years provide as varied a set of weather conditions as one would expect, and it seems legitimate to infer that any phenomenon common to them all is independent of casual climatic influences. They also have the advantage of covering a fair interval of time. Since sugar beet was not fully established in this country in the earlier years, it was excluded from the investigation.

Tables 1–4, therefore, lend support to the suggestion that an area in England at the present time has some kind of inherent capacity to produce good yields of a crop independently of which of the ten crops is grown. Of course this does not imply that any area will do equally well at every crop or that it is impossible to find an area with a high yield of one crop and a low yield of another. But it seems to me that on this evidence one may speak of the "productivity" of an area with genuine meaning, always bearing in mind that it is an extrapolation to use the word in relation to crops other than those specified.

"Productivity" is not a synonym for "fertility." I use the word to express the power of agriculture in a particular locality to produce crops without regard to whether that power is due to the bounty of nature or to the efforts of man. It will depend not only on the quality of the soil and the climate, but on such factors as farming efficiency, availability of labor, the supply of capital, and state encouragement.

It is as well to emphasize at the beginning that no account has been taken of fruit and vegetables or of grazing pastures. From some points of view, it might have been preferable to include fruit and vegetable growing in the inquiry, but for a discussion of crop productivity (meaning by "crop" one of the ten products previously mentioned) they are irrelevant. During the past fifty years, British agriculture has tended to switch over to the production of physiologically protective foodstuffs, and there is no sign of any reversal of the trend. In obtaining a picture of existing crop productivity, therefore, one can safely disregard land under fruit and vegetables on the understanding that it is unlikely to revert to crop production for many years to come. Even in an intensive campaign which might be embarked on in an emergency, it may be hazarded that orchards and vegetable areas would be disturbed as little as possible.

If any comparable estimates of yields on grazing pastures had been available, I should have taken them into account. The recent interest in grass drying and the government's campaign for improving soil fertility by encouraging the use of lime and basic slag may, in the course of time, furnish some data from which regional estimates could be attempted. But at present there are very few data, and I have been able to take account of grassland productivity only through the inclusion of hay from permanent grass, which unfortunately makes allowance only for quantity.

These remarks are to be borne in mind in interpreting the results of the inquiry. For example, in a discussion of the comparative productivities of counties below, Worcestershire will appear as a county of low productivity, notwithstanding that it includes the Vale of Evesham, because the vale is mainly devoted to fruit and vegetable growing. Again, Leicestershire will appear as a poorly productive area, because most of the best land in that county is grazed and the arable land is indifferent.

The main interest attaching to the idea of crop productivity lies in variation from place to place. No very clear impressions on this subject can be got from an inspection of the crop yields themselves, and the problem thus arises of constructing some kind of coefficient to measure the productivity on a local basis. I proceed to describe four different coefficients which were tried out for the purpose. The first two (the "productivity" and "ranking" coefficients) are based on psychological work, and measure a factor which may reasonably be regarded as covariant with productivity by regarding crop yields as analogous to test scores.[1] The third and fourth (the "money-value" and "energy" indices) are spatial index numbers obtained by expressing the yields in terms of common factors: money value and energy content.

THE PRODUCTIVITY COEFFICIENT

The yields of the ten crops for a particular county may be regarded as the coordinates of a point in a ten-dimensional Cartesian space. The counties will then correspond to a swarm of forty-eight points in this space, and the importance of an individual county will be represented by its position relative to the general constellation. If the correlations were all perfect, the points would lie on a curve which would approximate to a straight line in virtue of the fact that crop yields are distributed in a nearly normal form. The order of the points on this line would enable us to rank the counties in order of productivity.

In practice, of course, the correlations are not perfect. I therefore attempted to determine the straight line of closest fit to the cluster and to rank the counties according to the order of their points of projection onto this line, which may be termed the "productivity axis."

Consider the general case of n crops and let the yields be denoted by $x_1 \ldots x_n$. I assume the x's to be expressed in standard measure about their respective means, e.g., if the yield of the first crop for a particular county is X_1, then for that county

$$(1) \qquad X_1 = \frac{x_1 - M_1}{\sigma_1}$$

where M_1 is the mean yield of that crop among all counties and σ_1 is its standard deviation. It is required to find the straight line of closest fit to a set of points represented by forty-eight sets of values of $x_1 \ldots x_n$. In accordance with the usual procedure in analogous cases, I define the line of closest fit as the line such that the sum of squares of the distances of the points from it is a minimum.

Suppose the line is

$$(2) \qquad \frac{\xi_1 - m_1}{l_1} = \frac{\xi_2 - m_2}{l_2} = \cdots = \frac{\xi_n - m_n}{l_n}$$

when the ξ's are current coordinates. Then D, the sum of the squares of the distances of the points from it, is given by

$$(3) \qquad D = S\{(x_1 - m_1)^2 + (x_2 - m_2)^2$$
$$+ \cdots + (x_n - m_n)^2\}$$
$$- S\{l_1(x_1 - m_1) + l_2(x_2 - m_2)$$
$$+ \cdots l_n(x_n - m_n)\}^2$$

the summation extending over the forty-eight points.

This is stationary only if the partial derivatives with respect to the m's vanish, i.e., if

$$(4) \quad S(x_1 - m_1) - S[l_1\{l_1(x_1 - m_1) + \cdots$$
$$+ l_n(x_n - m_n)\}] = 0 \qquad \text{etc.}$$

Since $S(x_1) = 0$, etc., by hypothesis, Eqs. 4 lead to

$$-\frac{m_1}{l_1} = -\frac{m_2}{l_2} = \cdots = -\frac{m_n}{l_n}$$

and hence the origin lies on the line. We may thus take

$$m_1 = m_2 = \cdots = m_n = 0$$

A further condition that Eq. 3 gives a stationary value is that the partial derivatives with respect to the l's shall be proportional to the l's (since $l_1^2 + l_2^2 + \cdots + l_n^2 = 1$). Hence we have

$$(5) \qquad \frac{S\{x_1(l_1x_1 + l_2x_2 + \cdots + l_nx_n)\}}{l_1}$$
$$= \frac{S\{x_2(l_1x_1 + l_2x_2 + \cdots + l_nx_n)\}}{l_2}$$
$$= \text{etc.}$$
$$= N\lambda \text{ (say)}$$

Now $S(x_1^2) = S(x_2^2) = \cdots = N$, the number of counties, and the cross products $S(x_1x_2) = Nr_{12}$, etc., r_{12} being the coefficient of correlation between x_1 and x_2. Thus Eq. 5 reduces to the equations

$$(6) \qquad \begin{aligned} l_1(1 - \lambda) + l_2r_{12} + \cdots + l_nr_{1n} &= 0 \\ l_1r_{21} + l_2(1 - \lambda) + \cdots + l_nr_{2n} &= 0 \\ \cdot \qquad \cdot \qquad \qquad \cdot \qquad \cdot \\ l_1r_{n1} + l_2r_{n2} + \cdots + l_n(1 - \lambda) &= 0 \end{aligned}$$

giving for λ the n–ic

$$(7) \qquad \begin{vmatrix} 1 - \lambda & r_{12} & \ldots & r_{1n} \\ r_{12} & 1 - \lambda & \ldots & r_{2n} \\ \cdot & \cdot & \cdot & \cdot \\ r_{1n} & r_{2n} & \ldots & 1 - \lambda \end{vmatrix} = 0$$

The n roots of this equation give n stationary values of D. The *minimum* value of D is given by the greatest value of λ. For, from Eq. 3

$$D = S(x_1^2 + x_2^2 + \cdots + x_n^2)$$
$$- S\{l_1x_1 + l_2x_2 + \cdots + l_nx_n\}^2$$

and the second part on the right is seen from

Eq. 5 to be equal to $N\lambda$. Thus D is a minimum when λ is a maximum.

To find the productivity axis, it is therefore necessary to solve Eq. 7 for the greatest root of λ. The direction cosines of the axis may then be derived from $n-1$ of Eqs. 6 and the equation $l_1^2 + l_2^2 + \cdots + l_n^2 = 1$. The points may then be projected onto the axis by equations of the type

$$(8) \qquad p = l_1 x_1 + l_2 x_2 + \cdots + l_n x_n$$

and it is possible to rank the counties in order according to the values of p, which I therefore call the *productivity coefficient*. A county with high yields will lie high up along the axis, one with low yields low down on the axis, and counties with moderate yields or with a mixture of high and low yields will occupy intermediate positions. The value of p may therefore be expected to provide a measure of productivity, so far as measurement within the compass of a single number is possible.

The problem just considered and the associated determinant (Eq. 7) occur in a wide variety of mathematical contexts, from the factor theory of intelligence to the quantum theory. In essence, the question is one of determining the principal axes of an ellipsoid in an n-dimensional flat space.[2] Methods have been suggested by various psychological writers for obtaining an approximate solution of Eq. 7 or for arriving at the quantities p of Eq. 8 by short cuts. But I know of no method which is unattended by great arithmetical labor in the ten-dimensional case, and I should have been repelled from the calculations if I had not been fortunate enough to be able to use the Mallock calculating machine. This machine will obtain the roots of a set of ten linear equations, and by a simple method of trial and error the values of λ may be quickly found. In the process of finding λ, the direction cosines are given directly by the machine. [Through] the machine . . . , the necessary solutions were obtained for each of the four years for which the correlation coefficients are given in Tables 1–4. From the values of the l's, the productivity coefficients were calculated and are given in Table 5.

A discussion of the results is given below (pp. 398–403). There is no obvious limit to the absolute value of coefficients obtained in this way, but in practice values greater than $3\sqrt{n}$ are very improbable.[3]

THE RANKING COEFFICIENT

The labor required to reach Table 5 prompted me to look for a coefficient which, though perhaps of doubtful theoretical meaning, might lead to similar results in practice and save a good deal of the calculation. The following process was selected:

For each of the ten crops the forty-eight counties were ranked in the order of yield, beginning at the highest yield; e.g., in 1925, Buckinghamshire had rankings of 32 for wheat, 30 for barley, 32 for oats, 11 for beans, 4 for peas, 12 for potatoes, 16 for turnips, 11 for mangolds, 19 for hay (temporary grass), and 40 for hay (permanent grass). These ranks were considered as cardinal numbers and their arithmetic mean obtained; e.g., for Buckinghamshire in 1925, the figure obtained would be 20.7. This mean I call a "ranking coefficient." The ranks of counties which had equal yields were allotted by splitting in the usual way, i.e., if the rth, $(r+1)$th . . . $(r+s)$th counties had equal yields, each was allotted a rank $\{r + (r+1) + \cdots + (r+s)\}/(s+1)$, and the next county was ranked as $(r+s+1)$. It might have been possible to evade the difficulty by working out the crop yields to further places of decimals than those published in the *Agricultural Statistics*, but the accuracy of the estimates does not justify more than one place of decimals, and in any case, I do not think the procedure adopted results in any material differences in the values of the ranking coefficient. From the theoretical standpoint, the problem of split ranks remains obscure, but trouble arises mainly in testing the significance of sampling results, not in the type of descriptive work considered on the present occasion.

It is clear that a county with relatively high yields will have low ranking, and thus a low ranking coefficient; and vice versa. The ranking coefficient may thus be expected to give some sort of guide to the relative importance of counties. It may take any value from 1 to 48, and in practice comes very near to those limits for some counties.

Table 6 gives the values of this coefficient for the four years already considered. The results are discussed below (pp. 398–403).

TABLE 5

Values of the productivity coefficient for the years shown

County	1925	1930	1935	1936
Bedford	−2.679	+ .333	−1.591	− .656
Berkshire	+ .054	− .469	−2.193	−1.860
Buckingham	+ .347	+2.237	− .558	+ .595
Cambridge	−1.929	− .649	−3.065	−1.279
Chester	+3.974	+1.243	+ .982	+2.727
Cornwall	+1.380	+2.794	+ .926	+ .584
Cumberland	−2.090	−4.384	+ .202	− .565
Derby	+ .175	−1.130	+ .636	+ .606
Devon	−1.030	+ .017	− .200	− .826
Dorset	− .507	+ .571	− .070	−2.265
Durham	− .184	−1.253	+ .044	+ .438
Essex	+ .326	+1.747	+ .380	+1.528
Gloucester	− .740	+1.303	−1.828	− .898
Hampshire	−1.249	−1.496	−1.542	−2.794
Hereford	−1.339	−1.843	−1.468	−1.782
Hertford	−1.874	− .437	−1.294	+ .241
Huntingdon	+1.231	−3.376	−2.163	−2.867
Isle of Ely	+7.868	+5.801	+6.271	+5.527
Isle of Wight	−3.651	−4.874	−5.045	−4.321
Kent	+1.361	+1.704	+3.240	+1.369
Lancaster	+ .963	+ .940	+1.925	+3.551
Leicester	−1.424	−1.080	+ .086	−1.159
Lincs. (Holland)	+7.235	+4.953	+7.811	+6.701
Lincs. (Kesteven)	+1.532	+ .182	− .406	−1.903
Lincs. (Lindsey)	+ .315	− .373	+ .734	− .374
Middlesex and London	−1.121	+1.388	+ .530	+ .107
Norfolk	+2.754	− .273	+ .623	+1.048
Northampton	−4.448	− .251	+ .186	− .952
Northumberland	+ .429	− .841	+1.641	+1.907
Nottingham	−1.459	− .967	− .826	−1.657
Oxford	− .697	+ .057	− .953	+ .232
Rutland	−2.388	−2.846	− .956	+ .027
Salop	− .473	− .118	+ .247	+1.490
Soke of Peterborough	+1.144	− .959	− .756	−1.311
Somerset	+ .670	+1.361	+ .994	− .182
Stafford	+ .543	+ .063	+1.327	+1.486
Suffolk, E.	+ .230	− .206	+1.103	+2.328
Suffolk, W.	− .113	− .889	− .686	+ .468
Surrey	−2.796	+ .346	− .781	−2.042
Sussex, E.	−2.373	+1.586	−1.287	−1.177
Sussex, W.	−2.146	−2.154	−1.051	−3.784
Warwick	− .503	− .384	−1.009	− .437
Westmorland	−2.302	−4.067	+ .105	−4.333
Wiltshire	+1.393	+2.887	− .018	+ .369
Worcester	−2.408	− .555	−1.820	−1.135
Yorks. E. R.	+1.856	−1.005	− .716	− .485
Yorks. N. R.	− .376	− .467	+1.244	+ .940
Yorks. W. R.	−1.138	− .227	+ .842	+ .492

TABLE 6

Value of the ranking coefficient for the years shown

County	1925	1930	1935	1936
Bedford	37.30	23.05	31.50	28.25
Berkshire	22.10	27.45	36.40	33.40
Buckingham	20.70	13.85	24.65	19.20
Cambridge	34.25	29.60	38.95	25.65
Chester	9.25	18.50	19.55	12.60
Cornwall	17.80	14.80	20.45	21.90
Cumberland	24.20[b]	29.61[b]	16.67[b]	20.17[b]
Derby	22.15	31.15	18.85	20.55
Devon	30.80	25.65	24.20	29.10
Dorset	26.80	20.60	20.45	31.90
Durham	24.40	29.60	23.70	21.00
Essex	20.55	14.35	21.25	15.35
Gloucester	27.50	22.10	32.05	27.85
Hampshire	30.40	33.65	30.45	34.80
Hereford	30.30	34.00	32.55	32.60
Hertford	33.75	26.70	30.90	22.60
Huntingdon	17.60	41.25	35.50	35.35
Isle of Ely	4.45	5.00	6.25	8.90
Isle of Wight	39.10	41.15	46.50	41.25
Kent	18.15	13.80	12.20	18.70
Lancaster	20.00	17.50	15.45	12.20
Leicester	32.80	30.60	23.35	30.65
Lincs. (Holland)	2.05	4.90	3.60	6.00
Lincs. (Kesteven)	15.75	22.65	27.30	34.30
Lincs. (Lindsey)	20.30	25.60	20.50	26.75
Middlesex and London	27.50	17.20	20.90	17.28[a]
Norfolk	12.25	25.55	23.75	17.80
Northampton	26.85	25.30	21.30	30.65
Northumberland	21.30	24.95	16.00	15.90
Nottingham	31.25	30.05	27.10	33.20
Oxford	26.25	25.30	27.65	19.65
Rutland	33.45	34.50	28.55	21.45
Salop	25.50	24.55	22.45	14.60
Soke of Peterborough	17.60	28.85	28.60	31.50
Somerest	19.85	18.00	18.70	25.35
Stafford	20.45	21.10	17.80	14.35
Suffolk, E.	22.45	24.35	16.15	11.45
Suffolk, W.	24.15	29.90	28.00	22.20
Surrey	37.85	21.25	26.80	34.35
Sussex, E.	34.70	17.30	31.45	32.30
Sussex, W.	34.30	30.40	30.95	42.95
Warwick	25.75	27.20	30.30	26.85
Westmorland	27.06[c]	28.00[c]	24.10	28.06[c]
Wiltshire	15.60	14.95	23.45	21.40
Worcester	34.30	28.65	35.10	29.70
Yorks. E. R.	14.10	29.55	26.75	26.10
Yorks. N. R.	25.55	26.05	15.40	17.90
Yorks. W. R.	31.10	22.20	18.40	20.45

[a] No peas. Figure given is average for nine crops. Average for ten crops, ranking peas at 48 is 20.35.

[b] No peas. Figure given is average for nine crops. Average for ten crops (ranking peas at 48) is:

  1925 ... 26.60   1930 ... 31.45   1935 ... 19.80   1936 ... 22.95

[c] No peas in 1925 or 1930 and no beans or peas in 1936. Figure given is average of nine crops in 1925 and 1930 and average of eight crops in 1936. Averages of ten crops in 1925 and 1930, ranking peas as 48, are 29.15 and 30.00, respectively. Average for ten crops in 1936, ranking beans and peas as 47.5 each, is 31.95.

THE MONEY-VALUE COEFFICIENT

The two foregoing coefficients are concerned only with the yields per acre and are not in any way weighted according to the volume of production. Consideration was therefore given to the possibility of evolving measures of crop productivity by recourse to the index-number technique. The principal difficulty is to express yields of different crops in terms of some common unit. There is no quantity in this case which is completely satisfactory. There are two, however, which offered reasonable promise, namely, money value (as expressed in price) and energy (as expressed in starch equivalent).

A money-value index is subject to the disability that for certain crops adequate prices are not available—in fact, do not exist. Wheat gives the best price material since nearly all wheat grown in England is marketed under the stimulus of the Wheat Act, and very representative prices for the country as a whole are available. At the other end of the scale we have beans and turnips, most of which are grown for consumption on the farm, and price data for which are very inadequate. In the circumstances, I was often compelled to use figures which can only be approximate, on the grounds that nothing better was to be had. As the data employed may be of general interest, they are given in full in Table 7, together with some notes on the methods by which they were obtained.

The next question for decision was whether the index for a particular area was to be calculated only from prices ruling in that area. The answer was found to be determined by the purely practical circumstance that no county prices were available. But even if they had been, it would still have been arguable whether they should have been used to bring the crop outputs to a common denominator. Crops are frequently not sold in the county of origin. Furthermore, local variations in price depend in many instances as much on circumstances like proximity to markets as on quality or relative nutritive character, and it is no part of the function of the index to measure the former class of price element.

The prices for the different crops were obtained for the twelve years 1925–36, inclusive, and averaged, the results being given in Table 8.

It is evident that the big differences in prices per cwt between the crops will weight the final result heavily in favor of the higher-priced commodities. On the basis of the prices of Table 8, the crop production of each county was valued by multiplying the volume of production of a particular crop by the price and adding the results for the ten crops together. The total, divided by the total acreage in the county *under the ten crops*, gives for each county a figure of money value per acre under the crops considered. The calculations were, as usual, carried out for all counties for each of the four years 1925, 1930, 1935, and 1936. The resulting figures are given in Table 9. The large differences between counties such as Ely and Westmorland are an interesting illustration of the diverse financial circumstances obtaining in English farming today.

The method of calculation of an index number depends largely on the use to which the resulting figure is to be put. Since the purpose of the money-value index is only to compare the productivity of different areas, independently of fluctuations in prices from year to year and of special price-determining factors, such as proximity to market, the index proposed seems reasonably adequate. But I should like to emphasize that the figures of Table 9 are not to be misinterpreted as measuring the actual gross income per acre, still less the profitability of crop farming in particular areas. In ordinary circumstances it would be unnecessary to labor this point. The words "money value" and "price," however, have such emotional associations in the agricultural mind that some specific disclaimer is desirable.[4]

THE ENERGY COEFFICIENT

Like the money-value index, an index based on nutritional factors has to ignore local variations because of the absence of data. Certain other theoretical considerations have also to be set on one side for practical reasons. It is, for instance, impossible to take any account of protective elements in the crops, although these may exercise an important effect on the growth and well-being of the creature to which they are fed. Similarly, the necessity of selecting a common unit entails that account cannot be simultaneously taken of energy-providing carbohydrates and body-building proteins (except, of course, to the extent that allowance may always be made for the starch equivalent of proteins). For the present purpose, starch equiv-

TABLE 7

Prices of certain crops for the years shown

(Shillings per ton)

	1925		1926		1927		1928		1929		1930	
	s.	*d.*	*s.*	*d.*	*s.*	*d.*	*s.*	*d.*	*s.*	*d.*	*s.*	*d.*
Wheat[a]	243	4	248	4	230	0	200	0	196	8	160	0
Barley[a]	235	0	206	8	235	0	220	0	198	4	158	4
Oats[a]	195	0	180	0	181	8	208	4	176	8	123	4
Beans[b]	208	4	196	8	193	4	213	4	216	8	161	8
Peas[c]	385	6	223	6	315	6	333	0	291	3	255	0
Potatoes[d]	160	3	120	$7\frac{1}{2}$	137	9	136	$7\frac{1}{2}$	92	$10\frac{1}{2}$	80	$1\frac{1}{2}$
Turnips and Swedes[e]	14	6	13	6	15	6	15	6	14	6	8	6
Mangolds[f]	16	0	16	0	18	0	17	0	16	0	10	0
Hay (Temporary)[g]	99	3	103	3	108	0	113	3	123	9	115	3
Hay (Permanent)[g]	87	3	92	9	92	3	98	3	110	0	102	0

	1931		1932		1933		1934		1935		1936	
	s.	*d.*	*s.*	*d.*	*s.*	*d.*	*s.*	*d.*	*s.*	*d.*	*s.*	*d.*
Wheat[a]	115	0	118	4	106	8	96	8	103	4	143	4
Barley[a]	158	4	151	8	158	4	173	4	158	4	165	0
Oats[a]	125	0	140	0	111	8	125	0	133	4	126	8
Beans[b]	123	4	128	4	120	0	125	0	128	4	126	8
Peas[c]	245	6	233	0	256	6	233	9	259	6	214	0
Potatoes[d]	151	$1\frac{1}{2}$	155	3	82	$4\frac{1}{2}$	93	6	105	6	145	6
Turnips and Swedes[e]	8	0	9	6	8	0	11	0	8	0	10	0
Mangolds[f]	9	0	11	0	10	0	14	0	10	0	13	0
Hay (Temporary)[g]	83	9	69	3	74	9	97	9	102	6	96	0
Hay (Permanent)[g]	74	0	60	0	60	0	76	3	84	0	71	9

[a] *Agricultural Statistics.* Annual average price. Prices ascertained under Corn Returns Act, 1882, and Corn Sales Act, 1921.

[b] *Agricultural Statistics.* English winter beans, feeding-stuffs price at Hull only. From 1925 to 1929 inclusive 6*d.* per cwt has been added for delivery charge.

[c] *Agricultural Statistics* and *Journal of Ministry of Agriculture and Fisheries.* Mean of annual average of market garden peas (average first and second quality) and feeding-stuffs price in annual table of farm values of feeding stuffs.

[d] *Agricultural Statistics.* Mean of first- and second-quality King Edward VII and Majestic and mean of resulting figures.

[e] *Journal of Ministry of Agriculture and Fisheries.* Mean of feeding-stuffs prices in annual table of farm values of feeding-stuffs.

[f] *Journal of Ministry of Agriculture and Fisheries.* Feeding-stuffs price in annual table of farm values of feeding-stuffs.

[g] *Agricultural Statistics.* Mean of annual average of first and second quality.

alent was obviously the most suitable unit to take.

To calculate a coefficient based on starch equivalent, it is necessary to decide:

1. whether a gross or net digestible energy figure is to be taken

2. whether any allowance is to be made for by-products, such as wheat straw and turnip tops

3. whether account need be taken of the fact that the energy in certain foods, such as hay, cannot be absorbed directly by the human stomach, but has to be fed in the first instance to livestock, with a consequent loss.

The bulletin of the Ministry of Agriculture entitled *Rations for Livestock* gives figures for the gross and net starch equivalents of the various crops considered in this paper. Net

TABLE 8

Average of 1925 to 1936 prices for the crops shown (cf. Table 7)

	Shillings per ton
Wheat	163.47
Barley	184.86
Oats	152.22
Beans	161.81
Peas	270.50
Potatoes	121.79
Turnips and Swedes	11.38
Mangolds	13.33
Hay (Temporary)	98.90
Hay (Permanent)	84.04

TABLE 9

Values of the money-value coefficient in shillings per acre for the years shown

County	1925	1930	1935	1936
Bedford	157.1	155.5	138.8	156.1
Berkshire	128.8	117.0	109.8	104.0
Buckingham	117.2	128.3	116.8	111.4
Cambridge	141.8	132.7	119.0	133.9
Chester	210.2	182.7	173.9	182.0
Cornwall	154.4	144.1	129.9	129.2
Cumberland	137.0	131.2	135.3	125.1
Derby	124.7	116.9	119.8	119.2
Devon	137.7	134.2	129.0	117.4
Dorset	116.7	120.2	121.1	101.5
Durham	147.0	137.4	143.3	149.1
Essex	153.6	151.2	148.4	150.0
Gloucester	123.4	121.3	108.4	108.8
Hampshire	129.3	122.1	117.8	108.0
Hereford	118.3	107.9	104.1	99.9
Hertford	135.2	129.3	130.8	129.9
Huntingdon	201.1	143.4	173.6	169.7
Isle of Ely	347.7	302.5	395.7	310.7
Isle of Wight	113.2	96.4	92.7	110.2
Kent	167.2	156.5	154.6	153.8
Lancaster	205.3	189.3	199.8	199.7
Leicester	115.2	112.4	107.7	106.3
Lincs. (Holland)	401.0	378.3	413.2	352.5
Lincs. (Kesteven)	183.0	169.5	175.3	159.1
Lincs. (Lindsey)	172.5	168.3	185.2	169.9
Middlesex and London	145.5	156.4	159.4	167.4
Norfolk	177.4	155.0	173.2	176.2
Northampton	123.7	117.6	118.1	107.2
Northumberland	138.4	129.9	143.0	141.2
Nottingham	138.5	133.5	129.9	125.6
Oxford	125.1	122.0	116.5	116.3
Rutland	109.3	103.2	109.3	121.2
Salop	130.9	124.8	120.1	123.7
Soke of Peterborough	189.1	150.8	158.5	151.6
Somerset	121.0	122.4	125.4	107.4
Stafford	158.9	152.3	145.1	149.0
Suffolk, E.	149.1	135.8	150.2	151.7
Suffolk, W.	146.0	127.8	138.9	140.5
Surrey	129.7	128.7	127.6	112.7
Sussex, E.	105.7	123.3	95.7	98.4
Sussex, W.	124.8	115.0	110.6	98.3
Warwick	136.5	124.3	116.4	115.6
Westmorland	104.7	97.3	94.2	91.0
Wiltshire	131.1	128.4	123.4	113.5
Worcester	123.4	130.3	107.4	115.0
Yorks. E. R.	164.4	139.9	136.0	143.4
Yorks. N. R.	140.3	133.1	136.8	138.0
Yorks. W. R.	139.2	144.7	142.9	142.9

energy is the amount of energy available for work and body building, whereas a gross figure includes the energy employed in the digestive processes of the consuming animal and similar nonrealizable forms. Inasmuch as the present inquiry was concerned with the *production* of energy, I worked with gross figures, which are given in Table 10.

The money-value coefficient takes no cognizance of the value of by-products of the crops; but a parallel omission of any allowance for the energy of the by-products in the energy coefficient would have a serious effect. There is nearly as much starch equivalent in the straw produced on an acre of wheat as in the grain itself. It was therefore necessary to estimate the proportion by weight of by-products to main products for wheat, barley, oats, beans, peas, and turnips and swedes. The by-products of potatoes and mangolds are negligible, and do not exist at all for the two kinds of hay. The figures adopted, together with some notes on the sources of the estimates, are given in Table 11. On the basis of these figures we get the energy ratios (as gross digestible starch equivalent) shown in Table 12.

For example, a hundredweight of wheat will, when allowance is made for the associated straw, yield about 1.471 cwts of starch equivalent. It is clearly irrelevant to the inquiry to make allowance for wastage after harvest or losses in keeping.

The energy shown in these tables is produced in the crop, but it is not available for use by the human body. The energy in hay, for example, can be absorbed only by ruminants and consumed by man in the form of meat or milk.

TABLE 10

Energy values of various arable crops
Gross Digestible Energy as Starch

	Per cent
Wheat	79.1
Barley	75.3
Oats	66.1
Beans	76.5
Peas	77.3
Potatoes	18.8
Mangolds	9.2[a]
Turnips and	9.2
Swedes	6.0
Hay (temporary)	48.6[b]
Hay (permanent)	48.1[c]

[a] Average of white-fleshed globe and yellow-fleshed globe or tankard (the most common types on farms).

[b] Hay (temporary) is taken to mean a mixture of clover (crimson; and red, damaged, poor, good, and very good); lucerne (before flowering, in full flower, and half flower); sainfoin (in flower and before flowering). A mixture of rye grass and clover, rye grass (before flowering, perennial and Italian); timothy and trefoil. If rye grass and clover only were included, the figure would be 51.3.

[c] Simple average of poor, good, and very good.

Source—*Rations for Livestock*, Ministry of Agriculture and Fisheries, Bulletin No. 48, 9th ed.

TABLE 11

Estimated proportion of by-products of certain arable crops

Product	Weight of by-product per acre (cwts)
Wheat	29[a]
Barley	23[b]
Oats	27[c]
Beans	25[d]
Peas	25[e]
Turnips and Swedes	51[f]
Mangolds	80[g]

[a] Assuming proportion of 33% grain to 67% straw and chaff.

[b] Assuming proportion of 42% grain to 58% straw and chaff.

[c] Assuming proportion of 37% grain to 63% straw and chaff.

[d] Assuming proportion of 40% grain to 60% straw.

[e] Assuming proportion of 43% grain to 57% straw and pods.

[f] Assuming proportion of 80% roots to 20% tops (turnips).

86% roots to 14% tops (swedes).

[g] Assuming proportion of 85% roots to 15% tops.

These figures are based on *The Agricultural Notebook*, by Primrose McConnell, 11th ed.

TABLE 12

Total energy values of various arable crops
Gross digestible energy expressed as starch—after adding the proportions assignable to by-products

	Per cent
Wheat	147.1
Barley	134.8
Oats	136.1
Beans	142.4
Peas	128.5
Potatoes	18.8[a]
Turnips and Swedes	8.7[b]
Mangolds	10.2[c]
Hay (temporary)	48.6[d]
Hay (permanent)	48.1[e]

[a] Potato haulms have been ignored.

[b] Average of two crops—both roots and tops.

[c] Average of white-fleshed globe and yellow-fleshed globe.

[d] See note b to Table 10.

[e] See note c to Table 10.

Now the animal is a very inefficient converter of energy, the most efficient beast, such as the cow or the pig, salvaging for the human stomach less than 20 per cent of the energy fed to it.

It might have been argued that an index expressed in terms of energy should make allowance for this fact, and should give only the energy available for human food, not the total energy produced. I rejected a procedure of this kind, not without reluctance, on several grounds: partly because the object of the inquiry is to compare productivity in general, not the production of types of food specially suited to human metabolism; partly because certain foods, such as English wheat, are mainly fed to livestock but could, if necessary, be consumed directly by human beings; and partly because it would be almost impossible to estimate with the requisite accuracy how much of the different crops in different areas are fed to the different types of stock.

The energy index was therefore constructed by ascertaining the production of energy per acre under crops on the basis of the data of Table 12. The figures are given in Table 13.

DISCUSSION OF RESULTS

In order not to put too great a strain on the four coefficients just described, I used them in the first instance only to divide the counties into four categories: good, moderate, indif-

TABLE 13

*Values of the energy coefficient in tons
of starch equivalent per acre
for the years shown*

County	1925	1930	1935	1936
Bedford	.855	.868	.811	.825
Berkshire	.874	.785	.742	.694
Buckingham	.768	.807	.736	.704
Cambridge	.981	.921	.856	.955
Chester	.969	.886	.843	.852
Cornwall	.956	.896	.795	.776
Cumberland	.789	.793	.803	.742
Derby	.768	.703	.740	.724
Devon	.869	.847	.829	.746
Dorset	.786	.775	.770	.639
Durham	.780	.734	.764	.775
Essex	.975	.943	.944	.942
Gloucester	.781	.755	.685	.678
Hampshire	.865	.801	.772	.702
Hereford	.768	.690	.693	.653
Hertford	.894	.851	.886	.858
Huntingdon	1.097	.791	.905	.884
Isle of Ely	1.491	1.235	1.514	1.268
Isle of Wight	.758	.633	.574	.653
Kent	.922	.857	.857	.800
Lancaster	.872	.846	.885	.863
Leicester	.731	.690	.683	.663
Lincs. (Holland)	1.389	1.243	1.403	1.219
Lincs. (Kesteven)	1.073	.952	.986	.899
Lincs. (Lindsey)	.997	.948	1.031	.941
Middlesex and London	.654	.718	.718	.704
Norfolk	1.147	.970	1.083	1.093
Northampton	.827	.775	.798	.717
Northumberland	.818	.769	.858	.842
Nottingham	.856	.819	.844	.803
Oxford	.837	.813	.794	.773
Rutland	.736	.701	.761	.806
Salop	.802	.756	.756	.766
Soke of Peterborough	1.100	.897	.932	.883
Somerset	.753	.747	.769	.657
Stafford	.842	.801	.787	.791
Suffolk, E.	1.068	.963	1.085	1.088
Suffolk, W.	1.031	.903	1.002	1.006
Surrey	.720	.732	.719	.639
Sussex, E.	.665	.764	.602	.605
Sussex, W.	.845	.762	.737	.643
Warwick	.781	.727	.703	.682
Westmorland	.610	.590	.568	.548
Wiltshire	.862	.817	.793	.722
Worcester	.695	.743	.635	.663
Yorks. E. R.	1.072	.930	.939	.977
Yorks. N. R.	.838	.805	.842	.840
Yorks. W. R.	.767	.784	.784	.773

ferent, and poor. This was done by dividing the counties into equal ranges determined by the median and the two quartiles, the number of counties fortunately being a multiple of four. Table 14 summarizes the results for the four coefficients for each of the four years considered. The letters A, B, C, D mean, respectively, that the county concerned falls above the upper quartile, between the upper quartile and the median, between the median and the lower quartile, and below the lower quartile. In one or two instances, two counties tied on a line of division, in which case they were given the benefit of the doubt and both assigned to the upper class. This accounts for the fact that two of the columns contain thirteen of one letter and eleven of another.

A casual glance at the table will show that the verdicts of the money-value index and the energy index in the same year are very close, as also are those of the productivity index and the ranking index; but the two former are not always in agreement with the two latter.

Which coefficient should be used in practice will depend to some extent on the purpose in view. By inspection of Table 14, and by examining the primary data in borderline cases, I suggest the following classification of counties as giving a general picture of the geographical distribution of crop productivity.

Excellent
  Isle of Ely
  Lincolnshire (Holland)
Good
  Cheshire
  East Suffolk
  Essex
  Kent
  Lancashire
  Lincolnshire (Kesteven)
  Lincolnshire (Lindsey)
  Norfolk
  Soke of Peterborough
  Staffordshire
Moderate
  Bedfordshire
  Cornwall
  Durham
  Hertfordshire
  Huntingdonshire
  Middlesex
  Northumberland
  Shropshire

TABLE 14

Summary of classification of counties into four categories according to the four coefficients

County	Prod. method				Rank method				Price method				Energy method			
	'25	'30	'35	'36	'25	'30	'35	'36	'25	'30	'35	'36	'25	'30	'35	'36
Bedford	D	B	D	C	D	B	D	C	B	A	B	A	B	B	B	B
Berkshire	B	C	D	D	B	C	D	D	C	D	D	D	B	C	C	C
Buckingham	B	A	C	B	B	A	C	B	D	C	C	C	D	B	D	C
Cambridge	D	C	D	C	D	C	D	C	B	B	C	B	A	A	B	A
Chester	A	A	A	A	A	A	B	A	A	A	A	A	B	B	B	B
Cornwall	A	A	A	B	A	A	B	B	B	B	B	B	B	A	B	B
Cumberland	D	D	Б	C	B	D	A	B	C	B	B	C	C	C	B	C
Derby	B	D	B	B	B	D	A	B	C	D	C	C	D	D	C	C
Devon	C	B	C	C	C	C	C	C	C	B	C	C	B	B	B	C
Dorset	C	B	C	D	C	B	B	D	D	D	C	D	C	C	C	D
Durham	B	D	B	B	B	C	B	B	B	B	B	B	C	D	C	B
Essex	B	A	B	A	B	A	B	A	B	A	B	B	A	A	A	A
Gloucester	C	A	D	C	C	B	D	C	D	D	D	D	C	C	D	D
Hampshire	C	D	D	D	C	D	D	D	C	C	C	D	B	B	C	C
Hereford	C	D	D	D	C	D	D	D	D	D	D	D	C	D	D	D
Hertford	D	C	D	B	D	C	D	B	C	C	B	B	B	B	A	B
Huntingdon	A	D	D	D	A	D	D	D	A	B	A	A	A	C	A	A
Isle of Ely	A	A	A	A	A	A	A	A	A	A	A	A	A	A	A	A
Isle of Wight	D	D	D	D	D	D	D	D	D	D	D	D	D	D	D	D
Kent	A	A	A	A	A	A	A	B	A	A	A	A	B	B	B	B
Lancaster	A	B	A	A	B	A	A	A	A	A	A	A	B	B	B	B
Leicester	C	D	B	C	D	D	B	C	D	D	D	D	D	D	D	D
Lincs. (Holland)	A	A	A	A	A	A	A	A	A	A	A	A	A	A	A	A
Lincs. (Kesteven)	A	B	C	D	A	B	C	D	A	A	A	A	A	A	A	A
Lincs (Lindsey)	B	C	B	C	B	C	B	C	A	A	A	A	A	A	A	A
Middlesex and London	C	A	B	B	C	A	B	A	B	A	A	A	D	D	D	C
Norfolk	A	B	B	A	A	C	B	A	A	A	A	A	A	A	A	A
Northampton	D	C	B	C	C	B	B	C	D	D	C	D	C	C	B	C
Northumberland	B	C	A	A	B	B	A	A	B	C	B	B	C	C	B	B
Nottingham	C	C	C	D	D	D	C	D	B	B	C	C	B	B	B	B
Oxford	C	B	C	B	C	B	C	B	C	D	D	C	C	B	C	C
Rutland	D	D	C	B	D	D	C	B	D	D	D	C	D	D	C	B
Salop	C	B	B	A	C	B	B	A	C	C	C	C	C	C	C	C
Soke of Peterboro'	A	C	C	D	A	C	C	D	A	B	A	B	A	A	A	A
Somerset	B	A	A	B	A	A	A	C	D	C	C	D	D	D	C	D
Stafford	B	B	A	A	B	B	A	A	A	A	B	B	C	B	C	B
Suffolk, E.	B	B	A	A	B	B	A	A	B	B	A	A	A	A	A	A
Suffolk, W.	B	C	C	B	B	D	C	B	B	C	B	B	A	A	A	A
Surrey	D	B	C	D	D	B	C	D	C	C	C	C	D	D	D	D
Sussex, E.	D	A	D	C	D	A	D	D	D	C	D	D	D	C	D	D
Sussex, W.	D	D	D	D	D	D	D	D	C	D	D	D	B	C	D	D
Warwick	C	C	C	C	C	C	C	C	C	C	D	C	C	D	D	D
Westmorland	D	D	B	D	C	C	C	C	D	D	D	D	D	D	D	D
Wiltshire	A	A	B	B	A	A	B	B	C	C	C	C	B	B	C	C
Worcester	D	C	D	C	D	C	D	C	D	C	D	C	D	D	D	D
Yorks. E. R.	A	D	C	C	A	C	C	C	A	B	B	B	A	A	A	A
Yorks. N. R.	B	C	A	A	C	C	A	A	B	B	B	C	C	B	B	B
Yorks. W. R.	C	B	A	B	D	B	A	B	B	B	B	B	D	C	C	C

West Suffolk
Wiltshire
Yorkshire (East Riding)
Yorkshire (North Riding)
Indifferent
Berkshire
Buckinghamshire
Cambridgeshire
Cumberland
Derbyshire
Devonshire
Dorset
Gloucestershire
Northamptonshire
Nottinghamshire
Oxfordshire
Somerset
Warwickshire
Yorkshire (West Riding)
Poor
East Sussex
Hampshire
Herefordshire
Isle of Wight
Leicestershire
Rutland
Surrey
Westmorland
West Sussex
Worcestershire

The Isle of Ely and the Holland parts of Lincolnshire are so outstandingly good as to justify their inclusion in a special class.

These results are shown pictorially in the map . . . [on page 402]. On the whole, I think, they will appear to agriculturists as reasonable, but for the reasons given below, they have to be accepted with reserve.

One belt of good-moderate area runs down the east coast to Kent; the other runs on the west coast, from Lancashire to Shropshire. The indifferent belt runs from the southwest through the midlands, up the Pennine chain and across to the lake district. The southeast is seen to be poorly productive in respect of crops. One or two counties are a little surprising. Cornwall is unexpectedly high and Berkshire, Leicestershire, Worcestershire, and Herefordshire rather low. But I think the coefficients have done their duty properly. In the last four counties, the land under crops (as distinct from fruit, vegetables, and grazing pasture) does

produce low yields. It is interesting to compare this map with geological or rainfall maps.

There is one shortcoming in this work arising from the fact that figures for crop yields are available only on a county basis. This means that no analysis of the area within a county boundary has been possible—a county which is recorded as moderate may in fact be a mixture of several very good and several very bad districts, or it may contain a large area on which no one of the ten crops is grown. The results can thus be taken to give only a general picture of the distribution of crop productivity over the country. A district which is homogeneous in type of farming rarely has boundaries even approximating those of a county. For instance, the productive Fen belt, which accounts largely for the position of Ely and Holland, extends beyond those counties into Norfolk, Huntingdonshire, and Kesteven, and influences the productivity ranking therein. In a piece of land the size of a county, the variations in productivity may be very great, and the description under one of the headings "good," "indifferent," and so on is therefore attended by the usual cautions one applies in using an average to characterize a heterogeneous aggregate. In the map, for instance, the whole of a county has been shaded in even where it is known that a considerable part of its area is under grass or is nonagricultural land.

Unfortunately, no figures of crop yields for areal units of less than a county are published. I hope that at some future time it will be possible to build up, from parish figures, estimates of yields and production in natural farming-type areas. It is to be expected that the results of such an investigation would modify quite appreciably the boundaries of the areas on the map and would pick out especially productive or nonproductive localities which at present can be shown only on the general county level.

The value of the coefficients is, of course, dependent on the reliability of the estimates of crop yields themselves. I do not propose to go over this . . . . But I should like to make the point that the coefficients, being designed to compare counties and not to give any absolute measure of productivity, are on that account less likely to be affected by bias in the estimates.

In particular, the productivity coefficient has the interesting property of being invariant under

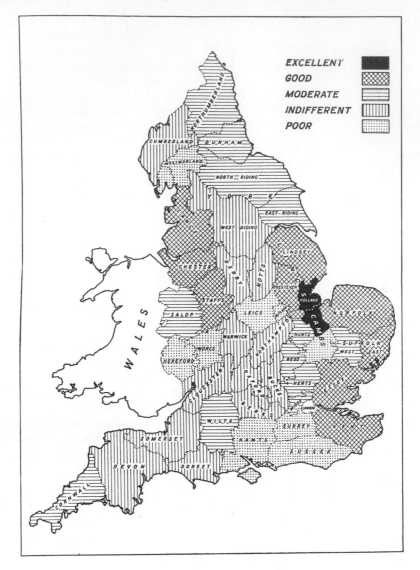

FIGURE 1. Showing the distribution of English Counties classified according to crop-productivity by the methods described in the text

one type of what might be called "linear" bias. If the true yields of wheat are in fact a_1, a_2, those of barley b_1, b_2 ... and so on, and if the estimated yields are

$$A_1 = l_a a_1 + m_a$$
$$A_2 = l_a a_2 + m_a$$
$$\cdot \quad \cdot \quad \cdot \quad \cdot$$
$$B_1 = l_b b_1 + m_b$$
$$\text{etc.}$$

the l's and m's being constant for any crop, but varying from crop to crop, then the pro-

ductivity axis is the same for the true as for the estimated yields, since the axis depends only on correlations between the yields, which are unaltered. The projections of the county points will also be unaltered, and thus the productivity coefficients are the same. It would, for instance, make no difference if all the crop reporters in the country went into an ecstasy of optimism about the wheat crop and doubled their estimates. The ranking coefficient has the same property.

So far as I know there is no evidence either way to show whether bias of this kind, operating over the whole country on one crop, exists in practice; but some little comfort may be derived from the reflection that two coefficients are independent of it. A more dangerous type of bias would be that in which all crops in one county were wrongly estimated. It is clear that no coefficient can remain superior to inaccuracies of this kind.

Precisely similar reasoning shows that in calculating the productivity and the ranking coefficients it is unnecessary to allow for associated by-products or such factors as wastage in cropping, provided that these factors apply universally to the crops affected. Nor would bad weather conditions affect the coefficients if they were prevalent over the whole country and affected crops in a linear way (though perhaps differentially). The productivity and ranking coefficients are thus unaffected by a variety of factors which may conceivably distort the other two coefficients to some extent.

COMPARISON OF THE FOUR COEFFICIENTS

It is evident from Table 14 that the correspondence between the productivity coefficient and the ranking coefficient is good, but I was not prepared to find it so extraordinarily good as a closer examination revealed it to be. An objective measure of correspondence was obtained by ranking the forty-eight counties in order of merit according to the two coefficients, and calculating the Spearman coefficient of rank correlation between the two sets of rankings so obtained. The following values were found for the four years concerned:

1925	.95
1930	.96
1935	.97
1936	.95

In 1925, half the counties had ranks either identical or differing only by one, and only six differed by five or more. The closeness of the two results, which are reached by widely different methods, is surprising. If the effect is typical, the ranking method is clearly far preferable to the productivity coefficient method because of the smaller amount of labor involved in computation. With some parental reluctance I feel bound to admit that the productivity coefficient, attractive as it is theoretically, can probably be replaced in practical work by the

ranking coefficient. It would be very interesting to know whether a similar problem has been studied in psychology. So far as I am aware, it has not been previously remarked that for reasonably high correlations the average rank will tend to give the same ranking as one type of general factor loading.

There is another practical objection to the productivity coefficient which also applies, though much less forcibly, to the ranking coefficient. If at any stage we wish to include additional areas in the inquiry (as for instance, if a county had been omitted by mistake, or it was desired to bring in the Welsh counties), the work has to begin practically *de novo*. All the correlation coefficients have to be calculated, and the determinantal equations have to be solved afresh. This would be a serious disadvantage, even if one were fortunate enough to have the services of the Mallock machine, if the work was concerned with farming-type districts or with parishes, whose boundaries are liable to alteration from time to time.

The relationship between the money-value coefficient and the energy coefficient, though close, is not so good as that between the other pair of coefficients. By the same method, I find the following values of the Spearman coefficient:

1925	.80
1930	.72
1935	.82
1936	.86

Some measure of divergence is hardly surprising in view of the very different points of view from which the two indices are constructed. The crops with the highest price are not necessarily those with the highest energy content. Perhaps in an enlightened community they would be. But it is common knowledge to the agricultural economist that certain crops, notably animal feeding-stuffs, have an affection value unrelated to their nutritive content, and in any case the energy coefficient takes account only of starch. Some difference might also be expected to arise from the fact that the money-value index includes no allowance for the value of by-products, though I should not expect the differences from this cause to be very great.

The correspondence between the productivity—ranking methods and the money-value—energy methods is quite good, though not so close as that between the individual members of the two pairs. For the Spearman coefficient between the productivity coefficient and the energy coefficient, I find:

1925	.69
1930	.48
1935	.62
1936	.61

The difference between the two pairs is probably due to the fact that one is weighted and the other is not. The productivity and the ranking coefficients take no cognizance of the amount of land under a particular crop, but only of the average yield where that crop is grown. A county with a yield of, say, sixteen cwts per acre of wheat on 1000 acres stands, so far as wheat is concerned, on an equal footing with a county which has only one acre producing sixteen cwts. There is an important difference in this respect between the crop yields regarded as scores in a test and the ordinary tests of psychology. I refer to the point again below.

Of the four coefficients, the ranking coefficient is probably the easiest to calculate in practice, and I should expect it to give a reasonable ranking of counties in order of productivity, particularly when it is only required to group them into broad categories. Further evidence would be needed before it could be assumed that the productivity coefficient may always be relied upon to give results in close conformity with those of the ranking coefficient. I have been unable to find any mathematical proof that a close correspondence will always exist, but the values given on page 403, column 1, can hardly be due to chance.[5] It is probable, however, that most agriculturists would prefer the money-value or the energy indices, partly because they have a more clearly comprehensible meaning and partly because they are weighted according to crop acreages.

RELATIONSHIP OF THE PRODUCTIVITY METHOD WITH THE FACTOR THEORY OF INTELLIGENCE

Without wishing to draw a red herring across the main line of the argument, I should like to venture a few remarks on the relationship between the productivity and ranking coefficients and the study of intelligence factors.

We can regard the capacity of a county to produce a certain crop as the ability of an individual. The method of appraising the ability is called a *test*, and the linear evaluation of the test performance a *score*. The yield of a crop may thus be regarded as the score of a county in a test of ability to grow that crop. The yields expressed about the mean in units equal to the standard deviation give what are known as the normalized standard scores in the ability concerned. The determination of the productivity coefficient is then formally equivalent to the determination of what Hotelling calls a "principal component."[6] Hotelling considers the normalized test vectors, corresponding to the points in the n-space (see p. 391), and determines principal reference axes by the condition that the sums of the squares of the *projections* of the test vectors onto a principal axis is stationary (which is the same thing as a condition that the sums of squares of the distances of the terminals of the vectors from a principal axis should be stationary). These projections he calls "principal components." By their means the test scores can be represented exactly as linear functions of n principal orthogonal components, but the utility of the method is mainly confined to cases in which the greater part of the score variance can be attributed to two or three components. Thurstone has criticized the method on the grounds that it is psychologically meaningless.

There are, however, some important differences between the productivity technique and the factor technique. In the first place, the test of crop growing is unlike the ordinary tests of psychology in one respect. In the latter, a subject is usually given a series of tests containing a fixed number of questions and marked in each test according to the proportion he answers correctly. In the growing of crops, regarded as a test of ability, the county is not allotted a specified number of tests consecutively, but is, so to speak, allowed to choose how many questions in which test it will answer simultaneously and marked according to the proportion of questions *attempted* which are answered correctly. The analogy would be closer if the brain were divided into sections and each section answered a different test simultaneously; or, alternatively, if the whole of the county were sown first to one crop, then to another, and so on. For this reason

I think one must be careful not to press the analogy with psychological work too far. At the same time, some psychologists appear to include in the same battery tests which vary considerably both in regard to the amount of psychic energy required and in regard to the regions of the central nervous system employed in answering them. It is not inconceivable that reactions to different tests may be localized in the brain in the same manner (though to a far less extent) that crop growing is localized in a county, but the present trend of opinion is, I understand, against this sort of phrenology.

Second, there are in psychology a practically infinite number of tests which can be applied to the same individual. Perhaps there are also an infinity of crops which can be grown in England, but in fact only a few can be grown commercially, and for purely descriptive purposes it is sufficient to consider only the crops which *are being* grown. This simple remark cuts away from the productivity method a great deal of the controversy which has clung to the factor theory of intelligence since its inception. For example, the arguments between the followers and the opponents of Spearman about the "existence" of a general factor do not affect the use of a productivity factor to describe the performance of the forty-eight counties *in the growing of the ten crops considered.*

They are, however, relevant if it is desired to extrapolate and infer that an area of high productivity would produce high yields of some crop as yet untried. Broadly speaking, I think it is true that the highly productive areas would do better than the others, although the evidence presented above does not allow a logical deduction to that effect. Sugar beet, for example, has developed mainly in the areas shown as good or excellent on the map; but to predict the fact would have required some knowledge of the crop. Without some such knowledge it would be a trespass on the data to attempt a forecast of the areas in which soybeans, for example, could find an economic foothold in this country.

It is almost impossible to resist a comparison between the productivity factor and a "general" factor for crop yields. So far as the two ideas are comparable, it seems to me that the case for the "existence" of a general intelligence factor is weakened by the evidence of this paper. Productivity is admittedly not a simple concept. It is merely the name given to an effect which is produced by a complex of causative influences. I hope the idea will not be found less useful on that account, but the fact remains that it is necessary to guard against hypostasizing the word. If forty-eight individuals were subjected to examinations in ten very different subjects and the results were found to be strongly correlated, this fact would be hailed by some psychologists as evidence for the existence of a general intelligence factor; and it is not, I hope, an injustice to say that some authorities would regard it as supporting the existence of a primary mental quality called general intelligence. This appears to me to be an error. As several psychologists, notably Prof. Godfrey Thomson, have pointed out, the phenomenon can equally well be explained by the overlapping of numerous abilities. This is undoubtedly the case for productivity, which is compounded of climatic, geographical, and pedological influences, to mention only a few, and with some diffidence I am therefore inclined to suggest that the evidence of this paper corroborates the views of Prof. Thompson and his followers.

In conclusion I should like to refer to a few aspects which have had to be left untouched in this study. The desirability of analysis by farming-type districts instead of counties has already been mentioned. This paper is, in fact, so far as its results go, only a tryout of technique preparatory to such an inquiry. It would also be interesting to compute indices over a series of years and to investigate such topics as which areas, if any, are improving or deteriorating, or which are most susceptible to changes in price or climate. And finally, on the theoretical side, it is worth inquiring whether the indices used can be simplified, e.g., by the omission of oats and barley, which, being highly correlated with wheat, probably contribute very little extra accuracy to the coefficients. All these topics would require much more time and space than can be spared on the present occasion. I mention them in order to make it clear that their importance has not been overlooked.

FOOTNOTES

[1] This approach was suggested by a paper of Dr. Rhodes, who appears to have been the first to contemplate the application of psychological methods to demographic statistics. E. C. Rhodes, "The Construction of an Index of Business Activity," *Journal of the Royal Statistical Society*, **100** (1937), 18–39.

[2] In this form the problem goes back for many years. The problem of fitting lines and planes to point clusters was discussed by Karl Pearson. Greenwood and Yule have used the method of principal axes for the two-dimensional case. K. Pearson, "On Lines and Planes of Closest Fit to Systems of Points in Space," *Philosophical Magazine*, **2** (1901), 559–572. M. Greenwood and G. U. Yule, "The Statistics of Anti-Typhoid and Anti-Cholera Inoculations and Interpretation of Such Statistics in General," *Proceedings of the Royal Society of Medicine*, **8** (1915), 113–194.

[3] For, if N be the number of counties

$$S(p^2) = S(l_1 x_1 + \cdots + l_n x_n)^2$$
$$= N\{1 + 2(l_1 l_2 r_{12} + \cdots)\}$$
$$\leqslant N\{1 + 2(l_1 l_2 + \cdots)\}$$
$$\leqslant N(l_1 + \cdots l_n)^2$$
$$\leqslant Nn$$

So that $\qquad \sigma_p \leqslant \sqrt{n}$

For correlational matrices in which the coefficients are materially less than unity, the probable limits to p are narrower.

[4] It is irrelevant to the present paper, but nevertheless a notable fact, that the areas with high money-value indices are, on the whole, areas wherein the financial conditions are generally regarded as satisfactory.

[5] If the correlations between crops are all unity, the two coefficients must give the same results. For the productivity coefficient then becomes a multiple of a single variate (which can be taken to be the yields of any one crop), and the ranking coefficient then becomes a multiple of the ranks for any one crop, i.e., a multiple of the ranks derived from the productivity coefficient. One expects a good correspondence if the correlations are close to unity, the surprising thing being that the correspondence is so good when some of the correlations are far from being equal to unity.

[6] H. Hotelling, "Analysis of a Complex of Statistical Variables into Principal Components," *Journal of Educational Psychology*, **24** (1933), 417–441, 498–520. I have adopted the nomenclature and definitions of Thurstone, who gives a formal exposition of various approaches in the factor theory and invariably says exactly what he means. L. L. Thurstone, *The Vectors of Mind* (Chicago: University of Chicago Press, 1935).

2

A GRAPH THEORY INTERPRETATION
OF NODAL REGIONS

JOHN D. NYSTUEN and MICHAEL F. DACEY

The purpose of this paper is to describe a procedure for ordering and grouping cities by the magnitude and direction of the flows of goods, people, and communications between them. Current theories of nodal regions and central place hierarchies provide the bases for the recognition of regionwide organization of cities into networks. These two theories were developed by students who recognized that the direction and magnitude of flows associated with social processes are indicators of spatial order in the regional structure of urban society. Whether the flow is local and to the city's hinterland, or regional and to the rank ordering of cities, the notion of central or nodal point is dependent upon the levels of strongest associations within the total flow.[1]

The present problem is to develop a method capable of quantifying the degree of association between city pairs in a manner that allows identification of the networks of strongest association. These associations may be in terms of interactions that occur directly between two cities, or indirectly through one or more inter-mediary cities. The magnitude of the combined direct and indirect associations is measured by an index that is related to certain concepts of graph theory. This index is used to identify the degree of contact between city pairs, and it provides a quantitative basis for grouping cities. The resulting subgroups of cities are analogous to nodal regions. When each city in a study region is assigned to a subgroup, it is possible to specify the rank ordering of cities and to evaluate the functional relations of the nodal hierarchy.

In this paper, pertinent geographic and graph theoretic concepts are discussed and are then used as a basis for deriving the method of isolating nodal regions. While this method is illustrated by the use of intercity telephone calls in Washington State, the techniques are quite general and may be adapted to many types of phenomena. A particular phenomenon is suitable

Reprinted from *Papers and Proceedings of the Regional Science Association*, **7** (1961), 29–42, by permission of the authors and editor.

for this type of analysis when it may be viewed as a relationship or flow that links objects that are properly mapped as points. In the present illustration, cities are conceptualized as puncti-form elements in a telephone network. Other suitable areas of application include the flow of information or material products between business firms in a metropolitan area, the flow of mail or freight between cities in a region, the interpersonal relations between the in-habitants of a city, or the political structure that connects federal, state, and local govern-ments.

RELATIONSHIP TO EXISTING THEORY

Cities may be viewed as nuclei of specialized activities which are spatially concentrated and functionally associated. Each activity has its own set of associations outside the city. To account for the many different external con-nections of each specialization, general state-ments concerning urban associations must be multidimensional. Accordingly, urban hinter-lands are normally defined by establishing a boundary from a composite of the spatial range of several central place functions, such as the trade area of the local newspaper, the extent of wholesale drug distribution, bus passenger volumes, governmental jurisdiction, and similar indices of central place functions.

Long-distance telephone communications may be considered a single index of this multidimen-sional association among cities. A grouping of cities on the basis of telephone data defines only a network of telephone traffic centers. The validity of interpreting these telephone traffic centers as an accurate indicator of multifunc-tional associations depends upon a correspond-ence of the hinterlands which are developed with those obtained from studies which evaluate many types of contacts. The authors are willing to accept that telephone flows are one of the best single indices of all functional contacts. It has an advantage over the use of a series of indices because it obviates weighing the indi-vidual contributions of the several indices.[2]

THE NODAL REGION OR HINTERLAND

Nodal regions are defined by evaluating the external contacts of small areal units. Each of these areal units is assigned to that place with which it has the dominant association. Usually, this will be a nearby city, and this city is defined as the central place or nodal point for the unit areas oriented to it. The aggregation of these unit areas, in turn, is called the nodal region.

This does not deny the existence of other flows or associations to and from each areal unit. Such flows do exist, so that each areal unit is connected to many other cities. News-paper circulation, for example, may be domi-nated by the local daily, while the nearest metropolitan paper may also be well represented, and *The New York Times* may find its way into a few homes in the area. Also, many sporadic contacts with former hometown papers may be present. Nevertheless, the "dominant association" remains the critical concept in defining a nodal structure. The remaining, non-dominant associations are not used, even though the magnitudes of some of these associations may be relatively large.

THE HIERARCHY OF CITIES

The nodal region describes the relationship between the hinterland, which is areal, and the central or nodal city, which is punctiform. Clearly, there is no loss of generality by con-sidering only paired contacts between points. In the hinterland concept, the areal units may be abstracted to the level of points, so that the association is in terms of many points being linked to a single central point.[3]

The hinterland of a major metropolitan center, such as Chicago, may encompass a large region and incorporate many of the region's functions. The strongest of the flows between Chicago and its hinterland are point-to-point associations of the cities within the region. At this scale, the relationship between nodal regions and the hierarchy of central places becomes clear. The major hinterland of Chicago is defined by its dominant association with many smaller metropolises. Each of these centers, in turn, is the focus of association from other, smaller centers within its immediate vicinity. These associations incorporate lower-order functions than those establishing direct associations to Chicago. In this fashion, city regions are nested together, intimately de-pendent upon the range of the functions which define the associations at each level.

A hierarchy of cities of this type may be

reduced to an abstract network of points and lines. The points represent the cities, while the lines represent the functional associations. Though a myriad of lines exist in the network, there is present a basic structure of strongest associations which creates the nested nodal regions and the hierarchy of cities. Both the direct and indirect associations are important in these intercity structures. In terms of the direct associations, for example, a wholesale establishment may receive orders directly and ship directly to some points within the system. Alternately, the associations are indirect when the orders are accumulated at various levels of the hierarchy and proceed upward to the regional headquarters. In the same manner, the outbound shipments from the central city proceed down the ranks to intermediary levels through middlemen, rather than directly to every point in the region.

Many associations are of this indirect type. For instance, political control moves up and down the ranks, rather than through direct communication between the national party leaders and the ward leaders. Most commodities are assembled and distributed through a hierarchical structure within the organization. This results in part from the economies of moving large lots over long distances and in part from the better control it affords over the operation. In evaluating the entire fabric of urban society, it is evident that subtle, indirect influences and associations are frequently exerted by one location on another. A system of analysis which accounts for both the direct and the indirect associations between cities is appropriate.

In summary, the nodal region is defined on the basis of the single strongest flow emanating from or moving to each of the unit areas in the vicinity of a central place. The region is delimited by the aggregation of these individual elements. The hierarchy of central places is determined by the aggregation of the smallest central places which are dependent upon a single, larger center for the functions they lack. This nesting of cities defines the organization of networks of cities and the position of each city within the network. Such nesting depends upon the available bundle of functions and the relative dominance of bundles.

In this study, we start with the cities and towns of a large area. Then the structure of

association among the cities is specified by assigning each city to one of several subgroups. By considering the system as a set of points and lines, where the lines represent the association between points, certain theorems of linear graphs become available for the analysis of the functional association of cities within an area.

A GEOGRAPHICAL APPLICATION OF SOME GRAPH THEORY CONCEPTS

Graph theory is a mathematics of relations. By specifying certain properties of the relations between cities and accepting the point-line abstraction of graph theory, certain theorems become available for analyzing intercity flows.[4] Consider the cities in a region as a set of points. Consider also a line joining a pair of points whenever there exists a certain flow between the cities they represent. The finite collection of points and lines, where each line contains exactly two points, is a linear graph of the relations established by the flows.

SOME CHARACTERISTICS OF LINEAR GRAPHS

A point is called *adjacent* to another point if it is connected to it by a line. The network of lines is the only information contained within the graph. Scalar distance and direction, the most striking aspects of geographical maps, are not defined for a graph. If the relationship is of equal value for every connected pair, the graph is a *binary graph*. Most graph theory relates to this type of construction, which simply indicates whether a line (a relation) exists or does not exist between any pair of points. The connections, however, may be considered to have intensity. *Intensity* is displayed on the graph by assigning a value to the lines.

Orientation of a relation between two points is displayed on the graph by an arrowhead $a \longrightarrow b$, and read "*a* is related to *b*." A graph with specified orientation is called a *directed graph*, or *digraph*. The relationship between two points on a directed graph need not be symmetrical, and when intensity of the connection is defined, the intensity may be different for each direction.

A path from the points a to e is a collection of points and lines of the form, $a, a \longrightarrow b, b, b \longrightarrow c, \cdots, d, d \longrightarrow e, e$, where the points $a, b,$

···, *e* are distinct. A *sequence* is a collection of points and lines from *a* to *e* in which the intermediate points need not be distinct. A graph is *weakly connected* if there exists a path between each pair of points, disregarding orientation. The points in a *component* of a graph are weakly connected and are not connected to any other points in the graph. The *degree* of a point is the number of points to which it is adjacent. In a directed graph, a point has an out-degree and an in-degree, depending on the orientation of the lines incident to it.

MATRIX NOTATION

For every linear graph there is an *adjacency matrix*, which completely describes the graph, and vice versa. The matrix notation is convenient for arithmetic manipulation. Every point in a graph is represented by a row and a column of the matrix. The element, x_{ij}, of the adjacency matrix takes the value of the line; if it exists, between the points i and j; if the line does not exist, the value of the x_{ij} is zero.

The diagonal elements, x_{ii}, of the adjacency matrix represent the relation of each point to itself. This relationship may or may not be defined. When it is not defined, all elements of the main diagonal are, by convention, put equal to zero.

PROPERTIES OF THE DOMINANT RELATIONS BETWEEN CITIES

The geographic theory reviewed above suggests that within the myriad relations existing between cities, the network of largest flows will be the ones outlining the skeleton of the urban organization in the entire region. The term "largest" implies an oriented relation, because a flow between a pair of cities may be the largest in terms of one city but not necessarily in terms of the other city. The relation "largest flow" may have various definitions, such as the largest outflow, inflow, or total flow. The present example uses the number of outgoing intercity telephone messages from each city to every other city in the study area. It is possible to construct a directed graph of these relations. Using the principle of dominant association, a single out-directed line is assumed to be associated with each point. When number of telephone messages is used to measure intensity of intercity associations, this assumption is easily accepted, because for any city the largest volume to any one city is typically several times greater than the next largest message flow. An assumption of this type is tenable only for intercity relations, which may be ranked or have a unique, largest interaction. In other situations, nodal region is most likely an inappropriate concept.

The collection of largest flow lines between city pairs defines a network of orientation among the points. Where each point has a largest flow, that largest flow may be found by simple inspection of a matrix of flows between all pairs, and it is the maximum element in each row when the matrix displays number of messages from the row city to the column city. The present intention is to use this notion of largest flow to aggregate cities associated with a central place. The resulting aggregation is said to be composed of the "subordinates" of the central city. The problem is the recognition of a "central city." In order to establish a "dominant center," three additional properties of the "largest flow" relation are now identified.

One property states that a city is "independent" if its largest flow is to a smaller city. A small city remote from large metropolitan centers may display this type of independence, because its largest flow is to an even smaller, nearby city. Conversely, in the same region, a large satellite city closely associated with a metropolitan center does not have this independence, because its largest flow is to the metropolis. So to identify independent cities, a measure of size is required. Size may be externally assigned, e.g., by population of each city, or it may be internally assigned, e.g., by the total volume of messages to or from all cities in the region. In the example below, size is assigned in accordance with the total in-message flow from all cities in the study region. This value is the column total of the matrix of flows between all pairs of cities. In these terms, an independent or central city is defined as one whose largest flow is to a smaller city. A subordinate city is a city whose largest flow is to a larger city. This assumes no ambiguities arise to obscure the dominant (largest) city of a pair. This occurs when largest flows are reflexive, that is, two cities whose largest out-connections are to each other.

A second property is transitivity. This property implies that if a city *a* is subordinate to city b, and b is subordinate to c, then a is subordinate to c.

A third property stipulates that a city is not a subordinate of any of its subordinates. A graph showing this relation is called *acyclic*. It is easily seen that an acyclic graph contains a *hierarchy*.

Two theorems

The largest flow from every subordinate city is called the *nodal flow*. These flows form the nodal *structure* of the region, and (for the particular relation under study) this skeleton displays the functional association of the cities in a region. This structure is analogous [to] the nodal region and contains a hierarchy of centers. It is important to recognize that in this nodal structure the out-contact from at least one point is zero. This particular case is called a *terminal point*, and in terms of an urban structure, this type of point is interpreted as a central city.

The following statements are useful deduc-

MATRIX OF NUMBER OF MESSAGES BETWEEN CITY-PAIRS

TO   CITY

		a	b	c	d	e	f	g	h	i	j	k	l
FROM	a	0	⑦⑤	15	20	28	2	3	2	1	20	1	0
	b*	69	0	45	50	58	12	20	3	6	35	4	2
	c	5	㊶	0	12	40	0	6	1	3	15	0	1
	d	19	㊿	14	0	30	7	6	2	11	18	5	1
	e*	7	40	48	26	0	7	10	2	37	39	12	6
	f	1	6	1	1	10	0	㉗	1	3	4	2	0
CITY	g*	2	16	3	3	13	31	0	0	3	18	3	1
	h	0	4	0	1	3	3	6	0	12	㊳⑧	4	0
	i	2	28	3	6	43	4	16	12	0	㊳⑧	13	1
	j*	7	40	10	8	40	5	17	34	98	0	35	12
	k	1	8	2	1	18	0	6	5	12	㉚	0	15
	l	0	2	0	0	7	0	1	0	1	⑥	⑫	0
Column Total		113	337	141	128	290	71	118	65	202	311	91	39

Largest flow circled. Largest flow determined by the number of out-going messages.

*Largest flow from these cities is to a "smaller" city where "size" is determined by the column totals.

GRAPH OF THE NODAL STRUCTURE BETWEEN CITIES

Graph of a,b,..., l cities in Region G.

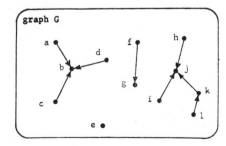

Adjacency Matrix of Graph G

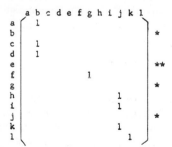

Blank spaces represent zero elements.

*Terminal point.   **Trivial terminal point.

FIGURE 1.   Graph of a nodal structure in a region (hypothetical)

tions concerning the graph of a nodal structure. Figure 1 illustrates the resulting concepts.

1. The components of a nodal structure partition the set of cities.

Proof: Each city is represented by a point in a graph of a nodal structure. Each point is weakly connected to every point in its component and to no point not in its component. A trivial component is an isolated point. Each point is therefore assigned to one and only one component. Such an assignment of a set is a partitioning.

2. Each component of a nodal structure has a unique central city (terminal point).

Proof: Every path has at least one subordinate point, and also a point to which all points on the path are subordinate by the transitive property of the relation. If this point is subordinate, it must be adjacent to a point not on the path because the relation is acyclic. Upon extending the path, an end point with zero out-degree will be found in the component, because at least one point is in the component and is not subordinate.[5] This end point is the only terminal point to which all points on the related paths are subordinate, because no branching occurs on any path (every subordinate point has an out-degree of 1).

Now assume distinct paths in a component and extend the paths to their terminal points. Any other point connected to a point in one extended path has no other connection, because each point has an out-degree no greater than 1. If their terminal points were distinct, the subgraphs associated with distinct paths by the method described would not be connected in any way. This contradicts the fact that all elements in a component are weakly connected. Therefore each extended path must have the same terminal point.

INTERPRETATION OF THE NODAL STRUCTURE

The nodal structure may be used to distinguish groups of cities that have maximum direct linkages, and the rank order of these cities may be calculated. The hinterland of the central city may also be determined by mapping the cities in a nodal structure and then drawing a line just beyond the cities which are most distant from the central city. In accordance with existing theory, the hinterland or nodal region contains the area in which the maximum association or flow is toward the central, or nodal, city. In addition, this plotting shows the hierarchy over which the central city is dominant.

AN EXTENSION OF THE THEORY TO INDIRECT ASSOCIATIONS

The operations and structure that [have] been described evaluate only direct contacts between city pairs. [They] do not incorporate the indirect associations, and these, conceivably, could be very influential in determining functional associations. Admittedly, direct contacts should receive the greater weight, but some evaluation of the indirect channels between city pairs would seem appropriate because of the indirect associations which occur within a hierarchy. Indirect associations may be evaluated by using matrix manipulations to adjust the nodal structure. It is postulated that the increment of indirect association or influence decreases with increases in the length of the channel.

POWER SERIES OF THE ADJACENCY MATRIX

The first step in accounting for indirect influence is to adjust the raw data matrix so that the direct association between each city pair is some proportion of the total association of the largest center in the area. This is accomplished by obtaining the maximum column total of the adjacency matrix ($\max_j \sum x_{ij}$) and dividing every x_{ij} element by this summation. Put: $y_{ij} = x_{ij}/\max \sum_j x_{ij}$. The following inequalities result for a graph of n points:

$$(1) \qquad 0 \leqq y_{ij} < 1 \qquad (i, j = 1, 2, \ldots, n)$$

$$(2) \qquad 0 < \sum_j y_{ij} \leqq 1 \qquad (j = 1, 2, \ldots, n)$$

The maximum column total equals 1.

The linear graph corresponding to this adjacency matrix has the appropriate, positive, decimal loading. Let the adjacency matrix be called Y. In terms of linear graphs, the power expansions of Y have interesting interpretations. The matrix Y^2, which is obtained by $Y \cdot Y$ under usual matrix multiplication, describes a graph when all sequences have a length of 2. The length of a sequence is the number of lines it contains. Further, the loading of the lines of each sequence of length 2 are obtained by multiplication. Since the initial loadings are decimal values, an attenuated value is associated with a contact that proceeds from point i to j through a sequence of length 2. The sum of all such two-step sequences from i to j is the value of all possible indirect contacts of length 2.

This assertion may be demonstrated as true by considering the meaning of the summation:

$$(3) \qquad a_{ij} = \sum_k y_{ik} y_{kj} \qquad (k = 1, 2, \ldots, n)$$

and where a_{ij} is an element in Y^2.

The y_{ik} is the loading on the line from point i to point k in the graph, and the y_{kj} has the same meaning for the link from k to j. The only terms which enter the summation are those where a sequence of length 2 exists. When a link from or to the kth point does not exist, the whole term is zero. The a_{ij} is the total value of all sequences of length 2. In a similar manner, it may be shown that the elements of Y^3 specify the attenuated value of all sequences of length 3, and so on. The meaning of the following summation is clear:

$$(4) \quad B = Y + Y^2 + Y^3 + \ldots + Y^n + \ldots$$

The element, b_{ij}, of B represents the total direct and indirect influence from i to j.

Some examples may be useful. Given the cities $a, b, \cdots, n$, a typical sequence from a to e might be $a \to b \to c \to d \to e$. Imagine an activity in city a as having influence on a respondent in b; this b in turn contacts a respondent in c, and continuing until a small response in e is effected. The probability of such a chain of occurrence depends in part on the magnitude of the flows in every link of the sequence. In general, the longer the sequence, the more remote is the probability of a response, and when a response occurs, it is less intense.

Alternatively, the flow of influence may be rechanneled through the same city more than once. For example, a sequence may have the form $a \to b \to a \to e$. All such summations are included in the matrix B.

The summation of the power expansion of Y is not demonstrated to be the correct form of the attenuation of flows in a sequence. It is extremely doubtful that the matrix B is the most appropriate measurement of the total direct and indirect influences. It is essentially a measure of chance indirect contact. The distribution of actual indirect association is very likely not at all random, but rather concentrated in certain flow channels, in which case the matrix B would be an underestimate of indirect influence. It does, however, have a greater appeal than the matrix Y, which incorporates only the direct influences. The choice of the particular power expansion is dictated by the ease of its computation. Several other methods may also be appropriate.[6]

COMPUTATION OF THE POWER SERIES OF THE ADJACENCY MATRIX

A convenient method of computing the matrix B is to use the following identity:

$$(5) \qquad (I - Y)^{-1} = I + Y + Y^2 \\ + \ldots + Y^n + \ldots$$

and then:

$$(6) \qquad B = (I - Y)^{-1} - I$$

where $\ldots$ I is the identity matrix. The inverse, $(I - Y)^{-1}$, is known to exist if $\ldots$ inequalities 1 and 2 hold.

THE NODAL STRUCTURE OF MATRIX B

The nodal structure of matrix B is established by isolating the network of largest flows in the same manner as was described for the direct associations. Because the associations enumerated in matrix B are adjusted for both direct and indirect flows, it is expected that a more reasonable structure is obtained.

AN EXAMPLE

Washington State was chosen as the study area. The utility of the nodal structure concept is evaluated by choosing a set of cities in this area and then determining the nodal structure that prevails. The nodal structure which emerges should resemble the known hinterland and ranking of the major cities in the area. Certain cities outside of the state were included in the study in order to examine the role they play in the network of city associations. Portland, Oregon, and Vancouver, British Columbia, were especially important additions.

The associations were defined by the number

of long-distance telephone messages between city pairs during one week in June, 1958.[7] Certain cities were omitted from the study due to characteristics of the data and in order to limit the size of the study.

Many pairs of neighboring cities have direct dialing service, and in these instances, the intercity calls were not recorded in long-distance data. Dormitory towns for Seattle and several "twin cities," such as Aberdeen-Hoquiam, Chehalis-Centralia, and Pasco-Kennewick, had direct-service exchange. This is not a serious deficiency in the data, because such cities very likely function as a single point in the statewide network, and one of the "twin cities" in each pair could be used in the study. Certain fairly large cities north of Seattle and along . . . Puget Sound were omitted for lack of data. These cities were served by a different telephone company. Because each year the telephone companies simultaneously take a one-week sample of intercity telephone calls, comparable data exist, but there was no attempt to obtain them. Finally, all cities above a certain population size were not included, in order to restrict the size of the study. Some small towns were chosen, however, in an effort to obtain samples of hierarchies with directed paths of length 2 or more. The map in Fig. 2 identifies the cities in the study. With the advantage of hindsight, it might have been preferable to have included more small towns in the study.

Certain channels of communication are omitted because they are not recorded in the long-distance data. Direct-line calls are an example. Probably the only large volume direct line in the state links Seattle with Olympia, the state capital. If these data were included, the maximum association of Olympia might shift from Tacoma to Seattle. Though beyond the scope of this study, interesting results could be obtained if all channels of communication were included, such as radio, telegraph, mail, and messenger service.

Table 1 is an example of the raw data tabulations. Forty cities were used in the study.[8] The entire table is the adjacency matrix of the almost completely connected graph of associations—there are a few zero entries. The row totals are the total out-contacts, while the column totals are the total in-contacts. The direction of the message flow is read from the "row" city to the "column" city. The main diagonal entries are zero, by convention.

Table 2 is the adjacency matrix B, which evaluates both the direct and indirect associations between the cities.[9] The nodal structure

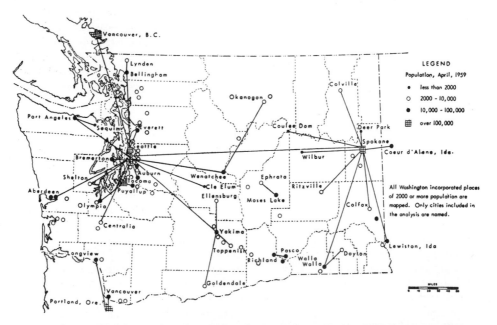

FIGURE 2.   Nodal structure based on telephone data, State of Washington, 1958

TABLE 1
A portion of the 40 × 40 table of number of messages between city pairs, for one week of June 1958

From city	Code	01	02	03	04	08	13	26	27	40
						To city				
Aberdeen	01	—	24	50	0	246	3671	54	4	1005
Auburn	02	26	—	35	0	8	7654	42	0	163
Bellingham	03	55	27	—	782	24	2494	101	3	356
Lynden	04	4	0	2250	—	4	357	9	0	110
Longview	08	329	15	32	0	—	1911	87	4	4773
⋮										⋮
Seattle	13	3427	4579	3843	308	1268	—	6168	269	16781
⋮										⋮
Spokane	26	61	32	119	6	85	9991	—	3842	3838
Couer d'Alene	27	0	4	4	0	6	254	5104	—	141
Portland, Ore.	40	802	210	304	22	4190	22179	3310	98	—

Largest column total: Seattle 154,192.

TABLE 2
A portion of the matrix B (Direct and indirect associations)

From city	Code	01	02	03	04	08	13	26	27	40
						To city				
Aberdeen	01	—	.248(4)	.395(4)	.551(6)	.166(3)	.245(2)[a]	.479(4)	.325(5)	.726(3)
Auburn	02	.303(4)	—	.364(4)	.109(5)	.108(4)	.508(2)[a]	.500(4)	.107(5)	.171(3)
Bellingham	03	.402(4)	.232(4)	—	.513(3)	.180(4)	.165(2)[a]	.739(4)	.247(5)	.254(3)
Lynden	04	.328(5)	.790(6)	.148(2)[a]	—	.307(5)	.239(3)	.716(5)	.689(7)	.753(4)
Longview	08	.221(3)	.150(4)	.252(4)	.341(6)	—	.131(2)	.699(4)	.325(5)	.316(2)[a]
⋮										⋮
Seattle[b]	13	.227(2)	.303(2)	.253(2)	.204(3)	.870(3)	—	.409(2)	.188(3)	.111(1)
⋮										⋮
Spokane	26	.568(4)	.421(4)	.953(4)	.536(5)	.688(4)	.649(2)[a]	—	.252(2)	.260(2)
Couer d'Alene	27	.650(6)	.332(6)	.340(5)	.560(7)	.459(5)	.191(3)	.335(2)[a]	—	.103(3)
Portland, Ore.[b]	40	.563(3)	.185(3)	.237(3)	.176(4)	.278(2)	.140(1)	.224(2)	.725(4)	—
Column Total		.548(2)	.588(2)	.613(2)	.866(3)	.585(2)	.102(0)	.229(1)	.311(2)	.563(1)

[a] Nodal flow.   [b] Terminal point.

REMARK: Figures are rounded to three significant digits. Data were processed to eight significant figures. The value in parentheses represents the number of zeros before the first significant digit.

contained in this matrix was determined by (1) identifying the nodal flow, (2) ranking the cities by their total incoming associations (column totals), (3) assigning an orientation from cities with smaller total associations to one with a larger total association, and (4) identifying the nonoriented cities as the center of its hierarchy. Figure 2 shows the results. Figure 3 is the adjacency matrix of the nodal structure derived from the direct and indirect associations.

CONCLUSIONS

The techniques defined in this paper will divide a set of cities into subgroups which specify a central place and its subordinate hierarchy. The association between cities is not the only system which may be defined as a network of points and lines. Nations or states may be thought of as points, with migrations or commodity flows as lines. The important step in the employment of abstract linear graph analysis is the assignment of plausible meaning to the points and lines, preferably in terms of some real-world phenomena. The usefulness of the attributes and the interpretation of the resulting hierarchy depend on the correspondence between an empirical example using graph theory analysis and other knowledge of the phenomena. The procedure described in this paper may be employed in a variety of ways, but the application is valid only when significant theoretical conclusions are produced and verified empirically.

IMPLICATIONS OF THE NODAL STRUCTURE IN WASHINGTON STATE

The nodal regions that are suggested by the nodal structure agree, in general, with expectation. Seattle is the dominant center, with nested hierarchies defined around Spokane and Yakima. Portland forms a system of its own by capturing nearby Washington State cities. The two small but independent hierarchies defined on Pasco and Moses Lake are most interesting.

Ephrata and Moses Lake are located on the

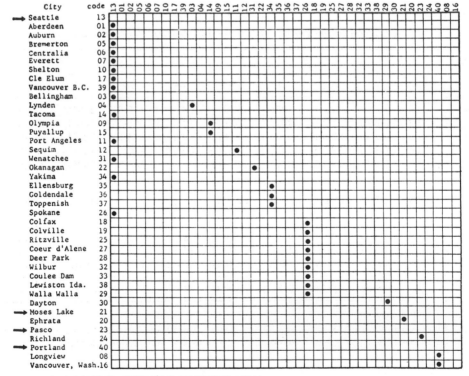

Arrows indicate cities which are terminal points.

FIGURE 3. Matrix of the nodal structure

boundary between two large hinterlands, where it is postulated that self-reliance or independence is most likely to appear.[10] In addition, these two cities constitute an anomaly, because, while Ephrata is an old city, Moses Lake was recently created by government fiat.

The small hierarchy with Pasco as the central point was anticipated by Ullman when he evaluated the growth centers of the western United States.

One hypothesis that occurs to me for the future is that Pasco-Kenneick-Richland . . . might develop as the subregional shopping center, supplanting the dominance of older (and more attractive) Yakima and Walla Walla.[11]

The effect of the national border is clear. Vancouver is subordinate to Seattle, and it does not dominate any city in the study, even though it is a large city and is much nearer to Lynden and Bellingham than is Seattle. It is probable that Vancouver would have been a terminal point if other Canadian cities had been included within the study. This is not a defect in the method. The results are only an evaluation of the associations between the cities in the study.

The nodal region of Tacoma, a large city south of Seattle, is also anticipated by theory. Tacoma is dominant in a nearby region. This region is off-center, in the direction away from the larger city of Seattle. The dominance of Seattle reasserts itself at even greater distances, so that Aberdeen and Centralia are directly associated with Seattle, rather than by a two-link path through the closer and larger city of Tacoma.[12] This and the other agreements with existing theory and accepted empirical evidence demonstrate the utility of the nodal structure for analyzing city associations.

FURTHER GRAPH THEORY APPLICATIONS

Given a set of cities in an area and a measure of association between them, a set of hierarchies has been obtained. Even more information is desirable. Spokane is obviously the second most important central place in Washington State, yet it is subordinate to Seattle in a hierarchy, while the much smaller places of Moses Lake and Pasco dominate their respective systems. Intuitively, a second-in-command position in a large organization is more important than the primary position in a tiny organization. Some measure of this difference in status is desirable. A further application of graph theory to this problem is suggested in a paper by Harary.[13] His ideas are adapted to this problem by the present authors in a further study of city associations.

FOOTNOTES

[1] B. J. L. Berry and W. L. Garrison, "A Note on Central Place Theory and the Range of a Good," *Economic Geography*, **34** (1958), 304–311; E. L. Ullman, "A Theory for Location of Cities," *American Journal of Sociology*, **46** (1941), 853–864; D. Whittlesey, "The Regional Concept and the Regional Method," in P. E. James and C. F. Jones, eds., *American Geography: Inventory and Prospect* (Syracuse: Syracuse University Press, 1954).

[2] C. Hammer and F. C. Iklé, "Intercity Telephone and Airline Traffic Related to Distance and the 'Propensity to Interact,'" *Sociometry*, **20** (1957), 306–316; C. D. Harris, *Salt Lake City: A Regional Capital* (Chicago: University of Chicago Press, 1940); E. L. Ullman, *Mobile: Industrial Seaport and Trade Center* (Chicago: University of Chicago Press, 1940).

[3] For example, see: W. Isard and D. J. Ostroff, "General Interregional Equilibrium," *Journal of Regional Science*, **2** (1960), 67–74.

[4] Some general statements of graph theory are: D. König, *Theorie der endlichen und unendlichen Graphen* (New York: Chelsea Publishing Co., 1950); C. Berge, *Théorie des graphes et ses applications* (Paris, 1958);

F. Harary, "Unsolved Problems in the Enumeration of Graphs," *Publications of the Mathematical Institute of the Hungarian Academy of Sciences*, **5**, Series A (1960), 63–95; Harary, "Some Historical and Intuitive Aspects of Graph Theory," *Siam Review*, **2** (Apr. 1960), 123–131. The utility of graph theory for geographic analysis has been demonstrated by W. L. Garrison, "Connectivity of the Interstate Highway System," pp. 239–249.

[5] Here only finite graphs are considered.

[6] For examples, see: R. D. Luce and D. Perry, "A Method of Matrix Analysis of Group Structure," *Psychometrika*, **14** (1949), 95–116; and L. Katz, "A New Status Index Derived from Sociometric Analysis," *Psychometrika*, **18** (1953), 39–44.

[7] We are indebted to the Pacific Bell Telephone and Telegraph Company and especially to Mr. Homer Moyer, a Seattle officer of that company, for this information.

[8] A copy of the entire matrix shown in Table 1 may be obtained from J. D. Nystuen, University of Michigan, Department of Geography.

[9] The computations were made possible by a grant

of computer time from the Western Data Processing Center, U. C. L. A.

[10] E. M. Hoover, *The Location of Economic Activity* (New York: McGraw-Hill Book Company, 1948); W. Isard, *Location and Space Economy* (New York: John Wiley & Sons, Inc., 1956); A. Lösch, *The Economics of Location* (New Haven: Yale University Press, 1954).

[11] E. L. Ullman, *Growth Centers of the West* (Seattle: University of Washington Press, 1955), p. 48.

[12] E. M. Hoover, *op. cit.;* W. Isard, *op. cit.;* A. Lösch, *op. cit.*

[13] Harary, F., "Status and Contrastatus," *Sociometry*, **22** (1959), 23–43.

3

A SYNTHESIS OF FORMAL
AND FUNCTIONAL REGIONS
USING A GENERAL FIELD THEORY
OF SPATIAL BEHAVIOR

BRIAN J. L. BERRY

Traditionally, three classificatory approaches have been used by geographers and other social scientists to define regions. The first stresses *homogeneity* of places located within the regions with respect to a given set of properties. The second emphasizes *nodality*, or *polarization*, usually of areas around some central urban place. The third is *programming*, or *policy-oriented*, concerned mainly with either administrative coherence and the identity between the area being studied and available political institutions for effectuating policy decisions, or else with the appropriate regional framework to insure achievement of a set of goals. Whether either of the first two approaches has anything to contribute to the third is a question that remains debatable.[1]

In this paper, we focus on the first two of these approaches, that of homogeneity, leading to *uniform*, or *formal*, *regions*, and the more general version of the second, dealing with the interactions between places that give rise to *organizational*, or *functional*, regions. The observation that identical procedures of numerical taxonomy could be used to derive an optimal regionalization in both cases[2] has led us to be able to integrate the two regional concepts by utilizing the techniques of system analysis. The result has been the development of a "general field theory of spatial behavior."[3]

We first review this general field theory, examine the mathematics which support both its structural and behavioral ingredients, describe the canonical formulation that makes the field theory operational, and finally outline, as an example, the main findings of a study of commodity flows and regional structure in India.

A FIELD THEORY

The field theory involves a spatial system that comprises places, the attributes of these places, and the interactions among them.

One can conceive of the places and their attributes being arranged in an *n*-place by *a*-attribute matrix, the attribute matrix, which describes the system. Each attribute shows some spatial variation over the places; each place is characterized by a particular combination of attributes. Mapping of the spatial variations and study of spatial associations by map comparison have long been the bases of traditional systematic geography; comparison of places in terms of their attribute-combinations, "formal" regionalization of places with similar sets, and areal differentiation of those with sets that are basically dissimilar have for an equally long period been the bases of traditional regional geography. We assert, however, that the infinity of attributes describing the places in the system actually index a finite number of independent basic concepts ("urbanization," "poverty") that together define the state of the system. The scores of places on the larger number of attributes may be used to estimate their scores on the fundamental spatial patterns that are the outward signs of the underlying concepts, and thus may be replaced by them, to create an $n \times s$ "structure matrix." Each of the s dimensions, in the sense of traditional systematic geography, reveals the fundamental pattern of spatial variation of a concept lying beneath the larger number of attributes that originally were used as overlapping indices of it. Places may be arrayed in the geometric space of one, several, or all of the dimensions, and the distances between pairs of places in this space vary directly with their degree of areal differentiation; traditional uniform or formal regions are clusters of places in the space.

Many kinds of interactions among the places can also be indexed. Each kind comprises a set of connections between pairs of places. A second matrix, an "interaction matrix," can thus be conceived in which the $(n^2 - n)$ possible pairs of places (dyads) occupy the rows (symmetry is not required, although in certain cases it may exist), and y kinds of interaction occupy the columns. Again, systematic and regional geographers have traditionally studied such matrices, examining spatial interactions, trying to define types of interaction, exploring the connectivity of places as expressed in some overall pattern of areal functional organization, and specifically resolving connectivities into nested sets of functional regions. We again assert that the infinity of interactions index a finite number of independent basic concepts ("complementarity," "intervening opportunity," "distance-

decay") that define the behavior of the system. Scores of dyads on the original interactions may be replaced by scores created for the types of spatial behavior, creating an $(n^2 - n) \times b$ "behavior matrix." This matrix then summarizes the basic types of spatial interaction and their patterns of areal functional organization, to use the common jargon.

Both the structure matrix and the behavior matrix are cross-sectional; they refer to a particular point or slice of time. Similar cross-sectional studies may be made at other times, and the results compared. There are several possible outcomes. Perhaps the underlying structure and behavior will be unchanged, although particular places or dyads may change their relative scores on the underlying dimensions. Alternatively, gradual changes in structure and/or behavior may be noted. Finally, quite radical transformations in spatial structure and behavior might have occurred.

To capture the exact nature of the changes taking place through time, we are led to a third repetition of our argument. Attributes and interactions may be studied at any of many points in time, and their values compared through time. These values in fact index a smaller number of spatial processes, however. The processes may relate to spatial changes within a framework of unchanging underlying dimensions, or they may reveal dramatic changes in structure and behavior.

It is now possible to postulate the basic theorems of the field theory and link spatial structure to spatial behavior in the dynamic framework of spatial process. Relevant functional forms, if we have read the theoretical literature properly, might equally well be:

1. (a) Dyadic spatial behavior is a function of the ways in which the fundamental spatial patterns characterize places.

(b) Changes in spatial behavior result from changes in the character of places as spatial processes run their course.

2. (a) The characteristics of any place are largely dependent upon its relationships with other places.

(b) Changes in spatial interactions give rise to changes in the character of places.

However, it is obvious from the reversal of the causal chains postulated in 1 and 2 that *it is more general to argue for a mutual equilibration of spatial structure and spatial behavior in a state of complex interdependency.* Thus, in the context of ongoing spatial processes, behavioral changes may call forth structural changes, as well as the converse.

The entire field theory may be stated mathematically using multivariate analysis, and appropriate modeling is suggested at every step. Yet to date, no one has made such a field theory operational. This fact notwithstanding, it does provide a useful framework to which to relate the different descriptive concepts of regions now in use.

For example, groups of places in the structural space form uniform regions, if contiguous, and regional types (for example, type-of-farming areas), if spatially separated. Similarly, sets of interconnected places in the behavior space are in fact functional regions. Theorem 1*a* of the field theory thus states that functional regionalizations are in some way dependent upon the character of places that may be expressed in some formal regionalization. Similarly, in Theorem 1*b*, changes in functional connections are attributed to the change in the character of places as a result of the operation of recognizable spatial processes. In this light, the field theory will be seen to have much in common with Philbrick's general scheme of "areal functional organization," in which there are alternating scales and levels of formal and functional regions, although it is isomorphic with it only in a special case, with the field theory being the more general.[4]

MATHEMATICAL METHODS

The field theory is supported and may be made operational by use of a set of multivariate techniques. These are, fundamentally, the methods of numerical taxonomy.

All taxonomic study involves three distinct elements:[5]

1. *systematics:* the scientific study of the kinds and diversity of objects and of all relationships among them

2. *classification:* the ordering of objects into groups (sets) on the basis of their relationships, that is, of their associations by contiguity, similarity, or both

3. *taxonomy:* the theoretical study of classification, including its bases, principles, procedures, and rules.

Thus in the inductive study of uniform or formal regions, the phase of systematics involves analysis of regional structure. Regionalization *per se* then becomes simply a process of classification. When we say, therefore, that the approach to regionalization taken is that of numerical taxonomy, we recognize the mathematical nature of the classificatory process, but also indicate that our concern is with the bases, principles, procedures and rules for regionalization. In short, the *procedures* of numerical taxonomy that we use for uniform regionalization involve:

1. *factor analysis*, as a tool for systematically exploring the many relationships between the variables we use to characterize places, to determine the precise nature and bases of regional structure

2. *dimensional analysis*, to determine the degrees of similarity of each place studied in terms of regional economic structure

3. *grouping analysis*, to cluster into regions contiguous sets of similar places.

The *principles* remain Aristotelian, however: Every place must ultimately be placed in a region; only under special conditions can a place belong to more than one region on any level of regionalization; regions may be arranged into a hierarchy by the successive splitting of larger regions into smaller regions; and the smaller regions should display less internal differences than the larger regions into which they are grouped.

The related *rules* for regionalization are simple. Once the degree of similarity of each pair of places being studied has been measured by a process of systematics, groups of places are formed on the basis of maximum similarity, subject only to the condition that places within the same region be contiguous. The steps of the complete process of numerical analysis are then as follows:

1. Determine the places which are to be grouped into regions and the characteristics (attributes) which are relevant to the regionalization.

2. Construct a table in which each of the places occupies a row and the characteristics each occupy a column. Enter the exact value of each place with respect to every characteristic. Such a table is known as a "data matrix."

3. Examine the spatial variations of the places with respect to each characteristic and the spatial associations among groups of characteristics, and determine whether the characteristics fall into groups because of the existence of certain underlying basic spatial patterns— the patterns that comprise regional structure. This step could be achieved by mapping each characteristic and by visually comparing and classifying the maps. However, cartographic analysis is extremely tedious if there are many places and characteristics, and visual comparisons are known to be treacherous. Thus it is more efficient and objective to calculate correlations among characteristics and to use multiple factor analysis to isolate the basic spatial patterns of regional structure.

4. Once identified, each of the basic spatial patterns can be mapped, and graphs can be drawn comparing the values of the places studied on each pattern. Dimensional analysis permits the exact measurement of the degree of similarity of each place and every other with respect to each pattern of regional structure, to any combination of patterns, or to all patterns considered simultaneously.

5. Finally, once the degree of similarity of each pair of places is known, grouping techniques can be used to link into regions those places which display maximum similarity. Orderly application of the technique successively links every place into the regional scheme, providing a complete picture of regional and subregional linkages in a "linkage tree." One possible outcome is a set of "regional types," for example, of areas with certain types of farming, which may be scattered over a whole territory. If regions comprising contiguous places are required, however, application of a contiguity constraint to the grouping process is necssary; places are grouped only if they are both very similar and contiguously located.

These procedures are adequate for both formal and functional regionalization. Characteristics may be properties of places (e.g., per capita income, population density), in which instance they are *scalar*, and the subsequent steps lead to a uniform regionalization. Alternatively, they may be connections among places (e.g., flows of traffic, commodities, people, messages, ideas), in which case they are *vector*, the cells of the data matrix record "dyadic behavior" (connections between pairs of places),

and the result of analyzing such a matrix is to achieve a functional or organizational regionalization. Each of the types of behavior contains self-defining organizational regions, because the dyads imply connectivity. However, if a multiconnection organizational regionalization over several different types of behavior is required, an additional grouping process will be necessary.

EXAMPLES IN THE LITERATURE

The first examples of experimentation with such procedures were Kendall's pioneering work on the distribution of crop productivity in Great Britain[6] and Hagood's studies of agricultural regions of the United States,[7] which may be contrasted with Odum's masterful exposition of traditional cartographic methods of regionalization using many variables[8] and the still classic statement of the National Resources Planning Board.[9] Attempts to develop alternative, simpler statistical procedures immediately postwar were made by Weaver[10] and Zobler,[11] but with the development of modern, large-scale computers in the United States after 1958, and their rapid adoption for scientific purposes, the much more satisfactory, but computationally more demanding methods proposed by Kendall could be used and extended. Berry applied factor and discriminatory analysis to the regionalization of economic development,[12] and later added improved dimensional analysis and grouping methods to the process.[13] In these studies, he showed how more than fifty variables used to characterize relative economic development of countries in fact displayed only four basic patterns of spatial variation, and he then proceeded to regionalize economic development based upon the scores of countries with respect to these four patterns. The methods have also been used to derive indices of economic health of areas from a variety of original variables,[14] to classify cities and towns,[15] and to analyze differences in regional development and welfare in Canada.[16] All of the above studies used scalar data and produced uniform regions. Stone, however, showed that vector data could be used in a similar analytic process.[17] Russett has extended the work in his examinational trading regions,[18] and Berry showed that identical procedures of taxonomy were relevant in the two cases.[19] Harman remains the basic source on factor analysis,[20] but see also Hotelling,[21] Kendall,[22] and Anderson.[23] Sokal and

Sneath,[24] Rubin,[25] and Ward[26] are useful sources on grouping methodology.

MATHEMATICAL STATEMENT

The complete procedure of numerical taxonomy, combining factor and dimensional analysis, may be stated as a mathematical process as follows:

Given a matrix A of order n by a, in which the n refers to observations (say, countries, counties, municipalities, or census tracts) and the a to attributes (say, proposed measures of social and economic disadvantage), form a matrix Z, again of order n by a, in which the original variables have been normalized if necessary, then in which every variable has been expressed in the standardized form of zero mean and unit variance.[27] Also form R, the a by a matrix of zero-order correlations among the variables. Then perform a principal axis factor analysis of $(R - U^2)$, where U^2 is a diagonal matrix containing the unique portion of the variance of each of the a variables. Generally, any u_i^2 is estimated as $(1.0 - h_i^2)$, where h_i^2, the communality of variable i, is approximated by computing the coefficient of determination resulting from the regression of i on the remaining $(a - 1.0)$ variables in the set. The choice of a principal axis factor analysis of $(R - U^2)$, rather than a principal components analysis of R, is made because of the "noise-reducing" properties of the former.

The principal axis factor analysis produces a matrix F of order a by s, such that $(R - U^2) = FF^T$ and $F^T F = \Lambda$. The solution is such as to require that for each column vector of F, F_j, and each diagonal element of Λ, λ_j, both $[(R - U^2) - \lambda_j I] = 0$, and $F_j^T F_j = \lambda_j$. Further, if $\lambda K_j^T K_j = \lambda$ then $K_j^T K_j = 1.0$ and also $[(R - U^2) - \lambda_j I]K_j = 0$. Any f_{ij} is a correlation coefficient of variable i with factor or dimension j, there being s dimensions of variation underlying the original a variables. Λ is a diagonal matrix containing the λs eigenvalues associated with each factor. The $k_{ij}s$ are thus $f_{ij}s$ in normalized form. An eigenvalue expresses that portion of the total common variance (given by the trace of $[R - U^2]$, which also equals the trace of Λ and of FF^T) accounted for by each of the underlying dimensions of variation. Since Λ is diagonal, the cross products of the factors are zero, i.e., they are not cor-

related, so that each dimension expresses an independent, additive part of the original whole given by the a variables. Which part of which of the original a variables has gone to constitute which of the factors may be determined by examining the factor loadings f_{ij} in the matrix F. In addition, one can compute the n by s matrix S by a pseudoinverse method, such that $S = ZF\Lambda^{-1}$, and then scale the column vectors of S to zero mean and unit variance. Each s_{ij} is a factor score, the score given to observation i on factor j. The spatial variation of each factor can be seen by mapping the factor scores.

The total degree of similarity of each pair of observations then may be computed using the procedures of dimensional analysis, as the taxonomic distance between observations i and j in the s space given by the dimensions, which, since they are independent, are also orthogonal, i.e., the dimensions intersect at right angles. Thus $d_{ij} = [\Sigma_r(s_{ir} - s_{jr})^2]^{1/2}$. This is simply the straight-line distance between the observations located as points in the scatter diagram of s dimensions, and distance increases, as does the dissimilarity of the observations. Of course separate distances could also be calculated for every one of the s dimensions, or on any desired combination, and it is in this form that such distances are used in the field theory. If every pairwise distance is computed, it is possible to prepare the array D of order n by n, an interobservation distance or similarity matrix, which is symmetric (the similarity of i and j is the same as j and i) and which has zeros along the main diagonal. A stepwise grouping procedure applied to this matrix will provide a near-optimal classification of the observations into as many subsets as are required. If a contiguous regionalization is required, this stepwise procedure is modified by use of a simple contiguity constraint. Iterative multiple discriminants will force the near-optimal classification to converge to the optimal classification or regionalization, such that within-group distance (and therefore variance) is minimized and, by definition, between-group variance (and therefore differentiation) maximized.

There are actually several alternative grouping algorithms, among which are:

1. *centroid grouping:* minimization of squared distance between groups
2. *total increment grouping:* minimization of the increment to within-group distances.

3. *gravity grouping.*

The first case of centroid grouping is the simplest, proceeding as follows:

Given the matrix D of order n by n, containing $n(n-1)/2$ distinct measures of interpoint distance (i.e., of similarity of the observations):

1. Identify that pair of observations for which d_{ij}^2 is a minimum.

2. Combine the row and column vectors of D represented by these observations into a single row and column vector representing the new group. The elements of these new vectors are the squared distances from the group centroid to all other points, and matrix D is now of order $(n-1)$ by $(n-1)$.

3. Go back to step 1 and repeat the process. Successive application of the stepwise procedure reduces the problem from n single-member groups to $n-1$, $n-2$, ... 10, 9, 8 ... 5, 4, 3, 2, 1 groups, and a "linkage tree" may be drawn showing how n outermost branches are successively linked up into a mainstem of the complete population. The problem is then to decide what "cuts" across this tree are most significant for the purposes of the problem at hand, so that instead of drawing a tree with $n-1$ separate branching steps, there is a hierarchy of regions with a finite number of levels at which subregions are recognized. Determination of the number and nature of cut-points, and therefore of levels of the regional hierarchy, may be entirely theoretical, beyond the scope of the mathematical manipulations. On the other hand, some quantitative criterion may be sought, such as a dramatic "jump" in the ratio of within- to between-group distances.

There is no guarantee that the groups defined in this manner will be nice, compact areas comprising sets of contiguous places. It is entirely possible that they will be regional types, such as type-of-farming areas. If the research analyst wants to be sure of uniform regions displaying contiguity, he must impose it on step 1 by selecting the minimum d_{ij}^2 for contiguous i and j, and—keeping check of contiguities in the updating process of step 2—any place contiguous to any member of a group is, by definition, contiguous to the group.

But even this will not insure compactness. One can conceive of a region comprising contiguous places that forms a complete circle around some other region, for example. If compactness is also required, it too must be imposed, by selecting i and j for which d_{ij}^2 is a minimum, provided that i and j are contiguous, and subject to minimization of the second moment of inertia of the geographic centroids of the areas.

The second and third types of grouping procedure are somewhat more elaborate. In the case of total increment grouping, a complete check is made of total within-group distances at every step, and groups are formed so that each step minimizes the increment to within-group distance. This is obviously much more desirable than the simple procedure described above, and has the added effect of maintaining groups that are much more nearly equal in size.

Gravity grouping moves in the opposite direction, permitting larger groups to reach out over longer distances than smaller groups to annex a new member. The familiar PP/d^2 formula is used. Both total increment and gravity grouping are subject to the same problems as centroid grouping in selection of significant cut-points to determine levels of the regional hierarchy, and whether contiguity and compactness constraints are needed.

THE FIELD THEORY: CANONICAL FORMULATION

Systematic analysis of the attribute matrix provides scores of areas on underlying spatial patterns. Dimensional analysis then provides distances for each dyad in the structural space. A single distance can be computed for each dyad, spanning all dimensions, or a separate distance may be recorded for each basic concept. Assume the latter. Then if there are s underlying dimensions describing the state of the system, there are s vectors of distance. Each will be $n^2 - n$ long, since there are that many distances recorded for every dyad. But each will only have $(n^2 - n)/2$ distinct distances because of the symmetry of the distance matrix. Call this similarity matrix for the structural space Δ. Factor analysis of the interaction matrix produces a similar matrix of order $n^2 - n$ by b, the behavior matrix B. Each vector of Δ provides the similarity measures for a particular independent kind of uniform regionalization, and each vector of B does the same for a functional regionalization. The field theory may be stated in canonical form as $B \sim \Delta$. If interest centers on the interdependencies of the two bases of regionalization, the procedure is then to estimate the successive canonical correlations λ and canonical vectors U and V, linking the s spatial patterns and the b types of behavior. Successive pairs of vectors U and V are produced from B and Δ, such that maximum correlations of the structural similarities of places and the behavior taking place between them are assured. In other words, relationships between the formal and functional regionalizations are specified.

Since the original vectors of both B and Δ are independent, if the various kinds of behavior and spatial patterns that can be identified have unambigous, one-to-one relationships, the canonical analysis should pick off pairs of vectors from B and Δ to create U and V without changing them in any way.[28] However, if the different forms of behavior result from complex overlappings of structural properties, new vectors of canonical variates will be created on either side expressing these complexities.[29] Thus the analysis results either in a reaffirmation of B and Δ, with an internal reordering of the column vectors so that similar vectors represent similar ideas, or else leads to new matrices U and V. Each vector of U is a linear combination of the vectors of B, and the same is true for Δ and V. Vectors of U and V are equal in number, and the canonical correlations between each successive pair of vectors are maximized.[30]

One problem of application does emerge at this point, however. Δ contains vectors in which there are only $(n^2 - n)/2$ distinct measures of similarity ($i - j$ and $j - i$ similarities are symmetric), but vectors of B usually will contain $(n^2 - n)$ separate pieces of behavioral data (only in special cases are the flows from i to j and j to i identical). To this difficulty of duplicated distances we can propose no formal solution, although one attempt to overcome it is described in the example that appears later.

MATHEMATICAL STATEMENT

The mathematics of canonical analysis are as follows. Let Σ_{BB}, $\Sigma_{\Delta\Delta}$, $\Sigma_{B\Delta}$, and $\Sigma_{\Delta B}$ be within- and between-group covariance matrices of B and Δ. Further, define column vectors U_j

with respect to B and V_j with respect to Δ as linear combinations with column vectors of parameters α_j and γ_j, such that $U_j = B\alpha_j$ and $V_j = \Delta\gamma_j$, requiring unit variance, such that $\alpha_j^T \Sigma_{BB} \alpha_j = 1.0$ and $\gamma_j^T \Sigma_{\Delta\Delta} \gamma_j = 1.0$, and with the expected means of U_j and V_j zero. Then $\lambda_j = \alpha_j^T \Sigma_{B\Delta} \gamma_j$ is the correlation of U_j and V_j, and is the canonical correlation which is maximized. α_j and γ_j are canonical vectors akin to factor loadings for B and Δ, and U_j and V_j are the canonical variates akin to factor scores. The solution for each set of λ_j, α_j, γ_j, U_j and V_j is where

$$
\begin{bmatrix} -\lambda_j \Sigma_{BB} & \Sigma_{B\Delta} \\ \Sigma_{\Delta B} & -\lambda_j \Sigma_{\Delta\Delta} \end{bmatrix} \cdot \begin{bmatrix} \alpha_j \\ \gamma_j \end{bmatrix} = 0
$$

Successive extractions will then, in the same manner as components analysis, produce sets of roots and related vectors and variates in decreasing order of significance, such that the sets are independent of one another, or $\alpha^T \Sigma_{BB} \alpha = 0$, $\gamma^T \Sigma_{\Delta\Delta} \gamma = 0$, and $\gamma^T \Sigma_{\Delta B} \alpha = 0$. If we let ∇ be the matrix of the vectors α_j, Γ the same for the $\gamma_j s$, Λ for the $\lambda_j s$ and U and V for the $U_j s$ and $V_j s$, respectively, then we can write $\nabla^T \Sigma_{BB} = I$, $\Gamma^T \Sigma_{\Delta\Delta} \Gamma = I$ and $\nabla^T \Sigma_{B\Delta} \Gamma = \Lambda$, with $U = B\nabla$ and $V = \Delta\Gamma$.

Restating in terms of between- and within-group correlation matrices,[31] we can write the fundamental canonical equation as $(R_{\Delta\Delta}^{-1} R_{\Delta B} R_{BB}^{-1} R_{B\Delta} - \lambda_i I)\gamma_i = 0$ and $\alpha_i = (R_{BB}^{-1} R_{B\Delta} \lambda_i)/\lambda_i^{-1/2}$.

FORECASTING WITH THE FIELD THEORY

Postulate 1b derived from the literature was that changes in spatial behavior result from changes in the character of places as spatial processes run their course. Spatial processes and changes in the character of places are thus considered to be exogenous; it is the behavior which is determined endogenously. Let us take this idea and show how the field theory lends itself to forecasting use. Arguing that, at least in the short-run, the differences among places observed by structural analysis of cross-sectional data and the changes of places observed by study of longitudinal data take place within the framework of the same underlying dimensions, parameters ∇, Γ, and Λ will remain unchanged.

Consider now as an example the policy formulation of a set of goals to be achieved by areas (levels of production, income, housing conditions, etc.). What types of interaction would be implied by these goals? From the structural analysis equation $S^* = ZF\Lambda^{-1}$, new scores for areas are achieved, and then new dyadic distances Δ^* are created. The canonical formulation then yields $V^* = \Delta^*\Gamma$. Now since $\nabla\Sigma_{BA}\Gamma = \Lambda = \nabla^T B^T \Delta\Gamma$ or $U^T V = \Lambda$, so that $\Lambda^{-1}U^T V = I$, we can write $\Lambda^{-1}U^{*T}V^* = I$. In other words, the specification of certain structural targets had led us to be able to forecast related behavior.

GENERALIZATION

The symmetry of the canonical formulation also permits it to be exploited in reverse. For example, forecasted or planned changes in connectivity can be specified exogenously and then used to predict the changes in character of places resulting from or required to support them. The interdependency implied undoubtedly leads to useful generality, particularly in cases where alternative kinds of forecasting ability are required.[32]

AN OUTLINE OF AN EXAMPLE

As part of an ongoing research program, the complete field theory formulation is being made operational for India.[33]

One phase of the study involves analysis of the spatial structure of the Indian economy using data for the 300-plus districts of that country. For each district, statistics have been compiled on a variety of the characteristics of the resident population, including occupational and income data, plus measures of economic activity, urbanization, accessibility, and the like. In all, more than 100 different variables have been assembled.

Factor analysis of these data produced one general factor relating urbanization, accessibility, income levels, growth rates, and the location of the modern (secondary and tertiary) sectors of the economy. Major industrial urban growth poles were identified, together with distance-decay functions relating intensity and level of activity in related community-of-interest areas to these centers. A second factor identified higher- and lower-income agricultural areas, and further dimensions pointed up well-known differences in regional specialization of

activity (for example, dryland crops of the northwest), or extracted the identifiable effects on the statistics of differences in district size. In most of these cases the nature of the formal regionalization is clear.

The behavioral aspect of the study involved commodity flows. For each of the thirty states which existed prior to the last reorganization, plus six major cities, we had available 36×36 flow matrices for each of sixty-three different commodities for each of ten years. Since the structural analysis related to 1960, the 1959–60 flow data were taken and organized into a $(36^2 - 36) \times 63$ interaction matrix listing flows of sixty-three commodities for each of the 1260 dyads.

Factor analysis of the interaction matrix yielded several distinct behavioral dimensions that differentiated between the functional economic regions focusing on Calcutta, Bombay, and Madras; subdivided the Bombay region into two parts (one maintaining its Bombay ties and the other oriented to Delhi); showed the national economy to be integrated by virtue of flows between the main metropolitan nodes; and pointed up facets of regional specialization —dryland grains moving out of the northwest, coal and iron from the northeast, and the like.

In the field theory formulation, we used the special postulate $B = f(\Delta)$. Factor scores from the commodity flow analysis yielded B, of order 1260 dyads by twelve behavioral dimensions. However, we were faced with a problem in creating Δ for states and cities, given a structural analysis based upon districts. In solving this problem, we may have arrived at a general way of linking different spatial levels of observation into one analytic frame that faces the problem of modifiable units squarely.

The approach taken was stimulated by Rao's canonical formulation of discriminatory analysis.[34] In the original space of the 100-plus variables, the districts form thirty-six swarms of points corresponding to their grouping into thirty-six states and cities. From the factor analysis, an orthonormal basis is provided for this space, and the factor scores represent projections of the districts onto this basis. Distances among districts accurately index their degrees of similarity. By the same token, distances among centroids of the thirty-six groups of districts ("generalized distances") index the similarity of the larger spatial units. Therefore,

Δ is created by computing distances among projections of the group centroids onto each separate dimension of the orthonormal basis, and will have as many vectors of distances as the basis has dimensions.

With a set of distances thereby available for the districts, it was possible to prepare matrix *B*, involving five behavioral dimensions for 1260 dyads, and matrix Δ, including distance measures on seven separate structural factors for the same 1260 dyads. Application of canonical analysis revealed three statistically significant dimensions of interrelationship between behavior and structure:

1. flows within each of the four main metropolitan regions of the economy (the great economic regions centering on Calcutta, Bombay, Madras, and Delhi) and the accessibility, potentials, modern economy structure of the country.

2–3. specialized agricultural production and flows, and specialized primary production and flows, respectively.

Further work is now proceeding to evaluate these results, but it appears that they embody all of the results expected from theories of international trade and spatial interaction.

FOOTNOTES

[1] J. R. Meyer, "Regional Economics: A Survey," *American Economic Review*, **53** (1963), 19–54; B. M. Russett, "Delineating International Regions," in J. D. Singer, ed., *Empirical Studies of International Relations*, International Yearbook of Political Behavior Research, Vol. VII (1965); E. O. Heady and M. D. Skold, "Analysis to Specify the Regional Distribution of Farm Production," in *Research and Education for Regional and Area Development* (Ames: Iowa State University Press, 1965). See also the experimental results in B. Stevens and C. A. Brackett, *Regionalization of Pennsylvania Counties for Development Planning* (Philadelphia: Regional Science Research Institute, 1965); and Stevens and Brackett, *Regionalization of Michigan, Minnesota, and Wisconsin Counties for Development Planning* (Philadelphia: Regional Science Research Institute, 1966).

[2] B. J. L. Berry, "The Mathematics of Economic Regionalization," *Proceedings of the Brno Conference on Economic Regionalization* (Brno: Czech Academy of Sciences, 1966).

[3] K. Lewin, *Field Theory in Social Science* (New York: Harper & Row, Publishers, 1951); R. Rummel, "A Field Theory of Social Action with Application to Conflict Within Nations," *General Systems*, **10** (1965), 183–211.

[4] A. K. Philbrick, "Principles of Areal Functional Organization in Regional Human Geography," *Economic Geography*, **33** (1957), 299–336.

[5] R. R. Sokal and P. H. Sneath, *Principles of Numerical Taxonomy* (San Francisco: W. H. Freeman & Company, 1963).

[6] M. G. Kendall, "The Geographical Distribution of Crop Productivity in England," pp. 387–406.

[7] M. J. Hagood, N. Danilevsky, and C. O. Geum, "An Examination of the Use of Factor Analysis in the Problem of Subregional Delineation," *Rural Sociology*, **3** (1941), 216–234; Hagood, "Statistical Methods for the Delineation of Regions Applied to Data on Agriculture and Population," *Social Forces*, **21** (1943), 287–297.

[8] H. W. Odum, *Southern Regions of the United States* (Chapel Hill: University of North Carolina Press, 1936).

[9] National Resources Committee, *Regional Factors in National Planning and Development* (Washington: The Committee, 1935).

[10] J. C. Weaver, "Crop-Combination Regions in the Middle West," *Geographical Review*, **44** (1954), 175–200.

[11] L. Zobler, "Statistical Testing of Regional Boundaries," *Annals of the Association of American Geographers*, **47** (1957), 83–95.

[12] B. J. L. Berry, "An Inductive Approach to the Regionalization of Economic Development," in N. Ginsburg, ed., *Essays on Geography and Economic Development*, University of Chicago, Department of Geography, Research Paper No. 62 (1960), pp. 78–107.

[13] B. J. L. Berry, "A Method for Deriving Multi-Factor Uniform Regions," *Przeglad Geograficzny*, **33** (1961), 263–282. A full application of the process described in this paper is found in B. G. Jones and W. W. Goldsmith, *Studies in Regional Development: A Factor Analysis Approach to Subregional Definition in Chenango, Delaware and Otsego Counties*, Cornell University, Center for Housing and Environmental Studies (1965).

[14] J. H. Thompson, S. C. Sufrin, P. R. Gould, and M. A. Buck, "Toward a Geography of Economic Health: The Case of New York State," *Annals of the Association of American Geographers*, **52** (1962), 1–20; W. H. Bell and D. W. Sanderson, "An Index of Economic Health for Ontario Counties and Districts," *Ontario Economic Review*, **2** (1964), No. 5.

[15] C. A. Moser and W. Scott, *British Towns* (Edinburgh: Oliver & Boyd, Ltd., 1961).

[16] D. M. Ray and B. J. L. Berry, "Multivariate Socioeconomic Regionalization: A Pilot Study in Central Canada," in T. Rymes and S. Ostry, eds., *Regional Statistical Studies* (Toronto: University of Toronto Press, 1966); B. J. L. Berry, "Identification of Declining Regions: An Empirical Study of the Dimensions of Rural Poverty," in R. S. Thoman and W. D. Wood, eds., *Areas of Economic Stress in Canada* (Kingston: Queen's University Press, 1965).

[17] R. Stone, "A Comparison of the Economic Structure of Regions Based on the Concept of Distance," *Journal of Regional Science*, **2** (1960), 1–20.

[18] B. M. Russett, *op. cit.*

[19] B. J. L. Berry, "The Mathematics of Economic Regionalization," *op. cit.*

[20] H. H. Harman, *Modern Factor Analysis* (Chicago: University of Chicago Press, 1960).

[21] H. Hotelling, "Analysis of a Complex of Statistical Variables into Principal Components," *Journal of Educational Psychology*, **24** (1933), 417–441, 498–520.

[22] M. G. Kendall, *A Course in Multivariate Analysis* (London: Charles Griffin & Company, Ltd., 1957).

[23] T. W. Anderson, *Introduction to Multivariate Statistical Analysis* (New York: John Wiley & Sons, Inc., 1958).

[24] R. R. Sokal and P. H. Sneath, *op. cit.*

[25] J. Rubin, *An Approach to Organizing Data into Homogeneous Groups* (New York: IBM Corporation, System Research and Development Center, 1965).

[26] J. H. Ward, Jr., "Hierarchical Grouping to Optimize an Objective Function," *Journal of the American Statistical Association*, **58** (1963), 236–244.

[27] This first sentence is written for the case of an attribute matrix. Appropriate changes will translate the statement into one for an interaction matrix, viz., replace n by $(n^2 - n)$, a by y, s by b, A by Y, and S by B, as in our earlier usage. A similar family of notational changes is appropriate in the investigation of spatial process.

[28] This is what we would expect from Philbrick's theory of areal functional organization, with its successive formal and functional "layers."

[29] This, then, is the more general case, and Philbrick's postulate is a special case.

[30] In this sense, the separate structural and behavioral dimensions of the canonical analysis are "mapped" into each other's spaces so that maximum coincidence is assured.

[31] See, for example, W. W. Cooley and P. R. Lohnes, *Multivariate Procedures in the Behavioral Sciences* (New York: John Wiley & Sons, Inc., 1962), pp. 35–37. The Bartlett and Wilks criteria for determining the number of significant canonical correlations is outlined in this study, with examples. Refer also to C. R. Rao, *Linear Statistical Inference and Its Applications* (New York: John Wiley & Sons, Inc., 1965).

[32] It is not clear that this reversibility is logical in every case. On the one hand, blockade of Cuba has affected the structure of that country's economy. But conversely, a United States airline strike cannot effect a reduction in the physical size of airports.

[33] The full results are being published in B. J. L. Berry, ed., *Essays on Commodity Flows and the Spatial Structure of the Indian Economy*, University of Chicago, Department of Geography Research Paper No. III (1967).

[34] C. R. Rao, *op. cit.* L. King of Ohio State University, in an unpublished paper entitled "A Discriminatory Analysis of Regional Urban Growth in Canada, 1951‑61," uses Rao's canonical form, as follows: Let G be a between-group dispersion matrix for k groups in a space a, and W be the pooled within-group dispersion matrix. Now write $C = GW^{-1}$. Successive vectors and roots corresponding to the solution of $(C - \lambda_i I) = 0$ and $(C - \lambda_i I)\psi_i = 0$ will provide an orthogonal basis for the space, and the $\psi_i s$ enable projectons of the points within groups and the group centroids to be made onto this basis, such that differences between groups are maximized. Distances between group centroids in this space are "generalized distances" in the strict sense in which that term is used in the statistical literature.

VII

PROBLEMS IN THE ANALYSIS
OF SPATIAL SERIES

1

ADDITIONAL COMMENTS ON WEIGHTING VALUES IN CORRELATION ANALYSIS OF AREAL DATA

EDWIN N. THOMAS and DAVID L. ANDERSON

BACKGROUND

In recent years, the concept of areal association has been assigned a role of increased importance by persons interested in the philosophy and methodology of geography. Although a variety of factors have contributed to the increased stature of the notion, one of the more significant events was the recognition by geographers that they could operationally define certain aspects of areal association within the framework provided by simple and multiple regression and correlation.[1]

The infusion of regression and correlation techniques into geographic research has not been an unmixed blessing. Although the use of these statistical tools permits the geographer to attain certain research goals which heretofore were unattainable, their adoption also has presented the geographer with methodological problems which were not important to him or which he did not clearly recognize when his research was conducted at a less precise level.

One of these methodological problems arises when a given study area is divided into different numbers of areal units, e.g., the United States may be divided for the purposes of study into townships, counties, states, and other units. In this instance, the regression and correlation parameters which are employed to describe the areal associations between spatial distributions within the study area may differ according to the size and number of areal units into which it has been divided.[2]

The differences in parameters arising from differences in areal units also may affect the results and conclusions of comparative regional studies. If different sizes of areal units affect the regression–correlation parameters representing conditions in the *same* study area, then such differences also may affect the values

Reprinted from *Annals of the Association of American Geographers*, **55** (1965), 492–505, by permission of the authors and editor.

depicting relationships in *different* study areas. Thus geographers who are interested in establishing worldwide generalizations about associations between phenomena or in differentiating areas according to differences in the associations of the phenomena located within them are presented with problems of interpretation which are difficult to resolve. This paper, however, is restricted to comments concerning some of the problems which arise when the same study area is divided into different numbers and, therefore, different sizes of areal units. The more interesting and complicated problem of comparing regional regression and correlation parameters is deferred until later.

THE PROBLEM

The essence of the problem is identifying or eliminating differences in parameters which may be attributed merely to differences in the size of areal units from those differences which are owing to "truly different" relationships. Robinson was the first geographer to attempt a formal solution to this general problem.[3] His solution, which is discussed in the following section, is recommended by its simplicity. However, it can be shown that it is not general; i.e., when one is processing real world data, the number of instances in which Robinson's method of areal weighting will insure computationally equal correlation and regression parameters from study area to study area is very limited.

Accordingly, the broad goals of this paper are twofold. The first goal is to identify the limitations inherent in Robinson's solution. The second is to present an approach to the problem which appears to lead, ultimately, to a general solution. Although research is still in progress, a limited number of theoretical and real world examples are provided which demonstrate the utility of the approach which is presented.

ROBINSON'S SOLUTION

A BRIEF REVIEW AND EXPLICATION OF THE PROBLEM

Before proceeding, it is necessary to review Robinson's work in detail. The problem as he conceived it may be summarized in his words:

When the geographer attempts statistical analysis, and especially correlation of distributions having areal extent, he must in many instances modify the general statistical formulae in order to take into account his areal point of view. This generalization applies when the data with which one is working are averages, percentages, ratios, or densities distributed over area and localized by minor civil divisions, counties, or some other such areal units ... for correlation analysis has been designed for studying relationships between characteristics as distributed among units of equal importance.... When the areal units to which the values relate are not the same size, as is unfortunately usually the case, significant discrepancies in size should be taken into account; otherwise, the results of computations may be meaningless.... The reduction of each value to a comparable unit, such as an average, ratio, or density, e.g., population per square mile or average slope, does not take care of the problem.[4]

He later stated:

A simple example can make clear the difficulty of using nonweighted values in correlation analysis. Figure 1 shows three "states" of the same size within each of which there is an identical distribution of values X and Y over the entire area. State I is composed of six "counties" of equal area (A). States II and III, although they have exactly the same total distribution of X and Y, have different numbers and sizes of areal units or enumeration districts.[5]

The variation in results which is obtained from such differences is illustrated in Table 1. All of the basic regression–correlation statistics, the Y-intercept, a, the simple regression coefficient, b, and the coefficient of simple correlation, r, differ for each of the states.

TABLE 1

Basic regression and correlation parameters using unweighted density values for areal units of unequal size: Robinson hypothetical data

State	a	b	r
I	1.429	1.429	0.715
II	1.625	1.375	0.687*
III	3.000	1.000	0.500

* The value of r for state II which is shown by Robinson as 0.875 is incorrect. This does not affect the remainder of Robinson's paper.

THE AREAL WEIGHTING SOLUTION

Robinson stated:

Clearly the coefficient of correlation for X and Y is affected by the arrangement and size of counties regardless of the actual distribution of X and Y. The influence of the chance arrangement of boundaries may be removed by weighting the data by the area of the units to which they refer.[6]

When the values of the individual densities are weighted by the areas of the observations, the equations for the three basic parameters are modified as follows: the equation for b is modified from

$$(1) \qquad b = \frac{N \sum XY - \sum X \sum Y}{N \sum X^2 - (\sum X)^2}$$

to

$$(2) \qquad b = \frac{\sum A \sum AXY - \sum AX \sum AY}{\sum A \sum AX^2 - (\sum AX)^2}$$

the equation for a is modified from

$$(3) \qquad a = \frac{\sum X^2 \sum Y - \sum X \sum XY}{N \sum X^2 - (\sum X)^2}$$

to

$$(4) \qquad a = \frac{\sum AX^2 \sum AY - \sum AX \sum AXY}{\sum A \sum AX^2 - (\sum AX)^2}$$

and the equation for r is modified from

$$(5) \qquad r = \frac{N \sum XY - \sum X \sum Y}{\sqrt{N \sum X^2 - (\sum X)^2}\sqrt{N \sum Y^2 - (\sum Y)^2}}$$

to

$$(6) \qquad r = \frac{\sum A \sum AXY - \sum AX \sum AY}{\sqrt{\sum A \sum AX^2 - (\sum AX)^2}}{\times \sqrt{\sum A \sum AY^2 - (\sum AY)^2}}$$

where X and Y refer to density values and A refers to the area of a particular areal unit.

When r, a, and b are computed according to Eqs. 2, 4, and 6, the respective parameters are equal in each of the three study areas comprising Robinson's exemplary data (Table 2).

TABLE 2

Basic regression and correlation parameters using weighted density values for areal units of unequal sizes Robinson hypothetical data

State	a	b	r
I	1.429	1.429	0.715
II	1.429	1.429	0.715
III	1.429	1.429	0.715

THE SPECIAL NATURE OF ROBINSON'S SOLUTION

Our goals in this section are twofold: (1) We will provide a numerical demonstration that Robinson's solution is not general, and (2) we will specify those special instances when it is effective.

To simplify our exposition, we will recognize two kinds of study areas. First, we will identify an *initial* study area in which all of the areal units are the same size. (Robinson's state I is an initial study area.) Second, we will recognize subsequent study areas in which the areal units are some combination of contiguous areal units in the initial study area. (In this sense, Robinson's states II–III are subsequent study areas.) In addition, the density values X and Y for the areal units in the subsequent study areas are defined as averages of the density values of the appropriate areal units in the initial area.

The casual reader may form the impression that regression and correlation parameters for initial and subsequent study areas will always be computationally equal when the data for subsequent study areas are areally weighted; this is compatible with the results which Robinson obtained using exemplary data (Table 2). However, this impression would not be correct, because computationally equal parameters do not always result even when density values are areally weighted.

This point may be illustrated with a simple numerical example. We will begin with an *initial* study area, I, which is identical to Robinson's state I. From I we will establish, in the manner prescribed above, subsequent study areas B and C (Fig. 2). The spatial distributions of X and Y in B and C will differ from the distributions obtaining in Robinson's II and III because the areal units in I which we will combine to form the subsequent areal units in B and C will differ from those which Robinson combined to form the areal units in II and III (compare Figs. 1–2).

Magnitudes of a, b, and r for study areas I, B, and C, computed from unweighted density values of X and Y, are presented in Table 3. As expected, they are not equal. If areal weighting is a general solution to the problem presented by the inequalities in Table 3, we would expect that the magnitudes of the various parameters computed from weighted density values according to Eqs. 2, 4, and 6 would be equal. This is not the case (Table 4). The particular

parameters for the various study areas are *not* equal. Areal weighting is not a general solution to the problem.[7]

TABLE 3

Basic regression and correlation parameters using unweighted density values: derived from Robinson hypothetical data

State	a	b	r
I	1.429	1.429	0.715
B	−1.000	2.500	0.829
C	0.000	2.000	1.000

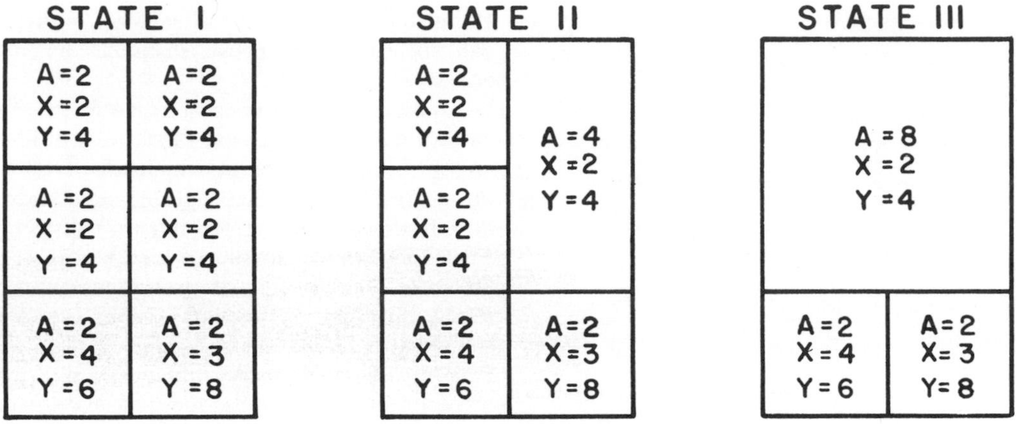

FIGURE 1. The sizes and shapes of areal units in three study areas: Robinson hypothetical data

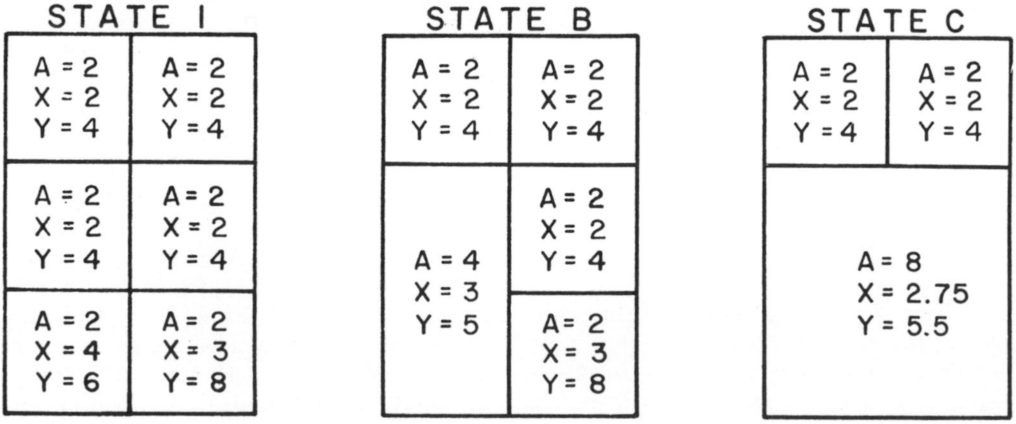

FIGURE 2. State I is Robinson's State I. The areal units in State I are combined to form the areal units in States B and C.

TABLE 4

Basic regression and correlation parameters
using weighted density values for
areal units of unequal size:
derived from Robinson hypothetical data

State	a	b	r
I	1.429	1.429	0.715
B	0.000	2.000	0.707
C	0.000	2.000	1.000

SPECIAL CASES WHEN AREAL WEIGHTING GIVES EQUAL PARAMETERS

There are only two instances when areal weighting is an effective implement in securing computationally equal results. The first case is the one treated by Robinson and illustrated by his exemplary data. In this case, the spatial distributions of X and Y for initial and subsequent study areas have, as Robinson stated, "exactly the same total distribution." In this case, each of the density values in the initial study area which is aggregated to give a density value in a particular areal unit in a subsequent study area is equal. Whenever this relationship obtains, the numerators and denominators in Eqs. 2, 4, and 6 will have the same numerical value whether data for initial or subsequent study areas are entered into the computations which are specified. Consequently, the values of a, b, and r will be equal for initial and subsequent areas.

Let us now consider the second case. If the density values for the aggregated areal units in the initial study area are not equal, then the values of X and Y in the areal units in subsequent study areas will not be equal to the respective values in the initial area, i.e., the initial and subsequent spatial distributions will not have "exactly the same total distribution." It follows that the numerators and denominators, respectively, in Eqs. 2, 4, and 6 for initial and subsequent areas will be unequal. But the values of a, b, and r *may* be equal for initial and subsequent study areas if the changes between study areas in numerators and denominators of Eqs. 2, 4, and 6 are exactly proportional. However, this event is strictly a chance occurrence, and is fully as much a function of special chance relationships among the initial X and Y values as it is a function of areal weighting.

When executing real world research, the number of times when either the first or second case is encountered is rare. For this reason, areal weighting must be considered only a special solution to the general problem of unequal correlation and regression parameters in initial and subsequent study areas.

AN INFERENTIAL APPROACH TO THE PROBLEM

INTRODUCTION

In the preceding sections we noted that the basic correlation and regression parameters which summarize the relationships between two variables for different study areas may differ according to the size and number of areal units into which the study areas are divided. We also suggested that the areal weighting solution to this problem which was asserted by Robinson is special.

In this section we will present the elements of an inferential solution to the problem in which we may accept computational differences in the magnitudes of the basic statistics, and then evaluate those differences within an inferential statistical framework. The position that we maintain is that, with some modification and augmentation, this inferential approach will lead to a general solution to the problem. We will comment on remaining questions and necessary additions in "Summary and Conclusions."

SAMPLES, POPULATIONS, AND UNIVERSES

Before proceeding, it is necessary to discuss briefly the kinds of aggregates or groups which are considered when statistical studies are executed. It is customary to consider statistical techniques as treating two groups. One group is the *sample*, which is a relatively small collection from a much larger group about which we desire information. The other group is the *population*, which is the larger body whose properties we are attempting to determine.[8] In this formulation, the word "universe" and "population" frequently are used interchangeably.

For certain kinds of problems, it is meaningful to identify three distinct levels of statistical inquiry by differentiating between a population and a universe.[9] Within this formulation, the definitions of "sample" and "population" remain the same, but "universe" is redefined so that the term refers to a more abstract group than population, and "contains all events as they happened and as they *might have* happened if everything else had remained the same but the random shocks."[10] Thus we recognize:[11]

Level I: *sample:* things that both happened and where observed. It is drawn from

Level II: *population:* things that happened but where not necessarily observed. It is drawn from

Level III: *universe:* all things that could have happened. (In the nature of things, only a few did).

The justification for this construct apparently lies with Fisher, who stated specifically that:

Any body of numerical observations, or qualitative data thrown into numerical form as frequencies, may be interpreted as a random sample of some hypothetical population of possible values.[12]

RATIONALE FOR TREATING DIFFERENCES BETWEEN REGRESSION–CORRELATION PARAMETERS WITHIN AN INFERENTIAL FRAMEWORK

The preceding discussion was necessitated by Robinson's model, in which all of the areal units in each state are employed in estimating the regression–correlation parameters. If we are dealing with all events which occurred within each study area, rather than a small collection of events, then, technically, we are treating populations and not samples. If we do not recognize the existence of three levels of statistical inquiry, then the application of inferential statistical techniques to our problem does not appear to be appropriate.[13] However, if we do recognize the three levels, then the data for each of the several study areas may be treated as a random sample from some hypothetical universe of possible values, although each is, in fact, a population.

Once we accept the notion that our study area populations may be regarded as random samples, then we may evaluate differences between parameters which describe areal associations within the study area populations by the same methods applied when attempting to evaluate the magnitudes which arise within any random samples, i.e., by employing appro-

priate tests of statistical significance. The question about which we wish to secure an answer is whether or not the parameters for the various study areas appear to have arisen from the *same* theoretical universe.

THE EXPECTED BEHAVIOR OF THE POPULATION PARAMETERS

For the purposes of clarity, let us briefly restate our problem and specify some of the assumptions which underlie its solution. First, we are dealing with several, s, study areas which have the same total area, but which are divided into different numbers of areal units. Second, two phenomena, W and Z, are distributed in each areal unit in each study area, such that the total magnitude of W and Z is equal in each study area or

$$(7) \quad \sum W_\mathrm{I} = \sum W_\mathrm{II} = \sum W_\mathrm{III} = \ldots = \sum W_s$$

and

$$(8) \quad \sum Z_\mathrm{I} = \sum Z_\mathrm{II} = \sum Z_\mathrm{III} = \ldots = \sum Z_s$$

Third, we will focus attention on density values, X and Y, of W and Z, such that for each areal unit in each study area we have

$$(9) \quad \frac{W_i}{A_i} = X_i$$

and

$$(10) \quad \frac{Z_i}{A_i} = Y_i$$

where A is area and i refers to the ith areal unit. Fourth, we will identify one study area, I, which is divided into the largest number of areal units, i.e., which is initial, and further specify that the areal units in all of the other study areas are formed of some combination of the areal units in I, i.e., all other study areas are subsequent. This implies that the values of W and Z, and hence X and Y, in all study areas are determined by the spatial distribution of W and Z in I. Fifth, in order to simplify the problem, we will specify that the pairs of W and Z values for each areal unit in I are randomly allocated to the particular areal units.[14] Sixth, and lastly, we will accept the notion that each set of paired

(X, Y) values for each study area is a population from a universe.

If the assumptions specified in the preceding paragraph are fulfilled, the regression-correlation parameters for the various study areas are affected, as Robinson stated, "by the chance arrangement of boundaries."[15] This being the case, if we evaluate the differences between parameters within a formal inferential statistical framework, we will expect that the tests of statistical significance which we may execute within that framework will indicate that those differences would have arisen through the operation of chance, i.e., that the area-to-area differences in the parameters may be attributed to random "shocks" within the same universe.

If the differences between the particular statistics for the various study areas can be attributed to random affects, then, for the purposes of geographic analysis, the various regression and correlation parameters for the several study areas may be treated as characterizing areal associations within the same universe, and the differences between them may be ignored.

THE PROCEDURE AND THE TESTS OF STATISTICAL SIGNIFICANCE TO BE EMPLOYED

It is necessary to comment briefly on the general procedure to be followed and the specific tests of significance that will be employed. Our general procedure will be to compute basic simple regression and correlation statistics for sets of study areas in which the study areas *per se* and the variables distributed within them fulfill the six assumptions specified above. Next, the differences between particular parameters for each of the study area sets will be hypothesized as arising solely from the operation of chance. Finally, each hypothesis will be tested, using whatever test of statistical significance is appropriate for the parameter in question.

Having specified the general procedure to be followed, we may now comment on the specific tests of statistical significance that will be used. We will employ z-transformations and z-tests to confirm the hypotheses concerning random differences between simple correlation coefficients according to

$$(11) \qquad \frac{(z_m - z_p)}{[1/(N_m - 3) + 1/(N_p - 3)]^{1/2}}$$

where z is a transformed value of a simple correlation coefficient r; N is the number of areal units in a given study area; and m and p denote the mth and pth study areas, respectively.[16] For a given value of r, z is defined as

$$(12) \qquad z = \tfrac{1}{2} \ln \left(\frac{1 + r}{1 - r} \right)$$

The random nature of differences between Y-intercepts and simple regression coefficients for various study areas will be demonstrated within one inferential model by using a modified analysis of covariance design.[17] The hypothesis concerning differences between regression coefficients for various study areas is tested directly according to

$$(13) \qquad \frac{(b_m - b_p)}{\sigma(1/\sum x_m^2 + 1/\sum x_p^2)^{1/2}}$$

where b denotes a simple regression coefficient, σ is an estimate of the standard error of estimate for the universe, $\sum x^2$ is the sum of the squared deviations from the mean of X, and m and p refer to the mth and pth study areas, respectively. The sampling distribution of $(b_m - b_p)$ has a t-distribution with $N_m + N_p - 4$ degrees of freedom.

The demonstration that the Y-intercepts for the various study areas do not differ significantly is not so straightforward. As Snedecor states: "The ultimate question about the elevation of the population regression lines has little meaning unless the lines are parallel."[18] Thus the demonstration that the Y-intercepts for the various study areas are equal is predicated on the prior demonstration that the differences between regression coefficients may be attributed to chance. Assuming that the study area regression coefficients have been shown to differ no more than would be expected from the operation of chance, the random nature of differences between Y-intercepts will be demonstrated according to

$$(14) \qquad \frac{(b^* - b^{**})}{S_{b^* - b^{**}}}$$

where b^* denotes the slope of the straight line connecting the mean points for X and Y in the mth and pth study areas, b^{**} denotes a common regression line, which is the weighted mean of the regression coefficients for the mth and pth study areas. The quantity $(b^* - b^{**})/S_{b^*-b^{**}}$ has a t-distribution with $N_m + N_p - 4$ degrees of freedom. The standard error of the difference between the coefficients, $S_{b^*-b^{**}}$ is determined according to

$$(15) \quad \left\langle \sigma^2 \left\{ \left[\frac{1}{(\bar{X}_m - \bar{X}_p)^2} \right] \left(\frac{1}{N_m} + \frac{1}{N_p} \right) + \left(\frac{1}{\sum x_m^2 + \sum x_p^2} \right) \right\} \right\rangle^{1/2}$$

where σ^2 is an estimate of the variance of the estimate in the universe, $\bar{X}$ is the mean of the X values, $\sum x^2$ is the sum of the squared deviations from the mean of X, N is the number of areal units in a given study area, and m and p denote the mth and pth study areas, respectively.

EXAMPLES OF DIFFERENCES IN REGRESSION AND CORRELATION PARAMETERS WHICH MAY BE ATTRIBUTED TO RANDOM EFFECTS

INTRODUCTION

In this section, following the procedures described above, we will provide theoretical and real world examples which demonstrate the random nature of differences between basic regression and correlation statistics which describe relationships in populations which,

to a greater or lesser extent, have the characteristics specified above (under "The Expected Behavior of the Population Parameters"). In addition to exemplifying the position taken [there], the real world examples also suggest that some of the assumptions which were specified may be relaxed somewhat without changing the random nature of the differences between parameters.

A HYPOTHETICAL EXAMPLE USING ROBINSON'S DATA

The series of tests of statistical significance described above were executed on the hypothetical parameters presented by Robinson. The results of these tests are presented in Table 5. The inferential evidence indicates that the Y-intercepts, a; the simple regression coefficients, b; and the simple correlation coefficients, r, for the three study areas treated by Robinson may be considered as describing relationships within the same universe. Differences may be considered to be chance occurrences, and substantive geographic significance should not be attached to them.

A HYPOTHETICAL EXAMPLE WHICH ALLOWS GREATER DEGREES OF FREEDOM

Data were prepared in order to provide a set of hypothetical study areas within which there were located greater numbers of areal units than in the study areas treated by

TABLE 5

Basic values employed in the tests of statistical significance and the results of the tests: Robinson hypothetical data

Statistic	Areas		
	I–II	I–III	II–III
Standard Error of Difference; z	0.833	∞^2	∞^2
Absolute Difference; z^1	0.039	0.338	0.299
Standard Error of Difference; b	1.078	1.423	1.584
Absolute Differences; b^1	0.054	0.429	0.375
Standard Error of Difference; $(b^* - b^{**})$	26.716	2.369	3.350
Absolute Differences; $b^* - b^{**1}$	0.597	0.727	0.769

[1] Differences in the magnitudes of the parameters for the various paired areas do not differ significantly at the 95 per cent confidence level.

[2] There are only three areal units in study area III. There is a loss of three degrees of freedom when executing a z-test. Hence the standard errors of the difference for z values involving study area III are infinitely large.

Robinson. An initial study area was established which was composed of fifty square areal units, each of which had an area of one square mile (Fig. 3). To fulfill the requisites . . . , paired (Z, W) values were selected from random normal deviates and were allocated to each areal unit to create the initial random spatial distribution of paired (X, Y) values.[19] The set of fifty paired values was purposely selected so as to have a coefficient of determination, r^2, of 0.5091, indicating that approximately 50 per cent of the variation in Y is explained by X.

The sizes and shapes of the areal units in subsequent study areas were created by randomly removing boundaries between adjoining areal units in the initial area. This was accomplished by using tables of random numbers.[20] If a random number was even, then the boundary between units was eliminated:

if the number was odd, then the boundary remained.

Boundaries were first removed between east–west neighbors. Randomly aggregating areal units resulted in a new map of the initial study area in which there were thirty areal units (Fig. 3). This subsequent study area then was treated like the initial study area, resulting in still another subsequent area with only eighteen areal units. This process was continued until no north-south boundaries existed between areal units. The east–west aggregation of areal units resulted in study areas with thirty, eighteen, thirteen, and ten areal units (Fig. 3).

After all of the east–west neighbors were aggregated, the entire process was repeated, starting with the original fifty units, but with north–south neighbors being consolidated. The removal of east–west boundaries gives rise to subsequent study areas having thirty-three,

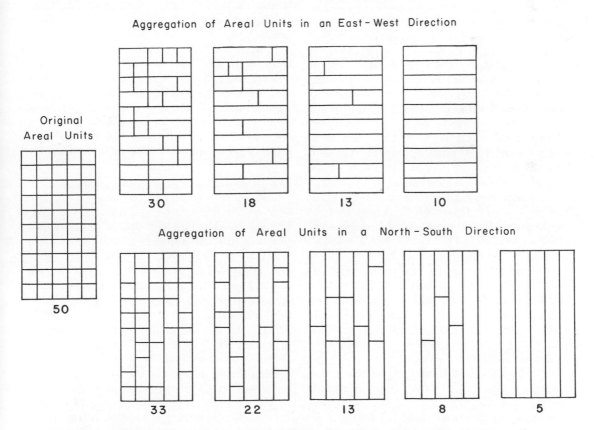

FIGURE 3.   The sizes and shapes of areal units: hypothetical data. The number under each study area refers to the number of areal units within it.

twenty-two, thirteen, eight, and five areal units (Fig. 3).

The magnitudes of Z and W for the areal units in the initial area were appropriately summed and divided by the areas of the modified units in order to determine the density values, X and Y, for the modified areal units in each of the subsequent study areas.

Basic regression and correlation parameters, i.e., r, a, and b, were computed for each of the ten hypothetical study areas. Differences between these values then were compared, using the series of statistical significance tests specified above (under "The Procedure and the Tests"). All of the inferential evidence indicates that the differences in the magnitude of the parameters may be considered as chance occurrences and that geographic significance should not be attached to them.

A REAL WORLD EXAMPLE WITHIN AN URBAN AREA

The following example, typical of one kind of problem which may be considered as a part of urban or social geography, is provided by Gehlke and Biehl.[21] The rate of male juvenile delinquency in areal units is the dependent variable; the independent variable is the median monthly rental value obtaining in the units. Neither of these variables is precisely a density; however, both of them are areal averages, and they both appear to represent phenomena which lie within the scope of the problem as Robinson defined it.[22]

The study area is Cleveland and its environs. "The 252 census tracts of Cleveland and its four largest suburbs were grouped successively in 200 areas, 175, 150, 125, 100, fifty, twenty-five, so far as possible of approximately the same size and consisting of contiguous territory."[23] Thus the design that Gehlke and Biehl followed generally fulfills the assumptions specified earlier. There is one particularly notable exception, however: the paired (delinquency and rental) values were not allocated within the study area randomly.

This example is restricted to the effect that aggregation has on the magnitude of simple correlation coefficients. None of the differences observed by Gehlke and Biehl [is] found to be statistically significant, and all of the values of r may be presumed to arise within the same universe. These empirical results also suggest

that the assumption concerning the random allocation of paired values may be relaxed somewhat, although it cannot be totally ignored.[24]

A REAL WORLD EXAMPLE WITHIN A NATIONAL AREA

The following example, representing one kind of problem which might arise in agricultural geography, is based upon data presented by Yule and Kendall.[25] The dependent variable is yield per acre of wheat in forty-eight agricultural counties in England; the independent variable is yield per acre of corn. The data for wheat and corn in the forty-eight agricultural counties is successively aggregated into data for twenty-four, twelve, six, and three areal units (Fig. 4). It should be noted that in the design adopted by Yule and Kendall, all of the aggregated values are not summations for contiguous areas. However, as they specify: "Since most of the areas are contiguous, this is the kind of result which we might get if larger areas than counties were recorded."[26]

The regression and correlation parameters were computed for the sets of forty-eight, twenty-four, twelve, six, and three areal units and were subjected to the tests of statistical significance. As was the case with all of the other examples, none of the differences is to be considered statistically significant. Geographic significance should not be attached to them.

SUMMARY AND CONCLUSIONS

We have briefly reviewed some of the effects upon regression and correlation parameters of differing sizes and numbers of areal units within study areas. In general, when the "same" study area is divided into different numbers and sizes of areal units, the particular parameters do not agree, and problems of interpreting the resulting differences arise.

The solution to this problem which Robinson presented has been acknowledged, and we have specified its special nature.

Employing inferential statistical notions, we have established the basic elements of a solution to the problem which we believe will prove to be general. However, it appears to the writers that three broad and related topics require additional thought before a complete and formal methodology can be specified:

FIGURE 4. The sizes and shapes of areal units: Yule and Kendall data. The number under each study area refers to the number of areal units within it.

1. Certain basic problems which appear to arise primarily from the nature of areal units deserve additional consideration. For example, it appears that both relative and absolute sizes of areal units may have to be given consideration, i.e., if a geographer is attempting to compare areal associations in two or more study areas which have unequal total areas, should the areal units in both have equal absolute areas, or would it be desirable for the areal units to contain some equal proportion of the total area of their respective study areas? In addition, what mathematical relationships, if any, can be established concerning the effects, between real world study areas, of differences in the average sizes of areal units, the variations in size of areal units, and the number of areal units?

2. Other basic problems appear to arise for the most part from the specific character of the data. For example, it is plausible that the effects of aggregating areal units may differ according to whether the relationship between X and Y variables is close or poor. In addition, if density values can be treated as merely linear transformations of absolute values, then the methodology ultimately specified may be equally applicable to both kinds of data.

3. Additional problems can be identified which can be attributed primarily to the

effects of differences in the spatial distributions of density values. It appears, for example, that the effects of aggregation in spatial distributions in which X or Y values in given areal units are systematically very similar or very different from the X or Y values in neighboring areal units may differ from the effects in spatial distributions in which systematic relationships do not occur. This problem in particular appears to be one which should be of special interest to geographers.

The preceding statements are not intended to be comprehensive, detailed, or technical. Contrariwise, they are specified merely to present three broad directions for inquiry, to exemplify some of the problems arising in each, and to indicate the directions in which the writers intend to proceed in the future.

MATHEMATICAL APPENDIX

THE MEANS OF WEIGHTED DENSITY VALUES FOR INITIAL AND SUBSEQUENT STUDY AREAS

Assume an initial study area, α, composed of N areal units which have the same area, A. Let X_i refer to the density value for the ith areal unit. Assume further that all X_i are not equal. For α, consider the weighted densities, AX_i and the mean, $\overline{AX}$. Following Robinson, we have

$$(1) \quad \overline{AX}_\alpha = \frac{\sum_{i=1}^{N} AX_i}{\sum_{i=1}^{N} A_i} = \frac{A \sum_{i=1}^{N} X_i}{NA} = \bar{X}_\alpha$$

where N is the number of areal units in α, i is the ith areal unit and $\bar{X}_\alpha$ is the mean of the unweighted density values.

Now aggregate certain areal units in α to form the areal units in a subsequent study area, β, according to "The Expected Behavior of the Population Parameters" (above). Then

$$\overline{AX}_\beta = \frac{\sum_{j=1}^{k} \left(\frac{\sum_{i=1}^{n_j} A_{ij} \sum_{i=1}^{n_j} AX_{ij}}{\sum_{i=1}^{n_j} A_{ij}} \right)}{\sum_{j=1}^{k} \sum_{i=1}^{n_i} A_{ij}} = \frac{\sum_{j=1}^{k} \sum_{i=1}^{n_j} AX_{ij}}{\sum_{i=1}^{N} A_i}$$

$$(2)$$

$$= \frac{\sum_{i=1}^{N} AX_i}{\sum_{i=1}^{N} A_i} = \overline{AX}_\alpha = \bar{X}_\alpha$$

where j and k, respectively, refer to a particular aggregation, and the number of aggregations and n refers to the number of areal units in a particular aggregation. Similar relationships obtain for $\overline{AY}_\alpha$ and $\overline{AY}_\beta$.[27]

In general, starting with all initial areal units the same size, the means of the weighted densities for initial and subsequent study areas are equal, and in turn are equal to the mean of the unweighted density values, i.e., with all initial areal units the same size, weighting does not affect the value of the mean.

SUMS OF SQUARES AND CROSS PRODUCTS FOR INITIAL AND SUBSEQUENT STUDY AREAS

Now consider, according to Robinson's formulation,

$$(3) \quad \sum_{i=1}^{N} Ax_\alpha^2 = \sum_{i=1}^{N} A(X_i - \bar{X}_\alpha)^2$$

where $\sum_{i=1}^{N} Ax_\alpha^2$ is the areally weighted sum of the squared deviations of the densities from the mean of the weighted densities for all areal units in α.

Again, aggregate certain areal units in α to form the areal units in a subsequent area, β, according to "The Expected Behavior" (above). Then

$$(4) \quad \sum_{i=1}^{N} Ax_\alpha^2 = \sum_{j=1}^{k} \sum_{i=1}^{n_j} A(X_{ij} - \bar{X}_j + \bar{X}_j - \bar{X}_\alpha)^2$$

which gives

$$(5) \quad \sum_{i=1}^{N} Ax_\alpha^2 = \sum_{j=1}^{k} \sum_{i=1}^{n_j} A(X_{ij} - \bar{X}_j)^2 \\ + \sum_{j=1}^{k} n_j A(\bar{X}_j - \bar{X}_\alpha)^2$$

Treating $\sum_{i=1}^{N} Ay_\alpha^2$ and $\sum_{i=1}^{N} Axy_\alpha$ similarly gives

$$(6) \quad \sum_{i=1}^{N} Ay_\alpha^2 = \sum_{j=1}^{k} \sum_{i=1}^{n_j} A(Y_{ij} - \bar{Y}_j)^2 \\ + \sum_{j=1}^{k} n_j A(\bar{Y}_i - \bar{Y}_\alpha)^2$$

and

$$(7) \quad \sum_{i=1}^{N} Axy_\alpha = \sum_{j=1}^{k} \sum_{i=1}^{n_j} A(X_{ij} - \bar{X}_j)(Y_{ij} - \bar{Y}_j) \\ + \sum_{j=1}^{k} n_j A(\bar{X}_j - \bar{X}_\alpha)(\bar{Y}_j - \bar{Y}_\alpha)$$

Let us now rewrite Eqs. 5, 6, and 7 in a simplified form. Equation 5 becomes

$$(8) \qquad \sum Ax_\alpha^2 = \sum Ax_w^2 + \sum Ax_\beta^2$$

Equation 6 becomes

$$(9) \qquad \sum Ay_\alpha^2 = \sum Ay_w^2 + \sum Ay_\beta^2$$

And Eq. 7 becomes

$$(10) \qquad \sum Axy_\alpha^2 = \sum Axy_w + \sum Axy_\beta$$

We may now comment on Eqs. 8, 9, and 10.[28] First, $\sum\limits_{i=1}^{N} Ax_\alpha^2$, $\sum\limits_{i=1}^{N} Ay_\alpha^2$, and $\sum\limits_{i=1}^{N} Axy_\alpha$ have been partitioned into two additive components. Second, the first term on the right side of Eqs. 8, 9, and 10 arises due to variation within aggregations, i.e., when we combine density values which are unequal, whereas the second term is due to variation between aggregations, i.e., it is precisely equal to the sums of squares and cross products for the subsequent area, β.

REGRESSION COEFFICIENTS FOR INITIAL AND SUBSEQUENT STUDY AREAS

The regression coefficient for the initial area, b_α, can be specified as

$$(11) \quad b_\alpha = \frac{\sum Axy_\alpha}{\sum Ax_\alpha^2} = \frac{\sum Axy_w + \sum Axy_\beta}{\sum Ax_w^2 + \sum Ax_\beta^2}$$

and b_β, the regression coefficient for the subsequent area, β, is given by

$$(12) \quad b_\beta = \frac{\sum Axy_\beta}{\sum Ax_\beta^2} = \frac{\sum Axy_\alpha - \sum Axy_w}{\sum Ax_\alpha^2 - \sum Ax_w^2}$$

We now may ask a critical question: "Do conditions exist under which $b_\beta = b_\alpha$?" One case immediately is apparent; from Eq. 12, we can see that if $\sum Axy_w$ and $\sum A_w^2$ are both equal to zero, then $\sum Axy_\beta = \sum Axy_\alpha$, and $\sum Ax_\beta^2 = \sum Ax_\alpha^2$, and b_β must be equal to b_α. The magnitude of $\sum Axy_w$ and $\sum Ax_w^2$ is an expression of the variation of weighted density values within aggregations. Therefore, if each of the X_i or Y_i within each aggregation is equal, then $\sum Axy_w$ and $\sum Ax_w^2$ will be equal to zero, insuring that $b_\beta = b_\alpha$.

This is the case treated by Robinson with three spatial distributions which have "exactly the same total distribution." In creating state II, he aggregates values for two areal units in state I. But both X values are equal to 2, and both Y values equal 4. For state III, four areal units in I are aggregated; again all X are equal (2) as are all Y (4).

We now will treat a second case. Rarely, when treating real world data, will $\sum Axy_w$ and $\sum Ax_w^2$ be equal to zero. In most instances, then, $\sum Axy_\beta \neq \sum Axy_\alpha$ and $\sum Ax_\beta^2 \neq \sum Ax_\alpha^2$. However, if

$$(13) \qquad \sum Axy_\beta = K \sum Axy_\alpha$$

and

$$(14) \qquad \sum Ax_\beta^2 = K \sum Ax_\alpha^2$$

where $K < 1$, then

$$(15)$$
$$b_\beta = \frac{\sum Axy_\beta}{\sum Ax_\beta^2} = \frac{K \sum Axy_\alpha}{K \sum Ax_\alpha^2} = \frac{\sum Axy_\alpha}{\sum Ax_\alpha^2} = b_\alpha$$

In other words, if $\sum Axy_\beta$ is in the same proportion to $\sum Axy_\alpha$ as $\sum Ax_\beta^2$ is to $\sum Ax_\alpha^2$, then $b_\beta = b_\alpha$. The strict proportionality must be maintained, because if

$$(16) \qquad \sum Axy_\beta = (K + C) \sum Axy_\alpha$$

and

$$(17) \qquad \sum Ax_\beta^2 = (K + E) \sum Ax_\alpha^2$$

where $K < 1$ and $C \neq E$, then

$$(18)$$
$$b_\beta = \frac{\sum Axy_\beta}{\sum Ax_\beta^2} = \frac{(K + C) \sum Axy_\alpha}{(K + E) \sum Ax_\alpha^2} \neq \frac{\sum Axy_\alpha}{\sum Ax_\alpha^2}$$

and $b_\beta \neq b_\alpha$.

The relationship specified in Eqs. 13 and 14 is strictly a chance event with a small probability of occurrence and, in spite of areal weighting, will occur infrequently within sets of real world data.

THE Y-INTERCEPTS FOR INITIAL AND SUBSEQUENT AREAS

We may now consider the value of the Y-intercept, a, in initial and subsequent areas. The Y-intercept may be computed according to

$$(19) \qquad a = \bar{Y} - b\bar{X}$$

We have already shown in Eq. 1 that $\overline{AX}_\alpha = \bar{X}_\alpha$ and $\overline{AY}_\alpha$ may be treated similarly. Thus the Y-intercept for weighted densities from the initial study area may be written as

$$(20) \qquad a_\alpha = \bar{Y}_\alpha - b_\alpha\bar{X}_\alpha$$

We also may write

$$(21) \qquad a_\beta = \bar{Y}_\beta - b_\beta\bar{X}_\beta$$

From Eqs. 1 and 2, we know that $\bar{Y}_\alpha = \bar{Y}_\beta$ and $\bar{X}_\alpha = \bar{X}_\beta$. Thus we may write Eq. 21 as

$$(22) \qquad a_\beta = \bar{Y}_\alpha - b_\beta\bar{X}_\alpha$$

From Eqs. 20 and 21, it is obvious that $a_\beta = a_\alpha$ if, and only if, $b_\alpha = b_\beta$. Thus equality of Y-intercepts is determined by equality of regression coefficients. From the preceding discussion, we know that we can expect regression coefficients for weighted density values from initial and subsequent study areas to agree only in two instances. Hence we conclude that, in general, Y-intercepts, even for areally weighted density values, will agree only in two instances which can be expected to arise only rarely within sets of real world data.

COEFFICIENTS OF CORRELATION FOR INITIAL AND SUBSEQUENT STUDY AREAS

Let us now consider r, the coefficient of correlation, which can be expressed as

$$(23) \qquad r = \frac{\sum xy}{N\sigma_y\sigma_x}$$

which gives

$$(24) \qquad r^2 = \frac{(\sum xy)^2}{\sum x^2 \sum y^2}$$

For our purposes, we can consider either r or r^2, and, inasmuch as r^2 leads to a less complicated formulation, we will treat it.

We will specify coefficients of determination for the α and β study areas as

$$(25) \qquad r_\alpha^2 = \frac{(\sum Axy_\alpha)^2}{\sum Ax_\alpha^2 \sum Ay_\alpha^2}$$

and

$$(26) \qquad r_\beta^2 = \frac{(\sum Axy_\beta)^2}{\sum Ax_\beta^2 \sum Ay_\beta^2}$$

We may now ask: "Under what conditions, if any, will $r_\alpha^2 = r_\beta^2$?" The answer is similar to the one secured for regression coefficients. First, from Eqs. 8, 9, and 10, we know that $\sum Ax_\alpha^2$, $\sum Ay_\alpha^2$, and $\sum Axy_\alpha$ can be partitioned into two additive components. For all aggregations, if, in each aggregation, the X_i are equal and the Y_i are equal, then

$$(27) \qquad \sum Ax_w^2 = \sum Ay_w^2 = \sum Axy_w = 0$$

and

$$(28) \qquad \sum Ax_\beta^2 = \sum Ax_\alpha^2$$

$$(29) \qquad \sum Ay_\beta^2 = \sum Ay_\alpha^2$$

$$(30) \qquad \sum Axy_\beta = \sum Axy_\alpha$$

Given Eq. 27, and hence Eqs. 28, 29, and 30, then

$$(31) \quad r_\beta^2 = \frac{(\sum Axy_\beta)^2}{\sum Ax_\beta^2 \sum Ay_\beta^2} = \frac{(\sum Axy_\alpha)^2}{\sum Ax_\alpha^2 \sum Ay_\alpha^2} = r_\alpha^2$$

This is the case represented by Robinson's exemplary data.

We may now turn our attention to the second case. If $\sum Ax_w^2$ and $\sum Ay_w^2$ and $\sum Axy_w \neq 0$, which is the most frequently encountered real world condition, and given the relationships in Eqs. 13 and 14, it may be that

$$(32) \qquad \sum Ax_\beta^2 = K \sum Ax_\alpha^2$$

$$(33) \qquad \sum Ay_\beta^2 = K \sum Ay_\alpha^2$$

and

$$(34) \qquad \sum Axy_\beta = K \sum Axy_\alpha$$

with $K < 1$. Then Eq. 26 becomes

$$(35) \qquad \begin{aligned} r_\beta^2 &= \frac{K^2 (\sum Axy_\alpha)^2}{K^2 \sum Ax_\alpha^2 \sum Ay_\alpha^2} \\ &= \frac{(\sum Axy_\alpha)^2}{\sum Ax_\alpha^2 \sum Ay_\alpha^2} = r_\alpha^2 \end{aligned}$$

And with $\sum Ax_w^2$, $\sum Ay_w^2$, and $\sum Axy_w$ not equal to zero, if, and only if, $\sum Ax_\beta^2$, $\sum Ay_\beta^2$, and

$\sum Axy_\beta$, respectively, are in the same proportion to $\sum Ax_\alpha^2$, $\sum Ay_\alpha^2$, and $\sum Axy_\alpha$ is $r_\beta^2 = r_\alpha^2$, because unless the strict proportionality is maintained, r_β^2 does not reduce to r_α^2. For example, let

$$(36) \qquad \sum Ax_\beta^2 = (K + E) \sum Ax_\alpha^2$$

$$(37) \qquad \sum Ay_\beta^2 = (K + D) \sum Ay_\alpha^2$$

and

$$(38) \qquad \sum Axy_\beta = (K + C) \sum Axy_\alpha$$

with $K < 1$ and $C \neq D \neq E$. Then

$$(39)$$

$$r_\beta^2 = \frac{(K^2 + 2KC + C^2)(\sum Axy_a)^2}{(K^2 + EK + KD + ED) \sum Ax^2 \sum Ay^2}$$

$$\neq \frac{(\sum Axy_\alpha)^2}{\sum Ax_\alpha^2 \sum Ay_a^2}$$

and $r_\beta^2 \neq r_\alpha^2$.

As stated above (under "Regression Coefficients for Initial and Subsequent Study Areas") in reference to regression coefficients, the kind of relationship specified in Eqs. 32, 33, and 34 can be expected to occur only infrequently within sets of real world data and are not insured by areal weighting, but rather are predicated on special characteristics of the density values and their corresponding spatial distributions.

FOOTNOTES

[1] The general approach of operationalizing the geographic concept of areal association using statistical methods is discussed by H. H. McCarty, J. C. Hook, and D. S. Knos, *The Measurement of Association in Industrial Geography*, State University of Iowa, Department of Geography (1956). See also R. Hartshorne, *Perspectives on the Nature of Geography* (Chicago: Rand McNally & Co., 1959), pp. 9–10, 160–163.

[2] H. H. McCarty, *et al.*, *op. cit.*, pp. 16, 98. Aspects of the general problem contemplated in this paper arise in one form or another in many disciplines. For examples see O. D. Duncan, R. P. Cuzzort, and B. Duncan, *Statistical Geography* (New York: Free Press of Glencoe, Inc., 1961), pp. 62–80; and G. U. Yule and M. G. Kendall, *An Introduction to the Theory of Statistics* (New York: Hafner Publishing Co., Inc., 1950) pp. 310–314, for a general treatment of the problem; and H. Theil, *Linear Aggregation of Economic Relations* (Amsterdam, 1954); J. Decker, "A System for Analysis of Forest Succession," *Forest Science*, **5** (1959), 154–157; and W. S. Robinson, "Ecological Correlations and the Behavior of Individuals," *American Sociological Review*, **15** (1950), 351–357, for disciplinary examples.

[3] A. H. Robinson, "The Necessity of Weighting Values in Correlation Analysis of Areal Data," *Annals of the Association of American Geographers*, **46** (1956), 233–236.

[4] *Ibid.*, 233.

[5] *Ibid.*, 233–234. Upper case X and Y are substituted into the quotation because of the conventional statistical use of capital letters to represent original data and lower case letters to represent deviations from the mean.

[6] *Ibid.*, 235.

[7] The values presented in Table 4 merely demonstrate that areal weighting does not always lead to computationally equal parameters; those data are not a mathematical proof that weighting is not usually effective. In addition, the two instances when areal weighting does give computationally equal regression and correlation parameters are specified without proof. A general formal proof of the limited success which can be expected from the process of areally weighting density values is presented in a mathematical appendix to this paper. The reader who is interested may refer to this appendix; others, who are willing to accept the writers' position on these points, may ignore it.

[8] G. W. Snedecor, *Statistical Methods Applied to Experiments in Agriculture and Biology* (Ames: Iowa State University Press, 1956), p. 1.

[9] The differentiation of the terms "universe" and "population" is not equally acceptable to all statisticians. For differing viewpoints, see L. Hogben, *Statistical Theory: The Relationship of Probability, Credibility and Error* (London: George Allen & Unwin, Ltd., 1957), pp. 96–105; and M. G. Kendall, *The Advanced Theory of Statistics* (London: Charles Griffin & Company, Ltd., 1948), I, 19, 187.

[10] S. Valanvanis, *Econometrics: An Introduction to Maximum Likelihood Methods* (New York: McGraw-Hill Book Company, 1959), pp. 12–13.

[11] *Ibid.*, p. 13.

[12] R. A. Fisher, "Theory of Statistical Estimation," *Proceedings of the Cambridge Philosophical Society*, **22**, (1925), 701.

[13] The problem of an adequate statistical rationale for making formal inferential statements when an entire population is treated is not restricted to this particular problem. It arises generally when a popula-

tion is treated as a sample, e.g., O. D. Duncan, *et al.*, *op. cit.*, p. 32.

[14] For detailed and scholarly treatments of the effects of highly systematic spatial allocations of X and Y, i.e., allocations in which near neighbors are very much alike, see R. C. Geary, "The Contiguity Ratio and Statistical Mapping," pp. 461–478; and P. A. P. Moran, "The Interpretation of Statistical Maps," *Journal of the Royal Statistical Society*, Series B, **10**, (1948), 243–251.

[15] A. H. Robinson, *op. cit.*, 235.

[16] G. W. Snedecor, *op. cit.*, pp. 178–179.

[17] A. Hald, *Statistical Theory with Engineering Applications*, G. Seidelin, trans. (New York: John Wiley & Sons, Inc., 1952), pp. 571–573.

[18] G. W. Snedecor, *op. cit.*, p. 398.

[19] E. C. Fieller, T. Lewis, and E. S. Pearson, *Correlated Random Normal Deviates* (London: Cambridge University Press, 1955), p. 56.

[20] H. Arkin and R. R. Colton, *Tables for Statisticians* (New York: Barnes & Noble, Inc., 1950), pp. 142–145.

[21] G. E. Gehlke and K. Biehl, "Certain Effects of Grouping upon the Size of the Correlation Coefficient in Census Tract Material," *Journal of the American Statistical Association*, **29**, supplement (1934), 169–170.

[22] A. H. Robinson, *op. cit.*, 233.

[23] G. E. Gehlke, *et al.*, *op cit.*, 169.

[24] The reader is again referred to R. C. Geary, *op. cit.*

[25] G. U. Yule and M. G. Kendall, *An Introduction to the Theory of Statistics* (New York: Hafner Publishing Co., Inc., 1950) pp. 310–114.

[26] *Ibid.*, p. 310.

[27] For the purposes of this formulation, areal units in α which are not modified, i.e., not aggregated to form an areal unit in β, will be treated as though they were combined but with $n_j = 1$, $AX_i = \overline{AX}_j$, and $AY_i = \overline{AY}_j$. This convention does not weaken the construct.

[28] A complete statement of the relationships which exist between the additive components in Eqs. 8, 9, and 10 could have been had by employing an analysis of variance–covariance model. The additional detail which this model would have provided is not requisite to the specific problem contemplated above, and therefore the more complete and detailed formulation was not employed.

The relevance of the analysis of covariance formulation is obvious from "The Expected Behavior" (above), in which the design of the inferential model is discussed.

2

SOME ALTERNATIVES
TO ECOLOGICAL CORRELATION

LEO. A. GOODMAN

The present article discusses some of the results reported in Robinson's paper on ecological correlation[1] and explores further the suggestions in earlier notes by the present author[2] and by Duncan and Davis.[3] The terminology used in these earlier papers will, for the sake of convenience, be used here, although it does have some disadvantages. "In an *ecological correlation* . . . the variables are . . . descriptive properties of groups . . . . An *individual correlation* is a correlation in which the . . . variables are descriptive properties of individuals. . . ."[4] The phrase "behavior of individuals" referred to the variables describing properties of individuals, while "ecological data" referred to the ecological variables describing properties of groups. An "ecological regression" study is a standard regression analysis for ecological variables. The problems of "aggregation," as discussed in some of the economics literature,[5] are related somewhat to the mathematical problems that have appeared in the discussion of ecological and individual correlations, although the terminology of this literature is quite different from that of the papers referred to earlier.

The variables in an ecological correlation are usually quantitative (e.g., percentages or means for each of the [fifty] states), while the variables in an individual correlation may be qualitative (e.g., race of each individual) or quantitative (e.g., height of each individual). The ecological correlation coefficient used in the earlier papers was the Pearsonian correlation coefficient for the joint distribution of two quantitative ecological variables. These papers dealt mainly, though not exclusively, with the situation in which both variables in the individual correlation study were qualitative and dichotomous and the individual correlation coefficient used was the fourfold-point (ϕ) correlation coefficient for the cross-classification table describing the joint distribution of the two dichotomous variables.[6] The present article

Reprinted from *American Journal of Sociology,* **64** (1959), 610–625, by permission of the author and the University of Chicago Press.

will also study this situation, as well as situations in which both variables considered in the individual correlation study are quantitative, or where both are qualitative and one is dichotomous. Situations in which one variable is quantitative and the other qualitative, or where both are qualitative but neither dichotomous, will not be considered here.[7]

It has been shown that ecological correlations cannot be used as substitutes for individual correlations.[8] However, ecological correlations may be of interest in themselves; the kinds of questions that can be answered by a study of ecological correlations are sometimes of direct concern to social scientists.[9] In some problems, both the ecological and the individual correlations and the relations between them may be of interest. Even if the investigator is concerned only with individual correlations, ecological data may be of service, though ecological correlations are not recommended.[10]

The author's earlier note[11] showed that, under very special circumstances, the analysis of the regression between ecological variables may be used to make inferences about "individual behavior," i.e., about the unknown data, for a population of individuals, describing the cross classification of two dichotomous attributes. In the present article, the general approach presented in the note will be developed further, and the inferences about "individual behavior" will be used to estimate individual correlations. (Since the individual correlation coefficient, ϕ, may not be an appropriate measure of association in many situations,[12] the author's note did not discuss individual correlations explicitly, but rather inferences about "individual behavior." However, since the individual correlation coefficient may sometimes be an appropriate measure, it will be investigated here. The general method developed here can also be applied to situations in which some other measure of association is of interest.) This article will also explore in some detail the method presented in the note by Duncan and Davis[13] and will suggest a few techniques that lead to further insight into it.[14]

If individual correlations are of interest, it is best to obtain the directly relevant data on individual behavior rather than ecological data. For example, if the individual correlation between color (Negro-white) and illiteracy

(illiterate-literate) is of interest, the appropriate data would be a fourfold table describing the cross classification of individuals according to Negro-white and illiterate-literate categories.[15] However, in some situations this table may not be available; thus the fourfold-point correlation coefficient cannot be computed from it. However, the marginal totals (i.e., the number of Negroes, whites, illiterates, and literates) for the total Negro-white population and also for the Negro-white populations of various subdivisions of the country may be known. Using these ecological data, methods will be presented for estimating the data, which would have appeared in the table, and the fourfold-point correlation coefficient for it. These methods can also be used to estimate the nonavailable data and the corresponding correlation coefficient for each subdivision of the country. These methods are simple, but they cannot be expected to lead to as accurate estimates as those obtained from relevant data on individual behavior. On the other hand, if the ecological data are easily available, then the amount of computation involved in using the methods suggested here costs very little in comparison with the cost of obtaining the directly relevant data from a special study.

ECOLOGICAL REGRESSION

The proportion, y, of individuals in the Negro-white population who are illiterate may be written as $y = xp + (1 - x)r$, where x is the proportion in the population who are Negro, p is the proportion of Negroes who are illiterate, $(1 - x)$ is the proportion in the population who are white, and r is the proportion of whites who are illiterate. Thus $y = r + (p - r)x = a + bx$, where $a = r$ and $b = p - r$. Hence if different populations or areas are considered where the proportion p is the same for each of these populations, and also the proportion r is the same for these populations, then there will be an exact linear relationship, $y = a + bx$, between the values of y and x for the different populations (assuming that not all the values of x are equal), where the slope will be $b = p - r$, and the y-intercept will be $a = r$. This straight line could be used to determine $r = a$ and $p = b + a$.

In practice, the actual values of p and r

will not be constant, but it may be the case that the average $E(p \mid x)$ of the values of p, for populations with the same proportion x of Negroes, is constant (i.e., $E[p \mid x]$ is the same for different values of x), and the average $E(r \mid x)$ of the values of r, for populations with the same x value, is also constant. In this situation, the main assumption of linear regression analysis, $E(y \mid x) = A + Bx$, holds true, where $A = E(r \mid x)$ and $B = E(p \mid x) - E(r \mid x)$. Thus standard methods of linear regression[16] can be used to estimate A and B. The variance $\sigma^2(y \mid x)$ of the observed y values from the straight line will depend on the variance $\sigma^2(p \mid x)$ computed for the probability distribution of the proportion p illiterate among Negroes for populations with the same proportion x of Negroes; the variance $\sigma^2(r \mid x)$ of the r for populations with a given x value; the covariance Cov $(p, r \mid x)$ of these two proportions; and the distribution of the x values. If $\sigma^2(y \mid x)$ is not approximately constant for the different x values, it will sometimes be worthwhile to modify the standard regression methods by the use of a "weighted regression."[17] (Another kind of modification, which will sometimes be appropriate, can be based on methods developed for the situation of "linear regression where both variates are subject to error"[18] rather than for the standard linear regression.) For a given x, $\sigma^2(y \mid x) = \sigma^2(p \mid x)x^2 + \sigma^2(r \mid x)(1 - x)^2 + 2\text{Cov}(p, r \mid x)x(1 - x)$. Thus, under the present assumptions, $\sigma^2(y \mid x) = 0$ only when all the p and r values equal $B + A$ and A, respectively, or when there is a specific negative linear relationship between p and r, for each x; viz., $px + r(1 - x) = A + Bx$, or $p = A + B - (r - A)(1 - x)/x$. (In the final section herein, different assumptions are made, which lead to quite different kinds of situations in which it is possible that $\sigma^2[y \mid x] = 0$.)

The expected values will be constant, and the variances will be small, when the probability of illiteracy, say, is much more a function of color (i.e., it depends on whether a person is white or Negro) rather than a function of the ecological area being considered. Where the phenomenon under investigation is more a function of the area (i.e., the p and r values differ widely in the different areas) than a function of color, the methods presented here are not recommended; however, in some situations the variance of p and r may be sufficiently small for them to be applicable, while in others the variance of p and r for a particular subset of ecological areas (e.g., for the states in a given geographic division of the United States) or for a set of combined ecological areas (e.g., for the nine geographic divisions of the United States) may be sufficiently small for the present method to be applied to the subset of ecological areas or to the set of combined areas. If the variance of p and r for the states in each division of the United States is small, then the methods may be applied to obtain separate estimates for each division, thus obtaining estimates where, in a certain sense, geographic divisions have been held constant.

If the scatter diagram of y and x does not suggest a linear relation between y and x, then the present strategy is not recommended (unless the scatter diagram of y and x for a subset of the areas or for a set of combined areas suggests linearity). If the scatter diagram does suggest a linear relation, then it may be applicable, but it is still possible that the variances of p and r are large. In this case, the present method leads to estimates of $E(p \mid x)$ and $E(r \mid x)$ when these average (expected) values are constant, but the estimate of the individual correlation for the total population based on these estimates of expected values may be quite poor if the variance of p and/or r is large.

From the scatter diagram of the per cent Negro and per cent illiterate in different areas, the slope B and the y-intercept A can be estimated by the usual methods of linear regression, obtaining the estimates $\hat{b}$ and $\hat{a}$, respectively. Then $E(r \mid x)$ and $E(p \mid x)$ can be estimated by $\hat{r} = \hat{a}$ and $\hat{p} = \hat{b} + \hat{r} = \hat{b} + \hat{a}$, respectively. The numbers of illiterate Negroes, illiterate whites, literate Negroes, and literate whites (i.e., the four entries in the fourfold "individual behavior" table) are estimated by $\hat{p}NX$, $\hat{r}N(1 - X)$, $(1 - \hat{p})NX$, and $(1 - \hat{r})N(1 - X)$, respectively, where NX is the total number of Negroes.

Since p and r lie between zero and 1, it is desirable that the estimates $\hat{p}$ and $\hat{r}$ also lie between zero and 1. When this is not the case, the underlying assumptions should be re-examined, although it is possible to obtain such estimates even if these assumptions are satisfied. A method for dealing with this situation was suggested in the author's earlier note.

The estimated proportion $\hat{Y} = \hat{a} + \hat{b}X = \hat{p}X + \hat{r}(1 - X)$ of illiterates in the Negro-white population should be close to the known proportion, Y, of illiterates. If this is not the case for a given set of data, this method is not recommended. In the special case where Y is, in fact, equal to the average, $\bar{y}$, of the illiteracy proportions in the various ecological areas, and X is equal to the average, $\bar{x}$, of the proportions Negro in the ecological areas, then this check on the underlying assumptions of the method does not apply, since in this case $\hat{Y} = \hat{a} + \hat{b}\bar{x} = \bar{y} = Y$, even if the assumptions are not met. A method for determining roughly whether or not $\hat{Y}$ is sufficiently close to Y will be mentioned later in this section.

Rather than compute the correlation coefficient c directly for the estimated fourfold table by the usual formula, a simplified formula is $\hat{b}\sqrt{X(1 - X)/\hat{Y}(1 - \hat{Y})}$. Since $\hat{Y}$ will be close to Y when this general approach is applicable, it will not matter much whether or not $\hat{Y}$ is replaced by the known proportion Y. Thus an estimate of the fourfold-point correlation is

$$\hat{c} = \hat{b}\sqrt{\frac{X(1 - X)}{Y(1 - Y)}}$$

Following standard correlation theory, the ecological correlation can be computed by multiplying b by the ratio of the standard deviation of the proportions of Negroes in the ecological areas and the standard deviation of the proportions of illiterates there. Since this ratio will usually be very different from $\sqrt{X(1 - X)/Y(1 - Y)}$ when ecological data are used, the ecological and individual correlations will usually be very different. However, the ecological correlation might also serve as a rough measure of whether the underlying assumptions are not satisfied for a particular set of data;[19] the present method is not to be recommended if it is rather small in absolute value.

The estimates $\hat{b}$ and $\hat{a}$ will be unbiased estimates of B and A, respectively, if $E(y \mid x) = A + Bx$. If $\sigma^2(y \mid x)$ does not depend on x (i.e., the special case of "homoscedasticity"), then the estimates $\hat{b}$ and $\hat{a}$ are the "best" unbiased estimates. When $\sigma^2(y \mid x)$ is not constant, which will usually be the case, the estimates will still be unbiased, but they may not be "best." When homoscedasticity can be

assumed and each y value, given x, is a statistically independent observation, the variances of the estimates of $\hat{b}$ and $\hat{a}$ are $\sigma^2(\hat{b}) = \sigma^2(y \mid x)/n\sigma^2(x)$ and

$$\sigma^2(\hat{a}) = \sigma^2(y \mid x) \sum_{i=1}^{n} \frac{x_i^2}{n^2 \sigma^2(x)}$$

where $\sigma^2(x)$ is the variance of the observed x values and n is the number of observations.[20] The variances of $\hat{p}$, $\hat{r}$, Y, and $\hat{c}$ can be written as follows: $\sigma^2(\hat{p}) = \sigma^2(\bar{y}) + (1 - \bar{x})^2\sigma^2(\hat{b})$, $\sigma^2(\hat{r}) = \sigma^2(\hat{a}) = \sigma^2(\bar{y}) + \bar{x}^2\sigma^2(\hat{b})$, $\sigma^2(\hat{Y}) = \sigma^2(\bar{y}) + (X - \bar{x})^2\sigma^2(\hat{b})$, $\sigma^2(\hat{c}) = \sigma^2(\hat{b})X(1 - X)/Y(1 - Y)$, where $\sigma^2(\bar{y}) = \sigma^2(y \mid x)/n$. These variances are all proportional to $\sigma^2(y \mid x)$, which depends on $\sigma^2(p \mid x)$, $\sigma^2(r \mid x)$, $\text{Cov}(r, p \mid x)$, and the distribution of x. When homoscedasticity can be assumed, the variances, $\sigma^2(\hat{p})$, $\sigma^2(\hat{r})$, $\sigma^2(\hat{Y})$, $\sigma^2(\hat{c})$, can be estimated, in an unbiased manner, by replacing $\sigma^2(y \mid x)$ in the formulae given above by the mean-square deviation of the observed y values from the least-squares regression line, $y = \hat{a} + \hat{b}x$.[21] The estimated variance of $\hat{Y}$ can be used along with the observed difference between $\hat{Y}$ and Y to determine roughly whether or not $\hat{Y}$ is sufficiently close to Y, which is another partial check on the underlying assumptions.

The formulae presented above must be interpreted with caution, since they compute only the variance of the estimate from its expected value, whereas the difference between the estimate and the actual (rather than the expected) population value would be of greater interest. Furthermore, if homoscedasticity cannot be assumed, the numerical values obtained by the formulae may be in error. In developing the formulae, it was not necessary to make any assumptions about the distribution of y for given x, except that of homoscedasticity and linearity of regression. If, in addition, the distribution of y for given x is a normal distribution, then it is also possible to obtain confidence intervals based on $\hat{b}$, $\hat{p}$, $\hat{r}$, $\hat{Y}$, and $\hat{c}$, using the variance formulae that are given above.

Our approach must begin, in each case, with a careful examination of the underlying assumptions;[22] however, the only necessary assumption for the justification of the use of the point estimates $\hat{b}$, $\hat{p}$, $\hat{r}$, $\hat{Y}$, and $\hat{c}$ is that p and r must be more or less constant for the different ecological areas, in such a way that the standard linear regression model can be applied.

If the proportion z of Negroes among the illiterates is approximately constant, and if the proportion v of Negroes among the literates is also approximately constnt, then an analogous approach to the one presented here could be used with the same ecological data to obtain estimates of the proportions z and v and the individual correlation c. Thus this approach may lead to two quite different estimates of c; the choice between them should depend upon whether p and r are more constant than z and v (see comments in the final section herein).

TWO NUMERICAL EXAMPLES

Let us first consider the example discussed by Robinson,[23] where, for the Census Bureau's nine geographic divisions of the United States in 1930, the ecological correlation between the per cent illiterate and the per cent Negro for the divisional Negro-white populations, ten years old and over, was .95, while the individual fourfold-point correlation for the 2×2 table giving the cross-classified color-illiteracy data for the correponding total Negro-white population was .20.[24] Using the present approach, we see that the graph (Robinson's Fig. 1) for the nine geographic divisions looks more or less linear and that the slope $b = .25$ and the y-intercept $\hat{a} = .02$. Also, the estimated proportion, $\hat{Y}$, of illiterates in the total population is .04, which is, in fact, equal to the known proportion $Y = .04$. This does not serve as a second partial check on the underlying assumptions, since, in this example, Y does not differ very much from the average, $\bar{y}$, of the proportions illiterate in the nine divisional populations and X does not differ from the average, $\bar{x} = .10$, of the proportions Negro in the nine divisional populations. (We shall see, in our second illustration, how the comparison of $\hat{Y}$ and Y can serve as a partial check on the assumptions. Differences between Y and $\bar{y}$, X and $\bar{x}$, are due to the fact that the percentages appearing in the graph are weighted by the relative population size of the corresponding area in the computation of Y and X, but not so in the computation of $\bar{y}$ and $\bar{x}$.) The fourfold-point correlation for the estimated table, based on the ecological data for the nine geographic

divisions, is $\hat{c} = .38$. The bounds for the individual correlation, obtained by the method suggested by Duncan and Davis, are $-.07$ and $+.60$.[25] Thus the estimate $\hat{c} = .38$, while not very close, is closer to the known value of the individual correlation than are the ecological correlation, .95, and the bounds.

We shall now consider the numerical example on the relation between color (nonwhite–white) and occupation (domestic service–other than domestic service) for employed females in Chicago in 1940, which is discussed in the note by Duncan and Davis. The individual correlation was .29, while their method, when applied to the available ecological data for community areas, led to the bounds .126 and .355. The scatter diagram for the proportion in domestic service and the proportion nonwhite among the employed females, computed from the available ecological data for each of fifteen community areas and the "balance of city,"[26] indicates that the relation is more or less linear, the ecological correlation is .93, $\hat{b} = .27$, and $\hat{a} = .07$. Also, the estimated proportion, $\hat{Y}$, of persons in domestic service in the total employed female population in Chicago is .08, which is, in fact, equal to the known proportion $Y = .08$. (Since $Y = .08$ differed from the average, $\bar{y} = .13$, of the proportions of employed females in domestic service in the various ecological areas, and $X = .07$, the proportion nonwhite among the total employed female population in Chicago, differed from the average, $\bar{x} = .24$, of the proportions nonwhite among the employed females in the ecological areas, the fact that $\hat{Y}$ was very close to Y gives us some further confidence in the application of this method to the present data.) The fourfold-point correlation for the estimated table is $\hat{c} = .25$. Thus the ecological data show that the individual correlation must lie in the interval between .13 and .35, and the estimate $\hat{c} = .25$ is quite close to the known value of .29. The computation of the bounds may be used as a third partial check on the estimate $\hat{c}$, as well as for determining the possible range of the individual correlations; we would not have recommended that $\hat{c}$ be used if it had not been within the interval determined by the bounds.

Duncan and Davis also determine that the possible range of the percentage of nonwhites in domestic service, based on the community area data, is between 21.1 and 44.5 per cent.

It can be seen that the ecological regression method leads to the quite accurate estimate $\hat{p} = .34$ in this particular case; the known value of this proportion is .38.

TABLE 1

Parameters	True values	Estimates	Estimated standard deviations
B	.32	.27	.03
$E(p\|x)$	.38	.34	.02
$E(r\|x)$	.06	.07	.01
Y	.08	.08	.01
c	.29	.25	.03

In this particular illustration, since Y and X differed from $\bar{y}$ and $\bar{x}$, respectively, there were three partial checks on the underlying assumptions, while in the preceding example, there were, in effect, only two. For the present illustration, the results may be summarized in Table 1, where the estimates are shown to compare favorably with their respective known true values and where the estimated standard deviations, computed from the formulae given earlier, are also presented. Since the true value of Y is known from the ecological data, a rough comparison between $\hat{Y}$ and Y can be made by using the information about the estimate of $\sigma(\hat{Y})$, another partial check on the assumptions underlying the present method.

THE METHOD OF OBTAINING BOUNDS

Robinson and also Duncan and Davis point out that different systems of areal subdivision give different results. Duncan and Davis mention that, for their illustrative material, substantially closer bounds to the individual correlation can be derived from the marginal frequencies for the census tracts than from the marginals for the community areas (which are combinations of tracts), and that the criterion for choice between the results of different systems of areal subdivisions is clear: "The individual correlation is approximated most closely by the least maximum and the greatest minimum among the results for several systems of areal subdivisions." Where one areal subdivision (e.g., community areas) represents a combination of another areal subdivision (census tracts), the least maximum and greatest minimum are obtained from the finer areal subdivision.[27] Thus, if the best bounds are desired, it is necessary only to compute the bounds for the finer subdivision. However, it is possible to combine the areas of the finer subdivision into not more than four combined areas, where all the areas in a given combined area are similar (in a sense to be defined in the following paragraph), so that the bounds computed by using only the data for the less fine subdivision will be equal to the best bounds determined by the finer subdivision.

Duncan and Davis indicate that substantially closer bounds are obtained for their data when the finer areal subdivision is used. It may sometimes happen that there is little or no difference between the bounds for the finer subdivision and the less fine subdivision. All tracts in which the number of nonwhite employed females was not more than the number of females in domestic service and the number of females in domestic service was not more than the number of white employed females can be combined into a single area without affecting the bounds (except for rounding errors); tracts in which the number of nonwhites was not less than the number in domestic service and the number in domestic service was not more than the number of whites can be combined without affecting the bounds; etc. Tracts that can be combined in this way will be called "similar" (this definition of "similarity" is convenient in this particular problem, but not necessarily so in other, quite different problems). Thus the fact that substantially closer bounds were obtained when census tracts rather than community areas were used indicates that some of the tracts that form a given community area were not "similar."

The color-illiteracy data for the [fifty] states and Washington, D.C., indicate that the nine geographic divisions were combinations of areas that were, in fact, quite "similar." More specifically, the number of Negroes was not more than the number of illiterates, and the number of illiterates was not more than the number of whites (or the number of Negroes was not less than the number of illiterates, and the number of illiterates was not more than the number of whites) in almost all the areas that were combined to form a given division. Only seven states had been combined with areas that differed in this respect. Thus the bounds $(-.07$ and $+.60)$ for the individual color-illiteracy correlation based on the data for the nine geographic divisions differ only slightly from the bounds ($-.07$ and $+.58$) based on the data for the [fifty] states and Washington, D.C. The method of combining areas so that the same bounds are obtained for the combined areas as for the finer subdivision is as follows: Draw two lines $y = x$ and $y = 1 - x$ on the graph of the scatter diagram of the observed ecological variables y and x. This divides the graph into four parts: A, B, C, D, where A contains all those points representing areas where the number of nonwhite employed females was not more than the number of females in domestic service and the number of females in domestic service was not more than the number of white employed females ($x \leq y \leq 1 - x$); B contains those points where $x \geq y \leq 1 - x$; C contains those points where $x \geq y \geq 1 - x$; and D contains those points where $x \leq y \geq 1 - x$. (If a point falls exactly on a diagonal line dividing the parts of the graph, it may be put in either one of the adjacent parts, but, of course, cannot be put in both parts.) All the points, or the ecological areas that they represent, that appear in the same part of the graph can be combined to form a single combined area, thus obtaining four areas: A, B, C, D. Bounds for the individual correlation computed by using the ecological data for the combined areas will yield the same result as the bounds computed by using the data for each of the points on the graph; i.e., the bounds computed by using each of the points on the graph could actually be computed from, at most, four points, A, B, C, D, placed on the graph, where point A is a weighted average (weighted by relative population size) of the points in part A of the graph, etc.

The bounds for the individual correlation are determined by first calculating the minimum number of nonwhite females that are in domestic service; based on the available ecological data, this can be seen to be zero for area A (or for any ecological area represented by a point in part A of the graph) and also for area B (i.e., the areas where $y \leq 1 - x$); it is equal to the difference between the number of females in domestic service and the number of white employed females for area C and also for area D (i.e., the areas where $y \geq 1 - x$). The maximum number of nonwhite employed females in domestic service can be seen to be equal to the number of nonwhite employed

females for area A and also for area D (i.e., the areas where $y \geq x$); it is equal to the number of females in domestic service for area B and also for C (i.e., the areas where $y \leq x$). Thus, at a minimum, the number of nonwhite females in domestic service for the total population under consideration (i.e., the combination of areas A, B, C, and D) will be equal to the difference between the number of females in domestic service and the number of white employed females for the combined population in areas C and D. At a maximum, the total number of nonwhite females in domestic service will be equal to the sum of the number of nonwhite employed females for the combined population in areas A and D and the number of females in domestic service for the combined population in areas B and C. From the available ecological data for community areas in Chicago, we find that these minimum and maximum numbers are 5826 and 12,271, respectively. Accordingly, the fourfold-point correlation coefficient is between .13 and .35. The difference, T, between the maximum and minimum numbers, $12{,}271 - 5826 = 6445$, can be shown to be equal to the sum, S, of the number of nonwhite employed females who reside in area A, the number white in area C, the number in domestic service in B, and the number not in domestic service who reside in area D. By obtaining S separately and comparing it with T, we have a partial check on our computations of the minimum and maximum numbers.

It can be seen that T multiplied by the total population is equal to the product of the possible range, R, of the fourfold-point correlation ($.35 - .13) = .22$) and the square root of the product of the four marginal totals in the fourfold cross-classification table for the population. Thus $T = S$ is directly proportional to R (the constant of proportionality depends on the population marginal totals). Hence the "accuracy" R of the bounds, for a given set of population marginal totals, depends on the magnitude of S, which can be determined very quickly in a rough fashion by an examination of the data described by the graph. These bounds will be quite accurate if all the points in part A of the graph are very close to the vertical line determined by $x = 0$, the points in part B are close to the horizontal line $y = 0$, the points in part C are close to the vertical line $x = 1$, and the point in part D

are close to the horizontal line $y = 1$. The exact value of the individual correlation can be determined $(R = 0)$ from the ecological data if $S = 0$; i.e., if all the ecological areas can be represented by points on some of the lines that form the sides (boundaries) of the graph. In other words, if in each ecological area employed females were either all white, all nonwhite, or all in domestic service, or all not in domestic service, we should, of course, be able to determine the exact value of the individual correlation from the ecological data alone. However, if each of the areas in, say, part B of the graph becomes more completely white (i.e., the percentage nonwhite decreases) or more completely nonwhite, but the areas still remain in part B (i.e., the percentage in domestic service still remains less than the percentage nonwhite and the percentage white), then the accuracy of the bounds need not be improved unless the percentage in domestic service in these areas also decreased. Using this general approach, an examination of the respective graphs describing the ecological data and a glance at the respective marginal proportions for the total populations would reveal that the bounds for the color-occupation data for the community areas or census tracts would be more accurate than the bounds for the color-illiteracy data obtained on either a divisional or a state basis.

Since it is possible, in computing bounds, to reduce the original ecological data to, at most, four areas (this simplifies somewhat the amount of computation; in any case, very little computation is required), the bounds are based essentially only on the information available for these four combined areas or their respective four points on the graph. The actual distribution of points on the graph is not used except insofar as it supplies data for the combined areas; the accuracy of the bounds depends on how closely these four points "hug" the four sides of the graph.

FURTHER COMMENTS ON ECOLOGICAL REGRESSION

The regression approach made use of the graph of the ecological data, and the results depended on these data. If some other areal subdivision of the population is of interest, quite different estimates of the slope and

y-intercept may be obtained, unless the underlying assumptions of this approach also hold true for this second areal subdivision, and the values of $E(p \mid x)$ and $E(r \mid x)$ remain unchanged. Sometimes it is possible to combine areas or to use some other method of defining areas or classes of individuals in order to obtain a new subdivision of the population for which the underlying assumptions of the regression approach are more reasonable than for the original area data. It is not necessary that this new subdivision actually divide the population into mutually exclusive classes or that the entire population be included in the subdivision. For the areas in the new subdivision and for the entire population, the underlying assumptions concerning p and r should be more reasonable. With additional information about the population, it may be possible to determine such a subdivision of the population. If this is the case, the regression methods should be applied to this new subdivision rather than to the original data.

None of the methods discussed here makes much use of the information about the spatial distribution of the areas under consideration. This information and the information concerning the relative population sizes of the areas are not contained in the graph. The information may be of interest in itself, and also it would probably be worthwhile to make some use of it in dealing with the present problem. For example, the method mentioned herein for "holding constant the geographic divisions" does make some use of the spatial distribution of the states. The spatial distribution, the population sizes, and any other relevant information should enter into the discussion of whether or not, in a particular case, the underlying assumptions are met. The information concerning relative population sizes can also be utilized (to a certain extent) as "weights" in the weighted linear regression analysis referred to earlier in this article.

RELATION BETWEEN TWO QUALITATIVE VARIABLES WHEN ONE OF THEM IS DICHOTOMOUS

We shall now consider the situation in which the "individual behavior" described by a $2 \times \beta$ cross-classification table for a population is of direct interest, but where the only available data are the marginal totals in the table for the population and the marginal totals for some subdivision of the population. Here both variables in the individual correlation study are qualitative; one of them has two categories (e.g., literate-illiterate) and the other has β categories (e.g., Negro-white-"other races"; $\beta = 3$). Using an approach similar to the regression approach described here for the case where $\beta = 2$, we see that the proportion y of individuals in the Negro-white-"other races" population who are illiterate may be written as $y = x_1 p_1 + x_2 p_2 + x_3 p_3$, where x_1 is the proportion in the population who are Negro, p_1 is the proportion of Negroes who are illiterate, x_2 is the proportion in the population who are white, p_2 is the proportion of whites who are illiterate, x_3 is the proportion in the population who belong to "other races," and p_3 is the proportion of people in "other races" who are illiterate. Since $x_1 + x_2 + x_3 = 1$, we have $y = x_1 p_1 + x_2 p_2 + (1 - x_1 - x_2)p_3 = p_3 + (p_1 - p_3)x_1 + (p_2 - p_3)x_2 = a + b_1 x_1 + b_2 x_2$, where $a = p_3$, $b_1 = p_1 - p_3$, and $b_2 = p_2 - p_3$. Hence, if different areas are considered where the proportion p_1 is the same for each area, the proportion p_2 is the same for each area, and the proportion p_3 is the same for each area, then there will be an exact multilinear relationship, $y = a + b_1 x_1 + b_2 x_2$, between the values of y and x_1, x_2 for the different areas, where the slopes will be $b_1 = p_1 - p_3$ and $b_2 = p_2 - p_3$, and the y-intercept will be $a = p_3$. This multilinear relationship could be used to determine $p_3 = a$, $p_2 = b_2 + a$, and $p_1 = b_1 + a$.

In practice, the actual values of p_1, p_2, and p_3 will not be constant, but it may be the case that the average $E(p_1 | x_1, x_2)$ of the values of p_1, the average $E(p_2 | x_1, x_2)$ of the values of p_2 and the average $E(p_3 | x_1, x_2)$ of the values of p_3 for populations with the same proportions x_1 and x_2 of Negroes and whites, respectively, are constant. Then the main assumption of multiple linear regression analysis, $E(y | x_1, x_2) = A + B_1 x_1 - B_2 x_2$, holds true, where $A = E(p_3 | x_1, x_2)$, $B_1 = E(p_1 | x_1, x_2) - A$, and $B_2 = E(p_2 | x_1, x_2) - A$. Thus standard methods of multiple regression can be used to obtain estimates $\hat{a}, \hat{b}_1, \hat{b}_2$, of A, B_1, B_2, respectively.[28] If the variances of p_1, p_2, and p_3 are not large, then these estimates can be used to obtain the estimates $\hat{p}_3 = \hat{a}$, $\hat{p}_2 = \hat{b}_2 + \hat{a}$, and $\hat{p}_1 = \hat{b}_1 + \hat{a}$ of the expected values of p_3, p_2, and p_1, respectively. The six entries in the 2×3 cross-classification table describing the relation between literacy and color can then be estimated by a method analogous to that described earlier for the case in which $\beta = 2$. The estimates $\hat{p}_1, \hat{p}_2, \hat{p}_3$ should be examined to see whether they all lie between zero and 1. Also the estimated proportion $\hat{Y} = \hat{a} + \hat{b}_1 X_1 + \hat{b}_2 X_2$ of illiterates in the total population (where X_1 is the proportion of Negroes in the total population and X_2 is the proportion of whites in this population) should be close to the known proportion Y of illiterates in this population, if the method suggested here is to be applied. Many of the comments discussed earlier for the case $\beta = 2$ can be generalized to the situation described in this section. This is left as an exercise for the interested reader.

RELATION BETWEEN TWO QUANTITATIVE VARIABLES

Many of the ideas presented above can be applied also in the case in which we are dealing with quantitative variables rather than categories—e.g., income rather than race. Let us consider the situation in which the individual Pearsonian correlation between income and size of family is of interest and the relevant cross-classified data for the entire population are not available. That is, for each individual in the population, information about both his income, x, and size of his family, y cannot be obtained, but it is possible to determine or to estimate the income distribution and the distribution of size of family for the population (i.e., the marginal totals). If the average income and the average size of family for, say, each of the [fifty] states is known, and if there is a linear relationship between income x and average size of family $E(y | x)$ when x is given, and it is more or less constant in these states (i.e., $E[y | x] = A + Bx$ is true for the individuals in each state, and A and B are constant for all states), then it is possible to use these ecological data for each of the states, to estimate the individual correlation for the population. The appropriate estimate of this Pearsonian correlation is obtained by multiplying $\hat{b}$, the estimate of the slope of the regression line of y and x obtained from the average income and average family-size data, by the ratio V of the standard deviation of the population income distribution and the standard deviation of the population family-size distribution. (This corresponds to the earlier multiplication of $\hat{b}$ by the $\sqrt{X[1-X]}/\sqrt{Y[1-Y]}$.) The usual ecological correlation, which cannot be used in general to estimate the individual correlation, is obtained by multiplying $\hat{b}$ by the ratio of the observed standard deviation of the distribution of the [fifty] average incomes for the states and the observed standard deviation of the distribution of the [fifty] average family sizes for the states; if Washington, D.C., is included, there will be [fifty-one] averages. If, as is often the case, this latter ratio is much larger than the ratio V, the usual ecological correlation will overestimate the individual correlation.[29] The ecological correlation may serve as a rough measure and partial check on whether the underlying assumption is not satisfied—i.e., whether $E(y\,|\,x) = A + Bx$, where A and B are constant for all states.

We have seen that it is not necessary to know the entire distribution of income and the distribution of size of family for the total population, but only the standard deviations of the two, in order to use the ecological data to estimate the individual correlation, since only these standard deviations enter into the computation of the ratio V and of the individual correlation estimate. These standard deviations can be determined from the standard deviations (or variances) and the averages of the respective distributions for the states, since the variance of the population income (family size) distribution is the weighted sum $\sum w(i)M(i)$ of the average squared deviations $M(i)$ of the income (family size) of a person in the ith state from the average income (family size) $\bar{X}$ for the total population, where $w(i)$ is the relative population size of the ith state, $M(i) = \sigma^2(i) + [\bar{x}(i) - \bar{X}]^2$, $\bar{x}(i)$ is the average income (family size) in the ith state, and $\sigma^2(i)$ is the variance of the income (family-size) distribution in the ith state. These data, together with the estimated slope $\hat{b}$ of the regression line obtained from the data on average income and average family size for the states, lead to the estimate bV of the individual correlation coefficient for the entire population, where there is a constant linear relationship between income x and average family size $E(y\,|\,x)$ when x is given.

We have seen that the variance $\sigma^2(X)$ of the population income (family size) distribution is $\sum w(i)M(i) = \sum w(i)\sigma^2(i) + \sum w(i)[\bar{x}(i) - \bar{X}]^2$; i.e., the population variance is the sum of two

terms: (a) the weighted sum of the variances for the states (the "within states" variance, $WS[X]$) and (b) the weighted sum of the squared deviations of the averages $x(i)$ for the states from X (the "between states weighted" variance, $BSW[\bar{x}]$), where the weights are the relative population sizes. Thus $\sigma^2(X) = WS(X) + BSW(\bar{x})$, and the variance of the family-size distribution is $\sigma^2(Y) = WS(Y) + BSW(\bar{y})$. The usual ecological correlation is

$$\hat{b}\sqrt{\frac{BS(\bar{x})}{BS(\bar{y})}}$$

where $BS(\bar{x})$ and $BS(\bar{y})$ are the observed (unweighted) variances of the average incomes $\bar{x}(i)$ and the average family sizes $\bar{y}(i)$, respectively, for the states. Since the estimate of the individual correlation is $\hat{b}V = \hat{b}\sqrt{\sigma^2(X)/\sigma^2(Y)}$, the ecological correlation will be larger than $\hat{b}V$ whenever $\sigma^2(X)/\sigma^2(Y) < BS(\bar{x})/BS(\bar{y})$, i.e., whenever $WS(X)/WS(Y) < [BS(\bar{x})/BS(\bar{y})] + E$, where $E = [BSW(\bar{y})\,BS(\bar{x}) - BS(\bar{y})\,BSW(\bar{x})]/WS(Y)BS(\bar{y})$. If the usual ecological correlation is modified to obtain the "weighted" ecological correlation, $\hat{b}\sqrt{BSW(\bar{x})/BSW(\bar{y})}$, then this "weighted" ecological correlation will be larger than the estimate of the individual correlation whenever $\sigma^2(X)/\sigma^2(Y) < BSW(\bar{x})/BSW(\bar{y})$, [or] whenever the ratio $WS(X)/WS(Y)$ of the "within states" variances is less than the ratio $BSW(\bar{x})/BSW(\bar{y})$ of the "between states weighted" variances.

The ratio of the usual ecological correlation and the estimate of the individual correlation is $\sqrt{[BS(\bar{x})/BS(\bar{y})]/[\sigma^2(X)/\sigma^2(Y)]}$. If the observed variances $BS(\bar{y})$ and $\sigma^2(Y)$ are replaced in the above ratio by their expected values computed under the usual independence assumptions of the linear regression model, where $E(y\,|\,x) = A + Bx$ for each state and $\sigma^2[y\,|\,x(i)]$ is the variance around the regression line in the ith state, then the so-called "expected" ratio obtained will be larger than 1 whenever

$$\frac{\sum\{w(i)\sigma^2[y\,|\,x(i)]\}}{\sigma^2(X)} > \frac{\sum\{\sigma^2[y\,|\,x(i)]/w(i)\}}{TN[BS(\bar{x})]}$$

where there are T states and a total population size of N individuals—i.e., whenever

$$BS(\bar{x}) > \frac{\sigma^2(X)\sum\{\sigma^2[y\,|\,x(i)]/w(i)\}}{TN\sum\{w(i)\sigma^2[y\,|\,x(i)]\}}$$

In the special situation where $w(i) = 1/T$, then this "expected" ratio will be larger than 1 whenever $BS(\bar{x}) > \sigma^2(X)T/N$—i.e., whenever $BS(\bar{x})$ is greater than $\sigma^2(X)$ divided by the average population size N/T of the states, which will often be the case. (If the x values observed in each state were a random sample of size N/T from the same population of x values with variance $\sigma^2[X]$, then the expected value of $BS[\bar{x}]$ would be approximately $\sigma^2[X]/[N/T]$.) By a similar approach, the "expected" ratio of the "weighted" ecological correlation and the estimate of the individual correlation will be larger than 1 whenever $BSW(\bar{x}) > \sigma^2(X)[\sum\{\sigma^2[y|x(i)]\}]/N \sum\{w(i)\sigma^2[y|x(i)]\}$. Where $\sigma^2[y|x(i)]$ is the same for each state (or where $w[i] = 1/T$), this "expected" ratio will be larger than 1 whenever $BSW(\bar{x}) > \sigma^2(X)T/N$, which will usually be the case. Since $\sigma^2(X) = WS(X) + BSW(\bar{x})$, the relationships being presented here can be described in terms of relationships between $WS(X)$, $BSW(\bar{x})$, and $BS(\bar{x})$. These relationships indicate to a certain extent why the (usual and the "weighted") ecological correlations are generally larger than the estimate of the individual correlation, and thus why they cannot be used as estimates of the individual correlation.

The standard deviation of the estimate of the individual correlation and confidence intervals for it can be determined, when certain additional assumptions are made, by using methods similar to those developed earlier herein; this will not be discussed here. The statements and formulae presented here should be understood to hold when the amount of data is sufficiently large to permit sampling fluctuations to be neglected; i.e., we assume that the estimate $\hat{b}$ of the slope B is quite accurate and that $\bar{Y}$, the average size of family in the population, is close to the numerical value $\hat{a} + \hat{b}\bar{X}$. The comparison between $\hat{a} + \hat{b}\bar{X}$ and $\bar{Y}$ can be used as a partial check on the underlying assumptions made in this section (except if the average $\overline{\bar{x}[i]}$ of the $\bar{x}[i]$ is close to $\bar{X}$ and the average $\overline{\bar{y}[i]}$ of the $\bar{y}[i]$ is close to $\bar{Y}$) in the same way that the comparison of $\hat{Y}$ and Y was used to check the assumptions made earlier in this article.

We shall now consider briefly what might happen if the method suggested here is applied where the underlying assumptions did not apply. Suppose that the simple linear relationship was not true, but that a multilinear relation, $E(y|x, z) = A + Bx + Dz$, did hold true for the individuals, where A, B, and D were constant for all states and where z was some relevant variable. In this case, the averages $\bar{y}(i)$, $\bar{x}(i)$, and $\bar{z}(i)$ for the ith state are related as follows: $E[\bar{y}(i)|\bar{x}(i), \bar{z}(i)] = A + B\bar{x}(i) + D\bar{z}(i)$. Then the standard methods of multiple linear regression can be applied to the ecological data, $\bar{y}(i)$, $\bar{x}(i)$, $\bar{z}(i)$, in order to obtain estimates of the constants A, B, D, in the multilinear equation for the individuals. However, if a simple linear relationship between $\bar{y}(i)$ and $\bar{x}(i)$ is incorrectly assumed and $\bar{z}(i)$ is neglected, then the standard estimates $\hat{a}$ and $\hat{b}$ for the regression line between y and x will have the following biases: $E\{\hat{b}\} - B = D\sigma[\bar{x}(i), \bar{z}(i)]/V[\bar{x}(i)] = D\delta$, $E\{\hat{a}\} - A = D[\overline{\bar{x}(i)} - \overline{\bar{z}(i)}\delta]$, where $\sigma[\bar{x}(i), \bar{z}(i)]$ is the covariance between $\bar{x}(i)$ and $\bar{z}(i)$ for the different states; $V[\bar{x}(i)]$ is the variance of $\bar{x}(i)$ for the states; and $\delta = \sigma[\bar{x}(i), \bar{z}(i)]/V[\bar{x}(i)]$. Thus if $D = 0$, the relation between y and x will be linear, and the standard estimates will be unbiased. However, if $D \neq 0$, the $\hat{b}$ will be biased unless the covariance between $\bar{x}(i)$ and $\bar{z}(i)$ is zero. Even in the situation where $\hat{b}$ is unbiased but $D \neq 0$, it will not be possible, except under special circumstances, to estimate the individual correlation between y and x from the ecological data $\bar{y}(i)$ and $\bar{x}(i)$, since the individual values of z and their relation to y and x will play an important role in determining this correlation if $D \neq 0$.

Let us now consider the special circumstance in which the individual value z measures a characteristic of the state in which the individual lives (e.g., its size), so that z will be the same for all individuals living in it. The value of D may be known, or it can be estimated, along with A and B, by the usual methods of multiple linear regression applied to the ecological data concerning $\bar{y}(i)$, $\bar{x}(i)$, and $\bar{z}(i)$, thus obtaining the estimates $\hat{d}$, $\hat{a}$, $\hat{b}$. In this case, there will be a simple linear relation between y and x, for the individuals in a given state, but the y-intercept of the line may differ for the different states; i.e., $E(y|x) = (A + Dz) + Bx$, where $z = \bar{z}(i)$, may differ from state to state. Thus the regression line for each state can be estimated, and each line will have the same slope, $\hat{b}$. If the variances of the y and x measurements, for a given state, are known, then it is possible to estimate the individual correlation coefficient for the population in that state. Furthermore, if these variances are known for each state, then they can be used, together with the values $\bar{y}(i)$, $\bar{x}(i)$, $\hat{b}$ and the relative size of each state, to estimate the individual correlation coefficient for the total population. Hence it is possible to obtain an estimate of the individual correlation coefficient for a population from the ecological data, even if there is no constant linear relationship, $E(y\,|\,x) = A + Bx$, as long as the situation is such that the slope B remains the same in the different states, while the y intercept may differ from state to state in a way that is linearly related to some measured characteristic, z, of the state.

RELATION BETWEEN TWO DICHOTOMOUS VARIABLES

The point of view described at the end of the preceding section can be applied to show that if the average $E(r\,|\,x)$ of the values of the proportion r of whites who are illiterate, for states with the same proportion x of Negroes, is a linear function of a measurable characteristic z of each state (i.e., $E[r\,|\,x] = C + Fz$), and if the difference between the average $E(p\,|\,x)$ of the values of the proportion p of Negroes who are illiterate (for states with the same proportion x of Negroes) and $E(r\,|\,x)$ is constant (i.e., $E[p\,|\,x] - E[r\,|\,x] = B$), then the average of the values of the proportion y of illiterates (for states with the same proportion x of Negroes) is equal to $E(y\,|\,x) = C + Fz + Bx$. The special situation where $F = 0$ has been studied earlier in this article. By standard methods of multiple regression applied to the ecological data (i.e., to the proportions y and x and the value of z for each state), estimates $\hat{c}, \hat{f},$ and $\hat{b}$ of C, F, and B, respectively, can be obtained, which can then be used to obtain the estimates $\hat{r} = \hat{c} + \hat{f}z$ and $\hat{p} = \hat{b} + \hat{c} + \hat{f}z$ of $E(r\,|\,x)$ and $E(p\,|\,x)$, respectively, for each state. These estimates $\hat{r}$ and $\hat{p}$ can be used along with the values of x and the size of the population of each state to estimate the four entries in the 2 × 2 cross-classification table describing the relation between the two dichotomous variables, race and illiteracy, for each state. These tables for the separate states can then be combined to estimate the four table entries for the total population; thus an estimate of the individual correlation between race and illiteracy can be obtained for the total population.

The magnitude of the estimate $\hat{b}$ of $B = E(p\,|\,x) - E(r\,|\,x)$, the average difference between the illiteracy rates for whites and the rates for Negroes for states having the same proportion x of Negroes might be interpreted as the "effect of race on illiteracy," while the magnitude of the estimate $\hat{f}$ of F might be interpreted as the "effect of z on the illiteracy of whites" (z might measure average income, average social status, per cent unemployed, etc., for each state). It should be noted that z cannot be taken equal to x (neither can z be a linear function of x), unless some additional assumptions are made, because if $z = x$, then $E(y\,|\,x) = C + (B + F)x$, in which case $B + F$ and C can be estimated by the methods of linear regression applied to y and x, but it will not be possible to obtain separate estimates of B and F unless additional assumptions are made about their relative magnitudes. For example, if the additional assumption that $F = 0$ is made (i.e., that the "effect of z on the illiteracy of whites" is zero), then the methods developed earlier can be utilized; but if the assumption that $B = 0$ is made (i.e., that the "effect of race on illiteracy" is zero), then the table entries for each state can be estimated as described in the preceding paragraph, and these table entries for the states can then be combined to estimate the individual correlation for the total population. In this particular example, in which $z = x$, if $F = 0$, then the effect of the percentage of population which is Negro in a state on the illiteracy rate for the whites there is zero, while if $B = 0$, then the average difference between the illiteracy rate for Negroes and the rate for whites is zero in states having the same proportion x of Negroes. In this situation, where $B = 0$, the estimated individual correlation between race and illiteracy computed for each state will be zero, but the individual correlation estimated for the total population may not be zero unless $F = 0$ as well. Since it is possible to obtain an exact linear relationship between y and x when either $F = 0$ or $B = 0$ (or even when neither F nor B equals zero), it is not possible to decide on the basis of the ecological data concerning y and x whether it should be assumed that $F = 0$, that $B = 0$, or that the ratio B/F is a known constant. The research worker will require additional data to help him choose between these models and the assumptions underlying them. This is an important choice, since they lead to different methods of analysis of the data and also to different interpretations of the results. It was assumed earlier that $F = 0$, and the methods described in that case led to estimates of the individual correlations which were different from what they would have been if it had been assumed that $B = 0$ or if it had been assumed that the ratio B/F was a known constant.

Let us now consider the situation where $E(r|x) = C + Fz$ and $E(p|x) = G + Hz$. (The preceding comments in this section dealt with the special situation where $H = F$, so that $E[p|x] - E[r|x] = G - C = B$.) In this case, $E(y|x) = C + Fz + [G - C + (H - F)z]x = C + Fz + (G - C)x + (H - F)zx$, and a multiple regression analysis of the ecological variable y on the three variables z, x, and zx will lead to estimates of C, F, $G - C$, and $H - F$. These estimates can be used to obtain estimates of C, F, G, and H, which in turn can be used along with the values of z for each state to estimate $E(r|x)$ and $E(p|x)$ for each state. From these estimates and the values of x and the size of the population of each state, the four entries in the 2×2 cross-classification table describing the relation between race and illiteracy in each state can be estimated, and the table entries for the states can be combined to estimate the table entries for the total population, thus providing an estimate of the individual correlation for the total population. If $z = x$ (or if z is a linear function of x), then the methods described in this paragraph cannot be applied unless some specific additional assumptions about the relationships between the constants are made, similar to those mentioned in the preceding paragraph.[30]

Let us now consider the situation in which $E(p|x)/E(r|x) = J$ is constant for the different values of x and $E(r|x) = C + Fx$. In this case, $E(y|x) = E(r|x) + E(r|x)[J - 1]x = [C + Fx][1 + (J - 1)x] = C + [F + C(J - 1)]x + F(J - 1)x^2$, and a multiple regression analysis of y on the variables x and x^2 will lead to estimates of C, $F + C(J - 1)$, and $F(J - 1)$.[31] These estimates can then be used to estimate C, F, and J. With these estimates and the values of x and the size of the population of each state, it is possible to estimate the entries in the cross-classification table describing the relation between race and illiteracy for each

state and then to combine these tables for the separate states to obtain an estimate of the cross-classification table for the total population. It is possible to perform a rough test of whether $F(J - 1) = 0$ by applying the standard test that the regression of y on x is linear rather than quadratic.[32] If $F = 0$, then the methods developed here earlier may be appropriate, while if $J - 1 = 0$ (i.e., the average illiteracy rate for Negroes equals the average rate for whites in states having the same proportion x of Negroes), then the method described in this paragraph can be applied. If $F(J - 1) = 0$, the decision as to whether to assume $F = 0$ or $J - 1 = 0$ should depend on the research worker's available knowledge or on some additional data related, directly or indirectly, to the magnitudes of F and $J - 1$. The magnitude of $J - 1$ may be interpreted, for the model under consideration, as the "effect of race on illiteracy." For this model, the scatter diagram of y on x can suggest whether (1) both F and $J - 1$ are different from zero (if the relationship between y and x is not linear, but it can be fitted by a second-degree polynomial in x); (2) either F or $J - 1$ is different from zero but not both (if the relationship is linear but the slope of the line is not zero); or (3) both F and $J - 1$ are equal to zero (if the relationship is linear with a slope of zero). The extent to which the scatter diagram can be fitted by a first- or second-degree polynomial in x can serve as a partial check on the assumptions underlying the methods described here. This is no more than a partial check, since, as we had seen earlier in this article, several different models may lead to a specified relationship between y and x, and the methods applied to the ecological data will depend very much on which model is chosen.

If $E(p|x)/E(r|x) = J$ and the relation between $E(r|x)$ and x is $E(r|x) = C + Fx + Kx^2$ or some more complicated relation, it is still possible to use a method similar to the one given in the preceding paragraph, in order to estimate the constants C, F, K, J, and then to use these estimates to estimate the individual correlation between race and illiteracy for each state separately and also for the total population. If $E(p|x)/E(r|x) = J$ and $E(r|x) = C + Fz$, where z is some measurable characteristic of each state, then it is also possible to estimate the constants C, F, and J from the relation $E(y \mid x) = (C + Fz)[1 + (J - 1)x] = C + Fz + C(J - 1)x + F(J - 1)zx$—a multilinear relation between y and the variables z, x, and zx. As a partial check on this model, the relations between the four constants in the multilinear relation can be examined to see whether they lead to a consistent set of estimates of the three constants G, F, and J.

The research worker who uses the methods described herein should be aware of the underlying assumptions of each method and should take advantage of all possible partial checks on them. The choice between the various models described here should be made on the basis of the research worker's knowledge or on some additional data pertaining to the underlying assumptions of the models.

FOOTNOTES

[1] W. S. Robinson, "Ecological Correlations and the Behavior of Individuals," *American Sociological Review*, **15** (1950), 351–357.

[2] L. A. Goodman, "Ecological Regression and Behavior of Individuals," *ibid.*, **18** (1953), 663–664.

[3] O. D. Duncan and B. Davis, "An Alternative to Ecological Correlation," *ibid.*, 665–666.

[4] W. S. Robinson, *op. cit.*, 351.

[5] For example, H. Theil, *Linear Aggregations of Economic Relations* (Amsterdam, 1954).

[6] See, e.g., H. M. Walker and J. Lev, *Statistical Inference* (New York: Holt, Rinehart & Winston, Inc., 1953), p. 272; and L. A. Goodman and W. H. Kruskal, "Measures of Association for Cross Classifications," *Journal of the American Statistical Association*, **49** (1954), 732–764, esp. 739.

[7] See L. A. Goodman, *et al.*, *op. cit.*, 735–738, for a description of some distinctions between these situations.

[8] W. S. Robinson, *op. cit.*, 357; L. A. Goodman, *op. cit.*, 663.

[9] H. Menzel's "Comment" on Robinson's paper, in *American Sociological Review*, **15** (1950), 674; L. A. Goodman, *op. cit.*, 663.

[10] Duncan, *et al.*, *op. cit.*, 665; L. A. Goodman, *op. cit.*, 664.

[11] L. A. Goodman, *op. cit.*

[12] See L. A. Goodman, *et al.*, *op. cit.*, for further discussion of this point.

[13] O. D. Duncan, *et al.*, *op. cit.*

[14] Cf. H. C. Selvin, "Durkheim's 'Suicide' and Problems of Empirical Research," *American Journal of Sociology*, **63** (1958), 615–618. Selvin refers to the results presented in an unpublished version of the present article.

[15] See, e.g., W. S. Robinson, *op. cit.*, 353 (Table 1).

[16] See, e.g., W. J. Dixon and F. J. Massey, Jr., *Introduction to Statistical Analysis* (New York: McGraw-Hill Book Company, 1951), Chap. 11.

[17] See, e.g., R. L. Anderson and T. A. Bancroft, *Statistical Theory in Research* (New York: McGraw-Hill Book Company, 1952), pp. 182–186.

[18] See e.g., M. G. Kendall, "Regression, Structure, and Functional Relationship," Parts I and II, *Biometrika*, **38** (1951), 11–25, and **39** (1952), 96–108; D. V. Lindley, "Regression Lines and Linear Functional Relationship," *Journal of the Royal Statistical Society*, **9**, supplement (1947), 219–244; J. W. Tukey, "Components in Regression," *Biometrics*, **7** (1951), 33–70.

[19] A statistical test for linearity of regression for certain kinds of data is described in H. M. Walker, *et al.*, *op. cit.*, pp. 245–246.'

[20] A somewhat different, but equivalent, set of formulas is given, for example, in A. M. Mood, *Introduction to the Theory of Statistics* (New York: McGraw-Hill Book Company, 1950), p. 294.

[21] See e.g., the discussion of regression analysis in W. J. Dixon, *et al.*, *op cit.*

[22] Relevant are two earlier papers: F. F. Stephan, "Sampling Errors and the Interpretation of Social Data Ordered in Time and Space," *Journal of the American Statistical Association*, **29**, supplement (1934), 165–166; and F. A. Ross, "Ecology and the Statistical Method," *American Journal of Sociology*, **38**(1933), 507–522.

[23] W. S. Robinson, *op. cit.*

[24] Further discussion and application of some of the methods developed here [are] in O. D. Duncan, R. P. Cuzzort, and B. Duncan, *Statistical Geography* (New York: Free Press of Glencoe, Inc., 1961); see also D. J. Bogue and M. J. Hagood, *Subregional Migration in the United States, 1935–40*, Vol. II: *Differential Migration in the Corn and Cotton Belts* (Oxford, O.: Scripps Foundation, 1953), Appendix A, for a somewhat different approach to the problem of ecological correlation.

[25] See O. D. Duncan and B. Davis, *op. cit.;* comments on this method will be presented in the following section.

[26] *Sixteenth Census of the United States: 1940: Population and Housing Statistics for Census Tracts and Community Areas, Chicago, Illinois* (Washington: U.S.G.P.O., 1943), Tables A-3 and A-3a, pp. 25–39, and Tables 3 and 3a, pp. 176–341.

[27] See reference to this finding in Selvin, *op. cit.*, 616–618.

[28] See, e.g., H. M. Walker, *et al.*, *op. cit.*, Chap. 13.

[29] See G. U. Yule and M. G. Kendall, *An Introduction to the Theory of Statistics* (New York: Hafner Publishing Co., Inc., 1950), pp. 313–314, for some related comments.

[30] See O. D. Duncan, R. P. Cuzzort, and B. Duncan, *op. cit.*, for some related comments.

[31] See, e.g., G. W. Snedecor, *Statistical Methods*, 4th ed. (Ames: Iowa State College Press, 1950), pp. 379–382, for a description of curvilinear regression methods for a second-degree polynomial.

[32] See *ibid.*, pp. 381–384.

3

THE CONTIGUITY RATIO
AND STATISTICAL MAPPING

R. C. GEARY

The problem discussed in this paper is to determine whether statistics given for each "county" in a "country" are distributed at random or whether they form a pattern. The statistical instrument is the contiguity ratio c defined by formula 1.1 below, which is an obvious generalization of the Von Neumann ratio used in one-dimensional analysis, particularly time series. While the applications in the paper are confined to one- and two-dimensional problems, it is evident that the theory applies to any number of dimensions. If the figures for adjoining counties are generally closer than those for counties not adjoining, the ratio will clearly tend to be less than unity. The constants are such that when the statistics are distributed at random in the counties, the average value of the ratio is unity. The statistics will be regarded as contiguous if the actual ratio found is significantly less than unity, by reference to the standard error. The theory is discussed from the viewpoints of both randomization and classical normal theory. With the randomization approach, the observations themselves are the "universe," and no assumption need be made as to the character of the frequency distribution. In the "normal case," the assumption is that the observations may be regarded as a random sample from a normal universe. In this case it seems certain that the ratio tends very rapidly to normality as the number of counties increases. The exact values of the first four semi-invariants are given for the normal case. These functions depend only on the configuration, and the calculated values for Ireland, with number of counties only twenty-six, show that the distribution of the ratio is very close to normal. Accordingly, one can have confidence in deciding on significance from the standard error.

The theory is also extended to regression problems. It is suggested that, if the dependent variables are found to be contiguous, the fact that the remainders after removal of the effect of independent variables are found to lack con-

Reprinted from *The Incorporated Statistician*, **5** (1954), 115–141, by permission of the author and editor.

tiguity constitutes a prima facie case for regarding the independent variables included as *completely* explaining the dependent variables. There are, of course, other, and perhaps better, reasons for developing the regression aspects. If the theory is to be applied to problems of contagion (morbidity and mortality rates or numbers), one cannot regard the fact of contagion in the narrow sense (i.e., that the disease has been transmitted by contacts) as established, or use the ratio as the measure of the strength of contagion, unless one has removed causative factors (independent variables) which may themselves have the property of contiguity. Contagion can only be established from the remainders when the effects of the causative factors have been duly allowed for. For instance, if a disease is known to vary according to social group, it is clearly necessary to correct for this effect, which itself is very likely to be contiguous.

In the present paper, most of the applications are derived from Irish county data. Dublin (city and county) has been excluded because of the highly urbanized character of this area which renders most of the statistics exceptional. The greater number of the statistics examined exhibit the statistical property of contiguity in high degree. This property was fairly well known from ordinary mapping. For example, the counties to the northwest of a line from north Louth to west Cork have generally a higher proportion of the population in towns and villages than counties to the northwest. Even the agricultural characteristics of the two zones are significantly different. The writer, at this stage, is mainly concerned to see how the theory works with actual data, even though the fact of contiguity might have been anticipated. The ratio, moreover, establishes not only the fact, but the relative strength of contiguity, and the exceptions have some interest.

In the final section of the paper proper, the statistical efficiency of the ratio, as a measure of contagion in the linear case, is discussed. It is found that the ratio is more efficient (by reference to a simple theoretical model of "contagion") than the "method of blocks" when the blocks contain but a few primary units, but the block method is to be preferred for larger sized blocks. In an appendix a method of orthogonalizing the independent variables by the use of latent roots and vectors is developed and applied to linear and quadratic terms of latitude and longitude of twenty-five Irish counties.

The Contiguity Ratio–Randomization Aspect

Let the number of counties be n, the measure of the tth county z_t, with number of connections k_t. The contiguity ratio c is given by

$$(1.1) \qquad c = \frac{(n-1)}{2K_1} \frac{\sum'_{i \neq t'} (z_t - z_{t'})^2}{\sum_t (z_t - \bar{z})^2}$$

where

$$(1.2) \quad \begin{cases} K_1 = \Sigma k_t \\ \Sigma = \text{sum over all counties} \\ \Sigma' = \text{sum over contiguous counties} \end{cases}$$

It is easy to show that

$$(1.3) \quad 2a = \Sigma'(z_t - z_{t'})^2 = 2(\Sigma k_t z_t^2 - 2 \sum'_{t<t'} z_t z_{t'})$$

The sampling theory of c can be discussed from two points of view: (1) randomization, or (2) classical sampling theory, which involves the assumption of universal normality of the z_t and also the concept of randomization.

Since the sum product in the denominator of c, namely

$$(1.4) \qquad b = \Sigma(z_t - \bar{z})^2$$

is symmetrical in the z_t it assumes the same value for every permutation of the variables. Accordingly, attention may be confined to

$$(1.5) \qquad a = \Sigma k_t z_t^2 - 2 \sum'_{t<t'} z_t z_{t'}$$

Denote the mean by the symbol M, so that, where z and z' are any different pair from the series $z_1, z_2, \cdots, z_n$,

$$nM(z^2) = \Sigma z_t^2$$
$$n(n-1)M(zz') = 2 \sum_{t<t'} z_t z_{t'}$$

It is evident that, without loss of generality, it may be assumed that

$$nM(z) = \Sigma z_t = 0$$

Then

(1.6)   (i) $n(n-1)M(zz') = 2\Sigma z_t z_{t'}$

$$= -\Sigma z_t^2 = -nM(z^2)$$

(ii) $n(n-1)M(z^2 z') = \Sigma z_t^2 z_{t'}$

$$= -\Sigma z_t^3 = -nM(z^3)$$

(iii) $n(n-1)(n-2)M(z\,z'\,z'')$

$$= 6\Sigma z_t z_{t'} z_{t''} = 2\Sigma z_t^3 = 2nM(z^3)$$

(iv) $n(n-1)M(z^3 z') = -\Sigma z_t^4 = -nM(z^4)$

(v) $n(n-1)M(z^2 z'^2) = 2\Sigma z_t^2 z_{t'}^2$

$$= n^2[M(z^2)]^2 - nM(z^4)$$

(vi) $n(n-1)(n-2)M(z^2 z' z'')$

$$= 2\Sigma z_t^2 z_{t'} z_{t''} = 2nM(z^4) - n^2[M(z^2)]^2$$

(vii) $n(n-1)(n-2)(n-3)M(z\,z'\,z''\,z''')$

$$= 24\Sigma z_t z_{t'} z_{t''} z_{t'''}$$

$$= 3n^2[M(z^2)]^2 - 6nM(z^4)$$

According to the randomization approach, the significance of the value of a, and hence of c, is judged by the position of the value actually found in the sequence of the $n!$ values of a (or c) found by permuting the n values of z in every possible way. From this point of view, the $n!$ values are regarded as a frequency distribution with calculable moments. For simplicity of notation, write

$$M(z^a z'^{a'} z''^{a''} \cdots) = (a\,c'\,a'' \cdots)$$

Then, from Eq. 1.5,

(1.7) $M(a) = K_1\{(2) - (11)\}$

$$= K_1 \frac{n(2)}{(n-1)}$$

from Eq. 1.6 (i), so that, from Eqs. 1.1 and 1.3

(1.8) $M(c) = 1$

Squaring a, as given by Eq. 1.5, and taking the mean of each term, bearing in mind that $\sum_{t<t'}'$ contains in all $K_1/2$ terms,

$$M(a^2) = (4)\Sigma k_t^2 + 2(22)\sum_{t<t'} k_t k_{t'} - 4(31)\Sigma k_t^2$$

$$- 4(211)\Sigma k_t\left(\frac{K_1}{2} - k_t\right) + 2K_1(22)$$

$$+ 4(211)\Sigma k_t(k_t - 1)$$

(1.9) $+ 4(1111)\left\{\frac{K_1}{2}\left(\frac{K_1}{2} - 1\right) - \Sigma k_t(k_t - 1)\right\}$

$$= K_2\{(4) - 4(31) - (22) + 8(211)$$

$$- 4(1111) + K_1(K_1 + 2)\{(22)$$

$$- 2(211) + (1111)\}$$

where
$$K_1 = \Sigma k_t$$
$$K_2 = \Sigma k_t^2$$

As a check it will be noted that the sums of the coefficients of the expressions in the brackets { } of Eq. 1.9 are zero. This is because when all the z are equal, the moments from zero [say $(4)'$, $(31)'$, etc.] are all equal, so that $M(a^2)$ is zero as it should be, since, in this particular case, each of the a's is zero. Finally, using the last four relations of Eq. 1.6, $M(a^2)$ is given by

(1.10) $(n-1)(n-2)(n-3)M(a^2)$

$$= K_2\{n(n^2 - n + 2)(4)$$

$$- n(n^2 + 3n - 6)(2)^2\}$$

$$+ K_1(K_1 + 2)\{-n(n-1)(4)$$

$$+ n(n^2 - 3n + 3)(2)^2\}$$

From Eqs. 1.1, 1.3, and 1.10, the $M(c^2)$ may be computed as the product of $M(a^2)$ by $(n-1)^2/n^2 K_1^2(2)^2$. It may be observed that, in practical applications, K_1 and K_2 will each be of order n, so that, as n tends toward infinity, $M(c^2)$ will tend toward a finite limit. In fact, if

(1.11) $K_1 = nk_1$

$$K_2 = nk_2$$

(1.12) $M(c) = 1$

$$M(c^2) \sim 1 + \frac{1}{n}\left\{\left(\frac{k_2}{k_1^2} - 1\right)\right.$$

$$\left.\left[\frac{(4) - (2)^2}{(2)^2}\right] + \frac{2}{k_1}\right\}$$

If the z can be regarded as a normal sample, (4) will be approximately equal to $3(2)^2$, so that

(1.13) $\text{Var}(c) \sim \frac{2}{n}\left(\frac{k_2}{k_1^2} + \frac{1}{k_1} - 1\right)$

Later (under "Regression Aspects of Contiguity"), the regression aspects of the problem are discussed from the viewpoint of classical linear theory. The problem is to determine if there is a contiguity effect, i.e., if c has a significantly low value after the elimination of q independent variables by the least-square method. As far as randomization is concerned, it would appear that the test developed in this section can be applied formally, the z being the remainders after the contributions of the independent variables have been removed. To a certain extent, the writer shares the misgivings of some other students about the validity of the randomization approach in its application to regression remainders. As each successive independent variable is removed, should not the degrees of freedom be diminished? It does not seem so. What happens is that the variance (or range) of the remainders diminishes as the effect of each independent variable is allowed for, the test becoming indeterminate when the number of independent variables (originally with mean zero) is one less than the number of observations n, i.e., when all the remainders are zero. Accordingly, the formal application of the randomization procedure, without diminution of the number of degrees of freedom, does not result in *obvious* inconsistency; we can conceive of cases where c will be significantly low even after removal of the effect of $(n-2)$ independent variables. Since doubts remain, however, the writer considered it desirable to examine the problem from the classical sampling aspect. In any case, it will be interesting to compare the results of the two approaches. In the practical aspect, the randomization method has the advantage that it can be applied without the assumption of universal normality in the n observations, regarded as a random sample.

The Two-Category Case

This is the case in which only two values (which, without loss of generality, may be taken as 1 and zero) appear in the county scheme. The present theory in its randomization aspect can be applied literally. The problem here is to determine if the two values are distributed at random in the pattern, or if, on the contrary, there is grouping or coagulation. If the number of counties is, as before, n, and if the number of ones is np and the number of zeros nq, we require only the values of the moments from the mean, namely (2) and (4). These are

(1.14)
$$(2) = pq$$
$$(4) = pq(p^2 - pq + q^2)$$
with $p + q - 1$

The randomization mean $M(c) = 1$ and $M(c^2)$ is found from Eqs. 1.1, 1.3, and 1.10.

Example: Has the Irish twenty-five-county scheme illustrated in Fig. 1 a pattern, or are the units and zero distributed at random?

For the twenty-five-county scheme, $n = 25$, $K_1 = 110$, $K_2 = 544$. For the particular example $np = 13$, $nq = 12$, and from Eq. 1.1, the actual value of c is found to be 0.6993. The variance is 0.014069, so that the standard error is 0.1186 and $R = (1 - c)\text{S.E.} = 2.54$, which should be judged significant.

Classical Theory: The Frequency Distribution of c in the Normal Case

Let the z_i be a random sample of n from a normal universe with mean zero and (unknown) variance σ^2. Since c is the quotient of a quadratic form by the estimated variance, the moments from zero of the ratio are the quotients of the moments of the numerator and denominator for normal supplies. Following are the first four moments of c:

(2.1) $\mu_1' = 1$

$$\mu_2' = \frac{\{n^2 k_1^2 + 2n(k_1 + k_2)\}(n - 1)}{n^2(n + 1)k_1^2}$$

$$\mu_3' = \frac{\{n^3 k_1^3 + 6n^2 k_1(k_1 + k_2) + 8n(3k_2 + k_3 - 6t')\}(n - 1)^2}{n^3(n + 1)(n + 3)k_1^3}$$

$$\mu_4' = \frac{\begin{aligned}&\{n^4 k_1^4 + 12n^3 k_1^2(k_1 + k_2) + 4n^2(3k_1^2 \\ &+ 30k_1 k_2 + 8k_1 k_3 - 48k_1 t' + 3k_2^2) \\ &+ 48n(-k_1 + 2k_2 + 6k_3 + k_4 - 2v_1 \\ &+ 8v_2 - 8v_3 + 8q')\}(n - 1)^3\end{aligned}}{n^4(n + 1)(n + 3)(n + 5)k_1^4}$$

where

(2.2) $n = $ number of counties

$nk_a = \Sigma_i k_i^a$, $a = 1, 2, 3, 4$,

$nv_1 = \sum_{i<j}' (k_i + k_j)^2$

$nv_2 = \sum_{i<j}' k_i k_j$

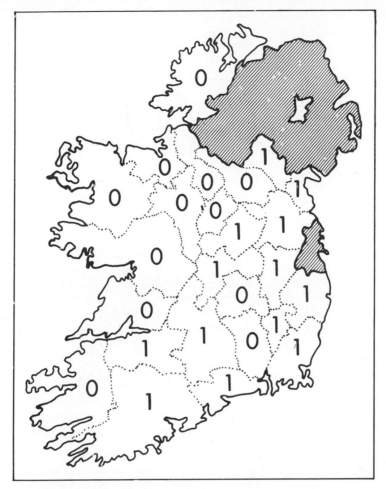

FIGURE 1.   Two-category example for twenty-five counties

$$nv_3 = \Sigma_i k_i T_i \quad \begin{cases} \text{where } T_i \text{ is the number of} \\ \text{triads at county } i \text{ and } T \\ \text{the total number of triads} \\ \text{in the system} \end{cases}$$

$$nt' = T$$

$nq' = Q$ the total number of quartets in the system

The meaning of the terms "triad" and "quartet" (as well as "connections") will best be understood by reference to Fig. 2 (of Ireland —twenty-six counties).

The capital letters A—Z indicate the counties arranged in alphabetical order from A (Carlow) to Z (Wicklow). The numbers on the map indicate the connections. Thus A is connected with I, J, K, Y, Z, $= 5$. Clearly, the total number of connections in the system is half the total of the numbers of the map. As regards triads, there are five at A, namely, AIK, AIZ, AJK, AJY, AYZ. Quartets at A number nine, namely, AFIZ, AIJK, AIKS, AIKZ, AIYZ, AJKV, AJKY, AJWY, AJYZ. Triads and quartets enter into the calculations of moments, because in raising $\sum_{ij} z_i z_j$ in a to the third and fourth powers, respectively, the product terms, like $(z_i z_j)(z_{i'} z_{j'})(z_{i''} z_{j''})$ and $(z_i z_j)(z_{i'} z_{j'})(z_{i''} z_{j''})(z_{i'''} z_{j'''})$, make nonzero contributions when triads and quartets are involved. For Ireland (twenty-six counties) the values of (2.2) are as follows:

$n =$	26	$nv_1 =$	6,168
$nk_1 =$	116	$nv_2 =$	1,472
$nk_2 =$	584	$nv_3 =$	519
$nk_3 =$	3,224	$nt' =$	33
$nk_4 =$	19,184	$nq' =$	42

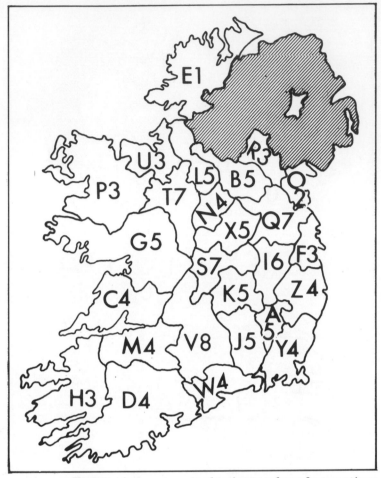

FIGURE 2. Twenty-six county map showing number of connections

The values of Eq. 2.1 are, then:

$$\mu_1' = 1$$
$$\mu_2' = 1.02226186$$
$$\mu_3' = 1.06690364$$
$$\mu_4' = 1.13553261$$

The values of the semi-invariants are

$$\lambda_1 = 1$$
$$\lambda_2 = 0.0222619$$
$$\lambda_3 = 0.0001179$$
$$\lambda_4 = 0.0000028$$

The values of $\sqrt{\beta_1} = \lambda_3/\lambda_2^{3/2}$ and $\beta_2 = \lambda_4/\lambda_2^2$ are, respectively, 0.0355 and 0.0057, so that, with n only 26 and in a system which may be regarded as well diversified, the distribution is obviously very close to normal. The writer does not consider that it is necessary

to furnish a formal proof of the normality of c for n indefinitely large, since, from the practical point of view, it is more important to establish that, for the sample sizes and the kinds of situation which are encountered, the assumption of normality is plausible, so that the standard deviation can be used as a test of significance.

To terms in n^{-4}, the values of the semi-invariants, computed from Eqs. 2.1 and 2.2, are as follows:

$$(2.3) \quad \lambda_1 = 1$$

$$\lambda_2 \sim \frac{2}{nk_1^2}(k_1 - k_1^2 + k_2) - \frac{2}{n^2 k_1^2}(2k_1 - k_1^2$$

$$+ 2k_2) + \frac{2}{n^3 k_1^2}(2k_1 - k_1^2 + 2k_2)$$

$$- \frac{2}{n^4 k_1^2}(2k_1 - k_1^2 + 2k_2)$$

$$\lambda_3 \sim \frac{8}{n^2 k_1^3}(2k_1^3 - 3k_1^2 - 3k_1 k_2 + 3k_2 + k_3$$

$$- 6t') - \frac{8}{n^3 k_1^3}(8k_1^3 - 15k_1^2 - 15k_1 k_2$$

$$+ 18k_2 + 6k_3 - 36t') + \frac{8}{n^4 k_1^3}(26k_1^3$$

$$- 51k_1^2 - 51k_1 k_2 + 66k_2 + 22k_3$$

$$- 132t')$$

$$\lambda_4 \sim \frac{48}{n^3 k_1^4}(5k_1^4 - 10k_1^3 - 10k_1^2 k_2 + 2k_1^2$$

$$+ 16k_1 k_2 + 4k_1 k_3 - 24k_1 t' + 2k_2^2$$

$$+ k_1 - 2k_2 - 6k_3 - k_4 + 2v_1$$

$$- 8v_2 + 8v_3 - 8q')$$

$$+ \frac{48}{n^4 k_1^4}(43k_1^4 - 96k_1^3 - 96k_1^2 k_2 + 20k_1^2$$

$$+ 172k_1 k_2 + 44k_1 k_3 - 264k_1 t'$$

$$+ 20k_2^2 + 12k_1 - 24k_2 - 72k_3$$

$$- 12k_4 + 24v_1 - 96v_2 + 96v_3$$

$$- 96q')$$

Clearly, β_1 and β_2 are $0(n^{-1})$, lending a measure of verisimilitude to the algebra. For Ireland (twenty-six counties), the approximation to λ_4 is $0.337n^{-3} - 10.42n^{-4}$. It may be remarked that the coefficients of n^{-3} and n^{-4}, though they have a sharply increasing tendency, are very small in relation to the contributions of the different terms.

REGRESSION ASPECTS OF CONTIGUITY

The problem is to determine whether the value of c given by Eq. 1.1 is significantly small when the z_t are the remainders when the effect of a number of independent variables has been removed from the original dependent variable under examination. The typical procedure would consist in first establishing by the c test that the original observations were contiguous. The regression between the original observations and a series of correlative observations would be determined by least-square procedure. The remainders would then be tested for contiguity. If the original observations were highly contiguous and the remainders not significantly so, this might be a good test for the thesis that the independent variables completely "explain" the observations. As a more

practical application, if mortality or morbidity rates were being examined for evidence of contagion, given rates for n districts (parts of a city or county, for example), it would be highly desirable to correct the rates for, say, independent variables, such as income level, density of population, housing conditions, etc., each of which may also be significantly contiguous.

The model will be the usual linear one. In matrix notation, let y represent the $1 \times n$ matrix of original observations, x the $q \times n$ matrix of independent variables, q being the number of independent variables, a and b the matrices of coefficients determined by least squares. The absolute matrix will be $(a, a, a, \ldots n$ terms), i.e., $1 \times n$, whereas b will be $1 \times q$. The remainder matrix z will be $1 \times n$, i.e.

$$(3.1) \qquad y = a + bx + z$$

Without loss of generality, it may be assumed that the mean of each of the elements in x is zero. Then

$$(3.2) \qquad a = yN$$

where N is the $n \times n$ matrix, all of whose elements are $1/n$, and

$$(3.3) \qquad yx' = bxx'$$

where x' is the transpose of x. Since the means of all the elements in x are zero

$$(3.4) \qquad xN = 0$$

The matrix y is also given by

$$(3.5) \qquad y = \alpha + \beta x + u$$

where α and β are the (usually unknown) population or universal mean values of a and b, respectively, while u, of dimensions $1 \times n$, is a random normal sample of mean zero and (unknown) variance σ^2. It is first necessary to express z in terms of u. From the foregoing relations

$$(3.6) \quad z = y - a - yx'(xx')^{-1}x$$
$$= \alpha + \beta x + u - (\alpha + \beta x + u)N$$
$$- (\alpha + \beta x + u)x'(xx')^{-1}x$$
$$= u[I - N - X]$$

where I is the unit $n \times n$ matrix and $X = x'(xx')^{-1}x$. Since the square of the symmetrical $n \times n$ matrix $[I - N - X]$ is equal to itself, the universal variance-covariance matrix of z, namely V, is given by

$$(3.7) \qquad V = \sigma^2[I - N - A]$$

or

$$(3.8) \quad \frac{1}{\sigma^2}E(z_t z_{t'}) = \delta_{tt'} - \frac{1}{n} - \frac{1}{n}\sum_{i,i'} x_{it}s_{ii'}x_{i't'}$$

where x_{it} are the elements of x and $s_{ii'}$ the elements of $(xx')^{-1}$, and $\delta_{tt'} = 1$ for $t = t'$ and zero for $t \neq t'$. Using the relations $\sum_t x_{it} = 0$ it follows that

$$(3.9) \quad \frac{1}{\sigma^2}EM(z_t^2) = \frac{1}{\sigma^2}E\left(\frac{1}{n}\sum_t z_t^2\right) = 1 - \frac{1}{n} - \frac{q}{n}$$

$$= \frac{(n - q - 1)}{n}$$

and, for $t \neq t'$,

$$(3.10) \quad \frac{1}{\sigma^2}EM(z_t z_{t'}) = \frac{1}{\sigma^2}E\left(\frac{1}{n(n-1)}\sum_{t \neq t'} z_t z_{t'}\right)$$

$$= -\frac{1}{n} + \frac{q}{n(n-1)}$$

$$= \frac{-(n-q-1)}{n(n-1)}$$

The foregoing formulae in this section are, of course, well known. It has been judged expedient to develop them in some detail because they illustrate in the simplest case the processes by which the variance of c is derived. The universe which imparts variability to c is the resultant of two processes: (1) the independent variables being fixed and ordered, the variability being due to the normal variate u, superimposed on which is (2) variability due to the $n!$ permutations of the independent variables as a group. The combined process as it relates to the derivation of universal means is represented by the operational "product" EM, E relating to process 1 and M to process 2. It will be noted from Eqs. 3.9 and 3.10 that the process yields the classical results in its application to the variance-covariance.

Formula 3.6 shows that, in the conditions specified, z is a normal variate with variance-covariance matrix given by Eq. 3.8, which, it will be noted, is a function of the order subscripts t and t'. Given the order the moments from zero of c, with

$$(3.11) \qquad c = P\frac{a}{b'}$$

where

$$(3.12) \qquad a = \sum_t k_t z_t^2 - 2\sum_{i<t'}' z_t z_{t'}$$

$$b' = \sum_t z_t^2$$

$$P = \frac{(n-1)}{K_1}$$

the moment of any degree of c, i.e., $E(c^k)$, is the quotient of the moment of the numerator by the moment of the denominator. The final universal moments, on permutation of the orders represented by the process $ME = EM$, is found as the simple average of the E process, since at the second stage of averaging the denominators, which are symmetrical functions of the variables z and hence of the orders, are equal for all permutations. Symbolically, as regards any symmetrical function, $EM = E$. We now have

$$(3.13) \quad \mu_1' = EM(c) = \frac{PEM(a)}{E(b')}$$

$$= \frac{\dfrac{\sigma^2(n-1)}{K_1} \times \dfrac{K_1(n-q-1)}{(n-1)}}{\sigma^2(n-q-1)}$$

or

$$\mu_1' = 1$$

The second moment μ_2' of c is given by

$$(3.14) \quad \mu_2' = ME(c^2) = \frac{P^2\{ME(a^2)\}}{E(b')^2}$$

Since b' is a normal variance with $(n - q - 1)$ degrees of freedom, it is distributed as $\sigma^2\chi^2$, so that, in the last term of Eq. 3.14

$$(3.15) \quad \frac{P}{E(b')^2} = \frac{(n-1)^2}{K_1^2\sigma^4(n-q+1)(n-q-1)}$$

To find $ME(a^2)$, we take the square of a given by Eq. 3.12 and perform in succession the operations E and M on the various terms. The result is an expression of the form Eq. 1.9, where $(a\,b\,c\,\ldots)$ represents $ME(z_t^a\,z_{t'}^b\,z_{t''}^c\ldots)$, $t < t' < t''\ldots$. Now z_t, as a linear function of the normal variable u (see Eq. 3.6), is itself normally distributed with mean zero. Hence its moments of any dimension and of any even degrees are functions of the variances and covariances of the z_t, where the order of the subscripts, prior to the operation M, is fixed. We require only the following relations

$$(3.16) \qquad \mu(4) = 3[\mu(2)]^2$$

$$\mu(31) = 3\mu(20)\mu(11)$$

$$\mu(22) = \mu(20)\mu(02) + 2[\mu(11)]^2$$

$$\mu(211) = \mu(200)\mu(011) + 2\mu(101)\mu(110)$$

$$\mu(1111) = \mu(1100)\mu(0011)$$
$$+ \mu(1010)\mu(0101)$$
$$+ \mu(1001)\mu(0110)$$

The operation M is then performed on the various product terms on the right of Eq. 3.16. After M, it is obvious by symmetry that each of the three product terms in $\mu(1111)$ yields the same result.

To illustrate the process, consider $\mu(211)$. It will be convenient to regard the independent variables as orthogonalized by a nonsingular linear transformation, the same for all t, so that the matrix xx' reduces to a diagonal $q \times q$ matrix $n\sigma_1^2, n\sigma_2^2, \ldots, n\sigma_q^2$ and Eq. 3.8 becomes

$$(3.17) \qquad E(z_t^2) = \frac{\sigma^2}{n}(n - 1 - \Sigma_i\xi_{it}^2)$$

$$E(z_{t'}z_{t''}) = \frac{\sigma^2}{n}(-1 - \Sigma_i\xi_{it'}\xi_{it''})$$

$$\xi_{it} = \frac{x_{it}}{\sigma_i}$$

$$n\sigma_i^2 = \Sigma_t x_{it}^2$$

Therefore

$$(3.18) \qquad \frac{n^3(n - 1)(n - 2)}{2}M\{\mu(200)\mu(011)\}$$

$$= n^2\Sigma_t E(z_t^2) \sum_{t'\neq t''\neq t} E(z_{t'}z_{t''})$$

$$= n\Sigma_t E(z_t^2)\Big\{- (n - 1)(n - 2)$$

$$+ \sum_i \sum_{t'\neq t} \xi_{it}(\xi_{it} + \xi_{it'})\Big\}$$

using the second of Eq. 3.17 and the relation $\Sigma_t\xi_{it} = 0$. Using the further relation $\Sigma_t\xi_{it}^2 = n$, the second term in the brackets $\{\ \}$ becomes

$$qn - 2\Sigma_i\xi_{it}^2$$

Then, on substituting in the right side of Eq. 3.18 for $E(z_t^2)$ given by the first formula in Eq. 3.17 and summing for t, we find

$$(3.19) \quad M\{\mu(200)\mu(011)\}$$

$$= \frac{\sigma^2}{n^2(n - 1)(n - 2)}\{- (n - 1)^2(n - 2)$$

$$+ 2q(n - 1)(n - 2) - q^2n + 2\gamma\}$$

with

$$(3.20) \qquad n\gamma = \Sigma_t(\Sigma_i\xi_{it}^2)^2$$

All the other expressions required are derived in a similar way. Finally

$$(3.21) \quad ME(a^2) \times \frac{n(n - 1)(n - 2)(n - 3)}{\sigma^4}$$

$$= K_2\{2n(n - 1)(n - 2)(n - 3) - 2q(2n^3$$

$$- 9n^2 - 15n - 6) - q^2(n^2 + 3n - 6)$$

$$+ 3\gamma(n^2 - n + 2)\}$$

$$+ (K_1^2 + 2K_1)\{n(n - 1)(n - 2)(n - 3)$$

$$- 2q(n^3 - 6n^2 + 9n - 3)$$

$$+ q^2(n^2 - 3n + 3) - 3\gamma(n - 1)\}$$

As a check on Eq. 3.21, consider the use of $q = n - 1$. Then the least-squares fit to the observations y_t will be exact, so that all the remainder terms z_t will be zero and, from the first formula of Eq. 3.17, $\Sigma_i\xi_{it}^2 = n - 1$. Hence from Eq. 3.20 $\gamma = (n - 1)^2$. Substitution of these expressions for q and γ in Eq. 3.21 gives zero for the coefficients of K_2 and $(K_1^2 + 2K_1)$, as it should. From Eqs. 3.14, 3.15, and 3.21, $\mu_2' = ME(c^2)$ is found. The final expression is, of course, free of the error variance σ^2.

In Eq. 3.21, γ is a function of the orthogonalized independent variables. In terms of the original variables, γ is given in matrix notation by

$$(3.22) \qquad n\gamma = \Sigma_t\{x_t'(xx')^{-1}x_t\}^2$$

where x_t is the $q \times 1$ column matrix in the $q \times n$ matrix x. It may be of interest to add that $\gamma = 42,169$ when $n = 25$, $q = 5$ when the ξ_{it} are the quadratic orthogonal latitude-longitude terms, the "quolls" described in the Appendix.

CONTAGION: EFFICIENCY OF CONTIGUITY RATIO IN THE LINEAR CASE

The contiguity ratio c can, of course, be used to establish the fact, and to measure the degree, of contagion. The object of the present section is to compare the statistical efficiency of c as a measure of contagion (method 1) with that of another method (method II), which will presently be described.

Attention will be confined to the linear case. The method I mathematical model in the case of no contagion is as follows. A straight line of given length is divided into n equal divisions (e.g., a street or streets, each division representing a house). Each division is assigned a number 1 or zero, with probabilities p and q ($= 1 - p$), respectively, each assignment being independent. In the linear case

$$\text{(4.1)} \quad \begin{aligned} K_1 &= 2 + 2(n-2) = 2(n-1) = nk_1 \\ K_2 &= 2 + 4(n-2) = 2(2n-3) = nk_2 \end{aligned}$$

The moments (2) and (4) are given by

$$\text{(4.2)} \quad \begin{aligned} (2) &= pq \\ (4) &= pq(p^2 - pq + q^2) \end{aligned}$$

The mathematical model of contagion will be constructed by dividing the line into two parts containing n_1 and n_2 divisions so that

$$n_1 + n_2 = n$$

In the first part, the probability of assigning 1 in each division will be p_1 and in the second part p_2, so that the overall value of p as computed from the "observations" will be

$$\text{(4.3)} \quad p = \frac{(n_1 p_1 + n_2 p_2)}{(n_1 + n_2)}$$

If the probability p obtained uniformly throughout the $n = n_1 + n_2$ divisions, the average value of $M(c)$, from Eqs. 1.1 and 1.7 [would], of course, be unity. This is the "null-hypothesis" case, in which, from Eq. 1.7,

$$\text{(4.4)} \quad \begin{aligned} M_0(a) &= \frac{2(n-1)npq}{(n-1)} \\ &= 2npq \end{aligned}$$

In the "actual" case, the value will be

$$\text{(4.5)} \quad M(a) \sim 2n_1 p_1(1 - p_1) + 2n_2 p_2(1 - p_2)$$

when both n_1 and n_2 are large, as they will be assumed to be in the rest of this section. Then, from Eqs. 4.3 and 4.4

$$\text{(4.6)} \quad M_0(a) - M(a) \sim \frac{2n_1 n_2}{(n_1 + n_2)}(p_1 - p_2)^2$$

and

$$\text{(4.7)} \quad \begin{aligned} M_0(c) &- M(c) \\ &= 1 - M(c) \sim \frac{n_1 n_2 (p_1 - p_2)^2}{n^2 pq} \end{aligned}$$

Finally, we need the standard error in the null-hypothesis case. From Eq. 1.12, since $k_2/k_1^2 \sim 1$ and $2/k_1 \sim 1$,

$$\text{(4.8)} \quad \text{Var}(c) \sim \frac{1}{n}$$

We now introduce the *sensitivity* S defined as the ratio of the average deviation Eq. 4.7 to the null-hypothesis standard error, so that

$$\text{(4.9)} \quad S \sim \frac{n_1 n_2 (p_1 - p_2)^2}{n^{3/2} pq}$$

Method II envisages the divisions grouped in m blocks of d divisions each, so that $n = dm$, d being a small fixed number, so that m may be regarded as of the same order of magnitude as n. The test of contagion according to this method consists in comparing the number of blocks in $(d + 1)$ classes according to the number of units in each block with the theoretical distribution, on the assumption of no contagion using χ^2 with d degrees of freedom. In this nul-hypothesis case, the probability of x will be the binomial

$$\text{(4.10)} \quad \phi_x = \binom{d}{x} p^x q^{d-x}$$

For the contagion case, the line, as before, is divided into two parts, containing now m_1 and m_2 blocks, so that $n_1 = dm_1$ and $n_2 = dm_2$. The theoretical probability of x units in this case will be

$$(4.11) \qquad \phi_x' = \binom{d}{x}(\pi_1 p_1^x q_1^{d-x} + \pi_2 p_2^x q_2^{d-x})$$

where $\pi_1 = m_1/(m_1 + m_2)$, $\pi_2 = m_2/(m_1 + m_2)$, $\pi_1 + \pi_2 = 1$.

If the corresponding actual proportionate frequency (i.e., that found by classifying the blocks in a single experiment) be f_x', then the appropriate value of χ^2 is

$$(4.12) \qquad \chi^2 = m \sum_{x=0}^{d} (f_x' - \phi_x)^2 \phi_x$$

which, since $\Sigma_x f_1' = 1 = \Sigma_x \phi_{x'}$ gives

$$(4.13) \qquad \left(\frac{\chi^2}{m}\right) + 1 = \frac{\Sigma_x f_x'^2}{\phi_x}$$

Since

$$(4.14) \qquad m^2 E(f_x'^2) = m(m-1)\Sigma\phi_x'^2 + m\phi_x'$$

$$(4.15) \quad m^2 E\left(\frac{1+\chi^2}{m}\right) = m(m-1)\Sigma\phi_x'^2 + m\frac{\Sigma\phi_x'}{\phi_x}$$

Substituting for ϕ_x and ϕ_x' as given by Eqs. 4.10 and 4.11, the right side of 4.15 becomes

$$(4.16) \quad = m(m-1)\left\{\pi_1^2\left(\frac{p_1^2}{p} + \frac{q_1^2}{q}\right)^d \right.$$
$$+ 2\pi_1\pi_2\left(\frac{p_1 p_2}{p} + \frac{q_1 q_2}{q}\right)^d + \pi_2^2\left(\frac{p_2^2}{p} + \frac{q_2^2}{q}\right)^d\right\}$$
$$+ m\left\{\frac{\pi_1\left(\frac{q_1}{q}\right)^d\left[1 - \left(\frac{p_1 q}{pq_1}\right)^{d+1}\right]}{\left(1 - \frac{p_1 q}{pq_1}\right)}\right.$$
$$+ \left.\frac{\pi_2\left(\frac{q_2}{q}\right)^d\left[1 - \left(\frac{p_2 q}{pq_2}\right)^{d+1}\right]}{\left(1 - \frac{p_2 q}{pq_2}\right)}\right\}$$

The required value of $E\chi^2$ is found at once from Eqs. 4.15 and 4.16. It will be seen that if $p_1 = p_2 = p$, $E\chi^2 = d$, the number of degrees of freedom, as, of course, it should.

To compare the efficiency of the two methods, calculations of the associated probabilities were made for various sets of values of p_1 and p_2 and for block sizes 2, 4, and 8. The null-hypothesis value of p was taken as $(\pi_1 p_1 + \pi_2 p_2)$ throughout. To find the number of divisions n, S, given by Eq. 4.9, is written in the form

$$(4.17) \qquad S = \frac{\pi_1\pi_2(p_1 - p_2)^2 n^{1/2}}{pq}$$

and equated to its assumed critical value 2, which corresponds to a normal probability of 0.0455, i.e., it is assumed that c is approximately normally distributed. This given n as

$$(4.18) \qquad n = \frac{4p^2 q^2}{\pi_1^2 \pi_2^2 (p_1 - p_2)^4}$$

and then m is taken as n/d. Finally, the value of $E\chi^2$ is computed from Eq. 4.16 and its value compared with the χ^2 corresponding to the probability 0.0455. For each example, $\pi_1 = 0.7$, $\pi_2 = 0.3$.

The results of the computation are shown in Table 1 on page 472.

Method I will be regarded as more efficient than method II at the probability level 0.0455 if the χ^2 corresponding to this probability is greater than $E\chi^2$. It will be seen that for block sizes up to about 4, method I is at least as efficient as method II, but for $d > 4$ method II is to be preferred. This is a rather unexpected result; one might have thought that method I would always be superior because it *seems* to use more information than does method II, which "blankets" all the units within the block into a single figure (total number of units), whereas method I takes account of contagion (or contiguity) within blocks. For instance, if three units are found in a block of six houses, method II simply takes account of the total of 3, whereas in method I, the contiguity total can range from 1 (when the three units are together at either end) to 5 (when no two units are contiguous). The writer does not understand why the efficiency of method II seems to increase with block size. There must, in practice, be some limit to the block size of greater efficiency. It will be recalled that the number of blocks decreases in inverse proportion to block size. A point will be reached when there will not be a sufficient number of blocks for the χ^2-distribution to be deemed to apply; this may

TABLE 1

Comparison of values of χ^2 corresponding to probability 0.0455 with values of $E\chi^2$
(Formula (4.16)) for five examples each with three block sizes (d)

| Example | Assumed values of p_1, p_2 | | Number (d) of divisions in block | | | | | |
| | p_1 | p_2 | 2 | | 4 | | 8 | |
			χ^2	$E\chi^2$	χ^2	$E\chi^2$	χ^2	$E\chi^2$
1	0.1	0.2		3.57		8.98		19.23
2	0.2	0.1		3.95		10.43		26.23
3	0.2	0.4	6.19	4.08	9.71	11.25	15.79	38.30
4	0.4	0.2		4.05		10.61		26.83
5	0.4	0.6		4.18		10.46		19.98

be the solution of the anomaly. Of course the theory of infection being investigated will probably impose its own block size, but, though a very simple model has been assumed in the present case, the investigator should lean toward favoring larger rather than samller block sizes, if he can.

It is realized that a power function analysis would be more rigorous for comparing the efficiencies of the two methods. This would have involved the determination of the approximate frequency distribution of χ^2 given by Eqs. 4.12 or 4.13. The mean value of χ^2 has been given. For students who might be interested in pursuing the power function aspect, it will be useful to place on record the value of the second moment. It is derivable from

$$(4.19) \qquad m^4 E\left(1 + \frac{\chi^2}{m}\right)^2$$

$$= m_4\left(\Sigma_x \frac{\phi_x'^2}{\phi_x}\right)^2 + 2m_3\left(\Sigma\frac{\phi_x'^2}{\phi_x}\Sigma\frac{\phi_x'}{\phi_x} + 2\Sigma\frac{\phi_x'^3}{\phi_x^2}\right)$$

$$+ m_2\left\{\left(\Sigma\frac{\phi_x'}{\phi_x}\right)^2 + 6\Sigma\frac{\phi_x'^2}{\phi_x^2}\right\} + m_1\Sigma\frac{\phi_x'}{\phi_x^2}$$

with

$$m_r = m(m-1)(m-2)\cdots(m-r+1)$$

Furthermore, the author fully realizes that the model of contagion for the present purpose is far too rudimentary as a theory of contagion, considered *per se*. His object was only to form some impression of the efficiency of c in this application, for c can be applied in actual cases, however complicated the manner of spread of contagion.

APPLICATIONS

Twelve county series were selected for examination; they are displayed in the accompanying Table 2. Many of the figures for Dublin (city and county) are so exceptional on account of the highly urbanized character of that area that it was decided to exclude it from the calculation of the contiguity c, shown at the foot of the page. The number 0.1512 used for computing the significance R is the standard error computed from formula 2.1. It will be recalled that for this formula universal normality is assumed. On the other hand, the randomization procedure gives for c, for twenty-five Irish counties, mean unity and variance

$$\text{Var}(c) = 0\cdot00498737 \times \frac{(4)}{(2)^2} + 0\cdot00904961$$

This, in contradistinction to the normal value, varies with each series. If $(4)/(2)^2$ has the normal value 3, the variance (randomization theory) is 0.02401172, so that the standard error is 0.1550, very similar to the normal theory value. Except in the "unity-zero" (two category) and other cases where the distribution is extremely nonnormal, the difference between normal theory and randomization values of the variance are not important. It is immaterial which is used.

When the quolls (the five quadratic orthogonal latitude-longitude terms—see Appendix) have been removed by regression, the residuals have a normal theory variance of 0.027291 or a standard error of 0.1652. As formula 3.21 shows, in this computation due allowance is made for degrees of freedom involved in the

TABLE 2

Twelve statistical series for Irish counties, showing value of contiguity c and significance ratio R

| Serial letter | County (incl. county borough) | Percentage number Agricultural holdings in valuation groups (1950) | | | Per 1000 acres crops and pasture (1952) | | | | Town and village population as percentage of total (1951) | Per 1000 population (1951) | | Retail sales £ per person (1951) | Single males as % of all males aged 30–34 (1951) |
| | | £2–£10 | £10–£50 | Above £50 | Milch cows | Other cattle | Pigs | Sheep | | Private cars registered (1952) | Radio licences (1952) | | |
		(1)	(2)	(3)	(4)	(5)	(6)	(7)	(8)	(9)	(10)	(11)	(12)
A	Carlow	31.8	46.9	21.3	67	252	56	531	40.2	43	169	66	60.3
B	Cavan	40.1	56.0	3.9	99	231	97	56	17.3	26	56	49	73.4
C	Clare	38.8	54.4	6.8	110	285	32	116	24.4	22	67	28	68.3
D	Cork	33.2	50.4	16.4	146	256	137	148	52.6	38	130	66	60.1
E	Donegal	69.8	25.9	4.2	102	248	22	463	18.9	21	80	45	62.4
F	Dublin*	41.2	33.4	25.4	108	268	110	236	94.8	49	185	117	40.8
G	Galway	45.7	50.9	3.4	69	239	44	801	28.1	22	87	40	69.1
H	Kerry	51.4	45.1	3.5	194	283	84	354	26.7	20	76	41	68.2
I	Kildare	34.0	41.5	24.5	52	290	28	184	29.2	40	123	54	53.5
J	Kilkenny	25.0	50.6	24.4	91	283	63	157	31.1	41	82	45	64.8
K	Laoighis	32.7	51.7	15.6	69	269	54	87	26.7	38	121	46	67.2
L	Leitrim	60.2	38.4	1.4	102	231	37	84	13.7	20	70	29	73.4
M	Limerick	33.3	47.5	19.2	181	277	68	36	48.2	32	158	53	55.2
N	Longford	40.4	51.8	7.8	74	290	49	75	21.3	32	111	44	68.6
O	Louth	36.0	48.2	15.8	69	285	55	204	63.0	37	200	78	51.0
P	Mayo	68.0	30.8	1.2	97	289	50	393	18.5	17	84	37	67.4
Q	Meath	32.0	48.8	19.2	55	351	23	252	17.5	49	116	53	62.1
R	Monaghan	31.8	61.9	6.3	85	235	101	39	24.6	32	80	70	69.7
S	Offaly	31.2	55.7	13.1	55	262	50	112	35.6	33	110	55	65.2
T	Roscommon	44.6	51.7	3.7	66	275	24	299	13.2	22	115	28	74.9
U	Sligo	48.9	48.1	3.0	92	266	30	205	29.7	24	102	42	67.0
V	Tipperary	28.3	52.1	19.6	107	312	52	140	36.5	41	127	56	62.8
W	Waterford	34.3	39.1	26.6	122	292	96	199	56.4	41	164	74	54.6
X	Westmeath	28.4	54.4	17.2	43	323	25	188	35.8	37	157	57	56.9
Y	Wexford	27.0	52.1	20.8	64	219	68	288	34.6	34	122	66	56.4
Z	Wicklow	34.7	46.3	19.0	79	212	44	528	49.8	36	102	65	50.4
	Value of contiguity c	0.4193	0.8828	0.6160	0.3415	0.7876	0.6533	0.8686	0.6148	0.5185	0.8141	0.5267	0.6465
	Significance $R = (1 - c)/0.1512$	3.84	0.78	2.54	4.36	1.40	2.29	0.87	2.55	3.18	1.23	3.13	2.35

quolls (i.e., $q = 5$), while no such allowance has been made in the "normal" randomization value of 0.1550 already quoted. This comparison goes far to justify the use of the randomization method with the residuals without making allowance for degrees of freedom.

It will be remembered that the constants in c have been so determined that its mean value is unity. The twenty-five-county values of k_1 and k_2 are, respectively, 4.4 and 21.76.

Cows. Though for the original data $c = 0.3415$, with R having the highly significant value of 4.36, after removal of the quolls the value of c for the residuals is 1.03145, actually greater than unity, though not significantly so, since the randomization standard error of the residuals is 0.1724. The distribution of cows in Ireland at the county level is very largely due to geography alone. See analysis of variance in the Appendix.

Pigs. After removal of the quolls, the value of c is 0.8504, with a standard error of 0.1570. While the difference from unity is not significant, R is less than unity, and this fact, coupled with the fact that the original significance 2.29 was not very emphatic, does not permit us to asseverate with the same confidence as in the case of cows that the distribution is due to location.

Town and village population. The original ratio, as shown in the table, gives a significance of 2.55. This value is appreciably affected by the fact that County Meath, with some of the best land in Ireland, has a very low town and village population. While this is partly due to propinquity to Dublin, it is also influenced by the fact that the large border town of Drogheda is administratively assigned to County Louth, which has, partly in consequence, a very high town population ratio. When the county borders are "redrawn" so that Drogheda is assigned to County Meath, the significance becomes 2.83. When the quoll terms are removed, the value of c is 0.9375, with significance of 0.38, so that the geographical situation goes far toward explaining the distribution of the town and village population of Ireland. Incidentally, the residuals after removal of the linear terms of latitude and longitude give a value of c of 0.8750, with a significance of 0.72.

Private Cars. While the contiguity is highly significant, this is due entirely to motor cars on farms: as series 3 of Table 2 has shown, the larger farms have the property of contiguity in high degree. When attention is confined to nonagricultural motor cars (per 1000 nonagricultural population), the value of c becomes 0.9648, which is not significant. It is curious that, for county units, there is no significant correlation between estimated numbers of nonagricultural superior personnel and nonagricultural motor cars per 1000 population.

Retail Sales are highly correlated at the county level with town and village percentage (series 8), as would be expected: $r = 0.78$. What is very strange is that this correlation does not explain the contiguity of retail sales, for when town and village effect is removed by regression, the residuals have a value of c of 0.5325 (nearly equal to the original value) with a (randomization) significance R of 2.71. It may be observed that the "one-zero" example given in an earlier section of the paper was based on the retail sale distribution by assigning 1 to all counties with sales above the general (simple) average and zero to the remaining counties. It will be seen that this simplification of the pattern has the effect of reducing R from 3.13 to 2.54. On the other hand, if a five-grade classification be used and the numbers 1, 2, 3, 4, 5, assigned to the different grades, the apparent significance is greatly increased; in fact, $R = 4.04$. This is probably due to the exaggeration of the differences between the counties in the arbitrary numerical system used, thus increasing the general variance more than the contiguous variance.

Single Males show a significance R of 2.35. As was well known from the census analysis into town and rural areas, this percentage is highly correlated ($r = -0.80$) with the town and village percentage. Different from retail sales, the contiguity is largely explained by the town and village contiguity. In fact, when the latter is removed, $c = 0.8938$ and $R = 0.69$.

The only data, other than Irish county data, which the author has examined for contiguity are the death rates from tuberculosis (all forms) in the twenty-two Registrars' Districts in County Wexford, in the twenty-one years from

1906 to 1926 inclusive. These data [have] little current interest since the death rates have fallen considerably since the period in question, and conclusions valid then may not hold now. In a paper of many years ago it was shown that in the eight Registrars' Districts with marl subsoil there was a strongly linear relationship between the TB rate and marl area as percentage of total area.

The contiguity was not very significant in the original rates: $c = 0.8314$, $R = 1.09$. Even after allowing for the effects of the marl percentage and the town and village percentage, the contiguity ratio for the residuals was not perceptibly improved, for then $c = 0.8579$, $R = 1.02$. This is another example of the fact that independent variables, even if highly correlated with the dependent variables, do not necessarily "explain" the contiguity of the latter.

APPENDIX

Method of Orthogonalizing Independent Variables in Regression Analysis

The practical convenience of having independent variables orthogonal is obvious. For if the dependent variable is z_t $(t = 1, 2, \cdots, n)$ and the orthogonalized independent variables ξ_{it} $(i = 1, 2, \cdots, q)$, i.e., so that $\Sigma_t \xi_{it} = 0$, $\Sigma_t \xi_{it}^2 = n$, $\Sigma_t \xi_{it} \xi_{it'} = 0$, $t \neq t'$, the regression coefficients are found simply as

$$(1) \qquad b_i = \frac{\Sigma_t \xi_{it} z_t}{\Sigma_t \xi_{it}^2}$$

Furthermore, using orthogonal terms, the total variance of the dependent variable z can readily be analyzed to show the contribution of each term, and its statistical significance assessed from the residual variance.

A method to orthogonalize the original variables x_{it} consists in taking new variables x'_{it} as follows:

$$x'_{1t} = x_{1t}$$
$$x'_{2t} = x_{2t} - a_{21}x'_{2t}$$
$$x'_{3t} = x_{3t} - a_{32}x'_{2t} - a_{31}x'_{1t}$$

The constants a_{ij} are chosen in successive stages, so that $\Sigma_t x'_{1t} x'_{2t} = 0$, $\Sigma_t x'_{2t} x'_{3t} = 0$, etc. This method is very easy to apply in practice— far easier than the latent root method, which will presently be described—but it supplies $q!$ different orthogonal transformations, depending on the order of the variables, facing the computer with the problem of choice. Perhaps the logical order would be according to the correlation between the dependent and the several original independent variables, or the average of these for each independent variable when one is dealing with more than one dependent variable.

While the original independent variables can be transformed into orthogonal variables in an infinity of ways, it has seemed to the writer that the most logical method, and that which in certain cases imparts an objective meaning to the transformed variables, consists in determining the principal components of the original independent variables, having first standardized them, i.e., converting them individually so that each variance is unity. The procedure has the merit that it is symmetrical; it does not imply any particular order in the original variables and gives equal weight to all of them. As is well known, the process consists in finding the values of the coefficients a_i which maximize

$$(3) \qquad 2w = \Sigma_t (\Sigma_i a_i x_{it})^2$$

subject to

$$(4) \qquad \Sigma_i a_i^2 = 1$$

Introducing the Lagrange multiplier $n\lambda$, the equations to determine the a_i are as follows:

$$(5) \qquad \Sigma_j a_j m_{ij} = \lambda a_i, \; i = 1, 2, \cdots, q$$

where $\qquad nm_{ij} = \Sigma_t x_{it} x_{jt}$

The values of λ are found from Eq. 5 as the roots of the determinantal equation

$$(6) \qquad \begin{aligned} |m_{ij} - \lambda \delta_{ij}| = 0, \; & \delta_{ij} = 0 \\ \text{if } i \neq j, \; = 1 & \text{ if } i = j \end{aligned}$$

In the kind of applications contemplated, we shall not have to trouble about Eq. 6 having multiple roots. The orthogonal transformation required is

(7)
$$\xi'_{it} = \Sigma_j a_{ij} x_{jt}$$

where a_{ij} $(j = 1, 2, \cdots, q)$ are the solutions of Eq. 5 in a_i corresponding to the root λ_i of Eq. 6, arranged in descending order of magnitude. The ξ'_{it} are mutually orthogonal. These are then standardized by multiplication by $1/\sqrt{\lambda_i}$ to give the ξ_{it} with $\Sigma_t \xi_{it}^2 = n$ and, of course, $\Sigma_t \xi_{it} = 0$. When $q = 2$ the transformation is

(8)
$$\xi_{it} = \frac{(x_{it} + x_{2t})}{\sqrt{2}}$$

$$\xi_{2t} = \frac{(x_{it} - x_{2t})}{\sqrt{2}}$$

If x_{it} and x_{2t} are both positively or both negatively correlated to the dependent variable z, we can envisage the greater part of the variance being taken up by the ξ_{1t} term in the regression, the ξ_{2t} playing a subsidiary role; and inversely if the correlations of the x_{1t} and x_{2t} with y are of different signs.

This procedure of analyzing the independent variables into dependent components is a purely algebraic (or even arithmetic) one: it has no stochastic implications whatsoever. The stochastic element, in regression theory, enters via the dependent variable. As a more general point, it may be recalled that *any* nonsingular linear transformation results in the remainders for *each* dependent element which are identical with those which would have been obtained from regression on the original independent variables. Furthermore, the regression coefficients are consistent with the transformation in the sense that the two series of coefficients (i.e., on the original and, e.g., the orthogonal

TABLE 3

Latitude-longitude—twenty-five Irish counties. Quadratic orthogonal transforms standardized—the "quolls"

Serial letter	County	Latitude°	Longitude°	ξ_{1t}	ξ_{2t}	ξ_{3t}	ξ_{4t}	ξ_{5t}
A	Carlow	52.70	6.80	−0.575	0.896	−0.131	−0.538	−1.257
B	Cavan	53.97	7.30	−0.624	−0.360	−0.464	0.888	0.799
C	Clare	52.87	8.97	1.083	0.482	0.978	−0.180	0.937
D	Cork	51.97	8.73	2.020	−0.323	−1.810	−0.860	−0.081
E	Donegal	54.90	7.92	−0.408	−3.739	−1.148	0.081	−1.192
G	Galway	53.35	8.75	0.226	0.192	1.308	−0.402	1.059
H	Kerry	52.13	9.58	3.644	0.127	0.066	1.100	−0.348
I	Kildare	53.20	6.78	−0.609	0.946	0.044	0.591	−0.319
J	Kilkenny	52.55	7.22	−0.443	0.612	−0.660	−1.179	−0.544
K	Laoighis	53.00	7.32	−0.616	0.749	−0.269	−0.426	0.523
L	Leitrim	54.12	8.00	−0.646	−1.060	0.107	−0.079	0.744
M	Limerick	52.50	8.75	1.207	0.359	−0.223	−0.534	0.854
N	Longford	53.73	7.71	−0.688	−0.090	−0.027	0.059	1.212
O	Louth	53.93	6.53	−0.159	0.217	−0.391	2.559	−0.373
P	Mayo	53.95	9.33	0.483	−0.922	3.281	−0.466	−1.002
Q	Meath	53.63	6.67	−0.447	0.626	−0.103	1.633	−0.142
R	Monaghan	54.15	6.93	−0.356	−0.558	−0.811	1.869	0.258
S	Offaly	53.20	7.58	−0.609	0.577	−0.146	−0.348	1.097
T	Roscommon	53.73	8.27	−0.466	−0.284	0.677	−0.391	1.134
U	Sligo	54.17	8.67	−0.345	−1.420	1.428	−0.642	−0.104
V	Tipperary	52.62	7.88	−0.068	0.490	−0.682	−1.131	0.714
W	Waterford	52.22	7.58	0.040	0.120	−1.423	−1.819	−0.646
X	Westmeath	53.55	7.47	−0.702	0.289	−0.136	0.170	1.112
Y	Wexford	52.50	6.60	−0.503	0.828	−0.027	−0.789	−2.434
Z	Wicklow	52.93	6.35	−0.439	1.246	0.562	0.834	−1.999
	Sum	—	—	0	0	0	0	0
	Sum Squares	—	—	25	25	25	25	25

transforms) change into one another through the transformation as if the dependent variables were *exact* linear functions of the independent variables.

In order to determine the "quolls" (quadratic orthogonal components of latitude and longitude) for the twenty-five counties of the Irish Republic (i.e., excluding Dublin), the latitude and longitude of the center of each county was assessed by inspection from a large map. It was not considered necessary for the present purpose to have exact ordnance survey readings. For each county, the three products $x_{it}x_{jt}$ $(i,j = 1, 2;$ $t = 1, 2, \cdots, 25)$ were computed; these also were standardized. The latter three series $(x_{3t}, x_{4t}$ and $x_{5t})$ together with the standardized x_{it} and x_{2t} constituted the five independent variables. The latent root Eq. 6 was

$$(8) \quad \begin{vmatrix} 1-\lambda & -0.102478 & 0.415695 \\ & -0.258652 & 0.289645 \\ -0.102478 & 1-\lambda & -0.252129 \\ & 0.365408 & 0.086717 \\ 0.415695 & -0.252129 & 1-\lambda \\ & -0.326526 & 0.049330 \\ -0.258652 & 0.365408 & -0.326526 \\ & 1-\lambda & -0.220296 \\ 0.289645 & 0.086717 & 0.049330 \\ & -0.220296 & 1-\lambda \end{vmatrix} = 0$$

or

$$(9) \quad \lambda^5 - 5\lambda^4 + 9.303706\lambda^3 - 8.113070\lambda^2$$
$$+ 3.335669\lambda - 0.520925 = 0$$

the roots of which are

$$(10) \qquad \lambda_1 = 1.938867$$

$$\lambda_2 = 1.167814$$
$$\lambda_3 = 0.849644$$
$$\lambda_4 = 0.561003$$
$$\lambda_5 = 0.482672$$

It may be useful to place the transformed variables on record for students who may wish to compute regressions and remainders for the series in Table 2 or other Irish county series, of which there are many. It should be pointed out that, while in principle the quolls have the properties $\Sigma\xi_{it}\xi_{jt} = 25\delta_{ij}$ $(\delta_{ii} = 1, \delta_{ij} = 0, i \neq j)$, the actual totals are deemed correct only to the second decimal place.

Regression on the quolls have been computed for two series only for this paper, number milch cows and pigs per 1000 acres of crops and pasture—series 4 and 6 of Table 2. The five-term regression on percentage of population in towns and villages were worked from the original variables. The regressions were as follows:

Milch Cows

$$z_t = 91.60 + 30.705\xi_{1t} - 7.226\xi_{2t}$$
$$- 6.331\xi_{3t} - 6.003\xi_{4t} + 0.346\xi_{5t} + u_t$$

Pigs

$$z_t = 55.56 + 12.740\xi_{1t} + 2.729\xi_{2t}$$
$$-13.644\xi_{3t} - 2.263\xi_{4t} - 2.894\xi_{5i} + u_t$$

The analysis of variance in each case is shown in the following table.

With 1 and 19 degrees of freedom, the 5 per cent and 1 per cent points of the ratio are,

Term	Degrees of freedom	Milch cows		Pigs	
		Sum Squares	Ratio	Sum Squares	Ratio
1	1	23,570	62.79	4,058	7.14
2	1	1,305	3.48	186	0.33
3	1	1,002	2.67	4,654	8.18
4	1	901	2.40	128	0.23
5	1	3	0.01	209	0.37
u—total	19	7,133	—	10,805	—
u—mean	—	375.4	—	568.7	—
z	24	33,914		20,040	

respectively, 4.38 and 8.18, so that only the ξ_1 component in the case of cows and the ξ_1 and ξ_3 components in the case of pigs would be adjudged significant.

In the latitude-longitude case exemplified above, the five components appear to have but little objective significance; the method is merely a computational device. It would probably be otherwise if the original series were economic variables. It is intended, in Ireland, to analyze into orthogonal components an extended series of economic variables avail-able for (a) counties (including contiguous county boroughs) and (b) rural districts (including contiguous urban districts). Less elaborate research shows that there is a large degree of consistency between different economic statistics throughout Irish counties, so that the likelihood is that a few of the latent roots will be so much greater than the rest that the rest can be ignored. These components will then be available as independent variables to workers in many fields, e.g., for market research.

4

A REVIEW ON MEASURES OF CONTIGUITY
FOR TWO AND κ-COLOR MAPS

MICHAEL F. DACEY

Contiguity is evaluated for a study area partitioned into regions. While the particular geographic formulation of counties within a state is used, the general method applies to any set of nonoverlapping regions that exhausts the study area. In preparing a map for contiguity analysis, a property of each county is observed, and this property may be measured on a nominal, ordinal, or interval scale. Though a measure of contiguity for county data having an interval scaling is described briefly, this review stresses a nominal scaling of properties. In a nominal or classificatory scale, numbers or other symbols are used to identify classes of properties. For contiguity analysis of mapped data, it is convenient to associate each class with a separate color. The simplest case is the two-color map—say, black and white—and each county is colored black or white. The more general case concerns the k-color map, and each county is colored one of the k colors. The analysis of two- and k-color maps is described.

Mosaic maps are used to show the distribution of many phenomena. Two types of maps for which a test for areal contiguity seems particularly appropriate are identified.

ANALYSIS OF RESIDUALS

An assumption of correlation analysis is that residuals (the differences between the observed and calculated values) are mutually independent random variables. It is common to test for independence of residuals with respect to magnitude of observed values, temporal sequence, and other serial orderings by means of tests for serial- and autocorrelation. Where the observations have a geographic ordering, such as for county data, the assumptions of correlation analysis evidently require independence in the areal arrangement of residuals; Geary has forcefully stressed the need to satisfy this requirement in regional econometric models.[1] The methods discussed in this report include a test for independence in the areal arrangement of residuals; counties with positive residuals are colored, say, black, and counties with negative residuals are colored white.

"MEDIAN AND RUN" TESTS

A common hypothesis concerns whether observations have a random distribution. Where the observations have a natural serial order, such as on a time axis or in an areal traverse, several median and run tests are available. Analogous situations in map analysis occur on a county base map showing the pattern of some property counties where (1) values greater than the median are colored, say, black, and all other counties are colored white, or (2) counties in which some event occurred early are colored black, say, and all other counties are colored white. The methods discussed in this report include a test for a random areal arrangement in these types of map patterns.

The geographer has many applications for two-color maps, and the methods described in this report are appropriate for testing for presence of contiguity in any two-color map. The results easily generalize to the k-color map. County base maps showing the distribution of k classes of a phenomenon are a common cartographic product, so the methods described in this report have wide application in map analysis.

REGULAR LATTICE

The formal study of contiguity is in terms of a regular lattice of square cells, and each cell is colored. The tests for contiguity are based upon the distribution of adjacent cells of (1) the same color or (2) different colors. The color of a county may be any one of k specified colors. The two-color problem, $k = 2$, is stated in detail, and then results for any k are cited.

The study area is a regular lattice with m rows and n columns of cells. Each of the mn cells corresponds to a county and is colored black, B, or white, W. Cells may be represented by the symbol x_{ij} ($i = 1, 2, \ldots, m$; $j = 1, 2, \ldots, n$), and there is no loss of generality by letting $x_{ij} = 1$ if the ij cell is B, and $x_{ij} = 0$ if the cell is W.

Cells may be considered adjacent (1) if they have an edge in common or (2) if they have an edge or a vertex in common. In an obvious analogy to chess moves, the former is called the "rook's case," because only orthogonal relations are considered, and the latter is called the "queen's case," because diagonal relations are also included. Relations between adjacent cells are called "joins," and in the two-color formulation, a join connects a black and a white cell, two black cells, or two white cells, and these joins are denoted by BW, BB, and WW, respectively. The number of joins of each color combination is given by the following formulae:

(a) number of BW joins in rook's case:

$$Y = \sum_{i=1}^{m} \sum_{j=1}^{n-1} (x_{i,j+1} - x_{ij})^2$$
$$+ \sum_{i=1}^{m-1} \sum_{j=1}^{n} (x_{i+1,j} - x_{ij})^2$$

(b) number of BW joins in queen's case:

$$Y^* = Y + \sum_{i=2}^{m} \sum_{j=1}^{n-1} (x_{i-1,j+1} - x_{ij})^2$$
$$+ \sum_{i=1}^{m-1} \sum_{j=1}^{n-1} (x_{i+1,j+1} - x_{ij})^2$$

(c) number of BB joins in rook's case:

$$Z = \sum_{i=1}^{m} \sum_{j=1}^{n-1} x_{ij} x_{i,j+1} + \sum_{i=1}^{m-1} \sum_{j=1}^{n} x_{ij} x_{i+1,j+1}$$

(d) number of BB joins in queen's case:

$$Z^* = Z + \sum_{i=2}^{m} \sum_{j=1}^{n-1} x_{ij} x_{i-1,j+1} + \sum_{i=1}^{m-1} \sum_{j=1}^{n-1} x_{ij} x_{i+1,j+1}$$

(e) number of WW joins in rook's case:

$$X = 2mn - (m + n) - (Y + Z)$$

(f) number of WW joins in queen's case:

$$X^* = 4mn - 3(m + n) + 2 - (Y^* + Z^*)$$

The usual test for randomness involves evaluation of the standardized deviate:

$$\frac{J - E(J)}{\sigma(J)}$$

where J is the observed number of joins of a particular kind, $E(J)$ is the expected number of joins in a random distribution, and $\sigma(J)$ is the standard deviation. Contiguity, either positive or negative, in the pattern is indicated by a significant departure from the random expectation.

The computation of $E(J)$ and $\sigma(J)$ may be based upon two different assumptions. In free sampling, it is assumed that a cell is B, with probability p $(0 < p < 1)$, and W, with probability q $(q = 1 - p)$. In nonfree sampling, n_1 cells are B, n_2 cells are W, and $n_1 + n_2 = mn$. These cases correspond, respectively, to sampling with replacement and sampling without replacement. Lower-order moments have been obtained by Moran and Krishna Iyer and are listed in Table 1 with no attempt to assign priorities.[2] It is known that all cases listed in Table 1 approach the normal distribution as m and n become larger. In a following paragraph, the adequacy of the limiting form for small samples is evaluated.

Lattices with more than two colors have been studied. Krishna Iyer gives the first and second of all possible joins for the general k-color problem.[3] Freeman gives the first and second moments for the two-color lattice with vacancies, that is, some cells are not colored.[4] Levene reports lower-order moments for triangular joins on the plane two-color lattice.[5] Other plane lattices have been studied. Moran and Blömena gave results for the toroidal lattice.[6] The three-dimensional space lattice studied by Moran, and Krishna Iyer extended the results to higher dimensions.[7] Some results for k-color maps are listed in Table 2.

While not a common procedure, geographic investigations have been based upon a network of regular cells overlaid on a study region. An early example of this approach to map analysis is Matui's study of the distribution of houses and farms in the Tonami Plain, Japan.[8] Though the expressions for regular lattices have some practical geographic applications, the

TABLE 1

Computational forms for expectations and variances of joins on two-color regular and irregular lattices

---

Free sampling

BB joins
μ
$$p^2 A$$
σ^2
$$p^2 A + p^3 D - p^4(A + D)$$

BW joins
μ
$$2pqA$$
σ^2
$$2pqA + pqD - 4p^2 q^2(A + D)$$

(Expressions for WW joins are obtained from BB joins by replacing p with q.)

Nonfree sampling

BB joins
μ
$$n_1^{(2)} A/N^{(2)}$$
σ^2
$$(n_1^{(2)} A/N^{(2)}) + (n_1^{(3)} D/N^{(3)}) + (n_1^{(4)}\{A(A - 1) - D\}/N^{(4)}) - (n_1^{(2)} A/N^{(2)})^2$$

BW joins
μ
$$2n_1 n_2 A/N^{(2)}$$
σ^2
$$(2n_1 n_2 A/N^{(2)}) + (n_1 n_2\{n_1 + n_2 - 2\}D/N^{(3)})$$
$$+ (4n_1^{(2)} n_2^{(2)}\{A(A - 1) - D\}/N^{(4)}) - 4(n_1 n_2 A/N^{(2)})^2$$

(Expressions for WW joins are obtained from BB joins by replacing n_1 with n_2.)

Rook's case	*Queen's case*
$A = 2mn - (m + n)$	$A = 4mn - 3(m + n) + 2$
$D = 4[3mn - 3(m + n) + 2]$	$D = 8[7mn - 9(m + n) + 11]$
$N = mn$	$N = mn$

Counties
$$A = \tfrac{1}{2}\Sigma_k L_k = L$$
$$D = \Sigma_k L_k(L_k - 1) = K$$
$$N = N$$

$x^{(r)} = x(x - 1) \ldots (x - r + 1)$

TABLE 2

Computational forms for expectations and variances of joins
on k-color regular and irregular lattices

Free sampling

DEFINITIONS:

p_1—probability that a county is black A, D—see Table 1
p_2—probability that a county is white
p_α ($\alpha = u, v, w, \ldots$)—probability that a county is color α

BB joins

μ $p_1^2 A$

σ^2 $p_1^2 A + p_1^3 D - p_1^4(A + D)$

BW joins

μ $2p_1 p_2 A$

σ^2 $2p_1 p_2 A + p_1 p_2(p_1 + p_2)D - 4p_1^2 p_2^2(A + D)$

Joins of different colors

μ $2A\Sigma p_u p_v$

σ^2 $(2A + D)\Sigma p_u p_v - (8A + 5D)\Sigma p_u p_v p_w - 4(A + D)[\Sigma p_u^2 p_v^2 - 2\Sigma p_u p_v p_w p_x]$
          (If there are only three colors, $\Sigma p_u p_v p_w p_x = 0$.)

Nonfree sampling

DEFINITIONS:

n_1—number of black counties A, D—see Table 1
n_2—number of white counties
n_α ($\alpha = u, v, w, \ldots$)—number of counties with color
N—total number of counties

BB joins

μ $n_1^{(2)} A/N^{(2)}$

σ^2 $(n_1^{(2)} A/N^{(2)}) + (n_1^{(3)} D/N^{(3)}) + \left(n_1^{(4)} \dfrac{[A^2 - A - D]}{N^{(4)}}\right) - (n_1^{(2)} A/N^{(2)})^2$

BW joins

μ $2n_1 n_2 A/N^{(2)}$

σ^2 $(2n_1 n_2 A/N^{(2)}) + (n_1 n_2[n_1 + n_2 - 2]D/N^{(3)})$
          $+ \left(4n_1^{(2)} n_2^{(2)} \dfrac{[A^2 - A - D]}{N^{(4)}}\right) - (4n_1 n_2 A/N^{(2)})^2$

Joins of different colors

μ $2A\Sigma n_u n_v/N^{(2)}$

σ^2 $\Sigma n_u n_v[\{(2A + D)/N^{(2)}\} - \{4(A^2 - A - D)(N - 1)/N^{(4)}\}]$
          $+ \Sigma n_u n_v n_w[-\{(8A + 5D)/N^{(3)}\} + \{12(A^2 - A - D)/N^{(4)}\} + \{8A^2/N^{(3)}(N - 1)\}]$
          $+ [\Sigma n_u^2 n_v^2 - 2\Sigma n_u n_v n_w n_x][\{4(A + D)/N^{(4)}\} - \{2A^2(2N - 3)/N^{(2)} N^{(4)}\}]$
          (If there are only three colors, $\Sigma n_u n_v n_w n_x = 0$.)

main reason for studying regular lattices is that they provide a basis for extending measures of contiguity to irregular lattices, such as are formed by counties.

IRREGULAR LATTICES

The cells of an irregular lattice are not aligned in neat geometric arrays, and a county base map for, particularly, an eastern state is a pronounced example of an irregular lattice. The basic procedures for irregular and regular lattices do not differ. The application of the procedures is, however, quite different, because computational formulae are easily found to give the number of joins of any kind on a regular lattice, but for an irregular lattice such formulae are not available, and the number of joins is obtained by counting.

The procedure for a system of N counties labeled $1, 2, \ldots, k, \ldots, N$ follows. The number of counties contiguous to the typical county k is L_k. Two counties are called contiguous if (1) they have a common edge (boundary) or (2) they have a common edge or vertex. The definition of contiguity is arbitrary and depends on the nature of the problem at hand. Given the vector $\{L_k\}$, the total number of joins is

$$L = \tfrac{1}{2} \sum_{k=1}^{N} L_k$$

The quantity $1/2$ occurs because each join is counted twice.

The collection of joins is conveniently summarized by a connection matrix. Call this matrix $C = \|c_{kh}\|$ where $c_{kh} = 1$ if k and h are contiguous, and $c_{kh} = 0$ otherwise.

Each county is black, B, or white, W. Let $z_k = 1$ if k is B, and $z_k = 0$ if k is W. The total number of BB joins is

$$Z = \tfrac{1}{2} \sum_{k=1}^{N} \sum_{h=1}^{N} c_{kh} z_k z_h$$

the total number of BW joins is

$$Y = \tfrac{1}{2} \sum_{k=1}^{N} \sum_{h=1}^{N} c_{kh} (z_k + z_h)^2$$

and the total number of WW joins is

$$X = L - (Y + Z)$$

In actual map analysis, it may be quicker to simply count the number of joins of each kind.

The relations in Table 1 provide the basis for obtaining the expected values and variances of joins of each kind. The expected value is given by the product of the total number of joins and the probabilities listed in Table 1. The expectations for an irregular lattice are:

for BB joins

$$\mu(Z) = p^2 L$$

for WW joins

$$\mu(X) = q^2 L$$

for BW joins

$$\mu(Y) = 2pqL$$

The variance is based on the total number of contiguous counties and the total number of counties that have no county in common. For the latter term, define

$$K = \sum_{k=1}^{N} L_k (L_k - 1)$$

From Table 1, the variance for the several kinds of joins is seen to be given by:

for BB joins

$$\sigma^2(Z) = p^2 L + p^3 K - p^4 (L + K)$$

for WW joins

$$\sigma^2(X) = q^2 L + q^3 K - q^4 (L + K)$$

for BW joins

$$\sigma^2(Y) = 2pqL + pqK - 4p^2 q^2 (L + K)$$

For a county system, let X, Y, and Z give the observed number of WW, BW, and BB joins, respectively. The standardized deviates are

$$\frac{X - \mu(X)}{\sigma(X)} \quad \frac{Y - \mu(Y)}{\sigma(Y)} \quad \frac{Z - \mu(Z)}{\sigma(Z)}$$

The test for randomness may be evaluated by treating these quantities as standard normal deviates, provided that the assumption of a normal distribution is appropriate.

Since the distributions of the three types of joins for the rook's and queen's cases tend to the normal form as the numbers of rows and columns become large, it may be anticipated that the distribution of joins on an irregular lattice also tends to the normal form for a large number of counties. In many study areas of geographic interest, the number of counties or other regional divisions is, however, not large. The adequacy of the normality assumption for regions divided into a small or moderate number of counties needs evaluation.

DISCUSSION ON THE APPROACH TO THE NORMAL FORM

Although several writers have shown that the distribution of joins goes to the normal form as the lattice dimensions increase, I can find no statement of the suitability of the approximation for lattices of various dimensions. The limitation is that most studies do not contain explicit statements of the third- and higher-order central moments. Moran identifies the types of joins that contribute to the third and fourth central moments.[9] The third central moment is defined in terms of combinations of counties connected by three joins, and the fourth central moment is defined in terms of combinations of counties connected by four joins. For even a small lattice, the numbers of such combinations are large.

The third moment is considered in some detail, and the kinds of joins contributing to the third central moment are described. The third moment is defined by the following values (using Moran's notation):

n_4—terms corresponding to a single join occurring three times

n_5—terms corresponding to two joins having a single point in common, and such that one of the joins occurs twice

n_6—terms corresponding to three joins occurring in a chain, so that one join has a point in common with each of the other two points, which have no points in common with each other

n_7—terms corresponding to three joins which have only one point in common to all three

n_8—terms corresponding to three joins which join three points and, therefore, one point is common to each pair of joins.

Moran gives formulae for free sampling in the rook's case. The expression for the third central moment of BB joins is

$$\mu_3(Z) = n_4 p^2 (1 - p^2)(1 - 2p^2)$$
$$+ n_5 p^3 (1 - p)(1 - 2p^2)$$
$$+ n_6 p^4 (1 - p)^2$$
$$+ n_7 p^4 (1 - p)(1 - 2p)$$
$$+ n_8 p^3 (1 - p)^2 (1 + 2p)$$

where

$$n_4 = 2mn - m - n$$
$$n_5 = 12mn - 12(m + n) + 8$$
$$n_6 = 18mn - 25(m + n) + 28$$
$$n_7 = 4mn - 6(m + n) + 8$$
$$n_8 = 0$$

From Moran's identification of terms contributing to the third moment, values for free sampling in the queen's case may be obtained. For the corresponding values of n_4 to n_8, I have obtained

$$n_4^* = 4mn - 3(m + n) + 2$$
$$n_5^* = 56mn - 72(m + n) + 88$$
$$n_6^* = 180mn - 323(m + n) + 550$$
$$n_7^* = 24mn - 42(m + n) + 72$$
$$n_8^* = 4mn - 4(m + n) + 4$$

The fourth central moment depends upon fifteen separate terms. Computational formulae are given by Moran for the rook's case, and similar expressions could be worked out for the queen's case, but this is a fairly ambitious project that I have not undertaken.

There are no simple computational formulae for moments on an irregular lattice. While the number of terms of each kind can be obtained by counting, the number of terms can be very large, and for application of the contiguity ratio to real problems, counting is not very practical. As an alternative, I have tried to program the instructions for a computer. In actual counting from a map, each kind of join is easily identified, but it is difficult to enumerate all joins; in contrast, a computer counts joins very rapidly, but is very slow in distinguishing types of joins. Considering these two limitations, it is probably not feasible to compute moments for irregular lattices on any consistent basis.

Some appreciation of the appropriateness of a normality assumption for irregular lattices can be obtained by considering the rook's and queen's cases on a regular lattice. First, the appropriateness of the normal distribution to regular lattices is evaluated, and then these conclusions are applied to irregular lattices.

Moments and moment constants have been computed for BB joins on lattices of several dimensions in arguments of $p = .1(.2).9$. Table 3 gives the measure of skewness ($\beta_1 = \mu_3/\sigma^3$), the coefficient of variation ($c.\,v. = \sigma/\mu_1'$) and, for some lattices, the measure of kurtosis ($B_2 = \mu_4/\sigma^4$) for the rook's and queen's cases for several small lattices.

The following conclusions for joins of the same color are supported by the computed moment constants:

1. the assumption of normality does not lead

to serious error for small lattices if p is large, say, .7 or greater

2. the assumption of normality does not lead to serious error for lattices of moderate size if p is small, say, about .2 or less

3. the rook's case approaches the normal form more rapidly than the queen's case, but the difference between the two cases is significant only for small lattices

4. the coefficient of variation is smaller for the queen's case than the rook's case, a result obtained in more general fashion by Sukhame, but the difference between the two cases is significant only where p is small[10]

5. the difference between square and oblong lattices having equal number of cells is not great.

These conclusions are extended to irregular lattices by establishing a relationship that evidently will generally hold between the central moments for regular and irregular lattices. Each central moment, for any value of p, depends upon the number of combinations of joins of each n_z type. The value of n_z is a function of the number of contiguous cells or counties. For a regular lattice, the mean number of joins in the rook's case is

$$\bar{J} = \frac{4mn - 2(m + n)}{mn} \longrightarrow 4$$

and in the queen's case is

$$\bar{J}^* = \frac{8mn - 6(m + n) + 4}{mn} \longrightarrow 8$$

For most irregular lattices, the mean number of joins lies between 4 and 8, whether contiguity is defined by edges or by vertices. Since the value of a central moment depends upon number of joins, it is highly reasonable to expect that the value of a moment on an irregular lattice lies between values of the rook's and queen's cases on a regular lattice of roughly the same dimensions as the county map. Although this argument is highly tenuous, some conclusions for analysis of irregular lattices may be drawn without undue risk.

The assumption of normality does not lead to serious error if:

1. the study region is not highly elongated and

(a) the number of counties is moderately small and p is large

(b) the number of counties is moderately large and p is not small, or

(c) the number of counties is large

2. The study region is elongated and the number of counties is large.

If the normality assumption is questionable,

TABLE 3

Moment constants for **BB** *joins on two-color lattices of varying dimensions for rook's and queen's cases*

Lattice dimensions	Case	Statistic	p				
			.1	.3	.5	.7	.9
3 × 8	Rook's	β_1	5.96	.98	.26	.02	.17
		c. v.	1.94	.74	.45	.28	.14
3 × 8	Queen's	β_1	6.27	1.07	.28	<.01	.05
		c. v.	1.70	.71	.44	.28	.14
5 × 5	Rook's	β_1	5.73	.96	.08	.02	.16
		β_2	10.67	4.26	3.35	2.84	2.91
		c. v.	1.87	.73	.44	.28	.14
5 × 5	Queen's	β_1	6.07	1.07	.29	.01	.04
		c. v.	1.58	.70	.44	.28	.13
10 × 10	Rook's	β_1	1.38	.24	.06	.01	.04
		β_2	4.91	3.29	3.20	2.97	2.98
		c. v.	.90	.35	.22	.14	.07
10 × 10	Queen's	β_1	1.42	.26	.07	.01	.01
		c. v.	.79	.34	.21	.14	.07

a reasonably accurate estimate of the approach to the normal form may be obtained by computing β_1 and β_2 for the rook's case of a regular lattice having about the same number of cells and the same degree of oblongness (say, measured by m/n) as the county system under study.

These recommendations of course do not insure that errors will not occur in testing the hypothesis of random association. Accurate results may be obtained only by computing the measures of skewness and kurtosis for each irregular lattice. Because of the practical limitations to obtaining these measures, a nonparametric test of contiguity has a practical utility. Another reason for developing a nonparametric test is that, for many study regions, the measures of contiguity will be obtained for both BB and WW joins, and in these cases the assumption of normality is appropriate only where (1) the number of counties is large or (2) there is a moderate number of counties and p and q are approximately of equal value.

A NONPARAMETRIC TEST FOR CONTIGUITY

This test is obtained by an obvious extension of earlier work on black-white lattices. The study region is divided into N counties, and for the free sampling case a county is B or W with probabilities p and q, respectively. The typical county k is contiguous to r_k $(= J_k)$ other counties.

Denote by d_k the number of counties contiguous to county k that are of opposite color, and a definition in symbols is

$$d_k = \tfrac{1}{2} \sum_{h=1}^{N} c_{kh}(z_k - z_h)^2$$

In actual map analysis, d_k is easily obtained by counting. The test for contiguity is based upon a comparison of the observed frequency distribution of d_k, with the theoretical frequency distribution computed for a county system with no areal contiguity.

The theoretical distribution of d is obtained by a simple application of the binomial probability law. If county k is B and the distribution of B and W counties is random, the probability that d contiguous counties are W is

$$b(d; r, p) = \binom{r}{d} p^{r-d} q^d \quad d = 0, 1, \ldots, r$$

Alternatively, if k is W, the probability that d contiguous counties are B is

$$b(d; r, q) = \binom{r}{d} p^d q^{r-d} \quad d = 0, 1, \ldots, r$$

Since k is itself B with probability p and W with probability q, the probability that d contiguous counties are of the opposite color is

$$p(d; r, p) = pb(d; r, p) + qb(d; r, q)$$
$$d = 0, 1, \ldots, r$$

Let $f(r)$ give the number of counties in the study region contiguous to r other counties and select an integer R so that $f(r) = 0$ for all $r > R$. If the B and W labels are randomly assigned, the probability that an arbitrary county is contiguous to d counties of the opposite color evidently is

$$p(d) = \frac{1}{N} \sum_{r=d}^{R} f(r)p(d; r, p) \quad d = 0, 1, \ldots, R$$

The expected number of counties contiguous to d counties of the opposite color is $Np(d)$. Since contiguous counties of opposite colors produce a WB join, $Np(d)$ is also the expected number of counties having d joins of the WB kind. To test for areal contiguity, the observed number of counties having $0, 1, \ldots, R$ of the WB joins is compared with the distribution calculated for a random pattern; the goodness of fit may be evaluated by a nonparametric test, such as chi-square or Kolmogorov-Smirnov.

The computation of the expected frequency distribution is straightforward. If a table of individual terms of the binomial distribution is available, a convenient computational formula is

$$Np(d) = \sum_{r=d}^{R} f(r)[pb(d; r, p) + qb(d; r, q)]$$

where $b(\cdot)$ is a tabulated term. Alternatively, probabilities may be computed directly from

$$Np(d) = \sum_{r=d}^{R} f(r)\binom{r}{d}[p^{r-d+1}q^d + q^d q^{r-d+1}]$$

A short table of $p(d)$ is attached. This table gives probabilities of black-white joins for $r = 1(1)10$ and $p = .01(.01).50$. Because the probabilities are symmetrical about $1/2$, for

$p > .5$ the probabilities tabulated for $(1 - p)$ may be used.

Using this binomial model, the expected number of joins of each kind is given by

$$\mu(Y) = \frac{N}{2} \sum_{d=0}^{R} d\, p(d)$$

$$\mu(Z) = \left[\frac{p^2}{(q^2 + p^2)} \right] [L - \mu(Y)]$$

$$\mu(X) = \left[\frac{q^2}{(q^2 + p^2)} \right] [L - \mu(\chi)]$$

These values are identical to those given on page 482.

A similar set of equations may be derived for the nonfree sampling case with n_1 black counties and n_2 white counties, with $n_1 + n_2 = N$. Assuming no areal contiguity, the expected number of counties contiguous to d counties of the opposite color is

$$Np'(d) = \frac{\sum_{r=d}^{R} f(r) \binom{r}{d} [n_1^{(r-d)} n_2^{(d)} + n_1^{(d)} n_2^{(r-d)}]}{(N - 1)^{(r)}}$$

$$d = 0, 1, \ldots, R$$

where $m^{(x)} = m(m - 1) \ldots (m - x + 1)$.

APPLICATION OF THE TESTS FOR AREAL CONTIGUITY

The measures of contiguity described in this report may be used to test the hypothesis of randomness for any county data that have a meaningful binary coding. Two kinds of applications are illustrated. The first example is a test for randomness in the pattern of residuals resulting from a multiple regression analysis. The second example provided the motivation for this report and is an analysis of the county distribution of larger towns and cities in Iowa.

PATTERN OF RESIDUALS

An assumption of product moment correlation analysis is that the residuals from regression are independent. There are well-known methods for testing for serial correlation in residuals, but these methods are applied only to data having a serial order such as smallest to largest value or, in time-series data, earliest to latest observation. For correlation analysis of spatial data, the residuals are also assumed independent, and this evidently means that the spatial arrangement of residuals is random. This assumption may be tested by the contiguity measures for two-color maps.

The residual for county k is the quantity

$$\epsilon_k = (\text{observed value}) - (\text{calculated value})$$

where the latter value is obtained by a regression on the set of observed county values. A two-color map is obtained from the residuals by making a county B if the residual is nonnegative and W otherwise. If the residuals are random, each county has an equal probability of being B or W. So for the contiguity measures, $p = q = 1/2$ for any map whatsoever of residuals. For $p = q$, the distribution of joins may be assumed to follow the normal law. Accordingly, a test for randomness may use the standardized normal deviates

$$\frac{X - u(X)}{\sigma(X)} \quad \frac{Y - u(Y)}{\sigma(Y)} \quad \frac{Z - u(Z)}{\sigma(Z)}$$

The residuals may be taken as independent at the .05 significance if all three quantities are less than ± 2 and at the .01 level if all three quantities are less than ± 3.

Maps of residuals from a multiple regression of properties describing a transportation system in Ghana are given by Taaffe, et al.[11] On the two maps, regional divisions of Ghana are coded by map symbols indicating magnitude and size of each error term. To test for independence in these residuals, regions having positive residuals are coded B, and all other regions are coded W. The number of joins on each kind may be counted from the map. The numbers are

$$X = 22 \qquad Y = 45 \qquad Z = 26$$

and the total number of joins is $L = 93$. Also $K = \sum L_k (L_k - 1) = 774$. The normal deviates are

for BW joins $\quad \dfrac{45 - 46.5}{4.85} = -.31$

for BB joins $\quad \dfrac{26 - 23.25}{8.12} = .34$

for WW joins $\quad \dfrac{22 - 23.25}{8.12} = -.15$

The differences from random are not significant, so there is no evidence of areal contiguity in the pattern of county residuals. It is accordingly inferred that the residuals are areally independent. This conclusion, of course, does not mean that the assumption of independence in residuals is satisfied, because serial correlation of some other kind may be present.

Alternatively, the hypothesis of areal independence may be tested by comparing the observed and calculated frequency distributions of contiguous counties with the opposite color. For the Ghana residuals

d	0	1	2	3	4	5	6
Observed	1	11	12	12	1	3	0
Calculated	3	9	12	9	5	2	1

Combining the two right-hand cells for chi-square test, the calculated values is $X^2 = 2.98$, with 5 degrees of freedom. There is no evidence of significant departure from randomness.

PATTERN OF OBJECTS

Another use for measures of contiguity is to test for independence in the distribution of objects among counties. The pattern to be studied is formed by the 1950 arrangement of the ninety-three urban places in the ninety-nine Iowa counties. In another study, I showed that the distribution was more regular than random and that the probability a county contains x places may be represented to a high approximation by the density function

$$f(x; \lambda, \gamma) = \left[\frac{(1 - \lambda)\gamma^x e^{-\gamma}}{x!}\right] + \left[\frac{\lambda x \gamma^{x-1} e^{-\gamma}}{x!}\right]$$
$$x = 0, 1, \ldots$$

where $0 < \lambda < 1$ and $\lambda + \gamma =$ (number of places/number of counties).[12] In that report, the frequency distribution of places among counties was studied without regard to the arrangement of counties. The contiguity measures allow a more complete study of pattern.

The density function $f(x; \lambda, \gamma)$ has parameters λ and γ, and estimated values may be obtained by the method of moments. These estimated parameters are used in turn to estimate p and q for the contiguity measures.

For the Iowa data, the frequency distribution of places among counties is: 0–21, 1–64, 2–13, 4 or more —0. A place located in two or more counties was assigned to the county with the largest population. Two binary codings of this pattern are examined.

One two-color map is constructed by labeling a county B if it contains at least one place, and W otherwise. The probability p that a county is B is obtained from $f(x; \lambda, \gamma)$, and the estimated p is

$$p = 1 - f(0; \lambda, \gamma)$$

The estimated values of λ and γ were obtained by the method of moments, and numerical values for this pattern of urban places are

$$\gamma = .201 \qquad p = .79$$
$$\lambda = .728 \qquad q = .21$$

The presence of areal contiguity is evaluated by the nonparametric test.

The number of counties contiguous to d counties of the opposite color was obtained by counting the number of BW joins for each county. The frequency distribution $f(r)$ was obtained from the Iowa county structure. The observed and calculated frequencies are

d	0	1	2	3	4	5	6
Observed	26	38	14	8	11	2	0
Calculated	28	32	18	10	6	4	1

For a chi-square test of goodness of fit, the right-hand cells were combined. The calculated $x^2 = 7.92$, and for four degrees of freedom, the tabulated probability lies between .1 and .05.

The other two-color map is constructed by labeling a county B if it contains at least two places, and W otherwise. The probability p is obtained from $f(x; \lambda, \gamma)$

$$p = 1 - [f(0; \lambda, \gamma) + f(1; \lambda, \gamma)]$$

For the Iowa map, $p = .14$. The observed and calculated frequency distributions for joins of opposite colors are

d	0	1	2	3	4	5	6
Observed	51	22	9	9	4	4	0
Calculated	44	31	11	5	4	3	1

The two right-hand cells are combined for a chi-square test of goodness of fit. The calculated

$x^2 = 7.29$, and for four degrees of freedom, the tabulated probability lies between .2 and .1.

These two tests of areal contiguity do not strongly support the hypothesis of independence. There is evidence that nonrandom factors affect the county arrangement of places.

CONTIGUITY MEASURE FOR COUNTIES WITH INTERVAL VALUES

This report has concentrated on contiguity measures for areally distributed data having a nominal scaling. Contiguity measures for areally distributed data having an interval scaling are available, but these measures are not stressed because of bias in estimating the presence of contiguity. First, the corresponding measures for interval data are identified. Second, the inherent weaknesses of these measures are discussed.

A map divided into M counties is used. The typical county i has the value x_i, and to derive variance it is convenient to assume that the variable x is normally distributed with mean 0 and unit variance.

The number of counties contiguous to county i is J_i. Let $\|C_{ij}\|$ be the connection matrix and $c_{ij} = 1$ if i and j are contiguous, and $c_{ij} = 0$ otherwise. Also, as defined in Table 1

$$A = \tfrac{1}{2} \sum_{i=1}^{M} J_i \quad \text{and} \quad D = \sum_{i=1}^{M} J_i(J_i - 1)$$

Define

$$r = \frac{M}{A} \left[\frac{\sum_{i=1}^{M} \sum_{j=i+1}^{M} c_{ij} x_i x_j}{\sum_{i=1}^{M} x_i^2} \right] = \frac{M}{A} R$$

In large samples, r is an approximate estimate of the correlation coefficient between contiguous counties. To test for randomness, it is sufficient, however, to test only the quantity R.

The mean and variance of R have been obtained by Moran for the rook's case on a regular lattice, under the assumption that the variate X has the normal distribution.[13] Using relations already established, his results are readily generalized to irregular lattices.

The expectation of R for a county map is

$$E(R) = -\frac{A}{M(M-1)}$$

The expected value of R^2 for the county map is

$$E(R^2) = \frac{[A(1 + 2\rho^2)\sigma^4 + D(\rho + 2\rho^2)\sigma^4 + (A^2 - A + D)(3\rho^2\sigma^4)]}{(M+1)(M-1)}$$

where

$$\rho = \frac{1}{(M-1)}$$

and

$$\sigma^2 = \frac{(M-1)}{M}$$

The variance of R is

$$V(R) = E(R^2) - E^2(R)$$

To test for randomness in a county map, the quantity

$$\frac{R - E(R)}{V^{1/2}(R)}$$

is treated as a standard normal variate with unit variance. The distribution of R evidently tends to the normal form as M increases.

For many types of map analysis, the quantity R provides an acceptable test for randomness in the arrangement of county data. Results, however, must be interpreted carefully. If R is an unbiased measure of randomness, R will vary in a systematic fashion with changes in the underlying county structure. To illustrate, consider a county map P_o, with an assigned set of values $\{X_o\}$ and an index value R_o. Without changing the connection matrix $|C_{ij}|$ or the set $\{X_o\}$, a topological transformation on P_o may produce a new county map P_1 with $R_1 = R_o$, but for which we are willing to accept that the degree of randomness is unchanged. For example, the map P_1 may be constructed from P_o by the rule that county boundaries are shortened if they have values of the opposite sign, and are increased in length if the counties have values of the same sign. Alternatively, the area of counties may be changed, so that in one portion of the map the area of counties with positive values is greatly increased and the area of counties with negative values is greatly decreased, while for the rest of the map the area of counties with negative values is greatly increased and the area of counties with positive values is decreased. In situations of these types, an acceptable measure of correlation has different values. Because the quantity R is invariant over such topological transformations, r is not an acceptable measure of correlation. The difficulties in estimating correlation in areal data are well known; although in a different context, the results of Robinson and Thomas and Anderson illustrate the types of problems that arise.[14]

It is possible to write down at least some properties required in an acceptable correlation coefficient. Let a_i denote the area of the ith county and let b_{ij} denote the length of the boundary between counties i and j. A correlation coefficient in which area of county and length of common boundary are used to weigh contributions to the correlation coefficient is defined by

$$r^* = \frac{M}{A}\left[\frac{\frac{1}{2}\sum_{i=1}^{M}\sum_{j=1}^{M}c_{ij}\alpha_i\beta_{i(j)}x_ix_j}{\sum_{i=1}^{M}\alpha_ix_i^2}\right] = \frac{M}{A}R^*$$

where

$$c_{ii} = 0$$

$$\alpha_i = \frac{a_i}{\sum_{i=1}^{M}a_i}$$

$$\beta_{i(j)} = \frac{b_{ij}}{\sum_{j=1}^{M}b_{ij}}$$

The derivation of the distribution of r^* and R^* is not easy for any possible assumptions about the distributions of a and b. A rather inhibiting feature is that reasonable assumptions about the distributions of either a or b are not known.

FOOTNOTES

[1] R. C. Geary, "The Contiguity Ratio and Statistical Mapping," pp. 461–478; and Geary, "Some Remarks About Relations Between Stochastic Variables: A Discussion Document," *Revue de l'Institut International de Statistique*, **31** (1963), 163–181.

[2] P. A. Moran, "Random Associations on a Lattice," *Nature*, **158** (1946), 521; and Moran, "Random Associations on a Lattice," *Proceedings of the Cambridge Philosophical Society*, **43** (1947), 321–328; P. V. A. Krishna Iyer, "Random Association of Points on a Lattice," *Nature*, **160** (1947), 714; Krishna Iyer, "Random Association of Points on a Lattice," *Nature*, **162** (1948), 333; Krishna Iyer, "The First and Second Moments of Some Probability Distributions Arising from Points on a Lattice and Their Applications," *Biometrika*, **36** (1949), 135–141; Krishna Iyer, "Random Association of Points on a Lattice," *Journal of the Indian Society of Agricultural Statistics*, **2** (1949), 141–160.

[3] P. V. A. Krishna Iyer, "The Theory of Probability Distributions of Points on a Lattice," *Annals of Mathematical Statistics*, **21** (1950), 198–217.

[4] G. H. Freeman, "Spread of Diseases in a Rectangular Plantation with Vacancies," *Biometrika*, **40** (1953), 287–296.

[5] H. Levene, "A Test of Randomness in Two Dimensions," *Bulletin of the American Mathematical Society*, **52** (1946), 621.

[6] Moran, "Random Associations," *op. cit.* (1947); A. R. Blömena, "Random Association of Points on a Graph," *Statistic Neerlandica*, **14** (1960), 267–274.

Blömena, "On Probability Distribution Arising from Points on a Graph," *International Journal of Abstracts*, **1** (1964), 540.

[7] Moran, "Random Associations," *op. cit.* (1947); Krishna Iyer, "The First and Second Moments," *op. cit.*

[8] I. Matui, "Statistical Study of the Distributions of Scattered Villages in Two Regions of the Tonami Plain, Toyama Prefecture," pp. 149–158.

[9] P. A. Moran, "The Interpretation of Statistical Maps," *Journal of the Royal Statistical Society*, Series B, **10** (1948), 243–251.

[10] B. V. Sukhame, "Random Association of Points on a Lattice," *Journal of the Indian Society of Agricultural Statistics*, **2** (1949), 60–85.

[11] E. J. Taaffe, R. L. Morrill, and P. R. Gould, "Transport Expansion in Underdeveloped Countries: A Comparative Analysis," *Geographical Review*, **53** (1963), 503–529 (Fig. 9).

[12] M. F. Dacey, "Modified Poisson Probability Law for Point Pattern More Regular than Random," pp. 172–179.

[13] P. A. Moran, "Notes on Continuous Stochastic Phenomena," *Biometrika*, **37** (1950), 17–23.

[14] A. H. Robinson, "The Necessity of Weighting Values in Correlation Analysis of Areal Data," *Annals of the Association of American Geographers*, **46** (1956), 223–236; E. N. Thomas and D. L. Anderson, "Additional Comments on Weighting Values in Correlation Analysis of Areal Data," pp. 431–446.

TABLE 4

TABLE 4

Probabilities of black-white joins $r = 1(1)10$, $x = 0(1)r$, $p = .01(.01).1$

	x	.01	.02	.03	.04	.05	.06	.07	.08	.09	.10	x
r = 1	0	98020	96080	94180	92320	90500	88720	86980	85280	83620	82000	0
	1	01980	03920	05820	07680	09500	11280	13020	14720	16380	18000	1
r = 2	0	97030	94120	91270	88480	85750	83080	80470	77920	75430	73000	0
	1	01980	03920	05820	07680	09500	11280	13020	14720	16380	18000	1
	2	00990	01960	02910	03840	04750	05640	06510	07360	08190	09000	2
r = 3	0	96060	92237	88529	84935	81451	78076	74808	71643	68582	65620	0
	1	02911	05650	08222	10635	12896	15011	16987	18830	20545	22140	1
	2	00059	00230	00508	00885	01354	01909	02543	03250	04025	04860	2
	3	00970	01883	02741	03545	04299	05004	05662	06277	06848	07380	3
r = 4	0	95099	90392	85873	81537	77378	73390	69569	65908	62404	59050	0
	1	03842	07379	10624	13590	16293	18743	20954	22940	24711	26280	1
	2	00059	00230	00508	00885	01354	01909	02543	03250	04024	04860	2
	3	00039	00154	00339	00590	00902	01272	01695	02167	02683	03240	3
	4	00961	01845	02656	03398	04073	04686	05239	05735	06178	06570	4
r = 5	0	94148	88584	83297	78276	73509	68987	64699	60635	56787	53144	0
	1	04755	09039	12881	16308	19345	22018	24350	26365	28084	29529	1
	2	00096	00369	00798	01361	02042	02822	03686	04620	05609	06642	2
	3	00002	00015	00049	00113	00214	00359	00552	00797	01099	01458	3
	4	00048	00185	00399	00681	01021	01411	01843	02310	02804	03321	4
	5	00951	01808	02576	03261	03869	04403	04870	05273	05617	05906	5
r = 6	0	93206	86813	80798	75145	69834	64848	60170	55785	51676	47830	0
	1	05649	10630	14994	18786	22053	24835	27174	29105	30665	31887	1
	2	00143	00542	01159	01957	02902	03964	05115	06331	07589	08870	2
	3	00002	00015	00049	00113	00214	00359	00552	00797	01099	01458	3
	4	00001	00011	00037	00085	00161	00269	00414	00598	00824	01093	4
	5	00057	00217	00464	00783	01161	01586	02046	02533	03036	03548	5
	6	00942	01772	02499	03131	03675	04139	04529	04851	05111	05314	6
r = 7	0	92275	85077	78374	72139	66342	60957	55958	51322	47025	43047	0
	1	06524	12154	16968	21040	24442	27236	29483	31239	32556	33481	1
	2	00198	00744	01574	02630	03859	05216	06658	08150	09660	11162	2
	3	00003	00025	00081	00183	00339	00557	00840	01190	01608	02092	3
	4	00000	00001	00005	00015	00036	00071	00126	00205	00315	00459	4
	5	00002	00015	00049	00110	00204	00334	00504	00714	00965	01255	5
	6	00066	00248	00525	00877	01286	01738	02219	02717	03220	03721	6
	7	00932	01736	02424	03006	03492	03891	04212	04463	04651	04783	7
r = 8	0	91352	83375	76023	69253	63025	57299	52041	47216	42793	38742	0
	1	07382	13612	18810	23085	26537	29259	31336	32846	33858	34438	1
	2	00261	00972	02036	03366	04888	06537	08255	09997	11720	13393	2
	3	00005	00040	00126	00281	00515	00835	01243	01740	02321	02980	3
	4	00000	00001	00005	00015	00036	00071	00126	00205	00315	00459	4
	5	00000	00001	00004	00012	00028	00057	00101	00164	00252	00367	5
	6	00003	00020	00063	00140	00257	00417	00622	00870	01160	01490	6
	7	00074	00278	00582	00962	01397	01868	02359	02856	03349	03826	7
	8	00923	01701	02351	02886	03317	03657	03917	04106	04232	04305	8
r = 9	0	90438	81707	73742	66484	59874	53862	48398	43439	38942	34868	0
	1	08222	15008	20526	24931	28361	30942	32786	33996	34662	34868	1
	2	00332	01225	02539	04155	05971	07900	09871	11825	13713	15497	2
	3	00008	00058	00183	00404	00733	01177	01734	02399	03165	04018	3
	4	00000	00002	00009	00025	00058	00113	00197	00315	00474	00678	4
	5	00000	00000	00000	00002	00006	00014	00029	00055	00093	00149	5
	6	00000	00001	00006	00017	00039	00075	00131	00210	00316	00452	6
	7	00003	00025	00079	00173	00314	00504	00743	01028	01356	01722	7
	8	00083	00306	00635	01039	01493	01975	02468	02956	03428	03874	8
	9	00914	01668	02281	02770	03151	03438	03643	03777	03851	03874	9
r = 10	0	89534	80073	71530	63824	56880	50630	45010	39964	35437	31381	0
	1	09044	16341	22123	26593	29937	32317	33879	34751	35047	34868	1
	2	00411	01501	03079	04986	07090	09283	11475	13598	15598	17434	2
	3	00011	00082	00254	00554	00995	01580	02303	03153	04114	05166	3
	4	00000	00003	00014	00041	00092	00176	00304	00480	00713	01006	4
	5	00000	00000	00001	00002	00006	00014	00029	00054	00093	00149	5
	6	00000	00000	00000	00002	00005	00012	00025	00045	00077	00124	6
	7	00000	00002	00008	00023	00052	00101	00173	00275	00407	00574	7
	8	00004	00031	00095	00208	00373	00592	00864	01183	01543	01937	8
	9	00091	00333	00684	01108	01576	02063	02550	03022	03466	03874	9
	10	00905	01634	02212	02659	02994	03232	03388	03475	03505	03487	10

Table 4 (CONT.)

Probabilities of black-white joins $r = 1(1)10$, $x = 0(1)r$, $p = .11(.01).2$

	x	.11	.12	.13	.14	.15	.16	.17	.18	.19	.20	x
r = 1	0	80420	78880	77380	75920	74500	73120	71780	70480	69220	68000	0
	1	19580	21120	22620	24080	25500	26880	28220	29520	30780	32000	1
r = 2	0	70630	68320	66070	63880	61750	59680	57670	55720	53830	52000	0
	1	19580	21120	22620	24080	25500	26880	28220	29520	30780	32000	1
	2	09790	10560	11310	12040	12750	13440	14110	14760	15390	16000	2
r = 3	0	62757	59990	57318	54739	52251	49853	47542	45317	43177	41120	0
	1	23619	24989	26255	27422	28496	29482	30385	31208	31959	32640	1
	2	05751	06691	07675	08698	09754	10838	11945	13072	14211	15360	2
	3	07873	08330	08752	09141	09499	09827	10128	10403	10653	10880	3
r = 4	0	55842	52776	49846	47048	44378	41832	39405	37093	34893	32800	0
	1	27659	28858	29890	30765	31493	32084	32549	32897	33138	33280	1
	2	05750	06691	07675	08698	09754	10838	11945	13072	14211	15360	2
	3	03834	04460	05117	05798	06502	07225	07964	08714	09474	10240	3
	4	06915	07215	07472	07691	07873	08021	08137	08224	08284	08320	4
r = 5	0	49698	46441	43363	40457	37716	35132	32696	30404	28248	26221	0
	1	30719	31675	32414	32953	33310	33501	33541	33444	33225	32896	1
	2	07708	08796	09898	11005	12111	13208	14291	15355	16395	17408	2
	3	01877	02355	02893	03491	04145	04855	05618	06431	07290	08192	3
	4	03854	04398	04949	05503	06056	06604	07146	07677	08197	08704	4
	5	06144	06335	06483	06591	06662	06700	06708	06689	06645	06579	5
r = 6	0	44231	40868	37725	34793	32058	29509	27137	24929	22878	20973	0
	1	32802	33439	33825	33987	33949	33733	33360	32850	32220	31488	1
	2	10154	11428	12677	13890	15058	16170	17222	18209	19124	19968	2
	3	01877	02355	02894	03491	04145	04856	05618	06431	07290	08192	3
	4	01407	01766	02170	02618	03109	03642	04214	04823	05468	06144	4
	5	04062	04571	05071	05556	06023	06468	06889	07283	07650	07987	5
	6	05467	05573	05638	05665	05658	05622	05560	05475	05370	05248	6
r = 7	0	39366	35964	32821	29922	27249	24787	22523	20441	18530	16778	0
	1	34058	34329	34331	34097	33661	33052	32294	31414	30431	29367	1
	2	12631	14048	15397	16664	17838	18911	19877	20733	21476	22106	2
	3	02641	03251	03918	04638	05404	06213	07058	07932	08831	09748	3
	4	00643	00870	01146	01471	01850	02284	02775	03322	03927	04588	4
	5	01585	01951	02351	02783	03243	03728	04234	04759	05299	05849	5
	6	04210	04683	05132	05554	05946	06303	06626	06911	07159	07369	6
	7	04866	04904	04904	04871	04809	04722	04613	04488	04347	04195	7
r = 8	0	35036	31648	28554	25733	23162	20822	18694	16762	15010	13422	0
	1	34642	34525	34134	33512	32699	31728	30632	29436	28167	26845	1
	2	14986	16479	17853	19096	20200	21157	21966	22627	23140	23511	2
	3	03711	04505	05353	06244	07167	08114	09072	10034	10988	11928	3
	4	00643	00870	01146	01471	01850	02284	02775	03322	03927	04587	4
	5	00514	00696	00916	01177	01480	01827	02220	02658	03141	03670	5
	6	01856	02253	02676	03122	03584	04057	04536	05017	05494	05964	6
	7	04282	04708	05101	05456	05771	06045	06276	06465	06612	06717	7
	8	04330	04316	04267	04189	04087	03966	03829	03679	03521	03356	8
r = 9	0	31182	27850	24842	22130	19688	17490	15516	13745	12158	10738	0
	1	34685	34180	33409	32423	31268	29983	28602	27155	25666	24160	1
	2	17148	18643	19969	21113	22072	22845	23435	23846	24086	24165	2
	3	04946	05934	06966	08025	09097	10167	11218	12240	13220	14148	3
	4	00931	01236	01595	02010	02481	03006	03585	04215	04893	05615	4
	5	00226	00331	00466	00638	00849	01105	01409	01765	02176	02642	5
	6	00621	00824	01064	01340	01654	02004	02390	02810	03262	03743	6
	7	02120	02543	02985	03440	03899	04357	04808	05246	05666	06064	7
	8	04287	04661	04992	05278	05518	05711	05859	05961	06021	06041	8
	9	03854	03798	03712	03603	03474	03332	03178	03017	02852	02684	9
r = 10	0	27752	24508	21613	19032	16734	14692	12878	11271	09848	08590	0
	1	34300	33420	32295	30982	29531	27984	26377	24741	23099	21475	1
	2	19077	20508	21716	22696	23451	23987	24312	24439	24384	24161	2
	3	06288	07458	08654	09854	11038	12187	13284	14313	15263	16122	3
	4	01363	01784	02270	02819	03427	04089	04800	05554	06341	07157	4
	5	00226	00331	00466	00638	00849	01105	01409	01765	02176	02642	5
	6	00189	00276	00389	00531	00708	00921	01175	01471	01813	02202	6
	7	00778	01019	01297	01611	01958	02337	02743	03174	03624	04089	7
	8	02358	02797	03245	03695	04139	04570	04981	05367	05723	06046	8
	9	04239	04557	04826	05044	05212	05330	05403	05431	05419	05369	9
	10	03430	03342	03229	03098	02953	02798	02638	02474	02310	02147	10

TABLE 4 (CONT.)

Probabilities of black-white joins r = 1(1)10, x = 0(1)r, p = .21(.01).3

	x	.21	.22	.23	.24	.25	.26	.27	.28	.29	.30	x
r = 1	0	66820	65680	64580	63520	62500	61520	60580	59680	58820	58000	0
	1	33180	34320	35420	36480	37500	38480	39420	40320	41180	42000	1
r = 2	0	50230	48520	46870	45280	43750	42280	40870	39520	38230	37000	0
	1	33180	34320	35420	36480	37500	38480	39420	40320	41180	42000	1
	2	16590	17160	17710	18240	18750	19240	19710	20160	20590	21000	2
r = 3	0	39145	37249	35433	33694	32031	30444	28930	27488	26119	24820	0
	1	33256	33812	34311	34758	35156	35509	35821	36094	36333	36540	1
	2	16514	17668	18819	19962	21094	22211	23309	24386	25437	26460	2
	3	11085	11271	11437	11586	11719	11836	11940	12032	12111	12180	3
r = 4	0	30811	28923	27132	25435	23828	22309	20874	19521	18247	17050	0
	1	33333	33304	33203	33036	32813	32538	32222	31869	31486	31080	1
	2	16514	17668	18818	19962	21094	22211	23309	24386	25437	26460	2
	3	11009	11779	12546	13308	14062	14807	15539	16257	16958	17640	3
	4	08333	08326	08301	08259	08203	08056	07967	07872	07770		4
r = 5	0	24317	22531	20857	19289	17822	16452	15172	13980	12869	11838	0
	1	32470	31960	31376	30729	30029	29287	28510	27708	26890	26061	1
	2	18391	19341	20255	21133	21973	22773	23535	24255	24937	25578	2
	3	09132	10106	11109	12137	13184	14244	15314	16387	17458	18522	3
	4	09196	09670	10128	10566	10986	11387	11767	12128	12468	12789	4
	5	06494	06392	06275	06146	06006	05857	05702	05542	05378	05212	5
r = 6	0	19206	17568	16052	14650	13354	12159	11058	10044	09112	08257	0
	1	30670	29779	28831	27836	26807	25754	24686	23613	22543	21483	1
	2	20737	21431	22051	22597	23071	23477	23816	24093	24311	24476	2
	3	09132	10106	11109	12137	13184	14244	15314	16387	17458	18522	3
	4	06849	07580	08332	09102	09888	10683	11486	12290	13094	13892	4
	5	08295	08573	08820	09039	09228	09391	09526	09637	09725	09790	5
	6	05111	04963	04805	04639	04468	04292	04114	03936	03757	03580	6
r = 7	0	15171	13702	12358	11132	10013	08994	08068	07226	06462	05771	0
	1	28240	27065	25857	24628	23391	22157	20933	19728	18549	17401	1
	2	22625	23034	23338	23541	23648	23666	23601	23461	23254	22986	2
	3	10679	11616	12555	13491	14419	15336	16235	17115	17971	18800	3
	4	05302	06070	06886	07748	08652	09592	10565	11563	12581	13614	4
	5	06407	06969	07533	08095	08652	09201	09741	10269	10782	11280	5
	6	07542	07678	07779	07847	07883	07889	07867	07820	07751	07662	6
	7	04034	03866	03694	03518	03342	03165	02990	02818	02650	02486	7
r = 8	0	11985	10687	09515	08459	07509	06655	05888	05201	04586	04037	0
	1	25490	24117	22742	21377	20031	18715	17436	16199	15010	13872	1
	2	23745	23847	23828	23694	23456	23123	22706	22215	21661	21053	2
	3	12844	13730	14579	15388	16150	16863	17525	18133	18688	19189	3
	4	05302	06070	06886	07748	08652	09592	10564	11563	12581	13614	4
	5	04242	04856	05509	06198	06921	07674	08452	09250	10065	10891	5
	6	06422	06865	07290	07694	08075	08432	08762	09067	09344	09595	6
	7	06784	06813	06808	06770	06702	06607	06487	06347	06189	06015	7
	8	03186	03015	02843	02672	02504	02339	02180	02025	01876	01734	8
r = 9	0	09468	08336	07327	06429	05632	04924	04298	03744	03256	02825	0
	1	22652	21161	19698	18273	16897	15574	14311	13110	11976	10908	1
	2	24094	23885	23550	23103	22556	21924	21219	20454	19642	18794	2
	3	15014	15811	16533	17175	17736	18213	18607	18919	19152	19308	3
	4	06378	07176	08005	08859	09733	10622	11520	12421	13320	14213	4
	5	03167	03750	04390	05088	05840	06644	07496	08392	09326	10292	5
	6	04252	04783	05336	05906	06489	07081	07680	08281	08880	09475	6
	7	06434	06776	07085	07361	07601	07806	07974	08108	08208	08275	7
	8	06024	05971	05887	05776	05639	05481	05305	05114	04910	04698	8
	9	02517	02351	02189	02030	01877	01731	01590	01457	01330	01212	9
r = 10	0	07480	06502	05641	04886	04224	03644	03137	02696	02311	01977	0
	1	19884	18339	16852	15430	14079	12803	11605	10485	09443	08478	1
	2	23787	23279	22656	21933	21127	20255	19331	18370	17384	16387	2
	3	16882	17538	18085	18522	18848	19067	19180	19194	19114	18948	3
	4	07990	08835	09682	10525	11355	12167	12953	13709	14430	15111	4
	5	03167	03749	04390	05088	05840	06644	07496	08392	09326	10292	5
	6	02639	03125	03659	04240	04867	05537	06247	06993	07771	08577	6
	7	04566	05049	05533	06014	06489	06952	07402	07833	08246	08635	7
	8	06331	06577	06782	06945	07068	07150	07193	07198	07168	07106	8
	9	05286	05173	05035	04874	04695	04501	04296	04082	03863	03641	9
	10	01988	01834	01685	01543	01408	01280	01160	01048	00944	00848	10

TABLE **4** (CONT.)

Probabilities of black-white joins $r = 1(1)10$, $x = 0(1)r$, $p = .31(.01).4$

	x	.31	.32	.33	.34	.35	.36	.37	.38	.39	.40	x
r = 1	0	57220	56480	55780	55120	54500	53920	53380	52880	52420	52000	0
	1	42780	43520	44220	44880	45500	46080	46620	47120	47580	48000	1
r = 2	0	35830	34720	33670	32680	31750	30880	30070	29320	28630	28000	0
	1	42780	43520	44220	44880	45500	46080	46620	47120	47580	48000	1
	2	21390	21760	22110	22440	22750	23040	23310	23560	23790	24000	2
r = 3	0	23591	22430	21337	20311	19351	18457	17627	16862	16159	15520	0
	1	36718	36870	36999	37107	37196	37270	37329	37376	37412	37440	1
	2	27452	28410	29331	30213	31054	31850	32601	33304	33958	34560	2
	3	12239	12290	12333	12369	12399	12423	12443	12458	12471	12480	3
r = 4	0	15927	14875	13893	12978	12128	11342	10618	09954	09348	08800	0
	1	30656	30220	29778	29334	28893	28459	28037	27631	27244	26880	1
	2	27452	28410	29331	30213	31054	31850	32602	33304	33958	34560	2
	3	18301	18940	19554	20142	20702	21234	21734	22203	22639	23040	3
	4	07664	07555	07444	07333	07223	07115	07009	06908	06811	06720	4
r = 5	0	10881	09994	09175	08420	07726	07090	06509	05981	05504	05075	0
	1	25230	24404	23588	22789	22012	21262	20545	19863	19221	18624	1
	2	26180	26743	27268	27756	28207	28623	29004	29352	29668	29952	2
	3	19573	20606	21617	22599	23549	24461	25331	26155	26929	27648	3
	4	13090	13372	13634	13878	14104	14312	14502	14676	14834	14976	4
	5	05046	04881	04718	04558	04402	04252	04109	03973	03844	03725	5
r = 6	0	07474	06757	06103	05508	04967	04476	04034	03636	03280	02963	0
	1	20440	19421	18430	17473	16555	15679	14850	14071	13344	12672	1
	2	24590	24660	24689	24684	24649	24589	24508	24412	24305	24192	2
	3	19573	20606	21617	22599	23549	24461	25331	26155	26929	27648	3
	4	14680	15455	16213	16950	17662	18346	18999	19616	20196	20736	4
	5	09836	09864	09876	09874	09859	09836	09803	09765	09722	09677	5
	6	03407	03237	03072	02912	02759	02613	02475	02345	02224	02112	6
r = 7	0	05146	04583	04074	03618	03209	02843	02517	02227	01970	01745	0
	1	16292	15223	14200	13226	12303	11434	10621	09864	09166	08526	1
	2	22666	22303	21904	21478	21032	20575	20113	19655	19206	18773	2
	3	19600	20368	21102	21800	22460	23082	23663	24204	24703	25160	3
	4	14654	15694	16728	17750	18751	19726	20667	21567	22422	23224	4
	5	11760	12220	12661	13080	13476	13849	14198	14522	14822	15096	5
	6	07555	07434	07302	07159	07011	06858	06704	06552	06402	06258	6
	7	02327	02175	02029	01889	01758	01633	01517	01409	01309	01218	7
r = 8	0	03548	03112	02725	02382	02079	01812	01576	01370	01190	01034	0
	1	12789	11763	10796	09887	09039	08251	07523	06853	06242	05689	1
	2	20403	19721	19016	18298	17576	16858	16154	15470	14814	14193	2
	3	19637	20033	20380	20679	20935	21150	21328	21472	21587	21676	3
	4	14654	15694	16728	17750	18751	19726	20667	21568	22422	23224	4
	5	11723	12555	13383	14200	15001	15780	16533	17254	17938	18580	5
	6	09818	10017	10190	10340	10467	10575	10664	10736	10794	10838	6
	7	05829	05635	05433	05228	05022	04817	04615	04420	04233	04055	7
	8	01599	01470	01349	01236	01130	01031	00940	00857	00780	00711	8
r = 9	0	02447	02115	01824	01570	01349	01157	00990	00845	00721	00615	0
	1	09908	08975	08108	07307	06570	05895	05280	04722	04219	03769	1
	2	17922	17036	16147	15264	14395	13548	12732	11952	11214	10524	2
	3	19393	19412	19372	19279	19139	18962	18754	18522	18276	18022	3
	4	15092	15955	16796	17611	18395	19145	19857	20529	21157	21738	4
	5	11284	12294	13315	14339	15357	16361	17342	18293	19203	20066	5
	6	10062	10637	11197	11740	12263	12763	13238	13686	14104	14492	6
	7	08311	08320	08303	08262	08203	08127	08037	07938	07833	07724	7
	8	04480	04259	04037	03816	03599	03387	03183	02988	02804	02631	8
	9	01101	00997	00901	00812	00730	00655	00587	00525	00469	00419	9
r = 10	0	01688	01438	01222	01036	00876	00739	00622	00523	00438	00367	0
	1	07589	06772	06026	05346	04730	04174	03674	03228	02832	02482	1
	2	15388	14398	13426	12480	11567	10693	09863	09082	08354	07681	2
	3	18704	18391	18019	17597	17136	16647	16138	15620	15104	14598	3
	4	15751	16347	16897	17402	17860	18274	18643	18971	19258	19508	4
	5	11284	12294	13315	14339	15357	16361	17343	18293	19203	20066	5
	6	09403	10245	11096	11949	12798	13634	14452	15244	16003	16721	6
	7	09001	09341	09655	09944	10206	10442	10653	10840	11005	11148	7
	8	07014	06897	06757	06599	06426	06243	06052	05858	05664	05474	8
	9	03419	03200	02984	02773	02571	02376	02192	02018	01856	01707	9
	10	00759	00677	00603	00535	00473	00417	00368	00323	00283	00248	10

TABLE 4 (CONT.)

Probabilities of black-white joins r = 1(1)10, x = 0(1)r, p = .41(.01).5

	x	.41	.42	.43	.44	.45	.46	.47	.48	.49	.50	x
r = 1	0	51620	51280	50980	50720	50500	50320	50180	50080	50020	50000	0
	1	48380	48720	49020	49280	49500	49680	49820	49920	49980	50000	1
r = 2	0	27430	26920	26470	26080	25750	25480	25270	25120	25030	25000	0
	1	48380	48720	49020	49280	49500	49680	49820	49920	49980	50000	1
	2	24190	24360	24510	24640	24750	24840	24910	24960	24990	25000	2
r = 3	0	14943	14428	13975	13583	13251	12980	12770	12620	12530	12500	0
	1	37461	37475	37486	37492	37496	37498	37500	37500	37500	37500	1
	2	35109	35605	36044	36428	36754	37022	37230	37380	37470	37500	2
	3	12487	12492	12495	12497	12499	12500	12500	12500	12500	12500	3
r = 4	0	08308	07871	07487	07157	06878	06651	06475	06350	06275	06250	0
	1	26541	26231	25951	25704	25493	25317	25179	25080	25020	25000	1
	2	35110	35605	36044	36428	36754	37022	37231	37380	37470	37500	2
	3	23406	23736	24030	24285	24502	24681	24820	24920	24980	25000	3
	4	06635	06557	06488	06426	06373	06329	06295	06270	06255	06250	4
r = 5	0	04693	04356	04062	03810	03598	03427	03294	03200	03144	03125	0
	1	18073	17573	17126	16734	16398	16122	15905	15750	15656	15625	1
	2	30206	30430	30626	30793	30935	31049	31137	31200	31238	31250	2
	3	28310	28911	29448	29919	30322	30654	30914	31100	31212	31250	3
	4	15103	15215	15313	15397	15467	15524	15569	15600	15619	15625	4
	5	03615	03515	03425	03347	03280	03224	03181	03150	03131	03125	5
r = 6	0	02683	02438	02227	02046	01896	01775	01681	01615	01576	01562	0
	1	12058	11504	11010	10580	10214	09913	09678	09510	09409	09375	1
	2	24076	23962	23853	23751	23660	23583	23521	23475	23447	23438	2
	3	28310	28911	29448	29919	30322	30654	30914	31100	31212	31250	3
	4	21232	21683	22086	22440	22742	22990	23185	23325	23409	23438	4
	5	09631	09585	09541	09500	09464	09433	09408	09390	09379	09375	5
	6	02010	01917	01835	01764	01702	01652	01613	01585	01568	01562	6
r = 7	0	01548	01377	01231	01108	01006	00924	00861	00816	00790	00781	0
	1	07945	07428	06969	06571	06234	05959	05744	05591	05499	05469	1
	2	18362	17980	17630	17317	17046	16820	16640	16511	16432	16406	2
	3	25574	25945	26272	26556	26797	26994	27147	27256	27322	27344	3
	4	23969	24649	25262	25802	26266	26650	26952	27169	27300	27344	4
	5	15345	15567	15764	15934	16078	16196	16288	16354	16393	16406	5
	6	06121	05993	05877	05773	05682	05606	05547	05504	05478	05469	6
	7	01136	01061	00995	00939	00891	00851	00821	00799	00786	00781	7
r = 8	0	00899	00783	00685	00603	00536	00483	00442	00413	00396	00391	0
	1	05193	04752	04366	04034	03754	03527	03351	03225	03150	03125	1
	2	13612	13077	12594	12166	11797	11491	11250	11077	10972	10937	2
	3	21743	21792	21826	21848	21862	21870	21873	21875	21875	21875	3
	4	23968	24650	25262	25803	26267	26650	26952	27169	27300	27344	4
	5	19175	19720	20210	20642	21013	21320	21562	21736	21840	21875	5
	6	10872	10896	10913	10924	10931	10935	10937	10937	10938	10937	6
	7	03889	03736	03598	03476	03371	03283	03214	03165	03135	03125	7
	8	00649	00594	00546	00504	00469	00441	00419	00403	00394	00391	8
r = 9	0	00524	00448	00384	00330	00287	00253	00227	00210	00199	00195	0
	1	03370	03020	02716	02456	02240	02065	01930	01834	01777	01758	1
	2	09886	09305	08784	08327	07935	07612	07359	07177	07068	07031	2
	3	17768	17520	17284	17068	16876	16712	16580	16484	16426	16406	3
	4	22271	22752	23182	23557	23876	24139	24344	24491	24580	24610	4
	5	20873	21617	22290	22888	23403	23832	24170	24413	24560	24610	5
	6	14847	15168	15454	15704	15917	16093	16230	16328	16386	16406	6
	7	07615	07508	07408	07315	07233	07162	07106	07065	07040	07031	7
	8	02472	02326	02196	02082	01984	01903	01840	01794	01767	01758	8
	9	00374	00336	00302	00273	00249	00229	00214	00204	00197	00195	9
r = 10	0	00307	00257	00216	00182	00155	00133	00117	00106	00099	00098	0
	1	02175	01908	01680	01487	01327	01199	01101	01032	00990	00976	1
	2	07066	06512	06019	05591	05227	04928	04695	04528	04428	04394	2
	3	14111	13653	13229	12847	12513	12233	12011	11849	11751	11719	3
	4	19724	19907	20061	20188	20291	20372	20432	20475	20500	20508	4
	5	20873	21616	22290	22888	23403	23832	24170	24413	24560	24610	5
	6	17394	18014	18575	19073	19503	19860	20141	20345	20467	20508	6
	7	11271	11375	11463	11536	11595	11641	11676	11700	11714	11719	7
	8	05292	05120	04961	04817	04692	04587	04504	04443	04407	04394	8
	9	01570	01447	01338	01242	01161	01095	01043	01006	00984	00976	9
	10	00217	00191	00168	00149	00133	00120	00110	00103	00099	00098	10

INDEX

M